D1131527

INTRODUCTION TO GEOPHYSICS

McGraw-Hill Series in the Geological Sciences

ROBERT R. SHROCK, *Consulting Editor*

DE SITTER · Structural Geology

EWING, JARDETZKY, AND PRESS · Elastic Waves in Layered Media

GRIM · Clay Mineralogy

HEINRICH · Microscopic Petrography

HEISKANEN AND VENING MEINESZ · The Earth and Its Gravity Field

HOWELL · Introduction to Geophysics

OFFICER · Introduction to the Theory of Sound Transmission

SHROCK AND TWENHOFEL · Principles of Invertebrate Paleontology

Introduction to Geophysics

BENJAMIN F. HOWELL, JR.

Professor of Geophysics and Head, Department of Geophysics and Geochemistry, The Pennsylvania State University

McGRAW-HILL BOOK COMPANY, INC.

New York Toronto London

1959

INTRODUCTION TO GEOPHYSICS

 Library of Congress Catalog Card Number 58-11175.

THE MAPLE PRESS COMPANY, YORK, PA.

PREFACE

This work was written as a beginning college textbook in geophysics. Its principal objectives are to familiarize the reader with the scope of geophysics in relation to the other sciences, to give him some insight into the methods used by geophysicists to study the earth, and to outline some of the most important discoveries of these researches.

When the author first began to teach geophysics in 1949, he found that several excellent books on geophysical prospecting were available. In general geophysics, on the other hand, all the available texts in English either were concerned with some individual subdivision of this science such as seismology, to the exclusion of all others, or appeared to be written on the assumption that the reader already knew a great deal about the subject. This lack of a comprehensive introductory text led to the present work. It has been written with a course composed half of juniors and seniors and half of graduate students in mind. The students in the author's course are drawn from many curricula: physics, geology, mineralogy, petroleum engineering, mining engineering, as well as geophysics and geochemistry. The book is intended to satisfy the needs of a broad range of specialists for a basic knowledge of the fundamental principles of geophysics. It is assumed that the student using the text will be familiar with the terminology of both geology and physics. One semester of geology and one year of college physics should be sufficient preparation for understanding the ideas presented here.

A nodding acquaintance with calculus is also assumed. It is the author's observation that the average geology student has the same opinion of calculus that a small boy has of castor oil. He has a high respect for it but avoids it with a terror which cannot be touched by reason. This is indeed unfortunate, but since it is the case, the use of mathematics has been kept at a minimum. Yet geophysics is an exact science, and geophysical ideas can in many cases be adequately presented only with the help of formulas. Elementary calculus has therefore been employed wherever its use leads to greater clarity or conciseness in presenting information. Where formulas are derived, all steps are included in the derivation so that the student who is not quick in mathematics will have no difficulty in understanding what is being stated. In the few cases, such as in Chap. 10, where moderately complex mathematical treatments are necessary for thorough presentation of fundamental concepts, the text is so written that the sections containing the mathematical proofs can be skipped over by students unable to appreciate them. This material has been included for the physicist using this text, since he will ordinarily desire a rigorous treatment.

It is planned that this book should serve not only as a textbook but as a reference work. Since geophysics has developed relatively rapidly as a science in recent years, there is a great deal of basic information which is still published only in one or two places, usually in technical journals. Because of this, an extensive bibliography has been included, especially for those subjects not thoroughly treated in more specialized works. All references are at the end of the book, and throughout the text, references are made simply by stating the author's name and the year of the publication. Since this is a textbook and not a technical paper, the references used are intended, in general, to direct the reader to a readily available, more detailed treatment of the subject, wherever possible a book or summary paper. References to original sources can usually be found in these secondary sources. It is hoped that advanced students and others using this book will find these references a stimulating introduction to geophysical literature.

The writing of this book would not have been possible without the help of many friends and fellow geophysicists who gave generously of their time and advice. The author particularly wishes to thank the following for reading chapters related to their specialties and suggesting improvements and additions to the material presented: O. Frank Tuttle, Leonard F. Herzog, and E. James Moore of The Pennsylvania State University; Beno Gutenberg of the California Institute of Technology; Sigmund Hammer of Gulf Research and Development Company; Harry H. Hess and the author's father, B. F. Howell, of Princeton University; and E. H. Vestine of Rand Corporation.

The kind cooperation of the many individuals and organizations who supplied a large part of the illustrations used is greatly appreciated. Specific acknowledgement will be found in each case in the text.

Benjamin F. Howell, Jr.

CONTENTS

CHAPTER 1

INTRODUCTION

Geophysics has an unusual position in the organization of science.[1] It has neither a unique methodology nor a particular area of interest which it can claim peculiarly for its own. By definition, geophysics is the application of the principles and practices of physics to the solution of problems related to the earth. It grew out of physics and geology and has no sharp boundaries which distinguish it from either. It constitutes a point of view toward earth science as a whole involving the experimental approach to an understanding of the planet we inhabit.

This approach is a logical step in the development of the methodology of science. Before the industrial revolution began to give men plentiful leisure to examine the world about them, so little of nature's pattern had been recognized that a man could aspire to learn all that was known of it at the time he lived. The early natural philosophers were interested in all manifestations of reality. However, as science developed, the body of accumulated data rapidly became so great that no one individual could study all of it, to say nothing of understanding the meaning of what he had examined. As a result, the idea of specialization developed. Today the physical sciences have become so subdivided that it would be difficult even to list all their branches. It has been said that as successive investigators seek to learn more and more about less and less, they may soon reach the point of knowing everything about nothing.

Early in the process of subdivision, four branches of science were recognized. These are chemistry, the study of the properties of matter; physics, the study of the forces acting on matter; geology,[2] the study of matter as it occurs in the earth; and biology, the study of matter as it occurs in living organisms. To these are often added astronomy, which

[1] Throughout the discussion which follows, the word science will be used as a synonym for physical science unless otherwise noted.

[2] The term geology is commonly used with two different meanings. In its broader sense, used here, it is synonymous with all of earth science including the study of the air and the oceans. In its more restricted use, geology means the study of the accessible rocks of the earth's crust.

deals with the rest of the universe aside from the earth, and mathematics, the science of forms and numbers. Because it does not deal with matter directly, mathematics is often not included among the physical sciences. Astronomy is often treated as a branch of physics. From this point of view, science can be portrayed as a tetrahedron, as shown in Fig. 1.1. Each field of study has its place somewhere in the tetrahedron.

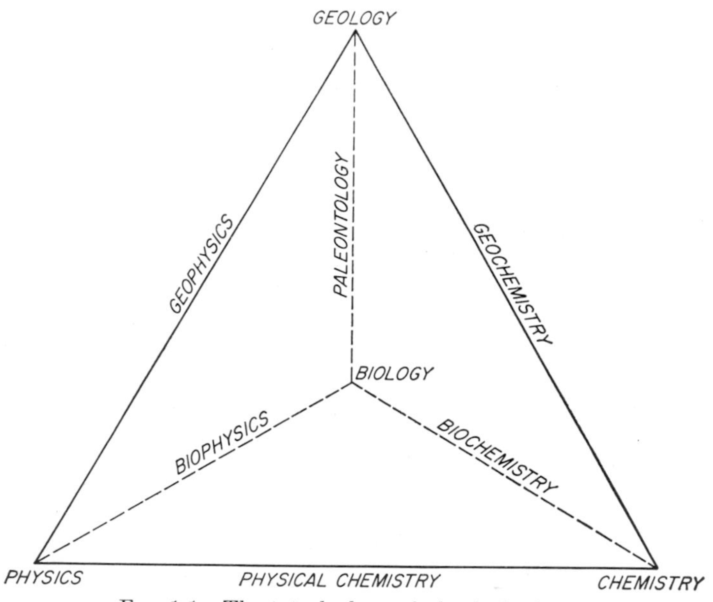

FIG. 1.1 The tetrahedron of physical science.

Until science began to diversify, the investigator was not tempted to emphasize one subject over any other. Thus, Sir Isaac Newton, who is often thought of as a physicist, also contributed to what we now call geology when he proposed the contraction theory of mountain building. As knowledge increased, certain fields were investigated more thoroughly than others and came to be considered as separate and distinct. Classification of knowledge into individual subjects tended to separate scientists and left the intermediate areas relatively undeveloped. When this overemphasis was recognized, new specialities developed which dealt with these in-between fields. Geophysics is one of these.

Science begins with observation. The recognition that experiment and not reference to authority is the best way to solve a problem marks the beginning of modern times and the end of the Renaissance. Our modern science and technology grew in their entirety from this single basic principle. In the beginning all science was largely descriptive. Kepler is remembered for his description of the motions of the planets; Harvey, for his demonstration of the circulation of the blood. The science of geology, probably because of the complexity of the medium with which it deals, has remained largely descriptive until recently. On the other hand, physics, which deals with forces and the relationships of bodies to one another regardless of their occurrence in nature, developed early into a laboratory science. Because conditions in the laboratory could be carefully controlled, the physicist soon progressed to the point of measuring quantities he could not see directly, such as gravity and electric current.

When the geologist finally reached the point where he understood the earth well enough to be ready to test his hypotheses by experiment, physicists and chemists had already developed the techniques of making the necessary measurements. As a result, the most rapidly expanding frontiers in earth science today are those where specialists in other fields are working with geologists. Geophysics is an example of such a domain.

The science of geophysics came into being as a result of the need of the geologist for new tools. As various techniques of experiment were applied to earth problems, whole new areas of investigation developed. Because of their relation to the older sciences of physics and geology, it was natural to group all these specialties under the one general name geophysics, even though they were diverse in nature. The American Geophysical Union breaks geophysics into eight subdivisions:

Meteorology—the science of the air
Hydrology—the science of ground water, both surface and underground
Oceanography—the science of the oceans
Seismology—the science of earthquakes and other ground vibrations
Volcanology—the science of volcanoes and related phenomena
Geomagnetism—the science of the earth's magnetic and electric phenomena
Geodesy—the science of the earth's shape and gravitational field
Tectonophysics (tectonics of geodynamics)—the science of the deformations of rocks, as in mountain building and other diastrophism

Four other fields are commonly named in classifications of geophysics:

Glaciology—dealing with water where it occurs as ice, usually considered to be a branch of hydrology
Geothermometry—dealing with the heat of the earth. Geothermometry is related to volcanology but is broader in conception. It is concerned with the temperature of the earth and with the effect of temperature on physical and chemical processes and the flow of heat. It includes the sources of the earth's heat, such as natural radioactivity. Volcanology is best classed as a subdivision of geothermometry.
Geocosmogony—dealing with the origin of the earth
Geochronology—the dating of events in the earth's history

The American Geophysical Union includes two other fields which it links with volcanology in its classification. The first of these is geochemistry, which relates geology to chemistry as geophysics relates it to physics. In any logical classification geochemistry deserves a position as an independent field of equal rank with geophysics, though it is often hard to say where the one science ends and the other begins. The second field is petrology, the science of the origin, evolution, and description of rocks. Petrology overlaps both volcanology and geochemistry in its area of interest.

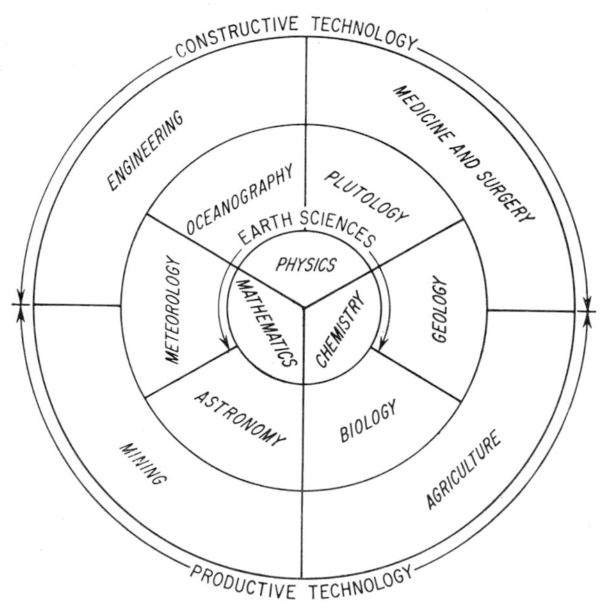

FIG. 1.2 The bull's-eye classification of physical science.

It is difficult to fit such a diverse collection of subdivisions into the simple picture of the organization of science presented above. Figure 1.2 is a rational classification which is better suited to showing the organization of science as it is today. In the center are the basic sciences of physics, chemistry, and mathematics, on which the other sciences depend. The basic sciences are concerned with the properties of matter independent of its natural occurrence. Thus the chemist may discuss properties of oxygen which it possesses whether it occurs as a gas in the air, combined with water in the ocean, or in a silicate molecule deep within the earth.

The second circle contains the applied sciences, divided into the realms with which they deal. Oceanography, meteorology, and astronomy are concerned with the oceans, the air, and the universe outside our terrestrial globe. Biology is concerned with the organisms which live upon it.

The realm of geology (used here in its more restricted meaning) is the exposed rocks of the earth's crust, from its surface to the bottom of the deepest wells. Beneath the thin shell which we can observe directly is the bulk of our earth, seen only by means of the tools of the geophysicist and geochemist. This realm of science is here named plutology.

This book might well have been called "Introduction to Plutology," as this subterrain is the area with which it is concerned. The scope of geophysics is too great to be treated adequately in one text, no matter how elementary. Meteorology, oceanography, and hydrology each would require as much discussion as all the chapters of this book which follow this one. Although the physical methods used in studying the air and water of the earth are in many cases similar to those involved in plutology, the differences between the gaseous and liquid environments and the solid part of the earth make great modifications in the details of these methods.

The principal objective of plutology is the determination of the composition and structure af the earth's interior and the history of its changes, past, present, and future. This objective is shared with geology. The geophysicist seeks to reach it by indirect measurements. Geologists depend largely on direct observations of rocks for knowledge of the earth. Geophysics is distinguished from geology by its emphasis on field and laboratory experiments.

Geology, biology, astronomy, and the geophysical sciences constitute a ring in Fig. 1.2 of applied sciences. They are "applied" because in them the "basic" sciences are used to explain the behavior of matter in its varied natural forms. They have sometimes been called descriptive sciences because in the past so much of the research in these fields has been devoted simply to studying the various forms in which matter can and does occur in nature. However, study of the universe and its inhabitants has not been limited to statements of what was found in it. The great progress man has made in mastering his own fate has resulted from his ability to capitalize on past experiences. For example, study of earthquakes has given a way of prospecting for oil, study of heredity in plants has shown how to grow better crops, and study of the atmosphere has taught us to predict weather.

The term "applied science" is often misused to refer to the outer ring of technologies. The latter are not sciences at all, though they depend on the sciences for the basic principles which guide their operations. The confusion arises from the intimate connection between basic information about the physical world and its practical applications. Science is systematic knowledge; it is the description and understanding of the universe in which we live, regardless of whether or not this knowledge has practical value. Technology is the use of this knowledge to benefit mankind.

The classification described above is two-dimensional only. Physical science cannot be properly comprehended unless we relate it to the less tangible activities of man. The social sciences connect to those shown in the chart through geography and psychology. Geography takes all of science and technology and relates them to man. Psychology describes man's reactions to the stimuli of his encounters with different aspects of the physical world and with his fellows.

In the chapters which follow, the different methods by which the geophysicist seeks information on the earth's interior will be outlined. In the last few decades, some of these methods have been highly developed in the search for petroleum and ore deposits. The special technological applications of geophysics to prospecting are the subject of numerous excellent texts (for example, Dobrin, 1952; Heiland, 1940). This work is a science text. It will concern itself with the broader problems of earth science and will leave the practical application of the methods described to the geophysical engineer.

Every earth scientist, especially the geologist, should be familiar with the various ways in which geophysics can help him understand the earth. This book is intended to show the potentialities and limitations of physical measurements made at or near the earth's surface as means of learning about the earth's hidden interior. The principal types of measurements which can be made will be outlined, and the significance of important data so far obtained will be discussed.

CHAPTER 2

ORIGIN OF THE EARTH

It is appropriate that a book dealing with the earth should start with how it came into being. One of the clearest lessons of geology is that everything we see is transient. Mountains are raised and worn away; great seas come and go. In the pages which follow, it will be shown that the features of the interior of the earth are no more permanent than its superficial appearance. What we observe today must be the result of what happened yesterday, and that, in turn, follows from earlier events, and so on as far back in time as one can go.

There is no true beginning to this history of change. Matter, either as mass or as energy, appears to be indestructible; so the rock, water, and air which make up the earth must always have existed in one form or another. When we refer to the origin of the earth, what we mean is not the creation of the matter of which it is composed, but the appearance of this matter as a single body which has had an individual existence from the time of its appearance to the present.

The omnipresence of change makes it certain that at some time the earth must have been very different from what it is now. There is a definite limit to the time that the earth can have existed in its present form. This is set by the changing proportions of the elements involved in radioactive disintegration (see Chap. 4). The fact that radioactive atoms exist at all on the earth today and have not completely disintegrated into more stable substances proves that the matter of which the earth is composed must once have been in a very different environment. The only place known where conditions may be right for the formation of the unstable elements is in the center of hot, dense stars. At some time, at least a part of the material from which the earth was formed must have been drawn from such a source. Since then great changes have taken place. The questions thus arise, what form could the material which today makes up the earth have had just before reaching its present general arrangement, and through what orderly transformation was the present condition reached?

2.1 Means of Studying the Universe. To approach the problem of what existed before there was an earth, a good method is to examine the forms in which matter exists elsewhere in the universe today. Since we can as yet rise only a little way above the solid surface of our planet, we must depend on information which comes to us from outer space. Such

FIG. 2.1 "Horsehead" nebula, a cloud of dark matter in Orion. (*Courtesy of Mount Wilson and Palomar Observatories.*)

information consists of two types: particles which enter our atmosphere and electromagnetic radiations such as light rays.

Most of the solid particles which strike the earth are evaporated by the heat generated by their passage through the air. Only in a few cases do some of the larger of these meteors reach the ground. They are found to consist of two principal types of material. The first of these is a stony substance composed largely of basic silicates such as are found in igneous rocks in the earth. The second type consists largely of unoxidized metal, mostly iron with some nickel.

In addition to the meteors which are large enough to see, we know that there is a steady hail of fine particles falling toward the earth. Polished metal plates carried high into the air by rockets become pitted by the impact of this cosmic dust. Thus we know that space is not really empty but is occupied by an invisible cloud of such material. At least in our part of the universe, it contains solid iron, nickel, and basic silicates, and probably includes hydrogen, helium, and other common elements in gaseous form. At some places in space, these clouds are so dense that they obscure the stars behind them (Fig. 2.1). In general, however, this matter must be spread very thinly to allow the light of the stars to pass through.

In contrast to this tenuous film of cold, dark matter there are many types of large, dense bodies in the universe. These include the stars which we see because of the light they radiate. The stars are grouped in galaxies, which are traveling through space at fantastically high velocities. Our sun lies in one such galaxy which we see in cross section as the Milky Way. The galaxies are in many cases rotating and have a peculiar spiral form as a result of this (Fig. 2.2).

Individual stars are composed of incandescent gas. They differ from one another in size and temperature and to a limited degree in the material of which they are made. Composition is determined from study of their light spectra. Most are believed to be similar to our sun.

Many stars occur in pairs, the two parts rotating about a common center of gravity. At one time such binaries were thought to be very rare, but so many stars have now been found to be double that it is probable that most have companions of some sort. Usually the two are unequal in size, one being much larger than the other. In some cases there may be more than two. These companion stars are not always luminous, their presence being detectable only by their gravitational effect on the motions of their companions (Urey, 1952). There may be many cold stars, both large and small, which we cannot see because they neither radiate nor reflect enough light.

Our sun may be thought of as a multiple star, the planets being its companions. It is possible that almost all stars have planets revolving about them. The planets in turn have their satellites, called moons. Mars, Jupiter, Uranus, Neptune, and Saturn all have moons. Saturn has a great cloud of tiny satellites which form its rings.

The sun has many satellites besides the planets. These include the asteroids, which are a countless group of small bodies moving in orbits between those of Mars and Jupiter. A large portion of the meteorites which strike the earth arrives on orbits similar to those of the asteroids.

It may be that most meteorites are simply small asteroids. At least some of the comets appear to move in highly eccentric elliptical orbits which bring them near the sun at infrequent but regular intervals.

2.2 Some Features of the Universe. Our sun is a relatively small star. The largest one known, Epsilon Aurigae, is 27×10^9 times as big.

Fig. 2.2 Meissier 51, a spiral nebula in Canes Venatici. (*Courtesy of Mount Wilson and Palomar Observatories.*)

The stars are scattered far apart in space. Their separation can be visualized by using an example proposed by the English physicist J. H. Jeans. If five apples were placed one on each of the five largest continents, the ratio of their average diameter to their separation would be about the same as the ratio of the diameter of an average star to the distance to other stars. The galaxies are a little more densely packed (Umbgrove, 1947). A typical galaxy might contain 10^{13} to 10^{14} individual stars. Its diameter might be of the order of 10^4 light-years (9.5×10^{16} km). For comparison, the earth's radius at the equator is 6,378 km (approximately 4,000 miles); the sun's diameter is 1,390,000 km; the average distance from the earth to the sun is 149,500,000 km and to Pluto, the outermost known planet, 5,908,000,000 km. The most remote known nebula is 150,000,000 light-years away, and there are known to be nearly a billion of them in the universe.

One of the most remarkable features of the universe is that it appears to be expanding. If one studies the frequency spectrum of light coming from any galaxy, the intensity is seen to be a maximum at certain frequencies. These frequencies are associated with certain chemical elements of which the galaxy is composed, and the same elements seem to

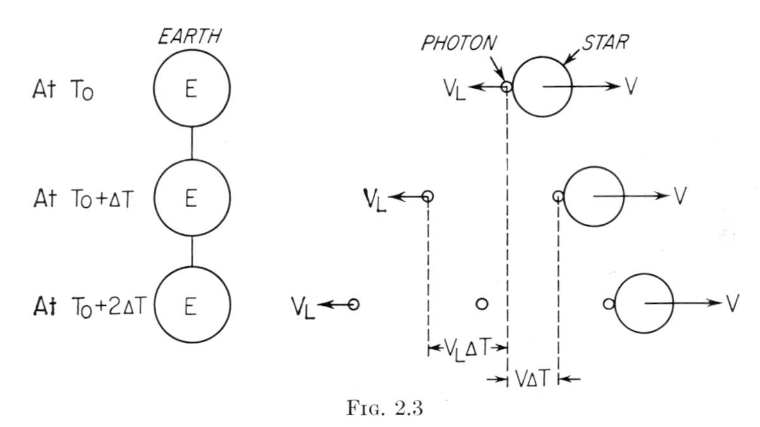

FIG. 2.3

predominate in all the stars. If one compares the spectra of different galaxies, it is found that although the patterns of relative intensity are nearly identical, the frequencies vary slightly. The more distant the galaxy, the lower the frequency of each spectral line.

The simplest explanation for this is that the more distant the galaxy, the faster it is moving away from the earth. We may think of the light as a series of photons, one leaving the galaxy every ΔT sec and moving toward the earth with the velocity of light V_L (Fig. 2.3). Between the times of the departure of two photons, the first will travel a distance $V_L\,\Delta T$. During this time the earth and galaxy will have become farther apart by a distance $V\,\Delta T$, where V is their rate of separation. Thus the second photon will be $(V_L + V)\,\Delta T$ behind the first, and the period of the light as it is observed on the earth will be $[(V_L + V)/V_L](\Delta T)$.

This doppler effect was first observed by E. Hubble of the Mount Wilson Observatory. He estimated that if one calculated V_L from the observed shift of the light toward lower frequencies (visible light is made to appear redder) and projected the galaxies back in time along the paths they are currently traveling, about 2 billion years ago all the galaxies would be concentrated into a small volume of the universe. Recent studies have indicated that Hubble's figure is probably too low, but that the convergence of the back projection in time is still true. The latest estimates are that 5 billion years have elapsed since the matter began to scatter (Ahrens, 1955).

The location of the source cannot be determined, as there is no way to tell what point in space is fixed relative to the others. The galaxies may be likened to points on the surface of a giant rubber balloon which is being inflated. No matter where one stands on the balloon, all the other points will be receding.

One quaint theory of the origin of the universe assumes that in the beginning there was a single superatom which, by rapid radioactive disintegrations, blew itself up into the whole mass and energy of what we observe today. This is an extreme view, and there is no valid reason to suppose that matter was ever so extremely concentrated. However, if Hubble is right and the galaxies were at one time closely gathered together, then we may seek the formation of the earth in the extraordinary events of the disruption of this concentration. Gamow (1951) has pointed out that in such a concentration the density of matter in the form of energy would be greater than the density of matter in the form of mass per unit volume. Under such conditions matter would be expected to behave quite differently from the way we see it under conditions as they are today.

Other explanations of the red shift have been proposed. It has been suggested that light in its transmission over large distances is slowed down slightly by a force like gravity tending to pull it back toward its source. However, there is no evidence that there is any such retardation. One can also postulate theories whereby the velocity of light is a function of time, which would account for the phenomenon (Krogdahl, 1952). However, there seems to be no reason other than the red shift to suspect that the velocity of light varies in this way, and these theories will not be discussed here.

2.3 The Solar System. There are similarities between the earth and the other planets of our solar system which suggest that all were formed by the same process, perhaps simultaneously. For instance, the compositions of the sun and planets, except for their hydrogen and helium content, are believed to be similar in so far as they can be determined. For this reason, the origin of the earth is usually discussed as a part of the origin of the solar system as a whole.

There are a number of features of the system which appear to be unchanging under conditions which currently exist. Therefore, these particular characteristics must have been created by the events associated with the origin of the system. We can test different theories of the earth's creation by seeing how satisfactorily they explain these features. One of the most striking characteristics of the solar system is that all the planets except Mercury and Pluto lie very nearly in a single plane and all revolve in ellipses in the same direction about the sun as a focus. Mercury's orbit is tilted only about 7° to this plane; Pluto's, 17°. The sun's axis of rotation is at an angle of 7° from perpendicular to the plane in which the planets lie. All the planets except Uranus rotate on their axes in the same direction that they revolve around the sun, and the sun rotates similarly. Uranus's axis is tilted 98° from the axis of its orbit. Of the 31 known moons, 25 revolve in the same direction that their planets rotate, and those which revolve oppositely are, with the exception of Neptune's Triton, the outer ones, for which it is easiest to postulate some special means of producing this unusual direction of motion. This nearly universal similarity in the sense of rotation must mean that almost all parts of the solar system acquired their angular momentum from a single source.

Another remarkable condition is the quantitative distribution of the energy of rotation. Although about 99 per cent of the mass of the solar system is in the sun, it possesses only one-thirtieth of the angular momentum. Jupiter, with 0.1 per cent of the mass, has about 59 per cent of the momentum (Jeffreys, 1929).

To a certain extent there can be exchanges of energy between the individual bodies. This is greatest in the case of the earth and the moon. It is brought about by tidal friction. If there were no friction, the gravitational force of the moon on the earth would cause tides on either side of the earth as shown in the upper diagram of Fig. 2.4. However, owing to friction, there is a tendency for the tides to be dragged past this position to that shown in the middle diagram of Fig. 2.4. Picture the earth as consisting of three masses, the main body of the earth E and the two tides A and B, and consider the gravitational forces acting between these three masses and the moon M as shown in the third part of Fig. 2.4. There will be a radial force

$$F_R = \gamma M \left(\frac{A}{R_A^2} \cos \theta_A + \frac{B}{R_B^2} \cos \theta_B + \frac{E}{R_E^2} \right) \tag{2.1}$$

which holds the moon near the earth, and a tangential force

$$F_T = \gamma M \left(\frac{A}{R_A^2} \sin \theta_A - \frac{B}{R_B^2} \sin \theta_B \right) \tag{2.2}$$

which will tend to accelerate the moon. F_T will act in the direction of the earth's rotation, since R_B is greater than R_A and θ_A is greater than θ_B. γ is Newton's constant of gravitation. At the same time, the earth's rate of rotation will be decreased. Angular momentum will be transferred from the earth's rotation to the moon's revolution about it. The acceleration given to the moon will lift it through the earth's gravitational field, causing it to move farther away from the earth. It will retreat until a new equilibrium is reached. This will occur when the centrifugal force equals the earth's attraction:

$$\frac{MV^2}{R} = \gamma \frac{MM_e}{R^2} \tag{2.3}$$

where $M_e = E + A + B$ = total mass of earth and $R \approx R_E$ = distance between the earth and moon. This is equivalent to

$$RV^2 = \gamma M_e \tag{2.4}$$

The product RV^2 must thus be a constant for equilibrium.

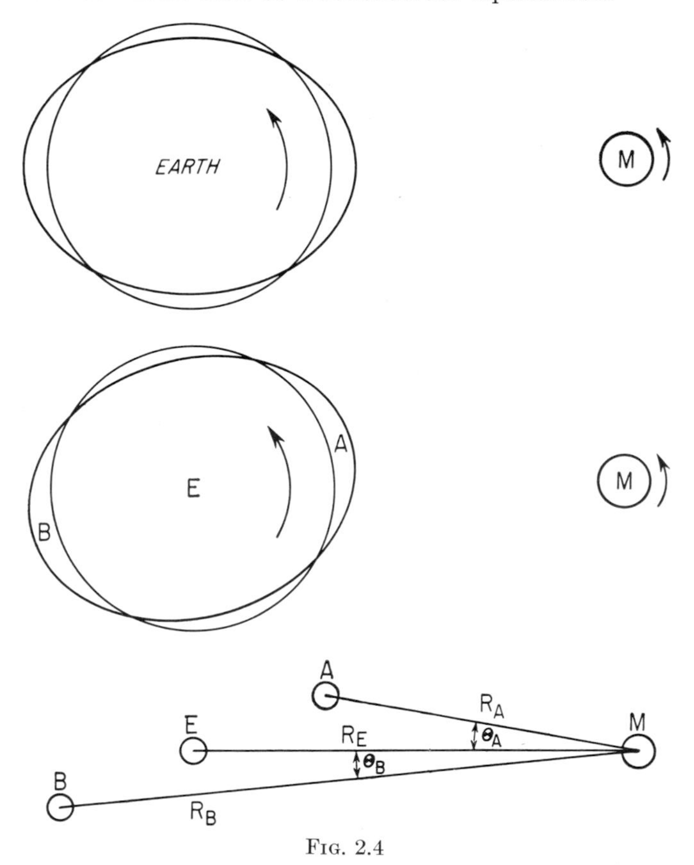

FIG. 2.4

The current rate of retreat is only a few feet per century. Jeffreys (1952) estimates that in about 5×10^{10} years the moon will move so far away that it will revolve about the earth at the same rate that the earth rotates. Before this occurs, if nothing else interferes, the moon will become so far away that the solar tides will have more effect than the lunar on the earth's rotation. They also act to decrease the earth's rotation. The day will become longer than the month. The tides will lag behind the position of the moon, and it will be drawn back to the earth, eventually falling into it.

Tidal effects in the past would have slowed the moon's rotation also. At present it always keeps the same face toward the earth. Similarly, Mercury always faces the sun.

Such exchanges of energy will occur whether there are fluid seas or not, as tides exist in the solid earth as well, and although of much smaller magnitude, they act similarly. The size of the effect in the case of the other planets can be shown to be so small that the present distribution of angular momentum cannot have changed much since the solar system was formed. Calculations of the rate of movement of the other satellites are difficult, as they depend on the unknown rigidities of the planets.

The moon is not perfectly round but is ellipsoidal in shape. The equatorial radius of the side facing the earth exceeds its average radius by about ½ km (Krogdahl, 1952). The amount of ellipticity is close to what a fluid moon would be expected to have had when it was only one-third its present distance from the earth. This is thought to indicate that the moon solidified from a liquid state at this distance.

One of the remarkable features of the revolution of the satellites is that some of them revolve about their planets faster than these rotate on their own axes. This is true of Phobos, the inner satellite of Mars. Thus the month of Phobos is shorter than the Martian day. The inner rings of Saturn also turn faster than the planet.

The retrograde satellites, those which revolve in the opposite direction from most of the solar system, may have acquired this motion since the origin of the planets. One of the retrograde satellites is Triton, which revolves around Neptune. Its direction of motion can possibly be explained by the behavior of the outermost known planet Pluto. The eccentricity of Pluto is so great that it could pass between Triton and Neptune. If this should occur with just the right relative positions of the three bodies, Pluto could be captured as a satellite by Neptune and the direction of revolution of Triton reversed. Conversely, if Pluto was once a satellite, a close encounter between it and Triton could have ejected the former and reversed the direction of motion of the latter. The outer retrograde satellites may have obtained their motion similarly, their companions having become comets or been lost altogether to the solar system.

One of the remarkable features of the planets is the spacing of their orbits. This is nearly regular, following a geometric progression known as Bode's rule. If one assumes that the asteroids are a planet, either partially assembled or broken up, then the radii from the sun to the planets, numbered outward with $N = 0$ for Venus, are given approximately by the equation $R = (0.4 + 0.3 \times 2^N)R_e$, where R_e is the distance of the earth from the sun (Table 2.1).[1] No theoretical reason is known why this rule should hold. Therefore, any method of formation of the

TABLE 2.1 DATA ON THE PLANETS

Body	Distance from sun, astron. units	Average radius, km	Average specific gravity	Number of satellites
Sun	.....	695,000	1.42	
Mercury	0.39	2,490	4.8	0
Venus	0.72	6,200	4.9	0
Earth	1.00	6,370	5.51	1
Mars	1.5	3,400	3.95	2
Asteroids	2.8			
Jupiter	5.2	71,300	1.34	12
Saturn	9.6	59,600	0.69	9
Uranus	19.25	25,800	1.36	5
Neptune	30.2	22,300	1.30	2
Pluto	39.6	2,900	....	0
Moon	.....	1,740	3.36	

planets which would require them to have this spacing would seem to be particularly likely.

In addition to the planets and asteroids, the solar system contains many smaller bodies which appear to be permanently held to the sun by gravitational forces. Much meteoric material may be simply gathered into the solar system from space, but there are also meteor clouds which the earth encounters at regular intervals, which must, therefore, be a relatively permanent part of the solar system. The presence of finely dispersed matter is also demonstrated by the zodiacal light, a faint cone of luminosity which can be seen near the sun. This light is believed to be scattered by gas or fine meteoritic material which fills the inner part of the solar system like a very fine mist. Such a layer of gas would have to be revolving about the sun to exist at all and even then would not be stable (Jeffreys, 1939). It would lose energy owing to viscous damping of its motion. Some of its mass would escape into outer space, and the rest would be gradually absorbed into the sun. What is seen today must, therefore, be only the remainder of a much larger cloud, and we can expect this to have played a role in the evolution of the present solar system.

Similarly, many of the comets, though they travel far from the sun, return periodically and must be considered a part of the solar system. Their attachment to the sun is such that they will be easily lost if their

[1] There are two exceptions to this rule. Using $N = -1$ for Mercury we get $R/R_e = 0.65$, whereas the actual distance of Mercury from the sun is $0.39R_e$. The position of Neptune does not fit Bode's rule at all. Pluto occurs approximately where the next planet beyond Uranus should be.

path should be changed slightly in a close encounter with a planet or any other large body. Similarly, the sun could have acquired them long after the formation of the rest of the solar system if they came close enough to be trapped by its gravitational field.

Another prominent feature is the variation in size and composition of the parts of the system (Table 2.1). The planets can be divided into two

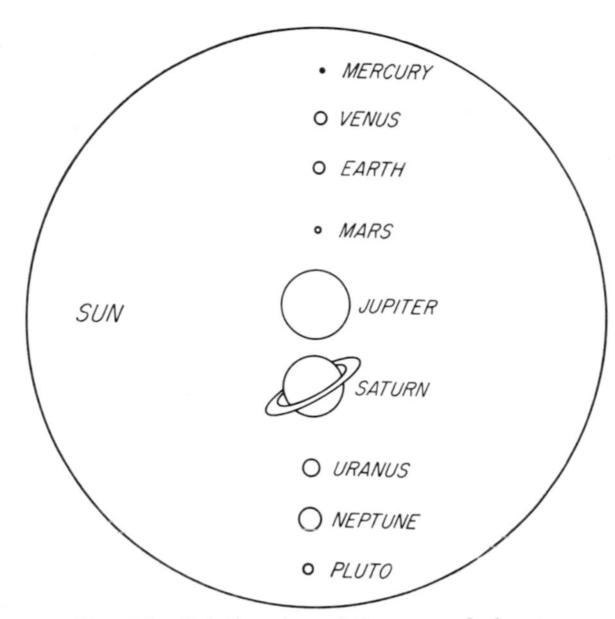

FIG. 2.5 Relative sizes of the sun and planets.

groups. The inner planets, Mercury, Venus, Earth, and Mars, are small and dense and contain little hydrogen and helium. The outer planets, Jupiter, Uranus, Saturn, and Neptune, are large and light and consist in great part of these two elements, as does the sun itself. The moon, while lacking the gases, is much lighter than the earth. Less is known about Pluto and the other satellites. The lack of light gases on the smaller planets is not surprising, as their gravitational fields are too weak to hold these materials, and they will escape if the atoms acquire sufficient velocity owing to their temperatures. Thus the larger planets, by their very size, tend to hold much matter which would be lost by the smaller bodies. Also, being farther from the sun, they are colder, and for that reason the gas escapes less easily. However, the jump in size (Fig. 2.5) from Mars to Jupiter is remarkable, and the variation in radius and density within the two groups is not regular.

The asteroids, which lie between Mars and Jupiter, are notable for their large eccentricities (average 0.15) which are greater than that possessed by any of the planets except Pluto (0.25). It has been suggested that a planet once existed here but was disrupted by tidal forces because of its proximity to Jupiter. It has also been suggested that these bodies are a partially assembled planet.

The physical appearance of the various bodies is also of significance. The Earth, Mars, and Venus all have atmospheres, so their present aspect

FIG. 2.6 Southern portion of the moon at last quarter. (*Courtesy of Mount Wilson and Palomar Observatories.*)

may be largely the result of erosion and other current processes. The moon, however, lacks any atmosphere. Its surface is highly pockmarked with craters (Fig. 2.6). At one time, these were thought to be volcanic in nature, but it can be proved that the ratio of their width to their depth is what would be expected for a surface explosion. They are, therefore, believed to result from the impact of large meteors striking the moon. Similar craters are found on the earth (Fig. 2.7) but become obliterated by erosion, whereas those on the moon may be very old.

One other feature of the solar system which is of importance relative to its origin is the rate of heat radiation by the sun. Study of paleoclimatology indicates that throughout geologic time there have been only minor variations in the earth's climate belts and hence in the amount of heat incident on the earth's surface. The simplest explanation of this is

Fig. 2.7 Air view of Meteor Crater, Arizona. (*Courtesy of Meteor Crater Museum.*)

that the sun has changed relatively little during the time for which we have a geologic record and that its distance from the earth has stayed nearly constant.

2.4 Condensation Hypotheses. There are two principal theories regarding the origin of the solar system. Both were first proposed about the middle of the eighteenth century, and both have been modified so greatly since their original conception that the men who first stated them would hardly recognize them today. One theory postulates that the planets were formed by the gathering together of smaller particles scattered through space. The other proposes that the planets are all fragments of a single larger body.

The one most popular at the present time is the condensation hypothesis. This originated with the German philosopher Immanuel Kant, who in 1755 speculated that the parts of the solar system condensed from a rotating, diffuse cloud of dust and gas. In 1796, Laplace, the French mathematician and philosopher, proposed a similar theory, apparently independently. Laplace went into more detail on the events of the earth's genesis than Kant had done. He postulated that the sun was originally a rotating disk of radius greater than the distance from the sun to the outermost planet. This disk was contracting, the energy thus obtained causing the whole mass to rotate faster. As the gas contracted, the velocity of the outer edge periodically became so great that a ring of material was left behind. These rings were later gathered together to form the planets. The satellites were formed as the planets condensed in a similar manner.

This theory was abandoned for many reasons. It was difficult to account for the angular momentum being largely in the planets when most of the mass condensed into the sun. To avoid this difficulty, it is necessary to assume that almost all the mass was in a central concentration from the start, and then the cloud would be so diffuse that gravitation would have been unable to draw the parts together.

Condensation is particularly unlikely if the gas cloud is hot. Even a mass concentration the size of the earth is unable to hold hydrogen and helium in its atmosphere at existing temperatures. The problem of getting a hot gas to condense has led all later proponents of the condensation hypothesis to suppose that the cloud was originally composed of cold particles.

G. H. Darwin and N. Lockyer postulated an original cloud of meteoroids of various sizes. They supposed that these were constantly colliding and that when they collided, their mutual gravitational attraction tended to hold them together. Because larger particles have a greater gravitational attraction than smaller ones, a few of the centers of condensation soon outstripped the others, becoming the sun and the planets. The cratered surface of the moon proves that bodies can grow in this manner, and indeed, matter is being added to the earth today by meteors. The principal weakness in this theory is that the impact of two small meteoroids would tend to disrupt both rather than to form a single body. Another difficulty is to explain how the material was gathered together in the first place into bodies the size of meteoroids. It is more generally believed that most interstellar material is gaseous.

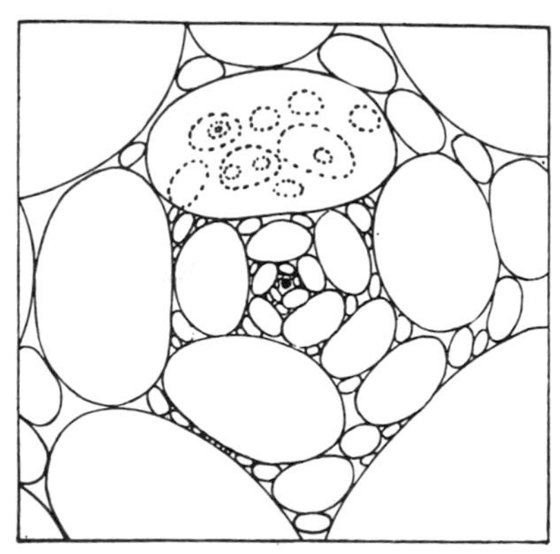

FIG. 2.8 Schematic distribution of eddies in the nebula from which the solar system condensed. (*Kuiper, 1951.*)

T. C. Chamberlain proposed that the matter was originally in the form not of gas or large meteoroids but of tiny dust grains which he called planetesimals. A cloud of these was rotating about the sun as a center, and as individual particles collided, they stuck to one another, gradually building up to form the planets and other large bodies. Regardless of the size of the particles, the same difficulties are encountered in trying to get the matter to condense at all.

Von Weizsacker and Kuiper have attempted to overcome this objection by proposing that the cloud of gas was in turbulent motion and that cells were formed in it (Fig. 2.8), small near the center and larger farther from the sun. Within these cells, the violence and irregularity of the motion were so great as to overcome the static gas laws which normally would apply. Because of this, the density of the matter was able locally to become so great that centers of mass were able to condense permanently. Eventually these condensations swept up a large part of the cloud of gas or dust. The arrangement of the cells is thought to have had the proper spacing to give planets at the distances from the sun required by Bode's rule.

The Von Weizsacker-Kuiper theory, like those of Laplace and Chamberlain, starts by postulating a system resembling the spiral nebulae so commonly seen in space (Fig. 2.2). It is logical to supose that the stars themselves condensed from such a cloud of matter, as we see them today distributed in such arrangements. The analogy is an uncertain one scaled down to planetary dimensions, as the size of nebulae is of an entirely different magnitude from that of the solar system. Mass distributions of stellar dimensions resembling spiral nebulae have not been observed. The theory does have the advantage that it starts with a star the size of the sun. This body is presumed to have pulled to itself by gravitational attraction a cloud of cold gas or dust as it passed through one of the parts of space where such clouds are known to exist. It is difficult to see where such a distribution of matter would have acquired its angular momentum; though once started, the present distribution of it is reasonable. The principal appeal of the theory is that it predicts that solar systems such as ours are common in the universe. Our world is not unique but may be duplicated a myriad of times elsewhere in our galaxy and in others.

A feature which this theory has difficulty explaining is the rapid rotation of Mars' satellite Phobos and the inner rings of Saturn. It is difficult to see why condensation from a cloud would result in a satellite which revolved faster than its planet rotates. Furthermore, the variation in the densities of the planets is peculiar. It is easy to understand why the large planets, with their strong gravitational fields, have low densities, since they were able to retain the light elements hydrogen and helium which the small planets cannot hold. However, if we arrange the inner planets (including the moon, which is big enough to be a planet) according to increasing density (Table 2.1), we find that the order is Moon, Mars,

Mercury, Venus, Earth, showing in general an increase of density with radius. No such systematic variation is apparent for the light, large planets. The densities of the planets appear to be due mainly to the relative sizes of their cores, whose radii are about half the total radius for the Earth and Venus and four-tenths for Mars (Urey, 1952). Mercury and the moon appear to have no core of this type. The condensation theory offers no explanation for this. It is also difficult to explain the large eccentricities of the asteroids and comets and the inclination of the orbit of Mercury.

Another problem is how to explain the presence of radioactive elements in the earth. It was previously pointed out that the only known place where radioactive elements can be formed is in the interior of extremely hot and dense stars. If this is the case, then the radioactive material which is now a part of the earth must at one time have been a part of such a star. Unless the earth acquired it after its formation, this material must have been scattered in space as a part of the cloud from which the solar system condensed. It will be shown in Chap. 4 that the material of which the earth is composed is not over 5.5 billion years old and that the most probable age of meteorites is about 4.5 billion years. Assuming that the meteorites were formed at the same time as the rest of the solar system, the scattering of the radioactive material in space must have taken place in less than 20 per cent of the age of the material. This means that there must have been a hasty (1 billion-year) period of dispersal previous to the concentration which finally yielded the relatively stable solar system as we see it today. The process by which this scattering took place is still to be explained.

Combine this with the evidence of Hubble's red shift which suggests that all the matter of the universe has been scattering for something like 5 billion years, and one may ask if it is necessary to scatter the material into a diffuse cloud at all only to reconcentrate it. Cannot the earth have been separated from a parent star directly in one piece, together with its radioactive elements? This brings us to the fragmentation theories.

2.5 Fragmentation Theories. The second group of hypotheses all require a special transient event for the creation of the solar system. In 1749, the French philosopher Buffon suggested that the planets were torn from the sun by a collision with another star. J. H. Jeans and T. C. Chamberlain suggested that an actual collision might not be necessary. A second star approaching closely would cause very large tides in the sun. It is known that sunspots are actually large clouds of matter thrown out of the sun to distances as great as 140,000 miles. These violent eruptions result from processes deep within the sun about which we know very little. The gravitational force of a star in a near approach to the sun might detach great pieces of the tidal prominences. Part of this matter would be carried away by the second star. Most of it would fall back into the sun, but part might be left circulating about the sun in elliptical orbits of high eccentricity. Material would be similarly drawn from the passing star, and some of it would be left behind. The angular momentum of this cloud of rotating matter would be provided by the velocity of the passing star relative to the sun.

The large chunks of gas drawn from the sun would expand and scatter, but owing to the expansion, they would also cool, allowing much of their mass to gather into dense concentrations to become planets, satellites, asteroids, and comets. The meteorites would be pieces of one or more of these concentrations, later broken up and scattered. The gas which was not captured by the largest concentrations would in part escape entirely, and the rest would be gradually drawn back into the sun. This reabsorption would be a gradual process. The zodiacal light may be a reflection from the last remnant of it, existing as a thin cloud near the sun.

The original, distended cloud of gas would tend to damp the motion of the planets through it and would thus reduce the ellipticity of the orbits of most of the bodies. The comets, since they followed the second star farther out into space, would be less affected and would retain highly elliptical orbits. The rotation of the sun and planets would be acquired from the angular momentum of parts of the gas cloud which they drew into themselves by gravitational attraction. The satellites in most cases would have been formed independently and captured at an early stage of the process. With the exception of the moon, whose origin will be treated in greater detail in the next chapter, all the satellites are much smaller than their planets. It is easier to see how some of the satellites might have acquired a retrograde sense of revolution starting with so violent and transient an event than in the more orderly development of the system by condensation.

The major objection to this theory is the difficulty of accounting for the distribution of angular momentum of the system. The sun possesses only 3 per cent of it, and Jupiter over half. Since Jupiter has only one-thousandth the mass of the sun, and since most of the matter drawn out by the passing star would eventually return to the sun, it is impossible to account for the present distribution of momentum if only one other star besides the sun were involved.

This objection was largely overcome by H. N. Russell, who pointed out that about 10 per cent of all stars are known to be binaries in which most of the angular momentum of the system lies in the rotation of the two about each other. It is now thought that the majority of stars are multiple. If the sun had had a companion and a third star had struck it or simply approached close enough to disrupt it, the angular motion of the

The two stars approaching each other could have been rotating in opposite directions so that they slowed each other down or one forced the other to even reverse its direction of rotation.

planets could have come from the previous motion of the companion star about the sun. Most of the mass of the sun's companion would have been carried away by the other star. Some of it would have fallen into the sun, giving it its rotation. The rest forms the planets and other satellites of the sun.

The principal objection to this theory is the unlikelihood of a close approach of two stars, considering how far apart they are at present. However, it must be remembered that Hubble's red shift suggests that at one time the stars were much closer together, thereby increasing the chance of such an encounter. Furthermore, collisions are not entirely unknown in the universe. The light spectrum of the nebula Cygnus A contains frequencies corresponding to a form of ionized neon which is believed to exist only when the atoms are traveling at speeds greater than 1,000 km (620 miles) per sec. They are most easily explained by supposing that Cygnus A consists of two nebulae in the act of colliding with each other.

The sun's companion may have been much smaller than the sun. If it were small enough to be liquid or even solid instead of gaseous, then it is perhaps easier to explain the variation in density and composition of the planets. The small star from which they were formed may have had an iron core, large parts of which helped to make the Earth, Venus, and Mars, but were not included in the composition of the moon or Mercury. It is thus easier to see why there are the several types of meteorites, which would have come from different parts of the parent star.

Hoyle (1950) has suggested that the sun may have had as a companion a very dense star which became a supernova. Because of their extreme rarity, relatively little is known of these unusual stars, but it is believed that they literally explode because of nuclear reactions. Such an event might completely destroy the star, leaving the sun with only a few small fragments of its original companion. These pieces, however, would possess most of what remained of the original angular momentum of the system. Such a parentage would make it easier to account for the observed quantities of the radioactive elements in the earth.

A major problem of this variation is to produce the present radii and narrow range of ellipticities of the planetary orbits. This is most easily accomplished if the planets were formed by the recombination of a large number of moderate-sized pieces of the parent star. In this case the various phases of the ellipticity of these pieces could average out to give nearly round paths for the final accumulation.

At the present stage of knowledge it is impossible to choose between condensation and fragmentation as the dominant process in the earth's formation. Both have probably been involved in the evolution of the galaxy. Both theories account equally well for the single plane of revolution of all the planetary bodies, the distribution of angular momentum, the zodiacal light, and most other features of the solar system. No one of the characteristics of the solar system can be said to provide proof of the impossibility of either theory.

It is of interest to compare the type of earth which would result from these two hypotheses with what we have today. In both cases, it would be expected to have a composition comparable to that of the sun and other stars, except for the lack of light gases. According to the condensation hypothesis, it would be formed by the coagulation of cold particles. If this is the case, then the interior of the earth must initially have been an unsorted mass of uniform composition, and any differentiation into layers which is observed today would most likely have occurred after the earth's formation, unless the material accumulated so fast that its energy of impact on arrival kept the growing earth molten.

A cold origin of this sort would impose upon the whole earth a very different set of initial conditions from that provided by the fragmentation hypothesis, which postulates that the original earth was a hot ball of gas or liquid which would quickly have sorted into layers on the basis of the density of its components as it initially began to cool. The present elliptical shape of the moon suggests that it solidified from a liquid when it was still much closer to the earth than it is now. This favors the fragmentation origin for the solar system with its hot source for the material of which the various bodies are made.

Much of the remainder of this book will deal with the interior of the earth. Its present structure must have developed from whatever form it had initially. Thus the chapters which follow will give us more evidence with which to judge these two hypotheses.

CHAPTER 3

ORIGIN OF THE MOON

Both the fragmentation and condensation hypotheses offer possible explanations of the origin of the moon. According to the former, it could be one of the pieces of stellar material left circulating about the sun following the breakup of a companion star. Its close relation to the earth would be a result of its initial proximity at the time equilibrium was established. In the case of condensation, the moon is presumed to have formed in a manner similar to the earth and at about the same radius from the sun as one of the turbulent, condensing cells postulated by Von Weizsacker and Kuiper. A later close approach of the two bodies resulted in the moon's capture.

The moon is unique among the satellites of our solar system in that its mass is 0.0123 that of the earth, being much larger with respect to its planet than any other satellite. The density of the moon is such that it is believed to be composed entirely of rocky materials, without any iron core such as the earth is thought to contain. This has led to the theory that the moon was formed from the earth at a time when the material of the earth had differentiated into two layers, a dense inner core and a lighter, rocky mantle. The moon is presumed to have been taken entirely from this outer part of the earth.

There is a second reason why it has been postulated that the moon was derived from the earth. As shown in Chap. 2, if one studies the tides on the earth, there is found to be an exchange of energy between the earth's rotation on its axis and the moon's revolution. This transfer of momentum causes the moon to move farther from the earth at the current rate of a few feet per century. The present average distance of the moon from the earth is 383,403 km. When it was nearer, its rate of retreat would have been faster because the tides would have been larger. Jeffreys (1952) estimates that the moon would have taken a little over 4 billion years to retreat to its present position by this process, starting very close to the earth's surface. Unless the moon has somehow been captured by the earth more recently or was formed at the same time and not over about 4 billion years ago, it must have been separated from the earth about that long ago.

If this is the case, before the separation the earth would have possessed all the angular momentum now resident in the earth-moon system. This would have resulted in its rotating with a period of about 4 hr (Jeffreys, 1952). The period of the solar tides would have been half this. If the earth were gaseous at this time, it would have had a free period of vibration which would also have been close to 2 hr. Resonance caused by coincidence of this free vibration and the solar tides could have built up the amplitude of the tidal bulges. If the motion became large enough, a big piece of the earth could have become detached to form the moon. Such disruptive resonance would be particularly likely if the earth's path at this time were more eccentric than it is at present and the resonance occurred as the earth passed close to the sun at perihelion, causing exceptionally large tides.

In support of this theory, it has been pointed out that the Pacific Ocean occupies a great depression in the earth's crust almost big enough to hold the whole mass of the moon. Furthermore, as will be shown later, certain types of rock prevalent on the continental masses and possibly under part of the Atlantic Ocean are missing under the Pacific. It is as though this material had been carried away with the separation of the moon.

This argument does not stand up under careful consideration. For the moon to have originated in this way, the earth must have been fluid at the time, preferably gaseous, or large tides would not have been possible. If the earth were fluid enough to be disrupted, it would have been fluid enough for subsequent mixing of the materials of which it is made to have obliterated completely any scar left by the moon's removal. Even if a thin solid crust had already formed, the part which was not carried away would have been broken up and redistributed so as to leave no evidence of where the moon had been.

Furthermore, it is extremely unlikely that resonant protrusions could have formed of sufficient amplitude to have allowed the crest of the tide to separate from the earth. Friction would have limited the height of the bulges. The greater the height, the greater the amount of friction and hence loss of energy from the tide.

If the moon was not drawn from the earth, it must have originated as a separate body, either by condensation, as Von Weizsacker and Kuiper suppose, or as a fragment of some larger body. Baldwin (1949) has shown that the dimensions of the lunar craters are what would be expected if they were formed by the impact of large meteorites on the moon's surface and that they are much too broad and shallow to be of volcanic origin. The prominence of the craters suggests that the moon was formed, in part at least, by the accumulation of small chunks of meteoric matter. The craters we see today were formed by the impact of these masses at a time when the surface of the moon was solid enough to permit them to remain as undisturbed topographic features throughout all subsequent time.

This is no proof of formation by the coalescing of small pieces. If the earth and moon are both fragments of a disrupted companion star of the sun, many smaller pieces were probably formed simultaneously. Some of these would later have been gathered up by larger bodies such as the earth and the moon. Thus the surface of the moon would have craters as a result of either mode of origin. On the earth the erosive action of wind and water, which is absent on the moon, would relatively quickly remove the traces of any craters that once existed, so their almost complete absence on the earth is to be expected.

Evidence for a formerly molten condition of the moon comes from its present shape. It has a bulge on the side toward the earth of such a size as to suggest that it solidified from a liquid at a time when it was distorted by a stronger gravitational field than now acts upon it. This shape can be most easily explained by supposing that the moon solidified when it was at a distance of only 140,000 km from the earth. It must have been formed so short a time before it acquired this shape that it was still fluid and deformable. A body the size of the moon would cool much more rapidly than the earth. Jeffreys (1952) estimates that the moon would retreat to about 240,000 km from the earth in not over 2×10^8 years; so it must have acquired its shape early in its history as a satellite. Apparently the moon has sufficient strength to have retained its bulge throughout its subsequent history.

CHAPTER 4

GEOCHRONOLOGY

Our world has not always existed in a form similar to what we observe today. The matter which constitutes the earth approached its present aspect at some time in the past. This time is the starting point of geologic chronology. The solid globe we occupy was not created in an instant but must have formed as a result of a systematic series of modifications of a part of the universe which existed previously in some other form. The rate of alteration of this distribution of matter and energy may be supposed to have been relatively rapid as the earth began to form. As a condition of equilibrium was approached, the rate of modification decreased. Changes are still taking place slowly, and gradual alterations will continue until a new cycle of rapid change is started in the future by some cataclysmic event such as the return of the moon to the earth. Because the earth evolved from some previous state rather than being created in an instant, the age we seek is no precise time in days, years, or even centuries. The best that can be hoped for is an approximate figure, whose value will depend on which stage of the early history of our planet is dated.

4.1 Age of the Moon. Several lines of evidence which give figures for the earth's age have been discussed in previous chapters. One of these is the retreat of the moon. Jeffreys (1952) has estimated that it would take the moon about 4×10^9 years to retreat to its present distance from a position close to the earth. This age value depends critically on the rate of dissipation of tidal energy in shallow seas. The distribution of shallow seas may have varied greatly throughout geologic time. The greater the tidal friction, the greater the rate of retreat of the moon. If tidal friction was substantially less in the past than it is at present, then the age could be greater than this. Tidal friction must also depend on the volume of water in the oceans. Water is being brought to the earth's surface currently by volcanoes and hot springs, and it is probable that the rate of release of juvenile water by this means has been at least as great in the past as it is at present. Mason (1952), Umbgrove (1947), and Rubey (1951) have summarized the theories on the rate of growth of the oceans. They conclude that a gradual growth, which would have changed the volume by only a small fraction since the pre-Cambrian, is most probable. Any growth of the oceans implies that the rate of exchange of energy between the earth and moon may have been less in the past, when the oceans were smaller and when shallow seas were correspondingly less extensive. Thus, it is quite possible that Jeffreys' figure of 4×10^9 years for the period during which the moon can have existed is too small. On the other hand, both Baldwin (1949) and Jeffreys have pointed out that tidal friction may be greater than the figure on which the 4×10^9-year age is based, so that this is at best only an estimate of the order of magnitude of the moon's maximum possible age.

The shape of the moon suggests that it solidified from a liquid at only a third of its present distance from the earth. Almost all the available 4×10^9 years of the moon's retreat would be involved in moving from one-third of its present distance to where it is now. Therefore, the earth must have existed for at least this length of time to allow the moon to move to its present position. On the other hand, a body the size of the moon would probably have solidified from a liquid state in much less than 4×10^9 years, so the moon cannot have been very old when it became a satellite of the earth. The simplest hypothesis is to assume that the earth and moon were formed at nearly the same time, which makes the earth also about 4×10^9 years old.

4.2 The Red Shift. A slightly larger figure for the maximum age is obtained from the shift of stellar spectra to longer wavelengths. We have seen that all parts of the universe appear to be retreating from the earth. If their present paths are projected backward, it is found that about 5 billion years ago all this matter would have been concentrated in a relatively small volume of the universe (Sec. 2.2). If this were the case, the concentration of mass and energy would have been so great that it is unlikely that our solar system could have existed as we know it today. This gives a maximum age for the whole universe in its present condition. The earth must be younger than this but may be almost this old.

4.3 Radioactive Disintegration.[1] Everyone is familiar with the use of an hourglass to tell time (Fig. 4.1). If we know that it takes 60 min for the sand to run from the top to the bottom part of the glass, then we know that on the average 1/3,600 of the sand falls from one chamber to the other per second. To get the approximate time in the middle of the hour, we could measure the amount of sand which had fallen up to that time and divide by the amount falling per second. To get the time accurately, it would be necessary to make a correction for any variation

[1] For a more thorough treatment of radioactive age determinations, see Knopf, 1931, and Faul, 1954.

in the rate at which the sand fell. A slight decrease in the rate at which it falls would be expected as the height of the column of sand in the upper chamber decreases.

In a similar manner, the radioactive disintegration of certain elements can be used to obtain figures for the age of the earth. Twelve natural radioactive series discovered up to 1953 are shown in Table 4.1, which is

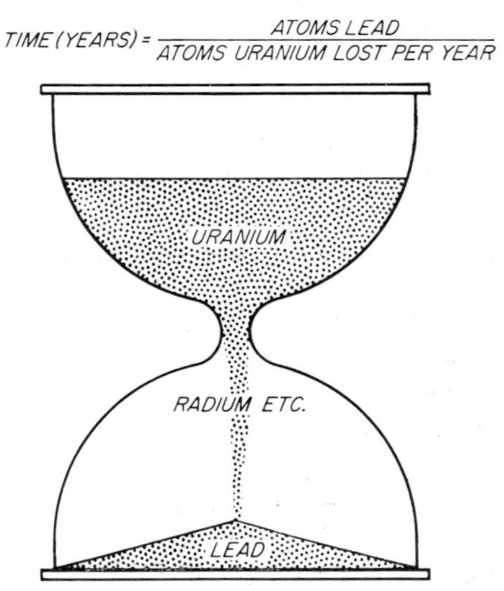

Fig. 4.1 Radioactive disintegration tells time like an hourglass.

taken in large part from data published by Hollander et al. (1953). In addition to these, neodymium 150, tellurium 130, and tin 124 are known to be radioactive with long half-lives; and hydrogen 3, beryllium 7, and beryllium 10 are produced in small amounts by natural processes in the atmosphere.

In the case of the isotope of uranium whose atomic weight is 238, 4.9×10^{-18} of whatever amount of this material is present decomposes into thorium 234 per second. The thorium decomposes into protoactinium, and so on down the series through radium and radon, eventually becoming lead of atomic weight 206. If we started with N atoms of uranium and after time T had L atoms of lead, then roughly

$$T = \frac{L}{\lambda_u N} \tag{4.1}$$

where $\lambda_u = 4.9 \times 10^{-18}$, the disintegration constant of U^{238}. The atoms which started as uranium but have proceeded through their disintegration only as far as radium or one of the other intermediate steps of the series correspond to the grains of sand in the hourglass which are in the act of falling from the upper chamber but have not yet reached the bottom of the hourglass. Except in the early stages of the process, they represent a small fraction of the total end-product atoms and can be neglected. Even in the early stages, we can calculate how many grains (atoms) are in the process of falling (disintegrating) and, after so calculating, correct for them.

If the time involved is large, we must take into account the fact that the number of atoms which disintegrate per unit of time changes. As noted above, λ_u of the atoms of uranium disintegrate per second. This means that during each succeeding second fewer atoms will disintegrate, as there are less total atoms present owing to those which broke up in previous seconds. Here our analogy breaks down. The sand will eventually all run down in the hourglass, but the radioactive disintegration will never end, although the disintegration will slow down asymptotically.

To see what happens more clearly, suppose we start with A_0 atoms of a radioactive element whose disintegration constant is λ_1. Let A be the number of atoms of the parent element present at any time t thereafter. The rate of disintegration will be

$$\frac{dA}{dt} = -\lambda_1 A \tag{4.2}$$

TABLE 4.1 THE NATURAL RADIOACTIVE SERIES*
Uranium Series

Element	Mass number	Atomic number	Half-life	Radiation
U	238	92	4.5×10^9 years	α
Th	234	90	24 days	β
Pa	234	91	6.7 hr, 1.2 min (2 isomers)	β
U	234	92	2.5×10^5 years	α
Th	230	90	8×10^4 years	α
Ra	226	88	1,620 years	α
Rn	222	86	3.8 days	α
Po	218	84	3 min	99.97% α, 0.03% β
Pb	214	82	26.8 min	β
or At	218	85	2 sec	α
Bi	214	83	20 min	99.96% β; 0.04% α
Po	214	84	1.6×10^{-4} sec	α
or Tl	210	81	1.3 min	β
Pb	210	82	22 years	β
Bi	210	83	5 days	β
Po	210	84	138 days	α
Pb	206	82		
				$8\alpha + 6\beta$

TABLE 4.1 THE NATURAL RADIOACTIVE SERIES* (*Continued*)

Actinium Series

Element	Mass number	Atomic number	Half-life	Radiation
U	235	92	7.1×10^8 years	α
Th	231	90	25.6 hr	β
Pa	231	91	3.4×10^4 years	α
Ac	227	89	22 years	β or α
Th	227	90	19 days	α
or Fr	223	87	21 min	β (small α alternate)
Ra	223	88	11.2 days	α
Rn	219	86	3.9 sec	α
Po	215	84	1.83×10^{-3} sec	α (small β alternate)
Pb	211	82	26 min	β
Bi	211	83	2.16 min	α (small β alternate)
Tl	207	81	4.8 min	β
Pb	207	82		
				7α, 4β

Thorium Series

Element	Mass number	Atomic number	Half-life	Radiation
Th	232	90	1.4×10^{10} years	α
Ra	228	88	6.7 years	β
Ac	228	89	6.1 hr	β
Th	228	90	1.9 years	α
Ra	224	88	3.64 days	α
Rn	220	86	54.5 sec	α
Po	216	84	0.16 sec	α (small β alternate)
Pb	212	82	10.6 hr	β
Bi	212	83	1 hr	63% β, 37% α
Po	212	84	3×10^{-7} sec	α
or Tl	208	81	3.1 min	β
Pb	208	82		
				6α, 4β

Potassium Series

Element	Mass number	Atomic number	Half-life	Radiation
K	40	19	1.2×10^9 years	β (90%) or K-orbit electron capture
Ca	40	20		
or Ar	40	18		

Carbon Series

Element	Mass number	Atomic number	Half-life	Radiation
C	14	6	5,600 years	β
N	14	7		

Rubidium Series

Element	Mass number	Atomic number	Half-life	Radiation
Rb	87	37	6×10^{10} years	β
Sr	87	38		

TABLE 4.1 THE NATURAL RADIOACTIVE SERIES* (*Continued*)

Lutecium Series

Element	Mass number	Atomic number	Half-life	Radiation
Lu	176	71	2.4×10^{10} years	β or electron capture
Hf	176	72		
or Yb	176	70		

Rhenium Series

Element	Mass number	Atomic number	Half-life	Radiation
Re	187	75	5×10^{10} years	β
Os	187	76		

Lanthanum Series

Element	Mass number	Atomic number	Half-life	Radiation
La	138	57	7×10^{10} years	Electron capture or β
Ba	138	56		
or Ce	138	58		

Indium Series

Element	Mass number	Atomic number	Half-life	Radiation
In	115	49	6×10^{14} years	β
Sn	115	50		

Samarium Series

Element	Mass number	Atomic number	Half-life	Radiation
Sm	147	62	1.4×10^{11} years	α
Nd	143	60		

* Data from Hollander et al., 1953; Ahrens, 1956; Aldrich et al., 1956*a* and *b*; Senftle, 1956.

Writing this in the form

$$\frac{dA}{A} = -\lambda_1\, dt \tag{4.3}$$

it can be seen that the solution will be of the form

$$\ln A = -\lambda_1 t + K \tag{4.4}$$

where ln stands for logarithm to the base e and K is a constant which can be determined from the boundary conditions as shown below. Throughout, ln will refer to natural logarithms—log to logarithms to the base 10.

Equation (4.4) can be written

$$A = e^{-\lambda_1 t + K} \tag{4.5}$$

At time $t = 0$, $A = A_0$, so

$$A_0 = e^K \tag{4.6}$$

and

$$A = A_0 e^{-\lambda_1 t} \tag{4.7}$$

The number of new atoms which have been formed from A up to any time t is

$$B_f = A_0 - A = A_0(1 - e^{-\lambda_1 t}) = A(e^{\lambda_1 t} - 1) \tag{4.8}$$

This is the number of atoms of element B of the series which is present at time t only if B is not radioactive. If B is radioactive,

$$\frac{dB}{dt} = \lambda_1 A - \lambda_2 B \tag{4.9}$$

It can be shown [by substituting in (4.9)] that the solution of this equation is

$$B = \frac{A_0\lambda_1}{\lambda_2 - \lambda_1}(e^{-\lambda_1 t} - e^{-\lambda_2 t}) = \frac{A\lambda_1}{\lambda_2 - \lambda_1}[1 - e^{(\lambda_1 - \lambda_2)t}] \tag{4.10}$$

In a similar manner, if the third element of the series C is radioactive

$$\frac{dC}{dt} = \lambda_2 B - \lambda_3 C \tag{4.11}$$

$$\begin{aligned} C &= A_0\lambda_1\lambda_2\left(\frac{e^{-\lambda_1 t}}{(\lambda_3 - \lambda_1)(\lambda_2 - \lambda_1)} + \frac{e^{-\lambda_2 t}}{(\lambda_1 - \lambda_2)(\lambda_3 - \lambda_2)} + \frac{e^{-\lambda_3 t}}{(\lambda_1 - \lambda_3)(\lambda_2 - \lambda_3)}\right) \\ &= A\lambda_1\lambda_2\left(\frac{1}{(\lambda_3 - \lambda_1)(\lambda_2 - \lambda_1)} + \frac{e^{(\lambda_1 - \lambda_2)t}}{(\lambda_1 - \lambda_2)(\lambda_3 - \lambda_2)} + \frac{e^{(\lambda_1 - \lambda_3)t}}{(\lambda_1 - \lambda_3)(\lambda_2 - \lambda_3)}\right) \end{aligned} \tag{4.12}$$

No matter how long the series, the form of the differential equation will be

$$\frac{dN}{dt} = \lambda_m M - \lambda_n N \tag{4.13}$$

where M and N are the number of atoms of two successive members of the series present at any time t, and λ_m and λ_n are their disintegration constants. The number of atoms of N will be

$$\begin{aligned} N &= A_0(F_1 e^{-\lambda_1 t} + F_2 e^{-\lambda_2 t} \cdots F_n e^{-\lambda_n t}) \\ &= A[F_1 + F_2 e^{(\lambda_1 - \lambda_2)t} \cdots + F_n e^{(\lambda_1 - \lambda_n)t}] \end{aligned} \tag{4.14}$$

These equations can be greatly simplified if λ_1 is much smaller than any of the other disintegration constants in the series. In this case, after a time long enough that $\lambda_2 t$ is much greater than unity, (4.10) becomes

$$B \approx \frac{\lambda_1 A}{\lambda_2} \tag{4.15}$$

Similarly, (4.12) will become

$$C \approx \frac{\lambda_1 A}{\lambda_3} \tag{4.16}$$

and by analogy, for any element N except the end-product element,

$$N \approx \frac{\lambda_1 A}{\lambda_n} \tag{4.17}$$

The end-product element P is not radioactive. Therefore, λ_p is 0, which is not small compared with λ_1.

The meaning of the approximation, $\lambda_n t$ is much greater than 1, can be seen if we note the relation of λ_n to the corresponding half-life T_H of an element. At $t = T_H$, (4.7) becomes

$$A = A_0 e^{-\lambda_1 T_H} \tag{4.18}$$

Solving this for T_H,

$$T_H = \frac{\ln 0.5}{-\lambda_1} = 0.69315\lambda_1^{-1} \tag{4.19}$$

This relation between T_H and the disintegration constant applies to any radioactive element. Therefore, the approximation $\lambda_n t$ is much greater than 1 means that $0.69315t/T_n$ greatly exceeds 1, or that many half-lives of the element under consideration have elapsed. Since the half-lives of all the intermediate elements in the uranium and thorium series are small compared with the half-lives of their parents, this is usually a good approximation.

To find the amount of the end product present, it is sufficient to note that the total number of atoms present at any time (not counting the helium nuclei formed) must always equal the number present originally:

$$A_0 = A + B + C \cdots + N + P \tag{4.20}$$

Solving this for P and using (4.7) and (4.17) to simplify the result,

$$\begin{aligned} P &= A_0 - B - C \cdots - N \\ &\approx Ae^{-\lambda_1 t} - A - \frac{\lambda_1 A}{\lambda_2} - \frac{\lambda_1 A}{\lambda_3} \cdots - \frac{\lambda_1 A}{\lambda_n} \\ &= A(e^{-\lambda_1 t} - 1 - \lambda) \end{aligned} \tag{4.21}$$

where λ is the fraction of the elements in intermediate stages of disintegration. After sufficient time has elapsed, λ approaches the value

$$\lambda = \sum_{m=2}^{m=n} \frac{\lambda_1}{\lambda_m} \tag{4.22}$$

which is a very small quantity for the uranium and thorium series ($\lambda \approx 0.74 \times 10^{-4}$ for the U^{238} series).

Equation (4.21) can be solved for t, giving

$$t = -\lambda_1^{-1} \ln \left(1 + \frac{P}{A} + \lambda\right) \tag{4.23}$$

If $(P/A) + \lambda$ is less than 1, the log term can be expanded as an infinite series

$$t = -\lambda_1^{-1} \left[\left(\frac{P}{A} + \lambda\right) - \frac{1}{2}\left(\frac{P}{A} + \lambda\right)^2 + \frac{1}{3}\left(\frac{P}{A} + \lambda\right)^3 \cdots \right] \tag{4.24}$$

When P/A is much less than 1 but much larger than λ, to a first approximation

$$-t \approx \frac{P}{\lambda_1 A} \tag{4.25}$$

This approximation is good to ± 5 per cent only when P/A is 0.1 or less, which means roughly that t is not over one-seventh the half-life of the parent element.

With the use of these equations, the age of any mixture of a radioactive parent element and its derivatives can be determined from the numbers of atoms of the different isotopes present. To get an approximate figure, if the amount of parent and end product present and the disintegration constant of the parent are known, Eq. (4.25) can be used. To get a more accurate age, Eq. (4.23) should be employed. If the intermediate elements have not reached equilibrium, then Eq. (4.14) must be used.

4.4 Age of Oldest Rocks. The method described above has been useful in dating not only rocks and minerals but also certain fossils and even charcoal and wood. The oldest rocks found to date come from Manitoba, Canada, from Western Australia, and from Rhodesia. Their ages are in the range 2 billion to 3.5 billion years (Ahrens, 1955; Jeffery, 1956). Since the earth must have formed before any of its component rocks, it would have to be older than this.

Ages calculated in this way are subject to certain unavoidable sources of error. First, there is frequently no way of knowing how much of the end product, Pb^{206} in the case of U^{238}, or of intermediate products were in the rock at the time it was formed. For this reason, there is a tendency to calculate too large an age. This error can be reduced by measuring the amount of nonradiogenic lead present and assuming that the ratio of such ordinary lead, Pb^{204}, to radiogenic lead was the same when the rock was formed as the average for all rocks at that time. From this the amount of radiogenic lead originally present can be calculated. Subtracting this from the total radiogenic lead gives the amount formed by disintegration during the life of the rock, which can be used to calculate its age. This correction is made more difficult by the fact that the ratio of ordinary to radiogenic lead must be constantly decreasing owing to formation of the latter by the disintegration of heavier elements.

In many rocks, uncertainty is introduced by the possibility of leaching or contamination. All rocks, at least those near the surface of the earth, have some porosity. The seeping of water through the rock may dissolve or deposit mineral matter. If some of the elements involved are a part of the disintegration series, an age calculated from what remains may be very much in error.

4.5 Age of Meteorites. The danger of loss is particularly great in the case of times calculated from the amount of helium formed by disintegration. In the case of the U^{238} series, eight alpha particles are given off by each heavy nucleus. Thus, we can use the amount of helium formed to determine age just as lead is used. In this case Eq. (4.21) would have the form

$$P_{\text{He}} = 8(A_0 - A) - 7B - 6C - 5D - 4E - 3F - 2G - H \quad (4.26)$$

where B, C, etc., are the various α-emitting stages in the sequence. Again using the approximation that sufficient time has elapsed for the intermediate stages to reach equilibrium with the parent uranium

$$\begin{aligned} P_{\text{He}} &= 8A_0 - A\left(8 - \frac{7\lambda_1}{\lambda_b} - \frac{6\lambda_1}{\lambda_c} - \frac{5\lambda_1}{\lambda_d} - \frac{4\lambda_1}{\lambda_e} - \frac{3\lambda_1}{\lambda_f} - \frac{2\lambda_1}{\lambda_g} - \frac{\lambda_1}{\lambda_h}\right) \\ &= 8[A_0 - (1 + \lambda')A] \end{aligned} \quad (4.27)$$

where $8\lambda' A$ is the number of alpha particles locked in elements B to H which will eventually be emitted. Equations (4.23) and (4.25) become

$$-T \approx \lambda_1^{-1} \ln\left(1 + \frac{P}{8A} + \lambda'\right) \approx \frac{P}{8\lambda_1 A} \quad (4.28)$$

Similar equations can be derived for the other series.

Since helium is a gas, it has a tendency to escape from the rock. This is particularly true when the sample is being prepared for analysis, and special precautions must be taken to preserve it. For this reason, helium/uranium ratios have not been so satisfactory for calculating rock ages as are lead/uranium ratios. Since helium is a gas and is a rare constituent of rocks, it is usually assumed that, when in the molten state helium escapes from any rock melt in which it is being formed. After solidification, the helium will be largely retained unless weathering, fracturing, or seeping waters aid it to escape. Therefore, times calculated from helium ratios will give the age of solidification of the rock. It is not necessary to make a correction for the helium originally present, as this can be presumed to be negligibly small. In general, because of the danger of loss of the gas, such measurements give only a minimum possible age of the sample.

Helium-ratio determinations have been most widely used in estimating the age of meteorites. Ages as great as 4.8×10^9 years are commonly calculated for these bodies. Since they appear to be a part of our solar system, it is generally believed that they most probably were formed at about the same time as the earth. This figure is consistent with meteorite ages of 4.55×10^9 years found from lead/uranium ratios (Patterson, 1956). However, helium is produced in meteorites by the action of cosmic rays, so that He-ratio age determinations may give too large figures unless a correction is made for the helium added during the life of the meteorite.

One of the elements of the uranium and thorium disintegration series most easily lost from a rock is radon, since it is also a gas. This danger is greater for the U^{238} series than for the U^{235} series, since Rn^{222}, the radon isotope in the U^{238} series, has a half-life of 3.8 days whereas Rn^{219} has one of only 3.9 sec. Radon loss is particularly likely in highly porous formations. This loss is easily demonstrated by measuring radon concentration in the air. The concentration will tend to rise when the barometric pressure is falling and fall when the barometric pressure is rising (Preibsch et al., 1937). Since most sediments have appreciable porosities, it is more difficult to make accurate age determinations for sedimentary rocks than for igneous rocks. The danger of disturbance by circulating ground water is also important here.

One other fundamental assumption is made in calculating ages by the radioactive disintegration method. This is that the rate of decay has always been the same. It is known that in the interior of the sun, nuclear reactions complicate the situation. At any temperature or pressure collisions with stray cosmic rays or the emmanations of other atoms may cause other changes than those of normal disintegration. Within the earth, at the low concentrations of radioactive matter which occur, such collisions must be so rare that their effects can be neglected. Even at the highest temperature and pressure which are probable at the earth's center, it is still unlikely that the rate of decay is different from what we observe at the surface. However, it is always possible that as our knowledge of nuclear reactions grows, this will be found to be untrue. With present knowledge, we can say only that there is no reason to suppose that there can have been any variation in the rate of radioactive decay since the world was formed.

Some typical ages of rocks are given in Table 4.2.

4.6 Age of the Crust. Uranium disintegration can be used in another way to solve the age problem. If we measure the average amounts of U^{235} and Pb^{207} (or U^{238} and Pb^{206}) in all the common types of rocks exposed at the earth's surface and then estimate the total amounts of each of these rocks in the outermost part of the earth, we can calculate the total of these isotopes present. If we then assume that the average composition of the earth's crust has been constant throughout geologic time and that originally it contained no Pb^{207}, we can calculate its age. The figure obtained is about 5 billion to 5.5 billion years (McCrady, 1952; Faul, 1954; Ahrens, 1955). Since there may have been some lead present originally, this figure gives a maximum possible age.

4.7 Other Radioactive Age Determinations. The other disintegration series listed in Table 4.1 can also be used in age determinations. Use of the uranium and thorium series is limited to the rare rocks in which these minerals are sufficiently concentrated to make accurate analysis possible. This is true also of the various minor series. Potentially, the most useful series is probably Rb-Sr^{87}. Although rubidium is usually a minor constituent in rocks, measurable amounts are present in a great many rocks. The main difficulty in its use at present in age determinations is that its half-life is less accurately known than those of the other common radioactive elements.

Potassium 40 also has potential value for age measurements. Although only 0.001 per cent of natural potassium is the unstable isotope, potassium also is widely distributed in rocks. However, K^{40} is more difficult to use than Rb^{87}. The calcium branch of the disintegration series is not useful because calcium is usually a common constituent in the same rocks as potassium, and much of the Ca^{40} is likely to have been in the rock since it was formed. The other product, argon 40, is an inert gas and can be easily lost during the life of the rock or even during analysis.

The relative scarcity of the different radioactive isotopes gives us another check on the age of the universe as a whole. It has been found that stable nuclei of similar complexity of the elements of atomic weight 40 or more are all about equally abundant, whereas the lighter nuclei become more common as their weights decrease. It is to be expected that when the elements were first formed, this rule applied also to the unstable elements. Of the two uranium isotopes which head disintegration series, U^{238} is 140 times as common as U^{235}. The latter has a little over two-elevenths the half-life of the former. If both were once equally abundant, it would take about 6×10^9 years to reach the present proportion. Furthermore, it would have required at least several billion years for U^{235}, with a half-life of 7.1×10^8 years, to decrease to its present relatively low concentration. On the other hand, the abundance of U^{238}, with a half-life of 4.5×10^9 years, is still so great compared with the other nuclides of the same size that it seems unlikely that more than several billion years could have passed since it was formed.

In the case of the trans-uranic elements neptunium, plutonium, americum, curium, berkelium, californium, einsteinium, fermium, and other possible radioactive nuclei which have never been found in the natural state, the half-lives are so short that nearly all of the element would be destroyed in a few billion years. This line of reasoning is a powerful argument in favor of the theory that, a few billion years ago, the matter of our whole universe was created from some previous state fundamentally different from the present one.

One other naturally occuring radioactive element is important in age determinations. C^{14} is formed from N^{14} in the upper atmosphere by reaction with neutrons produced by cosmic rays:

$$_0n^1 + {}_7N^{14} \rightarrow {}_6C^{14} + {}_1H^1 \tag{4.29}$$

The amount of C^{14} can be presumed to be constant with time provided neither the cosmic-ray flux nor the supply of N^{14} changes. The N^{14} removed as C^{14} is replenished by the disintegration of C^{14}:

$$_6C^{14} \rightarrow {}_7N^{14} + {}_{-1}\beta^0 \tag{4.30}$$

Because the end product, nitrogen 14, is a common nuclide, the equations such as (4.23) derived above cannot be used in this case. Instead, the ratio of the amount of C^{14} to the commoner nonradioactive C^{12} is used. It is assumed that the amount of C^{14} in the atmosphere has been constant for a long time, the amount forming being exactly equaled by the amount disintegrating at any time. Thus any carbon removed from the air and locked up in organic matter or a mineral will start with the C^{14}/C^{12} ratio characteristic of the air (or water) from which it was taken. When the organism dies or the mineral is buried, interaction with the air ceases, and the C^{14}/C^{12} ratio starts to decrease exponentially to zero. Analysis of the material can thus give an accurate estimate of its age until the C^{14} becomes so small as to be unmeasurable. This method has been used to date charcoal, bone, wood, peat, shells, Pleistocene and Recent clay, and oceanic oozes.

4.8 Rate of Erosion and Sedimentation. Man has kept a history of the world's evolution as it occurred for about five of the several million milleniums since its formation. Accurate calculations of time can be extended back a little further by counting growth rings in logs and clay varves in lake sediments. The latter method leads to another way of measuring the age of rocks. In many cases, the thickness of material deposited in a single year can be recognized by seasonal changes in the color, grain size, or other features of the sediments. By many such measurements, it is possible to obtain average rates of deposition for the different types of sediment. Further evidence can be obtained by studying the rate of accumulation of material in alluvial fans, delta deposits, and elsewhere today. By studying the exposed rocks all over the world it is possible to draw up a universal stratigraphic column. In this, the gaps in sedimentation at one locality are filled by entering the sections from other regions. When the thickness of each formation is divided by the normal rate of accumulation of that type of sediment, the time span represented by each unit can be estimated. Addition of these times gives a figure for the approximate age of any individual rock back to the beginning of the Cambrian period. This method has not been successfully extended into pre-Cambrian time, partly because of the incompleteness of the older stratigraphic section but mostly because the pre-Cambrian rocks have generally been so metamorphosed by heat and pressure that their original nature is often difficult or impossible to recognize.

In Table 4.2 the estimated maximum cumulative thickness of sediments for each of the geologic periods and some of the more recent epochs is compared with ages obtained by radioactivity measurements. At best, none of these ages are accurate to more than one or two significant figures. The estimated ages and durations of the periods represent little more than the order of magnitude of these figures. This is the case partly because of the limitations of the radioactivity method discussed above and partly because of the difficulty of determining the geologic age of specimens whose radioactivity age has been calculated in years. Specimens of sufficient radioactive-mineral content to measure accurately their uranium/lead, potassium/argon, or rubidium/strontium ratios are most commonly igneous, whereas the geologic time scale is based on the sedimentary sequences as determined by fossil evidence.

Comparison of the sediment thicknesses with the estimated ages based on radioactivity measurements (Fig. 4.2) shows that the two are not proportional to each other, as would be the case if the sediments accumulated at a steady rate. There are four reasons why exact proportionality should not be expected. First, the older the strata, the greater the chances that some part of the section is incomplete. It is difficult to correlate accurately the rocks of one region with those of another, and in order to get a complete section, the hiatuses at one place must be filled in with data from elsewhere. The older the rock, the greater the chances of its having been eroded away subsequent to its deposition. Therefore, progressively less complete sections are to be expected for the older periods.

TABLE 4.2 THICKNESS OF THE SEDIMENTARY SECTION COMPARED WITH AGES*

Eras and periods	Typical radioactive age figures	Estimated duration, millions of years	Estimated age of start of period, millions of years	Maximum known thickness of strata, thousands of ft	Cumulative maximum thickness, thousands of ft
Quaternary....	....	1	1	4	4
Tertiary:					
Pliocene.....	....	10	11	15	19
Miocene.....	....	12	23	21	40
Oligocene....	25	12	35	26	66
Eocene......	38	15	50	30	96
Paleocene....	60	15	65		
Cretaceous.....	95	65	130	69	165
Jurassic.......	147	30	160	27	192
Triassic........	....	35	195	30	222
Permian.......	225	30	225	19	241
Carboniferous..	240	35	260	46	287
Devonian......	260, 285	40	300	38	325
Silurian........	333	50	350	34	359
Ordovician.....	350	70	420	40	399
Cambrian.....	440	80	500	40	439
Proterozoic....	1,300	1,000	1,500		
Archeozoic.....	2,300–3,300	2,000	3,500		
Azoic..........	4,200	.....	5,000		

* After Ahrens, 1955; Davis and Aldrich, 1953; Faul, 1954; Kulp, 1955; Lipson, 1956; Folinsbee et al., 1956; and A. Holmes, 1947 and personal communication.

Second, the older the rock, the more likely that at some time since its formation, it has been deeply buried beneath other rocks. For sedimentary rocks, deep burial results in compaction with decrease in volume. A thousand feet of Cambrian rocks may have had considerably greater thickness when first deposited than they have today. This shrinks the known section with age.

Third, the type of sediment formed and preserved from the different periods has varied. The percentage of fine sediments is greater in some periods than others. These are deposited more slowly than the coarser sediments. The effect would be removed if we divided the thicknesses shown in Table 4.2 by factors proportional to the average rates of deposition in each period.

Lastly, the rate of erosion varies greatly. The present is thought to be an epoch of greater than average erosion and hence of rapid sedimentation. This condition may have held well back into the Tertiary. This variability upsets age calculations, as the rate of deposition of the rocks in older periods is not easily determined.

As a result of these difficulties, sedimentary thickness is rarely used to estimate the total ages of rocks. Instead, we depend almost entirely on the figures obtained from radioactivity. These are largely for igneous rocks. However, it should be possible to use sedimentary thickness to date formations of age intermediate between two rocks tested by the

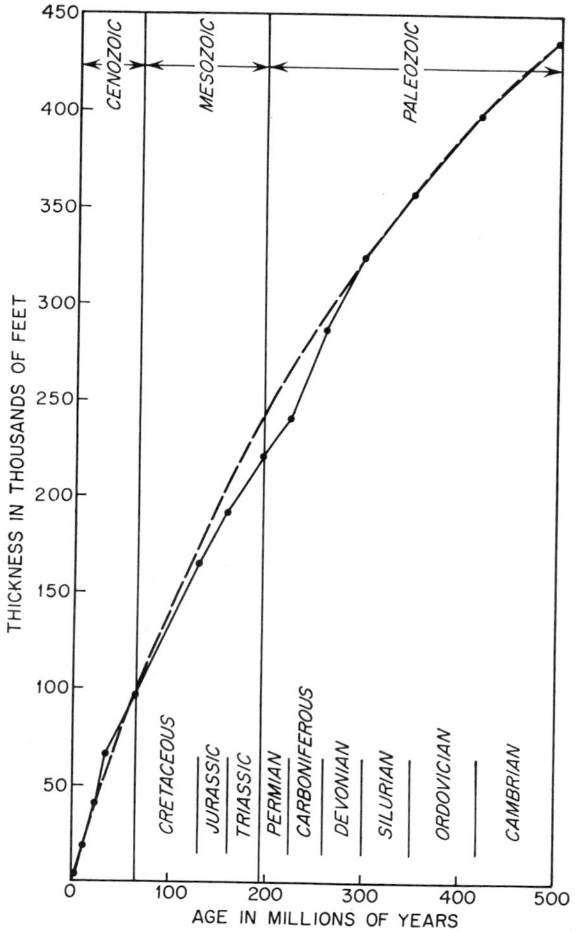

Fig. 4.2 Cumulative sedimentary thickness compared with ages. (*Data from Table 4.2.*)

more accurate method. Rough figures for the average rate of sedimentation can be obtained from Fig. 4.2. The effect of compression and incompleteness of the section is represented by the curvature of the dashed line.

4.9 Age of the Oceans. Each year rivers carry into the oceans 4×10^8 tons of salt. There are about 4×10^{16} tons of it there already. At the present rate of addition, it would have taken 10^8 years to salt an originally fresh ocean. Since the present rate of erosion is unusually great, we can expect the oceans to be several times this old. Furthermore, much of the salt being brought in today was formerly a part of the ocean, having been locked in sedimentary beds at the time of their formation. As a result, all that can be said is that the ocean is at least some hundreds of millions of years old.

Geologic information suggests that at least since the Cambrian, the extent of the well-preserved record, the oceans have been comparable in size to what they are today. It is probable, however, that they have gradually become saltier. The salt concentration in human blood is about one-third that in sea water. This may mean that our ancestors left the sea at a time when it was only one-third as salty as it is today.

4.10 Figures from Astronomic Evidence. All the evidence which has been discussed above appears to be consistent with an age for the earth and the rest of the universe of about 5×10^9 years. There are a number of other phenomena which tend to support this view (Gamow, 1951; Umbgrove, 1947). Astrophysicists have calculated that a galaxy can exist for only 10^9 to 10^{10} years without either condensing greatly or being largely dispersed. Spiral galaxies cannot rotate more than ten to fifteen times without changing greatly in form. A typical period of rotation is 2×10^8 years. At this rate, a spiral galaxy would have a life of only 2 to 3×10^9 years.

In the Pleiades is a cluster of stars of unusually great density. Such a star cluster is unstable. The estimated average life of such a cluster is about 3×10^9 years. Within our own galaxy, which we see as the Milky Way, there is believed to be a tendency for the velocities of all the stars to change toward a distribution wherein the energy is evenly distributed. The present situation is so far from this ideal that it seems unlikely that the galaxy can have existed for more than a few billion years.

Binary stars are unstable because of the tidal effects caused by other stars. The present state of observed binary stars is such that they cannot have existed over 10^{10} years, and probably not over half that long.

The brightness of a star is a measure of the rate at which mass is being converted into energy within it. In a normal star, this rate increases as the cube of the mass. The principal element believed to be involved in this conversion is hydrogen, which is changed into helium plus energy. The amount of hydrogen originally available H_0 was proportional to the mass M. Since only a small fraction of the mass is used up in the process, the the mass of the star changes very little. We can write this as an equation:

$$\frac{dH}{dt} \sim M^3 \sim H_0{}^3 \tag{4.31}$$

$$M^{-3}\, dH \sim dt \tag{4.32}$$

where H is the amount of hydrogen present at any time t. Solving this, we get for the time required to use up all the hydrogen

$$T \sim M^{-3}(H)_{t=0}^{t=T} = M^{-3}(H_0 - 0) = M^{-2} \tag{4.33}$$

Stars five times heavier than our sun seem to have just about used up all their hydrogen. They exhibit various kinds of unquiet behavior, ranging from regular pulsations (Cepheid variables) to terrific explosions (novae and supernovae). It would have taken these stars several billion years to use up their hydrogen if their original composition had been similar to that of normal stars.

All these figures are in good agreement with an age of a few billion years for a large proportion of the stars. It is possible that the formation of the earth was but a minor side show in the great spectacle of the formation of most of the major bodies of the universe.

4.11 Cooling of the Earth. Until the discovery of radioactivity provided a better explanation, it was believed that the increase in temperature as one goes down into the earth was due to its cooling from an originally gaseous state at the time of formation. It was supposed that the earth cooled largely by conduction. Assuming that at the time of solidification it had a uniform temperature of 7000°F, Lord Kelvin calculated that it would take 10^8 years to reach a state where the heat loss would be what we observe today. This figure is probably too big, as Kelvin's figures for the heat conductivities of rocks were inaccurate. Today we know that the earth's age cannot be even estimated in this way. As will be seen in the next chapter, the radioactive elements in the rocks probably generate enough heat by their disintegration to account completely for the heat rising to the earth's surface from its interior.

CHAPTER 5

TEMPERATURE OF THE EARTH

Almost everywhere on the earth, temperature is observed to increase with depth. Typical figures for this increase are given in Table 5.1. The average gradient is about 1°C per 30 m, but it is very variable. Values as great as 1°C per 6.7 m (0.149°C per m) have been observed (Van Orstrand, 1939). The gradient varies with depth, becoming greater with increasing distance from the surface in about 60 per cent of the places where it has been measured. Negative gradients (temperature decreases with depth) are occasionally observed, but it is probable that these are due to special conditions such as underground water circulation (see, for example, Krige, 1948).

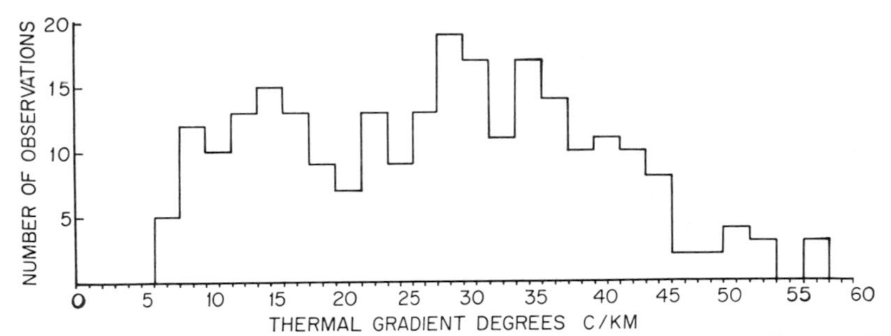

Fig. 5.1 Distribution of near-surface temperature gradients. (*After Tuttle, 1955.*)

5.1 Sources of Error in Measurements. Such figures as have been obtained are usually from wells and mines. Measurements of the normal temperature in such places are difficult to make. In drilling a well or excavating a mine, air, water, or mud is introduced into the opening from the surface and each has a tendency to cool the walls of the hole. This is particularly true in deep mines where cool air is pumped in continuously for the comfort of the workmen. The presence of water or air may also alter the thermal conductivity of the rock, making its value abnormal near a bore hole or mine shaft. Oxygen in the air or dissolved in water

TABLE 5.1 TYPICAL VALUES OF THE TEMPERATURE GRADIENT

Location	Effective average surface temp. (computed from gradient), °C	Gradient, °C/m	Depth, m	Authority
Albany, Ala	16.1	0.00472	30–305	1
Bakersfield, Calif	21.5	0.0286	30–1,295	1
Houghton, Mich	2.4	0.0168	1,470–1,905	1
Fort Collins, Colo	11.5	0.0304	30–305	1
Burns, Ore	6.1	0.0457	30–1,140	1
Vale, Ore	15.5	0.0834	30–395	1
Ardmore, Okla	17.0	0.0151	30–305	1
Kettleman Hills, Calif	21.7	0.0328	30–802	1
Long Bridge, Pa	8.3	0.0249	30–305	1
		0.0305	30–1,980	1
Panhandle, Tex	16.9	0.0194	30–305	1
		0.0195	30–602	1
Cody, Wyo	10.8	0.0293	30–305	1
		0.0310	30–1,295	1
Rawlins, Wyo	5.98	0.0263	30–305	1
		0.0319	30–914	1
Masjid-i-Sulaiman, Persia	26	0.0108	730–1,035	2
Witwatersrand, South Africa	20	0.00045	30–296	3
		0.0085	30–2,234	3
Paruschowitz, Germany	7.8	0.0314	31–1,954	4
Ontario, Canada	5.0	0.0136	175–910	5
		0.0118	175–2,300	5
Monche, Russia	2.15	0.00725	18–449	6
Boryslaw, Poland	−7.8	0.033	160–1,645	7
Tuxpan, Mexico	24.2	0.041	23–1,244	8

Authorities: 1. Van Orstrand, 1934; 2. Coster, 1947; 3. Krige, 1948; 4. Henrich, 1904; 5. Cleland, 1933; 6. Spicer, 1942; 7. Arctowski, 1925; 8. De Golyer, 1918

may react with the walls, raising their temperature. This may occur also at the earth's surface. The surface temperature of freshly extruded lava is sometimes greater than that a few inches beneath the surface. In the case of wells drilled with a rotating bit, although heat is generated in grinding the rock away, mud is usually circulated in the hole to cool the bit. In the case of wells, the escape of gases previously trapped in the rock has a tendency to cool it, as they expand on release.

5.2 Surface Temperature. At the surface the temperature is controlled primarily by five factors: (1) the radiant heat falling on the surface from the sun, (2) the albedo (reflectivity, the ratio of reflected radiation to the total radiation falling on a surface, the average value for the earth is 0.29), (3) the heat rising from below (temperature gradient), (4) the

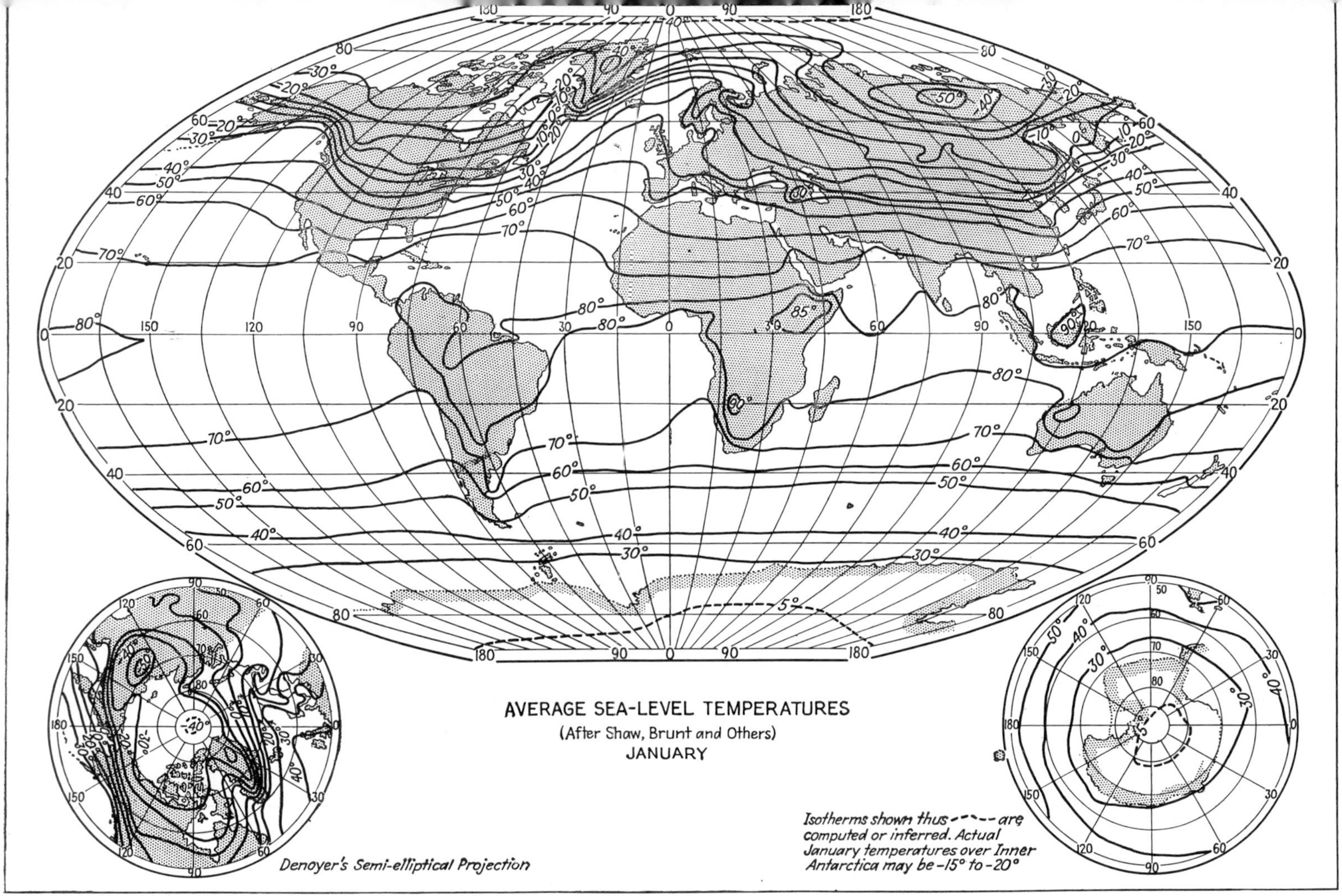

AVERAGE SEA-LEVEL TEMPERATURES
(After Shaw, Brunt and Others)
JANUARY

Denoyer's Semi-elliptical Projection

Isotherms shown thus - - - - are computed or inferred. Actual January temperatures over Inner Antarctica may be -15° to -20°

FIG. 5.2 Average sea-level temperature in January. (*Finch and Trewartha, 1957.*)

emissivity, and (5) the conduction loss to the air. In general the soil has an average temperature slightly above that of the adjacent air. As a result the air is warmed near the ground. This greater temperature results both from the earth's internal heat and from the fact that the rock is heated by the sun's rays during the day more rapidly than the heat can be reradiated. The heat gained during the day is lost during the night. The earth's thermal conductivity is so small that even the annual fluctuations of temperature at the surface from summer to winter are rarely detectable beneath 50 to 100 ft. As a result of this low conductivity of rocks, lavas of Pliocene and Pleistocene age a short distance beneath the surface in Oregon appear, in some cases, still to be warmer than the average for rocks of their composition and latitude.

Surface temperature is controlled almost entirely by the amount of solar radiation (Figs. 5.2 and 5.3). The presence of the earth's atmosphere has a blanketing effect which prevents large variations from day to night. The total range of average surface temperature is only from about -50 to $+40°C$. Compared with the temperatures reached a few kilometers beneath the earth's surface, this variation is small.

In the arctic regions, as a result of the low average surface temperature, the ground remains frozen all year to hundreds of feet in depth. This presents some peculiar problems to life in the far north. There can be no water wells, as there is no ground water, only ice. Where oil is produced, it is so cold that it is viscous and difficult to pump through pipes. In the summer the snow melts on the surface but cannot sink into the ground, which becomes soggy, sometimes to a depth of several feet. Buildings settle in the soft muck, to be squeezed out of the ground the next winter by the force of freezing water, like boulders in a New England pasture.

Advantage can also be taken of the cold. On at least one placer gold operation, water is dammed out of the workings by a wall of ice. This is formed during the winter by pumping brine through the ground in pipes until a barrier is solidly frozen around the area to be worked the next year.

5.3 Factors Affecting Temperature Gradient. A surface within the earth all points on which are at the same temperature is called an isogeotherm. Such surfaces commonly exhibit considerable irregularity in shape. In general, they rise under land masses, over peaks in the crystalline basement rocks, and in regions of current or recent volcanic activity and mineralization. Over areas of older mineralization they may be depressed by the greater conductivity of the ground. They drop also where no deformation has occurred for a geologically long time. The ocean bottom tends to be colder than the land surface at the same latitude.

H. S. Washington (1939) lists seven factors which may affect the temperature gradient:

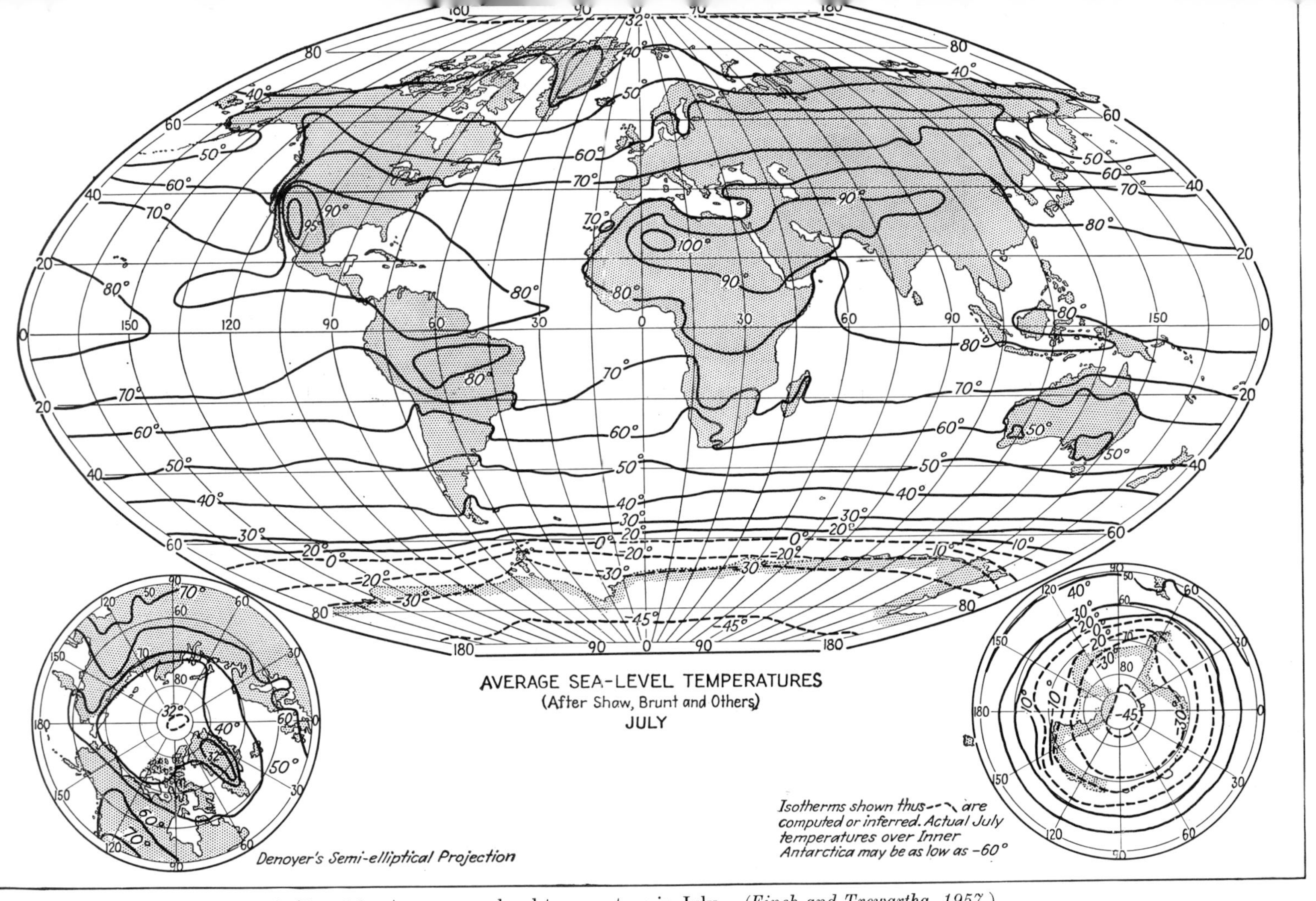

FIG. 5.3 Average sea-level temperature in July. (*Finch and Trewartha, 1957.*)

1. Variations of thermal conductivity with composition
2. Proximity to molten magma
3. Subterranean water circulation
4. Moisture content of the rock
5. Production or consumption of heat by chemical reactions
6. Effect of pressure and temperature on conductivity
7. Radioactivity

Conductivity is in large part controlled by the composition of the rock (Table 5.2). The presence of sulfides, oxides, or pure metals increases it. When conductivity is large, the temperature gradient is most commonly smaller than average and the isogeotherms are depressed.

TABLE 5.2 TYPICAL VALUES OF THE THERMAL CONDUCTIVITY OF ROCK AT ATMOSPHERIC PRESSURE*

Rock type	Temperature, °C	Conductivity, cal/sec/cm/°C
Granite	100	5–7 × 10^{-3}
	200	5–6.5 × 10^{-3}
Anorthosite	100	4.1–4.5 × 10^{-3}
	200	4.3–4.7 × 10^{-3}
Diabase	100	5.0–5.35 × 10^{-3}
Basalt	75	4 × 10^{-3}
Gabbro	100	5.25–5.75 × 10^{-3}
	400	4.8 × 10^{-3}
Dunite	100	9.4 × 10^{-3}
	200	8.1 × 10^{-3}
Limestone	100	4.9–7.0 × 10^{-3}
Sandstone	17	10 × 10^{-3}
Shale	17	1.4 × 10^{-3}
Rock salt	17	17 × 10^{-3}
Ice	0	22 × 10^{-3}
Silica glass	100	13–15 × 10^{-3}
Obsidian	100	15 × 10^{-3}
Sandy loam†	...	0.8–5.5 × 10^{-3}
Clay†	...	0.6–4 × 10^{-3}
River sand†	...	0.65–4.0 × 10^{-3}

* After Birch, 1942.
† Depends greatly on moisture content.

Near molten igneous bodies and hot springs the gradient is usually high. Hot springs are believed often to be due to the presence of magma near the surface. Near-surface igneous activity manifests itself in many ways (Fig. 5.4). In some active volcanoes, molten rock is pouring out or present as pools. It is more common for only gases to appear. These may rise with explosive violence as in the case of the eruption of Mount Pelée on the island of Martinique in 1902 (Leet, 1948, pp. 8–10).

The eruption of Mount Pelée was watched by observers on ships in the harbor. The crater had been active for some time. At night flames could be seen leaping from the mouth of the volcano. Hot mud and rock were thrown out; ash fell heavily on the surrounding country. The ground was shaken by numerous minor explosions. About 7:45 in the morning of May 8, this culminated in a single violent outburst of gas. This mass of gas, made heavy by the dust and rock fragments it carried with it, rolled down the side of the mountain as a density current. The

FIG. 5.4 Two hundred miles south of Tokyo, Japan, a new island, Myojin volcano, is rising from the sea floor. (*Official U.S. Navy Photograph.*)

city of Saint Pierre at the foot was engulfed by the hot, noxious fumes. Of the population of 40,000 persons, only one escaped, a prisoner in the jail. Seventeen out of eighteen ships in the harbor were destroyed, with most of their crews. All went in a few seconds in a puff of smoke.

At the other extreme are areas where the principal signs of igneous activity are hot springs and the unusual warmth of the ground. In Antarctica several areas have been found where the ice covering of that continent is absent, one possible reason being that the ground is kept, warmer than in surrounding areas by heat supplied from below (Byrd, 1947). Hot springs are common in such regions as Iceland and Yellowstone National Park. Where the heat supply is regular enough, geysers and like phenomena may result (Fig. 5.5).

Vulcanism can often be put to good use. In Italy the steam escaping from volcanic vents is used to generate electricity. Some mineralized waters are used for drinking or bathing because they are believed beneficial to health. They have provided the chief attraction of such resorts

Fig. 5.5 Old Faithful Geyser, Yellowstone National Park. (*Courtesy of E. W. Miller.*)

as Carlsbad, Germany. Hot springs are used to provide waters for swimming pools the year around in Iceland. Warm waters are pumped 10 miles to be used for heating houses and for washing. At places bread can be baked by burying a pan of dough in the hot ground (Clark, 1951).

Subterranean water circulation can either raise or lower the temperature locally. Water escaping from a solidifying magma will warm the rocks it penetrates. On the other hand, circulating ground waters help to cool rocks by carrying away heat and lowering the gradient. In general, the presence of water in a rock raises the conductivity and aids the heat to escape in this way also.

Especially near the surface where air can reach sulfides or other oxidizable material, the rock may be warmed by chemical reactions. The reactions also result in electrical currents, whose energy is dissipated as heat in the surrounding rocks through which they flow. These currents have been widely used to locate ore bodies, but little research has been done to investigate the possibilities of measuring temperature variations as a prospecting method.

There is reason to suppose that thermal conductivity depends on pressure and temperature, which increase with depth within the earth. Several lines of evidence all suggest that the conductivity increases with depth and hence that after an initial rise in the upper part of the crust the temperature gradient decreases (Gutenberg, 1951*a*). Wiedemann and Franz in 1853 showed that for many common materials the thermal conductivity is proportional to the electrical conductivity. It is known from studies of the fluctuations of the earth's magnetic field that beneath 200 to 250 km the electrical conductivity increases (see Chap. 23). At a depth of 700 km it may be as much as 10^5 times as large as at the surface. If the Wiedemann-Franz relationship holds, then thermal conductivity must increase also.

Bridgman has shown from theoretical considerations that the thermal conductivity σ should increase directly with the velocity of compressional waves V_p and inversely as the square of the mean distances between the centers of molecules d. If the density ρ of the rocks depended only on the spacing of the molecules, this could be written

$$\sigma = \frac{KV_p}{d^2} = KV_p\rho^{2/3} \tag{5.1}$$

where K is a constant of proportionality. In later chapters it will be shown that V_p and ρ both increase with depth. Therefore, the thermal conductivity would be expected to increase and the temperature gradient to decrease.

Conduction is not the only process by which heat may escape from the earth's interior. Some heat is carried upward by escaping volcanic gases and liquids. Where large parts of the earth are liquid, convection can be an effective agent in heat transfer. Radiation can also play a more important role in heat transfer than is generally realized. Because its effectiveness goes up as the cube of temperature, deep in the mantle and core it may become the main agent in heat transfer and may set an upper limit to the temperatures possible in the earth (Clark, 1956).

5.4 Sources of the Earth's Heat. The problem of determining the temperature gradient is complicated by the heat currently being generated at various depths. There are three major sources for the earth's internal heat and several minor ones. The most important source is the energy released by radioactive disintegration. When a uranium atom disintegrates, the sum of the masses of the lead atom which is finally formed and the alpha and beta particles given off is less than the mass of the original uranium. The difference m is converted into energy:

$$E \text{ (ergs)} = 9 \times 10^{20}\, m \text{ (grams)} \tag{5.2}$$

At the instant of disintegration this appears in the form of the kinetic energy of the two particles and as gamma rays. As the particle velocity is reduced to zero by passage through the rock, its kinetic energy is converted into heat (Tables 5.3 and 5.4).

Next in importance to radioactivity is the original temperature of the material from which the earth was formed. This would not be so important a source if it were not for the continual generation of new heat by

TABLE 5.3 TYPICAL VALUES OF ENERGY RELEASED BY RADIOACTIVE DISINTEGRATION*

Parent element	Daughter element	Energy released, Mev†
U^{238}	Th^{234}	4.25
Th^{234}	Pa^{234}	0.20
Pa^{234}	U^{234}	1.95
U^{234}	Th^{230}	4.85
Th^{230}	Ra^{226}	4.77
Ra^{226}	Rn^{222}	4.86
Rn^{222}	Po^{218}	5.59
Po^{218}	Pb^{214}	6.11
Bi^{214}	Po^{214}	3.17 (β)
	or Tl^{210}	5.61 (α)
Po^{214}	Pb^{210}	7.83
Tl^{210}	Pb^{210}	5.39
Pb^{210}	Bi^{210}	0.065
Bi^{210}	Po^{210}	5.06
Po^{210}	Pb^{206}	5.40
U^{235}	Th^{231}	4.66
Th^{232}	Ra^{228}	4.05
K^{40}	Ca^{40}	1.33 (β)
	or A^{40}	1.63 (K electron capture)
Rb^{87}	Sr^{87}	0.27
C^{14}	N^{14}	0.155
Re^{186}	Os^{186}	1.07

* Data from Hollander et al., 1953.
† Million electron volts. 1 Mev = 1.5921×10^{-6} erg.

other means. If the temperature were not kept high near the surface by the disintegration of radioactive elements, much of any original heat of the earth could have been lost in the last 5×10^9 years.

TABLE 5.4 TYPICAL VALUES OF HEAT GENERATED BY RADIOACTIVE DISINTEGRATION*

Material	*Cal generated/year/gm*
U^{238}	0.71
U^{235}	4.3
Th^{232}	0.20
K^{40}	0.22
Rb^{87}	0.00013×10^{-6}
Acidic igneous rocks	6×10^{-6}
Intermediate igneous rocks	3.5×10^{-6}
Basic igneous rocks	2×10^{-6}
Ultrabasic rocks	$0.02\text{–}0.9 \times 10^{-6}$
Stony meteorites	0.1×10^{-6}
Iron meteorites	0.01×10^{-6}
Sediments	2.3×10^{-6}

* For more extensive data and bibliographies see Evans et al., 1942; Gutenberg, 1951*a*; Jeffreys, 1952; Birch, 1954*a*; Bullard, 1954.

The third source is the heat of aggradation. If two particles moving in space collide and stick to each other, the energy of their relative motion must be changed into some other form such as the energy of rotation of the resulting single particle or as heat. If the particles strike head on, the energy might appear entirely as heat. Similarly, if a collection of particles already gathered together gradually shrinks further by rearrangement of the parts of which it is composed, the falling of the parts through the gravitative field of the whole may eventually appear largely as heat. Much of the earth's original warmth may have been generated in this way. A very small amount is still being added by the acquisition of meteoric particles.

The energy gained by a mass m falling through a gravitative field of strength g is

$$E = -\int gm\, dr \tag{5.3}$$

For a particle falling to the earth from a distance R to its surface at radius R_e this is

$$E = -\int_R^{R_e} \frac{\gamma M_e m}{r^2}\, dr = \gamma M_e m(R_e^{-1} - R^{-1}) \tag{5.4}$$

where γ is the universal constant of gravitation and M_e is the mass of the earth. In the case of a particle coming from very far away so that R^{-1} is small, the energy gained is 6.3×10^{11} ergs per gm.

It has been postulated that the earth is getting smaller, either by recrystallization to denser mineral varieties or by cooling or by both processes. Heat may be released or consumed by such recrystallization. If the earth were originally liquid, as it solidified much heat could have been released by this crystallization. This heat would tend to keep the earth's interior warm, opposing the tendency to shrink and to recrystallize. Where the earth is already solid, recrystallization to lower energy forms may release further energy even if no reduction in volume occurs. Chemical reactions within the earth may also release a minor amount of heat. Near the surface, reaction with atmospheric oxygen is of some local importance.

Regions of recent tectonic activity usually have higher temperature gradients than elsewhere, showing that the buried rocks are warmer than average. To some extent the heat may come directly from the same source which caused the deformation. At least a part of it results from the compression and shear of the rocks and from friction along fault planes which are common in such regions. The heat generated as rocks slip along a fault may be sufficient in some cases to melt a part of the rock. It has long been a question of debate how much of the metamorphism of rocks results from the heat and pressure of diastrophism and how much is a result solely of the high temperature associated with the depth of burial and the pressure of the overlying rocks. With present knowledge this is unanswerable.

5.5 Distribution of Radioactive Elements. The amount of radioactive material in some of the common rock types is given in Table 5.5.

TABLE 5.5 TYPICAL FIGURES OF CONCENTRATIONS OF URANIUM IN ROCKS*

Rock type	*Uranium concentration* $\times 10^6$ *gm/gm*
Acid igneous	2.77 – 4.02
Intermediate igneous	1.5 – 3.03
Basic igneous	0.6 – 0.95
Ultrabasic igneous	0.03
Volcanic glasses	0.80 –15.4
Iron meteorites	0.0033
Stony meteorites	0.001– 0.005
Ocean water	0.0013

* For more extensive data and references see Davis, 1950; Cooper, 1952; Adams, 1954; Larsen and Phair, 1954; Pettersson, 1954.

If the percentage concentration was the same throughout the earth as it is in granite or even in the basic igneous rocks, the amount of heat being generated currently would far exceed that lost through the surface, and the interior of the earth would be heating rapidly. The average heat current through the earth's crust is about 1.2×10^{-6} gm-cal per cm^2 per sec $\pm$ 50 per cent (Birch, 1954*a,b*). It appears to be about the same under the oceans as on land. For the whole earth this would result in a loss of about 6×10^{12} cal per sec. There is a little additional heat escaping from volcanoes in hot gases, perhaps 2×10^{10} cal per sec.

There are several reasons for believing that the concentration of radioactive matter decreases with depth. Studies of exposed rocks which were once deeply buried reveal that a large percentage of them have solidified from a liquid state. If the earth were once liquid, even if it were not all melted at the same time, differentiation would have occurred as the parts crystallized. The elements would have tended to separate in part according to their density. Thus the heavy metals such as iron would have sunk, and elements such as silicon, calcium, and magnesium would be concentrated nearer the surface. To the degree that the materials in this melt were immiscible, they would have sorted themselves into layers. In most of the universe iron is one of the common elements, and it is to be expected that any excess of it which did not combine with oxygen, silicon, and aluminum, the only commoner elements in rocks, would have sunk to the bottom of the melt.

One model of the earth which has been proposed is based on just such a differentiation. It is postulated that at the center of the earth there is a core composed largely of iron and nickel. Outside this is a layer of iron-rich silicates in which some metallic iron may be mixed. As one nears the surface, the amount of free metal decreases till at the top of this mantle of silicate rock which surrounds the metallic core the composition is close to that of an ultrabasic silicate such as dunite or peridotite. Above this lies a crust of average composition close to that of basalt at the bottom and granite at the top.

If this model is a good approximation to true conditions, then one would expect the concentration of radioactive elements to vary with depth. If the sorting were solely on the basis of atomic density, the heavy radioactive elements should sink to the center of the earth. However, other factors are more likely to control the distribution. It is the solid compounds formed by the solidifying melt which will determine which elements sink and which rise. The composition of exposed rocks will give evidence of where to expect the disintegrating elements. Granite contains more radioactive material than basalt. Therefore, in the granite-composition surface material there should be more radioactive elements than in the underlying basalt. The proportions should be approximately those in exposed granites and basalts. Exposed ultrabasic rocks contain even less radioactive material, so the subcrust would be expected to be even lower in activity.

The radioactivity of the deeper interior cannot be estimated by so direct a method as that of the crust. Probable values can be obtained by analogy with the compositions of meteorites. It is commonly believed that meteorites were formed from the same material as the planets and hence that they have a similar composition. They are of several types, the commonest being stony masses of ultrabasic composition, called aerolites, and metallic bodies composed mostly of iron and nickel, called siderites. Stony meteorites exhibit as little or less activity than do the ultrabasic rocks, and metallic meteorites possess even less than this. From this evidence it is suspected that the concentration of the radioactive elements decreases going down through the siliceous mantle and into the core.

This decrease in the concentration of the heaviest elements with depth is to be expected on theoretical grounds. Since the radioactive elements are uncommon constituents of rock, they tend to occur often, not as the principal atoms in mineral species, but as impurities in the minerals of other elements. The compounds whose crystal lattices contain them most easily and hence in which they most commonly occur are among the lighter silicates. As a result, in any differentiation process, the radioactive elements tend to be carried upward.

Except for iron, most of the elements in the interior of the earth probably occur as silicates. Although it has been postulated that a layer of oxides and sulfides would have separated from a once molten earth, there is little except speculative evidence to support this (Mason, 1952, pp. 34–35). In a silicate melt, sorting would occur largely by the floating upward and settling downward of solid particles crystallizing out of the melt, controlled by their relative weights. (See Chap. 17 for a more detailed discussion of magmatic differentiation.) Even a crystal of the same composition as the main body of magma would sink because of its greater density. However, progressive differences in composition between the crystals forming and the melt would be expectable, and material composed predominantly of the lighter elements would tend to collect at the top. The chemical affinities of the radioactive elements of the earth are with the light silicon-aluminum-rich compounds. It is to be expected that they would be concentrated in the uppermost part of a sequence of rocks which solidified from a single melt.

There is another reason why the radioactive elements would tend to be concentrated toward the surface. Studies of the solidification of large igneous bodies indicates that the original magma contained much water. This escapes in the last stages of differentiation, carrying with it whatever elements are left over from the separation of the common rock-forming minerals. The heavy radioactive atoms are large, which is why they do not fit easily into most crystal lattices. Therefore, they tend to be left in this residual solution and are carried upward as it escapes in the last stage of solidification.

The amount of radioactive material is constantly decreasing. Since the amount disintegrating at any one time is proportional to the amount present at that time, the amount of heat being produced in this way must be steadily decreasing. It is probable that there is enough radioactive material in the earth to account completely for the present heat loss. If this is the case, then the heat loss must formerly have been greater and the interior temperature correspondingly higher.

If there is not a decrease of the rate of heat generation with depth, then the temperature of the earth must be increasing. This would be expected if the earth was formed by slow accretion of cold, solid particles and was not initially a hot liquid. Because the rate of heat conduction by rocks is low (see Table 5.2), the internally generated heat may be forming faster than it can be conducted away, and if the deep rocks are rich enough in radioactivity, the center of the earth may be warming and gradually melting throughout a steadily increasing volume.

Under stable conditions inside a solid rock body, the amount of heat being carried away depends largely on the product of temperature gradient and conductivity. Evidence has been presented above that the temperature gradient within the earth probably decreases with depth. Therefore, for stable conditions to exist, the amount of radioactive material present must decrease with depth. If it does not decrease rapidly enough, the departure from stability will take the form of the rock heating and tending to melt. When it melts, differentiation will concentrate the radioactive elements toward the surface. Therefore, even if the original earth started its existence beneath the melting point throughout, wherever there were radioactive materials present, they would tend to melt their way toward the surface until they reached a depth where the thermal gradient was great enough to allow heat to escape as fast as it formed. When that depth was reached, the gradual decrease in undecomposed radioactive material would eventually allow the melt to cool and solidify.

As a result of either a single original differentiation or repeated melting and resolidifying of parts of the earth, the radioactive elements must have tended to become concentrated near the earth's surface. Beneath this zone of concentration the gradient must be only a small fraction of that at the surface.

The reason for the rapid decrease in gradient can be seen from the following argument. The heat generated within any spherical shell of thickness Δr and radius r within the earth is proportional to the concentration ρ_r of the enclosed radioactive material and the volume of the shell $4\pi r^2 \Delta r$. The total heat generated inside of a sphere of radius R is

$$E_H \sim 4\pi \int_0^R r^2 \rho_r \, dr \tag{5.5}$$

where R is the outer radius of the shell. The area through which the heat must escape is proportional to the area $4\pi R^2$. Therefore, the heat escaping E_A per square centimeter is proportional to $E_H/4\pi R^2$. For ρ_r a constant and for constant temperature,

$$E_A \sim R^{-2} \int_0^R r^2 \rho_r \, dr = \frac{\rho_r R}{3} \tag{5.6}$$

The gradient will be proportional to the heat flow times the inverse of the conductivity σ_t:

$$\frac{dT}{dR} \sim \frac{\int_0^R r^2 \rho_r \, dr}{\sigma_t R^2} \tag{5.7}$$

If σ_t increases and ρ_r decreases with decreasing R, as the evidence indicates that they do, the gradient must decrease very rapidly.

Up to this point it has generally been assumed that the earth is solid throughout. Where it is liquid, convection may aid conduction in allowing the heat to escape. This will tend to reduce the gradient in any part of the earth which is still liquid. However, a temperature difference is required to keep convection acting, so the gradient can never be reduced to zero by this means.

The above arguments all lead to the hypothesis that there is a concentration of much of the radioactive material of the earth in a thin crust or a crust plus the upper part of the underlying mantle. If such is the case, the existing heat loss can be equated to the amount being generated within the earth. This radioactive shell cannot exceed a few tens of kilometers in thickness, or more heat will be generated than is observed to be escaping.

5.6 Variation of Temperature with Depth. There is so much latitude to possible conditions that the temperature variation with depth cannot be accurately predicted. If the surface gradient of 1°C per 30 m continued to the earth's center, the temperature there would be over 200,000°. It is certainly much less than this, though one can do little more than guess at how much less with present knowledge. Birch (1955) estimates that beneath the continents at a depth of 30 km the temperature is somewhere of the order of magnitude of 500°C. Gutenberg (1951*a*) and Jeffreys (1952) have published curves showing higher temperatures at this depth. Beneath the crust the gradient probably decreases rapidly. Gutenberg (1951*a*) estimates that at the center of the earth the temperature may not be much over 2000°C. Figure 5.6 is based on Birch's estimate up to 30 km, but resembles more Jeffrey's at intermediate depth and Gutenberg's at the deep end. If the thermal conductivity increases with depth proportionately to the electrical conductivity, as predicted by Wiedemann and Franz, and if the amount of radioactive material in the rocks decreases with depth, then this temperature is reasonable.

The question of the temperature variation is of greatest importance in relation to the probability of the earth's being liquid at certain depths. It has been suggested that at the pressures which exist within the earth, the molecules may be so constrained that the distinction between solid and liquid disappears, just as gases cannot be distinguished from liquids above the critical temperature. There is, however, no evidence to show that this is the case.

It is impossible in the laboratory with known materials to duplicate the conditions of temperature and pressure which must occur below a few

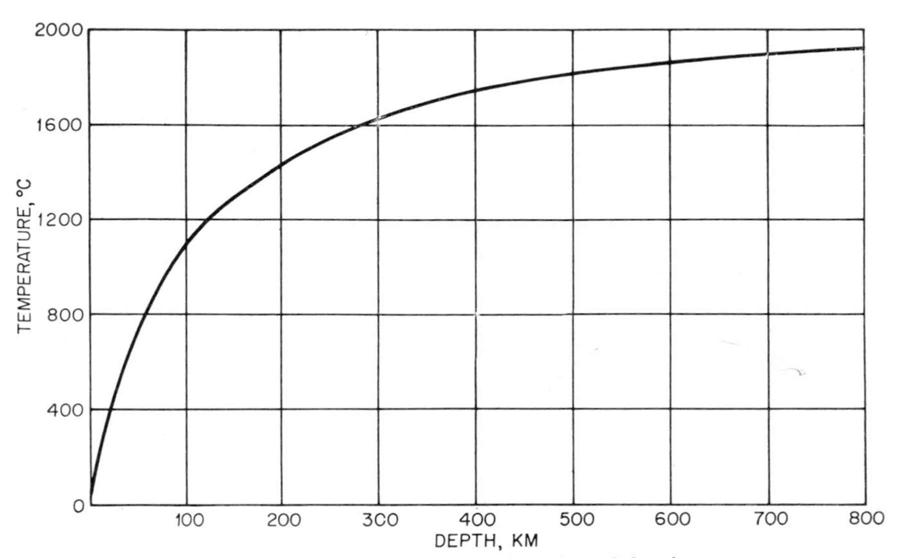

FIG. 5.6 Temperature as a function of depth.

tens of kilometers from the surface. Some minerals have been tested at pressures corresponding to 300 km and some metals at pressures corresponding to 900 km, but not at high temperature (Birch, 1952). Therefore, even the melting points of rocks at most depths are uncertain. This is made even more uncertain by lack of knowledge of how much water is in the rocks. The presence of water can greatly lower the melting point. The only evidence on composition is obtained by comparison with meteorites. The assumption that the earth's interior is similar in composition to meteorites can be checked against the known density variation with depth (Chap. 13) and the transmission velocities of seismic waves through the earth (Chap. 11) and is found to be reasonable.

With this degree of uncertainty, one can only conclude that at most depths the material could be either solid or liquid, as far as available evidence goes. The coarsely crystalline nature of igneous rocks indicates that much of the earth was once liquid. The existence of vulcanism proves that some of it is still liquid. A few measurements of the temperatures of lava are given in Table 5.6. Because the presence of volatile

TABLE 5.6 TYPICAL OBSERVED TEMPERATURES OF LAVA*

Locality	*Temperature, °C*
Kilauea	1200
Vesuvius (1904)	1100
Vesuvius (1913)	1200
Stromboli (1901)	1150
Etna (1892)	1060–1300
Sakura-jima	1048
Oshima	1200–1300
Paricutin	1200

* After Daly, 1933; Zeis, 1946.

material in molten magma may lower its freezing temperature greatly, it is probable that rocks are molten within the earth at much lower temperatures than this. In the chapters on seismology which follow, it will be proved that the earth contains a core which appears to be liquid but that the rest of the earth seems to be almost all solid.

CHAPTER 6

SEISMIC WAVES

6.1 Definitions. The most highly developed single branch of geophysics is seismology, the science of earthquakes and other ground vibrations. Its relatively great development is partly due to the spectacular effects of earthquakes, which have stimulated interest in the subject ever since man began to wonder about the causes of natural phenomena. We study earthquakes today in order to find out how to minimize the disastrous effects which result when a large quake occurs in an inhabited region. Since no accurate way of predicting earthquakes is known, much less of preventing them, all we can do is to try to be ready for them whenever they occur.

Seismology, however, is not restricted in its applications to the minimization of structural damage. The motions which constitute the earthquake are propagated through the ground, sometimes through the very center of the earth, and their characteristics are modified by the materials through which they pass. By a study of the vibrations and a knowledge of the paths they travel we can tell much about the interior of the earth. Earthquakes occur at depths as great as 700 km from the surface but are more common at certain depths than at others (Fig. 7.1). By understanding what causes earthquakes, by noting where they occur, and by studying the way their energy is propagated through the earth, we can make shrewd guesses as to what some of the conditions are which must exist at different depths within the earth.

Seismology deals primarily with earthquakes, and it is therefore desirable that we have a precise concept of just what is meant by this term. An earthquake is a sudden, transient motion or series of motions of the ground originating in a limited region and spreading from there in all directions. This definition is worthy of some study. If one measures the motions of one point on the earth's surface with respect to another, it is in general found that their relative positions are constantly changing. The magnitude of this movement varies with the rapidity at which it is occurring. There are slow displacements such as those involved in mountain building, which, if they are measured for centuries or milleniums, often reach thousands of feet. There are cyclic motions in the earth similar to the daily tides in the sea, caused by the same forces and having a height of a few inches. There are also more rapid vibrations constantly taking place with amplitudes of the order of a few thousandths or millionths of an inch. These last are called microseisms and are distinguishable from earthquakes by their continuity. An earthquake must be transient.

All the above motions, except earthquakes, are more or less continuous in time. They have no recognizable beginnings or endings, though the amount of motion varies from time to time. An earthquake, on the other hand, has a definite beginning, continues for a while, and then gradually dies out. Although its motion comes to no abrupt end, its duration can usually be estimated to within a few minutes at any place where it can be clearly recorded.

The above properties of an earthquake are purely descriptive. To a seismologist one of the principal properties of an earthquake is its cause. A movement of the ground, no matter how sudden or transient, is not an earthquake unless it is caused by a specific disturbance of some sort. If the disturbance is man made, we say the quake is artificial.[1] If it is due to normal earth processes, we say it is a natural earthquake. Such a disturbance may be either subterranean or superficial, but it must occur at some definite place. Explosions, either beneath or above the surface of the ground, can cause earthquakes if they are large enough. However, they must have size sufficient to cause a distinct, recognizable movement or series of movements of the ground. Thus a very small explosion which causes no measurable disturbance of the ground or the impacts of footsteps or of moving machinery are generally too weak to be classed as earthquakes. The dividing line is determined by distinguishability. Very small disturbances only add to the ever-present background of microseisms.

6.2 Microseisms. There are a variety of causes of microseisms. Some result from automobile, railroad, or other traffic; some are caused by surf beating on a beach; others are caused by rain soaking into the ground. Wind is a major cause of microseisms. It blows against trees, which in their swaying pull the ground with their roots. It presses against the sides of buildings and mountains, which must yield infinitesimally. Any variation of barometric pressure in the air will, to a certain degree, be transmitted into the ground, causing motion there.

Strong pressure gradients, particularly over shallow water, appear to be

[1] Some authorities do not include "artificial" disturbances among earthquakes but consider only vibrations resulting from faulting of the rocks to be earthquakes. The definition presented here is preferred because it is a practical one by which observed ground motions can be readily classified.

an important cause of microseisms. Such conditions are typical of the central portions of big storms, especially hurricanes. The resulting microseisms have a definite form, consisting of a series of trains of waves, each up to several minutes in duration (Fig. 6.1). They may last from a few hours to several days. They differ from earthquake waves in their lack of a sudden beginning.

The ground is never at rest. Microseisms are present at all times and places. Some locations are far quieter than others. The California Institute of Technology at one time operated a seismic recorder at La Jolla, on the seacoast near San Diego, California. As a result of this location, the microseism level was usually higher there than at its other recorders, which are located farther from the sea. The La Jolla instruments have now been moved a few miles inland to a new, quieter station, where they now record earthquakes more clearly.

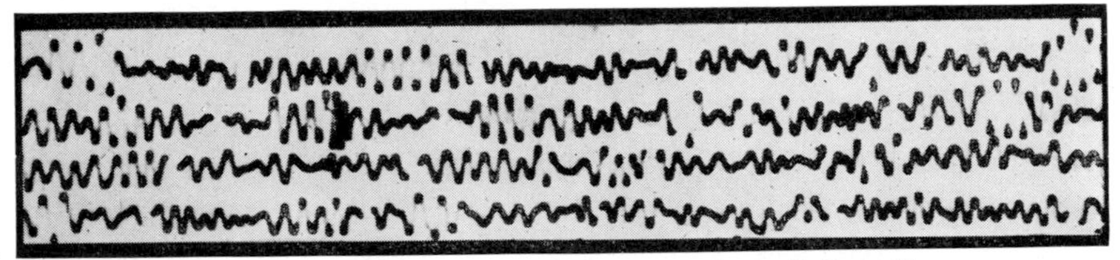

Fig. 6.1 Typical storm microseisms at State College, Pa.

Earthquakes are distinguishable from microseisms by their relatively sharp beginnings and more or less definite endings. When the quake is very small, the vibration may be too slight to be distinguished from the microseismic background. Thus earthquakes themselves contribute to this ground unrest. Any event which causes sudden motion of a part of the earth, such as a falling boulder, a slamming door, or an atom bomb, must cause a seismic disturbance. When we think of an earthquake, however, we generally think of those which are large enough to be felt by people or detected by sensitive instruments over an appreciable area. Gutenberg and Richter (1949) estimate that there are 150,000 natural earthquakes observed every year and that there are probably a million big enough to be recorded if suitable measuring devices were widely enough distributed.

6.3 The Assam Earthquake of 1897 (Oldham, 1899). We have seen that the smallest earthquakes are so weak that they cannot be distinguished from microseisms. Now we shall consider the other extreme, the largest earthquake. The earthquake which took place on June 12, 1897, in central Assam, India, is considered to be one of the most violent which has ever occurred. Whether or not there is any upper limit of size is uncertain, though Gutenberg and Richter (1949) have presented evidence which indicates that such a limit is probable. It is likely that the earth cannot store much more than that amount of energy which, if released suddenly, would result in an earthquake of about the size of the Assam earthquake. This earthquake was certainly as violent as any other of which we have as complete a description.

Fortunately, the area of most extreme shaking was sparsely inhabited, so that the number of fatalities was not great for so large a disturbance. Imamura (1937) estimates that only 960 persons were killed, while Davison (1936) places the figure at 1,542. However, the violence of the shaking can be realized when one notes that all brick and stone buildings were destroyed in an area of 30,000 square miles. The town hall and cathedral in Calcutta, 500 miles from the center of the shaken area, were

FIG. 6.2 Boulders displaced by the Assam earthquake of 1897. (*Oldham, 1899.*)

damaged. The water in lakes and rivers was set into oscillation as far away as 470 miles. The ground shook so hard that boulders which had been embedded in the earth on a hillside were found sitting on the surface several feet from the depressions they had previously occupied (Fig. 6.2). The intervening ground was undisturbed, indicating that the boulders had not rolled to their new positions, but that either they had been thrown through the air, or the ground beneath them had been jerked away so fast that they had been left unsupported, falling to their new locations. At one place a 3-ft-long stone pillar with a triangular base 12 by 10 by 9 in. was found 6½ ft from its original location. For this to have happened, the acceleration of the ground must have exceeded that of gravity.

Observers reported that the ground moved so violently that it was impossible to stand. The surface of the ground is reported to have vibrated visibly. Waves could be seen traveling along a road, and cracks appeared in the ground along their crests as they passed. The surface of the earth was reported to resemble a storm-tossed sea, except that the motion was more rapid. The waves traveled "faster than a walk but slower than a run." The wavelength was reported to be about 30 ft, and the height 1 ft.

An obelisk 60 ft high and 12 ft across at the base was broken off 45 ft above the ground. The part beneath this break which remained standing was cracked across at a height halfway to the ground, and the upper part rotated 30° with respect to the lower. At places the soil was loosened, so that houses sank into it until only their roofs showed about the surface. Water and sand fountained up through fissures in the ground. Railroad lines were twisted, and telephone poles shifted out of line.

A scarp was formed along the Chedrang fault with a maximum displacement of 35 ft vertically. The fault was located in a valley. Lakes

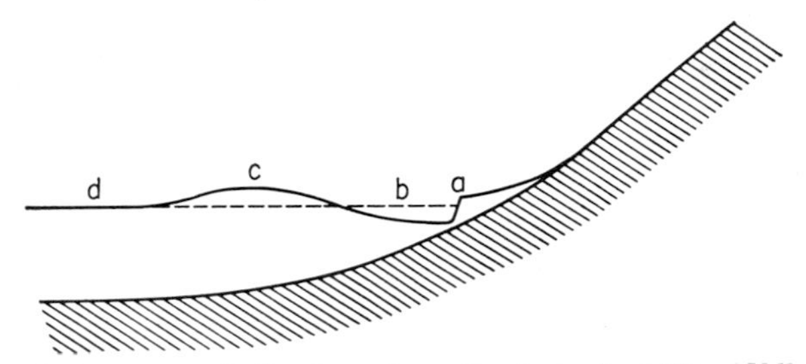

FIG. 6.3 Displacement of alluvium along the foot of a hill. *(Oldham, 1899.)*

and waterfalls were formed along it. Even beyond the section where the surface was broken, ponds were formed where the stream crossed the line of the fault from west to east, and rapids where it crossed from east to west. The depth of the ponds was as great as 24 ft. The tops of some hills were lowered so that more could be seen beyond them than had previously been visible. Nor was the movement all vertical. Retriangulation of geodetic stations showed that some had moved as much as 12 ft horizontally.

Huge landslides were produced. The whole south slope of two ranges of hills was thus stripped bare for a distance of 20 miles. In the soft ground along the base of these hills a mound was formed as though the whole range had shifted toward this valley, compressing the fill into a ridge, and then retreated (Fig. 6.3).

One of the most remarkable features was the Bordwar Fracture, a crack in solid gneiss 7 miles long, 1 in. wide, and of unknown depth. There was no evidence of faulting; the two sides simply moved apart, leaving the crack. Along the fissure tree trunks up to 6 in. in diameter were snapped off near their bases.

The earthquake was preceded by a low rumbling sound, which was heard before the first motion was felt. The ground continued to be disturbed intermittently for many months by additional smaller shocks, some of which were themselves large earthquakes. These quakes were so frequent that at one place a hanging lamp is claimed to have been kept swinging for over three days, and the surface of a vessel of water is said to have been agitated continuously for a week. The number of these additional disturbances exceeds 5,500, and the list is far from complete.

Another tremendous earthquake occurred in Assam on August 15, 1950. The center of the shaken area this time was about 500 km northeast of that of the 1897 shock. Many of the same phenomena were again observed.

6.4 The Seismograph. Seismology had its beginnings in the middle of the eighteenth century. The early work was largely confined to descriptive studies of the effects of earthquakes. The earliest written contribution of note is a memoir by John Michell, an Englishman, published in the Philosophical Transactions of the Royal Society of London in 1761. For over 100 years seismology remained predominantly descriptive. In 1830 Poisson published the fundamental theory of the transmission of elastic waves through solids, but not until toward the end of the century was it recognized that seismic waves were of this nature. Progress in seismology was very slow until after 1880, at which time John Milne, J. A. Ewing, and Thomas Gray in Japan developed instruments for accurate measurement of the ground motion during an earthquake.

Earlier seismic instruments did not make any record of the ground motions but simply indicated that vibrations had occurred. Such instruments existed in China at least as early as A.D. 132. One of these consisted of a ring of eight dragons facing at angles of 45° from one another and holding balls loosely in their mouths. When this device was shaken, the balls fell from the mouths of the dragons facing in the direction of ground motion. Another early device consisted of a bowl of mercury with a ring of spouts, from which some of the liquid flowed if the bowl was shaken. Instruments of this sort which indicate only the occurrence of an earth vibration are called seismoscopes.

The next step in recording was to measure the time of occurrence of the earthquake. Palmieri in Italy built the first instrument which would do this in 1855 (Davison, 1927). Palmieri's device made an electrical contact which stopped a clock and at the same time started a recording drum. A pencil was made to draw a line on the drum as long as the vibrations continued. Since such records indicated only the time of occurrence and duration of the motion, they contributed little to an understanding of the manner in which the ground vibrates. A recorder which makes a record of the occurrence of an earthquake is called a seismograph, and the record is called a seismogram.

Modern instruments make records wherein the deflection of the trace from a straight line is a function of the ground motion (Figs. 6.4 and 6.5).

FIG. 6.4 The Pennsylvania State University seismometer pier.

An instrument which measures the amount of ground motion is called a seismometer.

The basic problem in measuring ground motion is to find a place to stand from which to observe the movements of the earth. For most types of measurement the earth is assumed to be fixed in position, and motion is measured relative to it. Thus we say that the sun "rises" in the east or a wind blows from the southwest. Since the seismologist has no place to stand except upon the very earth whose motion he seeks to measure, he must resort to some sort of trick to make his observations. The commonest procedure is to suspend a mass with a minimum of

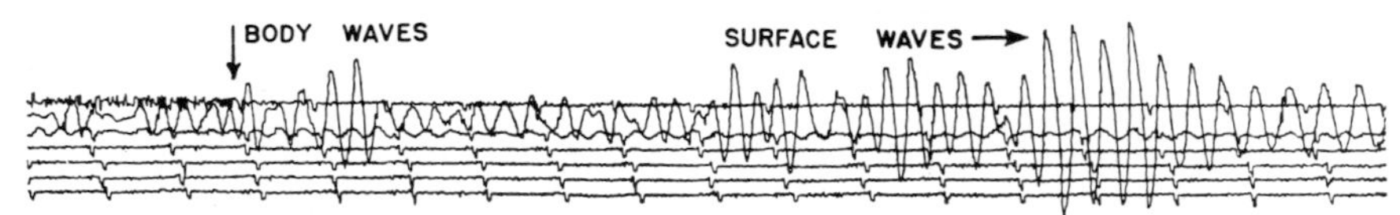

FIG. 6.5 Part of the seismogram of the Aug. 15, 1950, Assam earthquake recorded at State College, Pa.

attachment to the earth and depend upon its inertia to keep it fixed in position as the earth moves.

Seismometers are usually designed to measure only one component of ground motion. Three seismometers measuring three mutually perpendicular components of ground motion will give a complete picture of the ground motion. The simplest type of seismometer uses a pendulum (Fig. 6.6). The mass m of the pendulum tends to stand still as the supporting

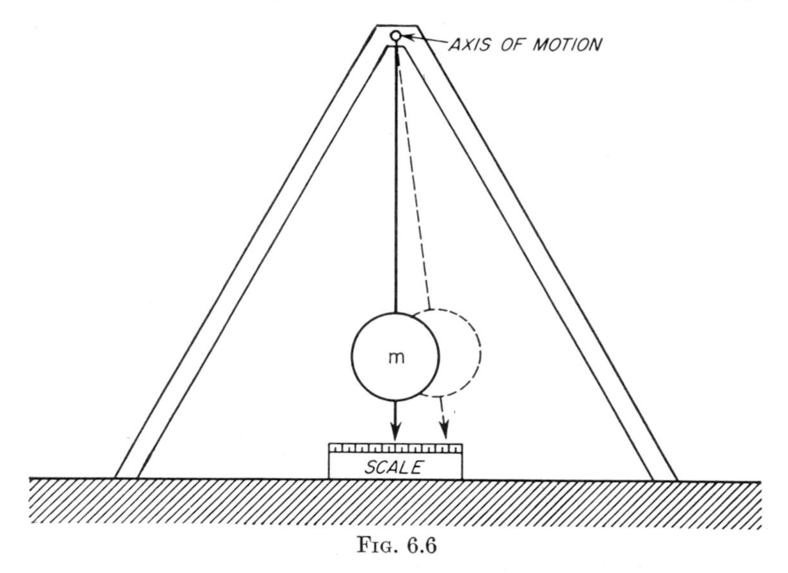

FIG. 6.6

frame moves. The motion of the ground can be noted by observing the relative position of a pointer on the mass and a scale attached to the ground.

But as the ground and frame move to one side, gravity pulls on such a pendulum, and the pendulum tends to follow the motion of the ground and to continue to swing after the ground comes to rest. A better system for earthquake observations is obtained by swinging the pendulum in a horizontal or nearly horizontal plane instead of a vertical plane (Fig. 6.7). If the pendulum swings about a vertical axis, there is no tendency for it to return to any particular position. If the axis is tilted slightly, the pendulum will be acted on by a small component of gravity, and if deflected, it will return slowly to its original position. Damping is easily provided by a plate attached to the mass and extending into a cup of oil on the ground. Such a horizontal pendulum is the basic principle of most earthquake seismometers (McComb, 1936).

In order to make the seismometer indicate the ground motion accurately, it is necessary that the rate at which the pendulum returns to its

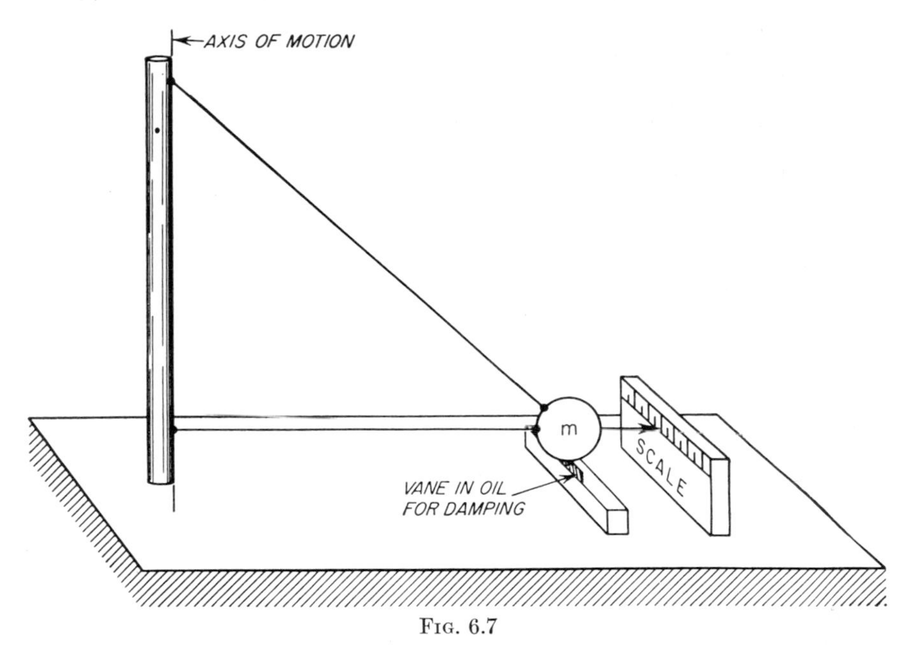

FIG. 6.7

rest position be very slow. This means that the natural period of oscillation of the pendulum must be long. The seismometer indicates clearly ground oscillations with periods short compared with its natural period. If the period of the ground motion is longer than that of the pendulum, the inertial mass tends to move with the ground and the motion is not accurately indicated. It can be shown that if the period of the ground motion greatly exceeds the pendulum period, the response is proportional to the acceleration of the ground instead of the displacement.

Vertical motion can be detected by swinging the pendulum about a horizontal axis (Fig. 6.8). The pendulum is supported against gravity by a spring. A long, weak spring can be used to keep the natural period of the pendulum long, or the spring can be adjusted so that it tends to increase whatever relative movement of the ground and inertial mass occurs. A diagonal spring, such as the one shown in Fig. 6.8, is the commonest type. If the ground rises, the angle θ decreases, and although the spring is stretched, the restoring moment about the axis of rotation of the pendulum is increased very little. If the ground drops, although the length of the spring, and hence its tension, decreases, θ increases, preventing a large decrease in the torque of the spring. A small restoring moment results in a long natural period of oscillation and a high sensitivity to ground motion. A spring system in which the restoring force is reduced in this fashion by the motion of the restrained mass is said to be

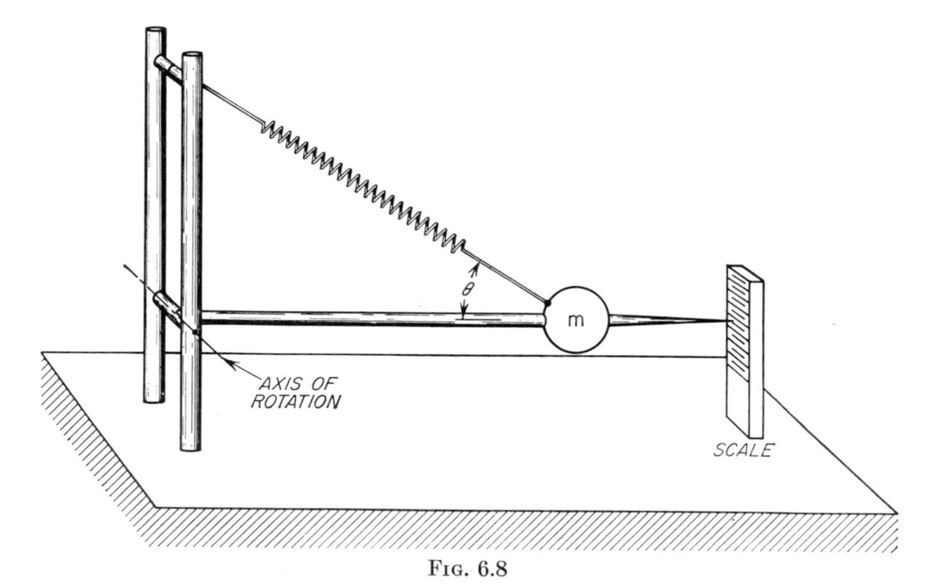

Fig. 6.8

astatized. Astatized pendulums of this sort are used to measure gravity, since the rest position of such a pendulum is very sensitive to the strength of the gravitational pull acting on it (see Sec. 14.2). There is a limit to the length of the free period of oscillation which can be obtained by astatization. If too much astatizing force is provided, the pendulum becomes unstable and will not return to its rest position if it is deflected from it.

It is normally desirable to make some sort of permanent record of the ground motion. This can be done by attaching a stylus or pen to the pendulum arm and letting it write a record on a rotating drum (Fig. 6.9). Some seismometers use a fine wire rubbing lightly on the surface of a piece of smoked paper. This gives a very sharp trace, but the smoked paper is difficult to manufacture and to store. More commonly, a fine ink line is drawn. In some modern instruments the recording paper is backed by a conductive material, and the stylus carries an electrical current which flows through the thin paper, burning a clear, sharp dark line on the surface.

All stylus-type recorders have the disadvantage that there is some friction between the stylus and drum, providing appreciable restraint to the relative movement of the ground and pendulum. This makes it difficult to record small ground movements. Furthermore, since the ground motion is usually very small, it is desirable to amplify it. The amplification provided by a mechanical recorder is only the ratio of the distance $L1$

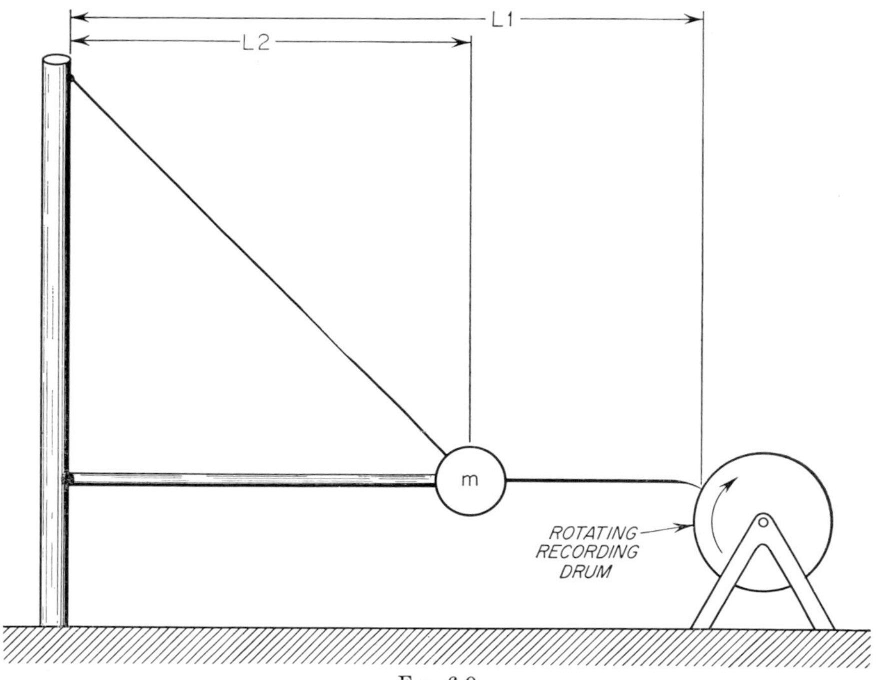

Fig. 6.9

of the recording stylus tip from the axis of motion to the distance $L2$ of the center of oscillation of the pendulum arm from the axis of rotation.[1]

Greater amplification can be obtained without the disadvantage of stylus or pen friction by use of photographic recording. A mirror is mounted on the seismometer, and a light beam is reflected from it onto a recording drum around which is wrapped a strip of film or photographic paper. When the recording drum is placed at a large distance from the

[1] For an ideal pendulum with all the mass concentrated at one point, the center of oscillation and center of mass are at the same point. The effective length of a pendulum is treated in more detail in Sec. 12.3. See Sohon (1932) for a detailed discussion of the mathematical theory of the seismograph.

seismometer, the effective length of the recording "arm" can be made much longer than the length of the pendulum. Furthermore, the light beam is deflected through twice the angle the pendulum rotates, giving another factor of 2 of amplification.

An example of a seismometer using this type of recording is the Wood-Anderson torsion seismometer (Fig. 6.10; Anderson and Wood, 1925). In this instrument, the mass is a copper cylinder attached to a torsion fiber along its side. The length of the pendulum is one-half the diameter of the cylinder, commonly less than 1 cm. By setting the recording drum several meters away, it is possible to get an amplification of several hundred times. Because its free period is short compared with the period of most seismic waves, the Wood-Anderson seismometer behaves

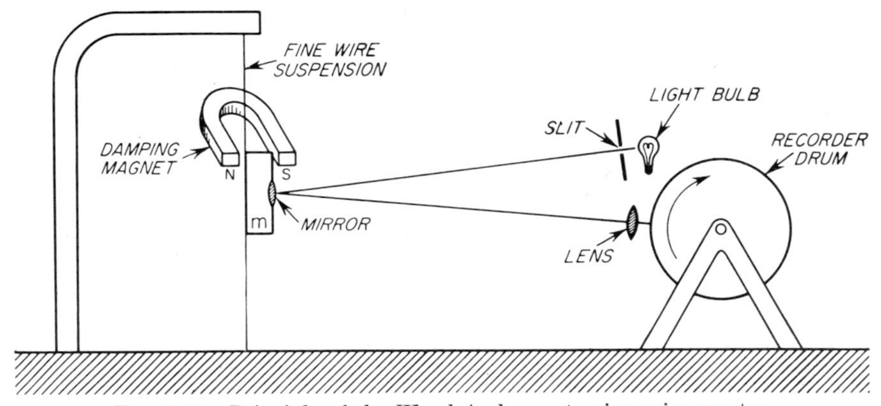

FIG. 6.10 Principle of the Wood-Anderson torsion seismometer.

for most earthquake waves as an accelerometer. Eddy-current damping is provided by making the inertia mass of copper and placing it in the field of a strong permanent magnet.

Even more amplification can be obtained by use of an electromagnetic transducer (Fig. 6.11). A coil fixed to the ground moves with respect to a magnet attached to the inertia mass (the positions of coil and magnet are interchangeable). This generates an electrical current which can be made to operate a galvanometer. In addition to the optical amplification of the galvanometer system, there is additional electrical gain obtainable. This is provided by the ratio of the inertial mass of the seismometer to the mass of the moving system of the galvanometer. The system is essentially a "heavy" generator running a "light" motor. Damping can be conveniently provided by the resistive losses in the electrical system.

The use of electromagnetic recording results in a seismogram wherein the deflection of the trace from a straight line is usually proportional to the velocity (= rate of change of displacement) of the ground. This is because the current generated by the coil and magnet is proportional to the rate at which the coil cuts the lines of magnetic flux, and hence to the velocity of the ground with respect to the inertial mass.

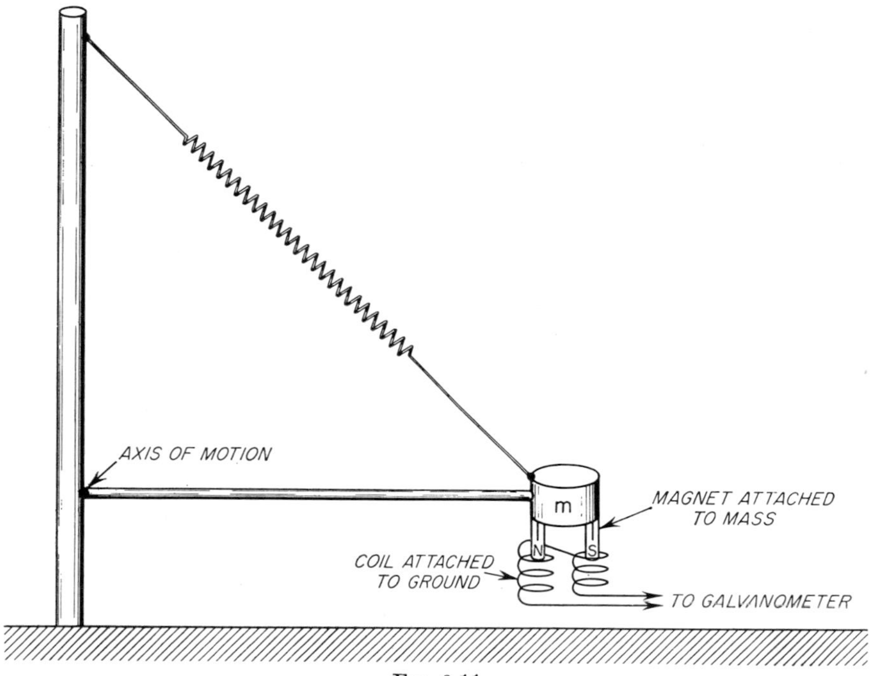

FIG. 6.11

6.5 Strain Seismometers. All the seismometers described above make a record of the displacement of the ground from rest or of some function of the displacement. It is also possible to measure the distortion of the ground in other ways. One variable which can be measured is the relative displacement of two points in the ground. The Benioff (1935) strain seismometer (Fig. 6.12) is an instrument of this sort. Two posts

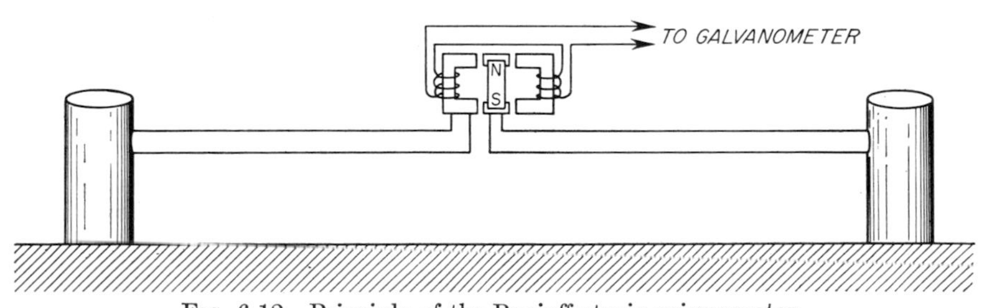

FIG. 6.12 Principle of the Benioff strain seismometer.

are sunk into the ground about 20 m apart. To one post is attached the magnet of an electromagnetic recording system, and to the other post the coil system. Motion of the magnet with respect to the coils operates a galvanometer and is recorded photographically. The Benioff seismometer uses a coil and magnet arrangement called a variable-reluctance element. Two U-shaped soft-iron frames on which the coils are wound are arranged so that in the undisturbed position half the flux of the magnet passes through each coil (Fig. 6.12). Any change in distance between the two posts moves the magnet nearer to one soft-iron core and farther from the other. When the gaps are made small, the reluctance of the magnetic system is very sensitive to the position of the armature. A small movement causes a large shift in flux, which produces a corresponding current in the coils to operate the recording galvanometer. Variable-reluctance elements are also used in pendulum seismometers to get high sensitivity.

Strain gauges made by cementing a gridwork of fine resistance wire to a rock surface have been used by Obert and Duvall (1949). As the rock deforms, the wire is stretched or compressed, changing its resistance. The strain can be measured by recording the change in current at a given applied voltage, or by making the resistance one element of a Wheatstone bridge and recording the unbalanced voltage.

Pressure-sensitive seismometers can also be made using piezoelectric crystals such as barium titanate, quartz, lithium sulfate, or Rochelle salt. These are particularly useful in model studies (e.g., Knopoff, 1955; Oliver et al., 1954; Tatel, 1954). Magnetostriction devices have been used to record pressure waves in water. Both piezoelectric and magnetostriction gauges are relatively insensitive to the low frequencies encountered in earthquake waves and are rarely used except in model studies and close to explosions, where peak pressures are large and of short duration. Carbon button microphones have also been used for recording seismic waves (Jakosky, 1940).

6.6 Seismograms. A typical seismogram made by a seismograph consists of an irregular line (Fig. 6.5). The amount of departure of any point on this line from a reference line is a measure of the amount of ground motion. Seismographs can be built so that they write records which are proportional to displacement, velocity, or acceleration of the earth. Since these are simply related, determination of one is equivalent to determination of all three. If x is the displacement of the ground from its rest position and t the time,

$$\text{Velocity} = v = \frac{dx}{dt} \tag{6.1}$$

$$\text{Acceleration} = a = \frac{dv}{dt} = \frac{d^2x}{dt^2} \tag{6.2}$$

On reversing the process,

$$v = \int a \, dt \tag{6.3}$$
$$x = \int v \, dt = \int\int a \, dt \, dt \tag{6.4}$$

Since each integration involves the introduction of an arbitrary constant, velocity cannot be determined exactly from acceleration, as any uniform velocity the particle may have will not be discovered. Similarly, displacement determined from velocity lacks also a fixed term. This, however, is no disadvantage in studying an earthquake, since it is the transient movements, not the fixed position and velocity, which are sought by such studies.

6.7 Types of Earthquake Waves. When the first seismograms of earthquakes were studied, they were found to consist of a long train of waves gradually increasing in amplitude to one or more maxima, then dying off somewhat more rapidly (Fig. 6.5). These principal waves were preceded by a number of relatively weak impulses, which were named "Vorlaufer" or "forerunners." The periods of the wave motions during the Vorlaufer were much shorter than during the later part of the record, of the order of 1 sec as compared with 10 sec; thus the latter came to be known as "long waves."

During the arrival of the vibrations from a large, distant earthquake, the ground at first moves largely up and down. These waves are called primary waves, abbreviated P waves. Following the arrival of a group of primary waves, Vorlaufer arrive with a motion predominantly at right angles to the motions of P. These secondary, or S, waves are usually larger in amplitude than the P waves.

Unlike P and S, which start relatively abruptly, the long waves generally start with gradually increasing amplitudes, without a distinct beginning. The earliest long waves usually have the longest periods. Sometimes a series of long waves is recognized arriving particularly early and with an exceedingly long period, over 25 sec. This pulse is called G, while the normal long waves are called L. The largest maximum of the long waves is called M, and the part of the earthquake which follows this maximum is called the coda.

The theory of transmission of elastic waves will be discussed in greater detail in Chap. 10. Most of this theory had already been developed when the first seismographs were made. Two types of waves can be transmitted through a homogeneous, isotropic, elastic solid. Dilatational (compressional) waves, of which sound waves are a familiar example, involve particle motions which are parallel to the direction of transmission of the energy, whereas transverse (shear) waves involve motion at right angles to this direction. It was recognized independently by R. D. Oldham and

E. Wiechert in 1899 that the P pulses were dilatational waves and S pulses shear waves. They travel through the interior of the earth and hence are called body waves.

The long waves are not so easily explained. If one plots their time of arrival against distance along the surface from their source, the resulting graph is a straight line showing that, unlike the body waves, they travel

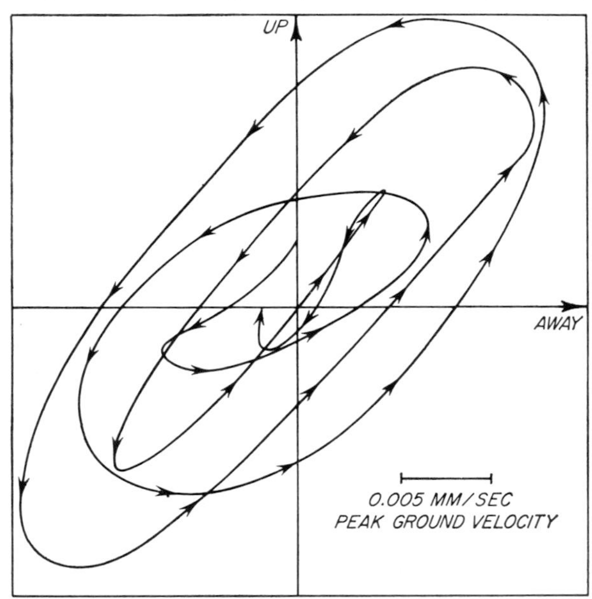

Fig. 6.13 Hodograph of the particle motion during the arrival of a pseudo-Rayleigh wave caused by a dynamite explosion.

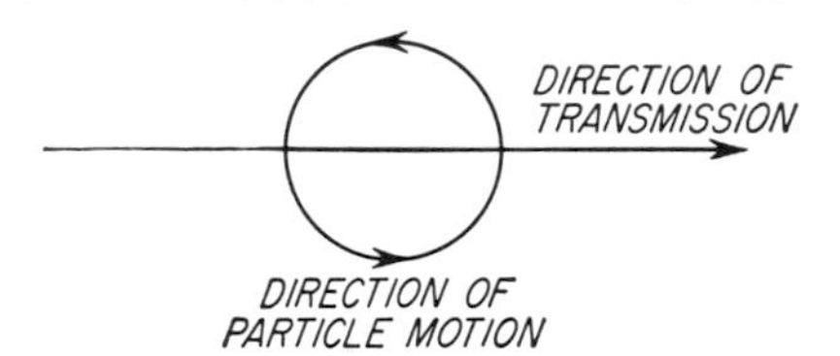

Fig. 6.14 Particle motion during the passage of a Stoneley wave.

along the earth's surface (Fig. 11.8). They are, therefore, called surface waves.

There are many types of surface waves which can exist in theory. In 1885 Lord Rayleigh showed that along a free surface bounding a homogeneous, semi-infinite, isotropic, elastic half space waves can be transmitted wherein the particles undergo a retrograde elliptical motion, with the long axis of the ellipse usually vertical (Fig. 6.13). R. Stoneley (1924,

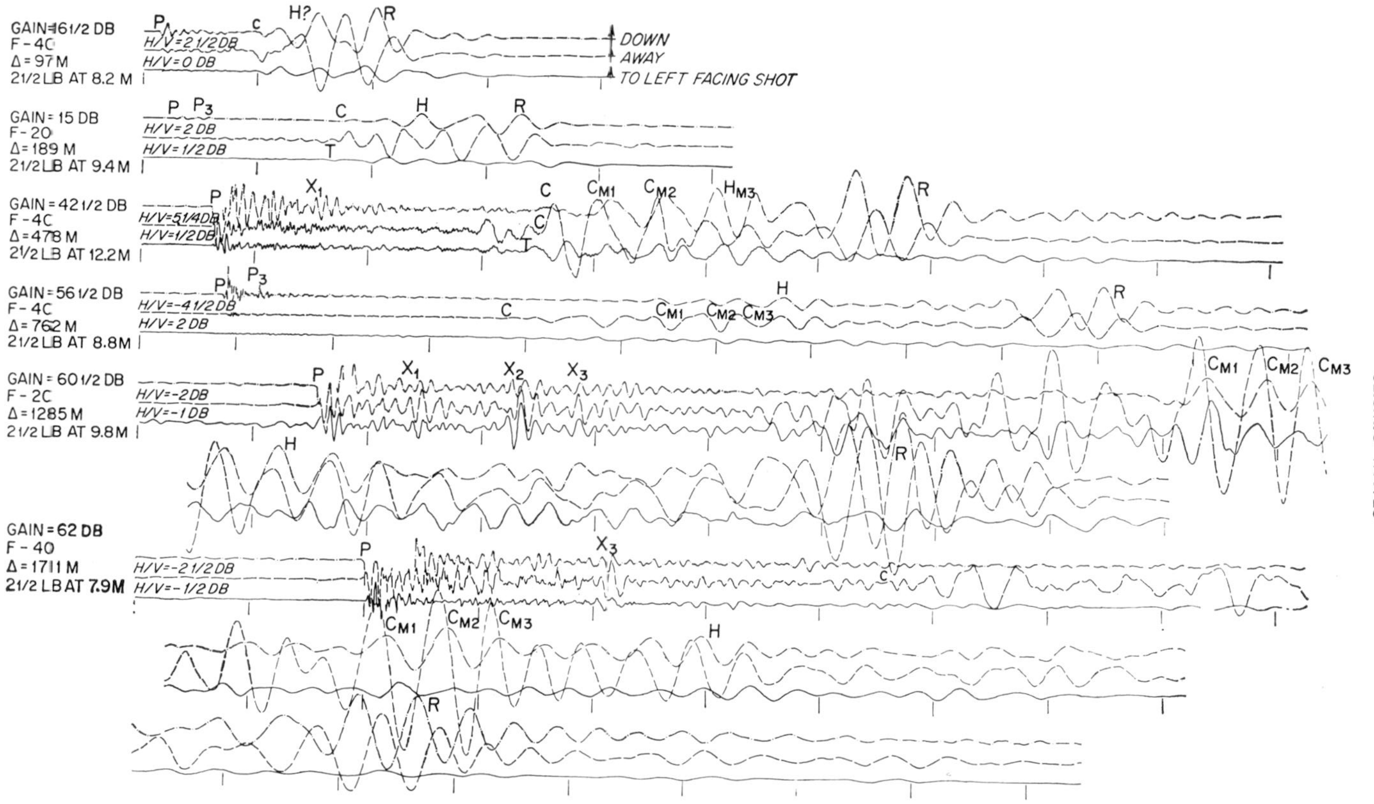

FIG. 6.15 Records of ground motion out to 1,711 m. P is the first arrival; P_3, X_1, X_2, and X_3 are later body-wave pulses; C is the beginning of the C pulse; C_{M1}, C_{M2}, and C_{M3} are a characteristic group of three maxima of C; T is the beginning of long-period motion on the transverse component; H is the maximum of the H pulse; and R is the maximum of R.

1926) and others have shown that such waves can exist even if the boundary is not free or if the medium is not homogeneous. Waves of this sort traveling along the boundary between two thick media are called Stoneley waves. In this case the motion can be either retrograde or direct depending on from which medium it is viewed (Fig. 6.14). Sezawa and Kanai (1935) have shown that the motion can be direct even on a free surface in certain cases.

The motion immediately preceding M and in the codas of earthquakes is similar to that predicted by the above investigators, except that the horizontal component of motion usually exceeds the vertical and the ellipses of motion are often tilted. This can be most clearly seen in the seismogram of a small explosion (Fig. 6.15). Such waves are often called Rayleigh-type or pseudo-Rayleigh waves to distinguish them from the theoretically predicted Rayleigh waves where the vertical amplitude would exceed the horizontal. The letter R is used as a designation where the particle motion is retrograde, H where it is direct.

In Fig. 6.15 there is motion preceding H which is largely confined to the longitudinal component (in the direction of transmission). This is an example of a pulse of a type first described by L. D. Leet (1939, 1946), and called "coupled waves" by him. The letter C designates this pulse. Although in the case illustrated the energy appears largely on only one component, it is often distributed on all three. In such cases it can often be recognized by the appearance of in-phase motion on all components. It is uncertain whether this is a body or a surface wave, as the manner of its transmission is unknown.

One other type of wave is common in the records of earthquakes. This is known as the Love wave, named after A. E. H. Love, who first derived the theory of its transmission in 1911. It is a surface shear wave, the motion being in the transverse direction (parallel to the surface, at right angles to the direction of transmission). The first part of L previous to R is often of this nature. In the records of underground explosions Love waves (and body shear waves also) are conspicuously weak. This is not surprising if we consider that the energy is initiated by a radial pressure around the charge, which sends out a compressional pulse through the ground but produces relatively little shear. The presence of strong shear waves with only relatively weak compressional waves in most earthquake records is evidence that earthquakes are not caused, in general, by an explosive phenomenon but by one in which shear of some sort is predominant. Other types of wave motion are involved in waves spreading radially from a source but have not been recognized in the records of earthquakes (Fu, 1947; Ewing et al., 1957).

CHAPTER 7

OBSERVATIONAL SEISMOLOGY

7.1 Earth Motion. In the last chapter it was shown that an earthquake consists of three groups of pulses: P, S, and L. These may sometimes be felt individually by observers during large earthquakes. However, this is generally not the case, as the ground motion is much more complicated than is suggested by the simplified discussion presented here. Where it can be recognized, P commonly consists of a distinctly vertical oscillation. It is felt by observers on ships as a sudden jarring motion, as though the ship had struck some submerged object. Often on ships it is not recognized as an earthquake, its nature being determined subsequently from a comparison of the time the event occurred at sea with that of the earthquake as observed ashore.

The compressional pulse is not usually so damaging to structures as are S and L. This is probably due to two factors. First, the compressional pulse usually has a smaller amplitude than either the shear waves or the long waves. Second, buildings have to be built to withstand the acceleration of gravity, which is a vertical force. The force exerted by compressional waves is in the direction of the ground motion, which also is usually nearly vertical, and only very rarely exceeds gravity. Since most structures are built with a considerable factor of safety, they will rarely be damaged by vertical earthquake forces unless the factor of safety is less than 2.

The same is not true for the other pulses, wherein the motion is either horizontal or has a strong horizontal component. The shear waves can sometimes be recognized as a violent tangential oscillation of the ground. Often, to an observer, they are indistinguishable from the long waves, wherein the motion differs primarily in that its period is greater and the pattern of the motion more complicated. Except when special care is taken to provide earthquake-resistant construction, buildings are rarely built with much thought of the effects of horizontal forces. The only other large force they must normally withstand is the wind, and it usually exerts a comparatively steady pressure, which is of an entirely different nature from earthquake forces. The force exerted by an earthquake vibration is dependent not only on the amplitude of motion but on its frequency, since

$$F = ma = m \frac{d^2x}{dt^2} \tag{7.1}$$

where m is the mass on which the force F acts, x is the displacement of the mass, a its acceleration, and t is time. If the motion is simple harmonic and of maximum half amplitude x_0, then

$$x = x_0 \cos \frac{2\pi t}{T} \tag{7.2}$$

where T is the period of the motion, and

$$F = m \frac{d^2x}{dt^2} = -m \frac{4\pi^2 x}{T^2} \tag{7.3}$$

The shorter the period, the greater the force for the same amount of displacement. S usually has a shorter period than does L, but the latter in many cases exerts the greater force because of its larger amplitude of motion. Furthermore, damage is also an effect of duration of the shaking (possibly of the number of shakes), and the long waves last longer than either P or S.

The duration of an earthquake is largely a function of the distance from the source of the motion, though it must also depend on the length of time during which the energy is being radiated from the source. It is also a function of the size of the earthquake, since much of the motion during a small earthquake at large distances is lost in the microseismic background. The different pulses travel at different speeds and along different paths, the body waves coming through the earth and the surface waves around the outside. P travels fastest, its speed varying from less than 1 km per sec in loose unconsolidated material near the surface to nearly 14 km per sec at the center of the earth. Shear waves travel everywhere more slowly than compressional waves, and Rayleigh waves slowest of all.

The long waves, because they travel along the surface, where the velocities are lowest, are the last to arrive. They are spread out because of dispersion, which results from the velocity of transmission being a function of wavelength. In general for earthquake surface waves, the longer the wavelength, the greater the velocity. For surface waves in the earth, dispersion is primarily a result of the greater depth of penetration of the long-period waves, which also have long wavelengths. The energy of surface waves travels largely in a layer adjoining the surface of the order of a wavelength thick, the amplitude of motion decreasing rapidly with distance from the surface. In the earth the velocity of transmission increases with depth. Therefore, the waves which penetrate most deeply reach the highest velocity regions, and hence travel fastest. As a result of this dispersion it may take several hours for a train of earthquake waves to pass a point at a large distance from the source of energy, while at a short distance the duration may be less than 1 min.

The shaking of the ground or of a building during an earthquake depends not only on the nature of the earthquake waves being received but also on the nature of the structure, natural (geological) or artificial (man-made), receiving them. There are three manners by which wave motion of any kind can be transmitted in any system. (1) The system can refuse to accept the arriving vibrations. This is called reflection and will be treated in greater detail later. As an analogy think of trying to pour water into a pail with a lid on it. The water will not enter the pail. (2) The energy may pass through the system, leaving it as quickly as it enters and completely unchanged by the medium. This is perfect transmission. It corresponds to a pail with no lid, but no bottom either. (3) The energy may accumulate in the system, appearing in other forms. This is called absorption. It corresponds to pouring water into a pail without a lid and with a bottom. There are, of course, also the intermediate cases of a pail with a partial lid, which accepts part of the energy, and one with a hole in the bottom, which retains the energy only temporarily.

This last case corresponds to resonance. In the case of an earthquake shaking a structure, resonance is of particular importance. If energy is passed on more slowly than it is supplied, it will accumulate with a gradual increase in amplitude of vibration. The result will be that the shaking becomes violent enough to do unusually heavy damage. This is common on certain types of ground, especially filled land, man-made fill, loose alluvial deposits, or river or lake beds. In such places the ground commonly vibrates much more than in adjoining sections of more solid rock.

Similarly buildings have certain natural frequencies of vibration, and if they are shaken at these frequencies, the amplitude may build up to much larger values than in the underlying ground. The limit on amplitude is controlled by the rate at which the energy can be transformed into other forms. If it is not so transformed or reradiated as vibrational energy, the amplitude increases until the structure is broken apart.

Such storage of energy due to resonance or other effects also contributes to dispersion. The storage causes a delay in reradiation of the energy. If the amount of delay depends on the frequency of the vibration, and it usually does, then the velocity of transmission depends on frequency (and hence on wavelength), which is dispersion.

The over-all result of dispersion and of transmission of the different pulses along different paths is that, at any given place, the earthquake arrives as a series of vibrations which take some time to pass. If two earthquakes occur at close to the same time, it may be impossible to distinguish them from each other.

7.2 Foreshocks and Aftershocks. In general an earthquake is not an isolated event. Earthquakes tend to occur more commonly in some regions than in others, and when they occur they tend to come in swarms. Sometimes, though rarely, the individual quakes of a swarm are all of about the same size, but usually one is the largest and is called the principal shock. Those preceding it are called foreshocks; those following it are called aftershocks.

Aftershocks are much commoner than foreshocks. All large earthquakes are followed by great numbers of aftershocks, but not all large earthquakes have foreshocks, and their number is relatively small when they do occur. The number of aftershocks, however, may be in the thousands. The duration of the swarm may run into weeks, months, or even years, since the frequency of occurrence dies off in general hyperbolically.

Theoretically, thus, the swarm is never over. Practically, however, when the time between aftershocks becomes of the order of a few months, it is no longer possible to distinguish an aftershock from a new principal shock. In general the size of aftershocks gradually drops off as well as the frequency, so that eventually their size is beneath the microseism level. There is not, however, a continuous decrease, as the size of the aftershocks varies irregularly, some of them being much larger than others occurring earlier in the sequence. The problem is further complicated by the fact that not all the shocks of a swarm occur in exactly the same location, though the source of all the energy is normally within a limited volume of the earth near the source of the main shock (Benioff et al., 1953, 1954). This variation of the location of the source makes it hard to tell an aftershock of a large earthquake in one region from a small principal shock in an adjoining region. Large aftershocks are commonly followed by their own sequences of smaller aftershocks. In a sense all earthquakes may be thought of as aftershocks of the original catastrophe of the earth's origin.

7.3 Epicenter and Focus. When an earthquake occurs, it does not take place simultaneously at all places where it is observed. The vibrations travel with definite, measurable velocities and seem to spread from a limited region, which is the source of the energy of the quake. This region is called the focus, or hypocenter, of the earthquake. Seismologists like to think of the focus as being a point and generally believe that, although the energy may be generated over a large area or throughout a large volume of the earth, radiation starts at some single point of this volume and spreads continuously to the rest of the source. This theory is consistent with observation, and hence the focus is usually defined as the point from which the energy is first radiated.

The focus of an earthquake is rarely at the surface of the earth, and no earthquakes are known to have originated at depths exceeding 700 km. Most earthquakes originate within the outer 50 km of the earth, a focal

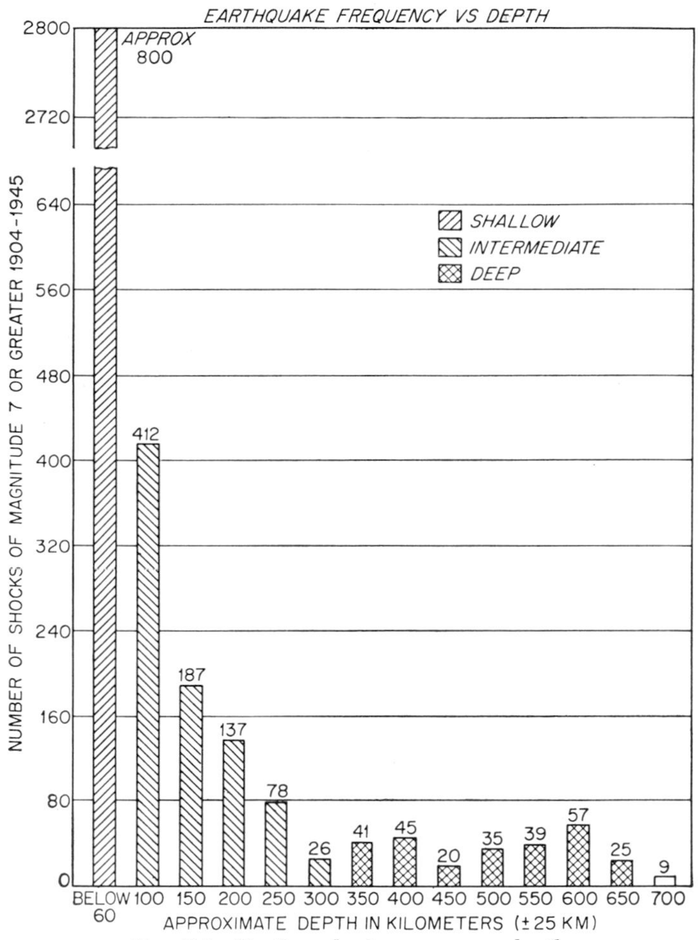

FIG. 7.1 Earthquake frequency vs. depth.

depth of the order of 25 km being most common. Earthquakes occurring at depths above 70 km are called shallow, or normal. If the focus is deeper than this but not over 300 km deep, the depth is called intermediate. Greater focal depths are spoken of as being deep, though sometimes this term is applied to all quakes of greater than normal depth of focus. Over 70 per cent of all earthquakes are shallow, the frequency of occurrence decreasing rapidly with depth down to 300 km, beneath which the rate of occurrence with depth is irregular (Fig. 7.1). Small earthquakes are more predominantly shallow than are deep earthquakes. Present accuracy of depth determination is such that depths are rarely known to closer than ± 25 km.

Abnormally deep earthquakes can be recognized in a number of ways. For one thing, the surface waves are unusually weak. This is presumably because large surface waves are not generated when the source is so deep that the earth's surface is not greatly disturbed by the shock. Deep earthquakes can be recognized by direct observation of damage, because the earthquake is felt over a very wide area, with the shaking being about equally severe at all places. In the case of shallow earthquakes, the severity of shaking usually decreases rapidly with distance from a point on the surface directly above the focus called the epicenter of the earthquake. The location of an earthquake is usually specified by giving the latitude and longitude of the epicenter and the depth of focus.

Earthquakes can be located by noting the place of most severe shaking. Such an "observational" epicenter may differ from the "instrumental" epicenter determined from a study of seismograms. This is because the point of maximum shaking at the surface is not necessarily directly over the point of first release of energy, or focus. The largest amount of energy may be released during the later part of the earthquake's generation when its source has left the original focus, or the nature of the ground may be such that the most easily shaken rocks are at some distance from the instrumental epicenter.

The determination of the location of the epicenter and focus of an earthquake is most often made from a study of seismograms. If the times of arrival of the different pulses are noted and their velocities of transmission through the earth are known, the distance of the focus from any recording station can be determined, and hence with the use of several stations the source can be located. This will be discussed further in Chap. 11.

7.4 Intensity. The violence, or "intensity," of the shaking caused by an earthquake is a measure of its size. The degree of violence is determined by noting the conditions under which the shaking is perceptible to humans, the degree to which man-made structures are damaged, and the nature of any visible deformation of the earth itself. Intensity is measured in terms of arbitrarily defined scales. One of the simplest of these is the Galitzin-Kirkpatrick scale (Wood, 1933). A series of round rods of different lengths but the same diameter are set on a flat, horizontal plate. When the ground or structure moves on which the plate sits, the longer rods fall. The more violently the ground shakes, the shorter the rod which will fall. Thus the longest rod left standing is a measure of the intensity of the shaking. The widest application of this simple scale has been in studying blast vibrations. It is so graphic a measure of intensity that it is particularly useful in court trials involving blast damage suits. Judge and jury readily comprehend its meaning. A building which was not damaged by a vibration such as that caused by a passing truck, which knocked down half the pins, probably would not be damaged by another similar vibration such as a quarry blast, which knocks down only one-quarter of the pins. Care should be used, however, to compare only similar vibrations.

J. R. Thoenen and S. L. Windes (1942) of the U.S. Bureau of Mines have made a study of the intensity of vibrations necessary to cause damage, and have found that the maximum acceleration applied to a structure during the passage of a seismic pulse is a measure of this ability. If the acceleration exceeds that of gravity, some damage is likely, but if it does not exceed one-tenth gravity, damage is unusual except in buildings which are very poorly built. The quality of the construction is an important factor in the ability of a structure to withstand earthquake vibrations.

E. J. Crandall (1949), on the other hand, has concluded from studies of blast vibrations that the energy represented by the vibrations is the best measure of their capacity to do damage. Kinetic energy is proportional to the square of velocity:

$$E = mv^2 \tag{7.4}$$

where m is the mass of the moving object and v is the maximum velocity with which it moves. If the motion is sinusoidal,[1]

$$E = m\left(\frac{a}{2\pi f}\right)^2 = \frac{ma^2}{4\pi^2 f^2} \tag{7.5}$$

where a is the corresponding acceleration and f is the frequency. This would mean that for constant acceleration the danger increases rapidly as the frequency of the vibrations decreases. On the other hand, in terms of displacement, larger amplitudes can be tolerated at low frequencies. This is consistent with earthquake-damage observations (Neumann, 1954).

The nature of the ground on which the building is built also affects the chances of damage. Structural failure is several times more likely on loose ground than on solid rock. This indicates that something more than just acceleration is involved in causing damage. A better measure, perhaps, is impact, which is defined as acceleration times frequency times duration. Impact is thus equivalent to acceleration multiplied by the number of times applied. In blasts, there is usually a single acceleration which is many times larger than all the others, so that impact and accel-

[1] The relation between velocity and acceleration of sinusoidal waves is considered in greater detail in Sec. 9.2.

eration are about equal on firm ground. On filled ground, however, where the rock stores some of the energy in resonance, there are commonly several successive cycles of motions of comparable amplitude, which would account for the greater intensity of damage.

In the case of earthquakes, the surface waves usually consist of a long sequence of vibrations of about the same amplitude, so that impact rather than acceleration should be used to measure intensity. Body waves on the other hand usually arrive as pulses of short duration, often with only one or a very few peaks of highest amplitude. There have been many cases of buildings surviving a large shock which were severely damaged by a smaller aftershock. Although in some cases it is possible that locally the aftershock was more intense than the main shock, these are equally likely examples of the damage being caused by the repeated application of acceleration adding up to sufficient impact.

A great many different intensity scales have been proposed. The first to be widely used was developed by M. S. Rossi in Italy between 1874 and 1878. A similar scale was developed by F. A. Forel in Switzerland in 1878. Later these two scales were combined into the still used Rossi-Forel scale (Table 7.1). According to their division, 10 grades of earthquake intensity were recognized, grading from shocks which were recorded by seismographs but not felt to those which caused visible deformation of the earth. A feature of this scale which seems quaint to us today is the emphasis in the middle grades on the ringing of doorbells.

TABLE 7.1 THE ROSSI-FOREL INTENSITY SCALE*

I. Shocks so weak as to be registered only by one type of seismograph and confirmed only by practical observers. Not perceptible on seismographs generally.

II. Shocks registered by seismographs generally. Confirmed only by persons who are in a condition of rest.

III. Shocks noticed by many persons. Strong enough for the duration and direction of shocks to be estimated.

IV. Shocks noticed by persons who are in a state of activity. Movable objects, windows, and doors shaken. Cracking sounds in houses.

V. Shocks generally noticed by the entire population. Large objects, beds, and other pieces of furniture are set in motion. Ringing of some doorbells.

VI. General awakening of people who are asleep. General ringing of doorbells, swinging of chandeliers, stopping of clocks, visible swaying of trees and bushes. Shocks strong enough to cause people to desert their houses in terror.

VII. Overturning of movable objects, falling of plaster from walls and ceiling, ringing of church bells. No damage to structures. Shocks powerful enough to cause general terror.

VIII. Throwing down of chimneys, appearance of cracks in the walls of buildings.

IX. Partial or complete destruction of certain buildings.

X. Great catastrophe. Ruined buildings, overturning of earth layers, appearance of clefts in the earth, landslips.

* Imamura, 1937, pp. 270–271.

These were mechanical bells, not the electrical variety we take for granted today but which were almost or quite unknown in Rossi's and Forel's time.

The Rossi-Forel scale has undergone many revisions. The first one of importance was made by Mercalli in 1888. He recognized that, particularly in the upper divisions, the earlier scale was not fine enough to divide earthquake intensities into as great detail as is desirable, and he proposed a scale with 12 subdivisions. In 1904 Cancani suggested that the degrees of the Mercalli scale be correlated with the maximum acceleration produced by the earthquake, thus giving the scale quantitative signifiance (Table 7.2). Because of the difficulty of determining the actual values of

TABLE 7.2 CANCANI'S (1904) MODIFICATION OF THE ROSSI-FOREL-MERCALLI SCALE

Degrees	Description	Corresponding acceleration, mm/sec^2
I	Instrumentally recorded shaking (*secousse instrumental*)	Less than 2.5
II	Very light (*bien légère*)	2.5–5.0
III	Light (*légère*)	5–10
IV	Easily noticeable or moderate (*sensible or mediocre*)	10–25
V	Rather strong (*assez forte*)	25–50
VI	Strong (*forte*)	50–100
VII	Very strong (*très forte*)	100–250
VIII	Ruinous (*ruineuse*)	250–500
IX	Disastrous (*désastreuse*)	500–1,000
X	Very disastrous (*très désastreuse*)	1,000–2,500
XI	Catastrophic (*catastrophe*)	2,500–5,000
XII	Very catastrophic (*grande catastrophe*)	5,000–10,000

acceleration, the more qualitative Mercalli scale has continued to be the most widely used measure of intensity in spite of the excellence of Cancani's proposal. The most widely used scale in the United States today is a modification of the Mercalli scale made by H. O. Wood and F. Neumann in 1931 (Table 7.3).

It should be remembered that intensity is not a measure of the size of the earthquake but of the degree to which it was observed and did damage. For this reason it is difficult, often impossible, to assign intensity values to earthquakes which occur in uninhabited regions or at sea.

The intensity in the most violently shaken region affected by an earthquake is sometimes spoken of as the intensity of that earthquake. From the point of view of persons living in regions where earthquakes are frequent, the resulting damage is the most important feature of a shock. It is, therefore, not surprising that the intensity was one of the first proper-

TABLE 7.3 THE MODIFIED MERCALLI INTENSITY SCALE OF 1931*

Scale degree	Effects on persons	Effects on structures	Other effects	Rossi-Forel equivalent	Equivalent shallow magnitude
I	Not felt except by few under favorable circumstances			I	
II	Felt by few at rest		Delicately suspended objects swing	I–II	2.5
III	Felt noticeably indoors. Standing cars may rock		Duration estimated	III	
IV	Felt generally indoors. People awakened		Cars rocked. Windows, etc., rattled	IV–V	3.5
V	Felt generally	Some plaster falls	Dishes, windows broken. Pendulum clocks stop	V–VI	
VI	Felt by all. Many frightened	Chimneys, plaster damaged	Furniture moved. Objects upset	VI–VII	
VII	Everyone runs outdoors. Felt in moving cars	Moderate damage		VIII	5.5
VIII	General alarm	Very destructive and general damage to weak structures. Little damage to well-built structures	Monuments, walls down. Furniture overturned. Sand and mud ejected. Changes in well-water levels	VIII–IX	6
IX	Panic	Total destruction of weak structures. Considerable damage to well-built structures	Foundations damaged. Underground pipes broken. Ground fissured and cracked	IX	
X	Panic	Masonry and frame structures commonly destroyed. Only best buildings survive. Foundations ruined	Ground badly cracked. Rails bent. Water slopped over banks	X	

TABLE 7.3 THE MODIFIED MERCALLI INTENSITY SCALE OF 1931* (*Continued*)

Scale degree	Effects on persons	Effects on structures	Other effects	Rossi-Forel equivalent	Equivalent shallow magnitude
XI	Panic	Few buildings survive	Broad fissures. Fault scarps. Underground pipes out of service	X	8.0
XII	Panic	Total destruction	Acceleration exceeds gravity. Waves seen in ground. Lines of sight and level distorted. Objects thrown in air	X	8.5

* After Wood and Neumann, 1931.

ties of earthquakes to be studied in detail. Scales of intensity have been used at least since 1811 (Wood, 1933). Maps showing the areas in which the intensities were of the various grades are called isoseismal maps, and the lines separating the areas of different grades of intensity are called isoseismal lines.

If the ground were completely uniform in character and the energy were radiated uniformly in all directions from a single source, the isoseismal lines would be circles. Actually this is never the case. A typical pattern is shown in Figs. 7.2 and 7.3. There are a number of factors which influence the radiation of the energy from the focus. First, the nature of the release of energy may be such that it is radiated more strongly in one direction than in another, just as the sound is stronger directly in front of a loud-speaker than it is to one side. Second, the source may extend throughout a plane or volume of the earth instead of being a point. Third, different types of ground transmit the vibrations with different efficiencies. Thus, hard rocks carry the energy better than unconsolidated sediments. On the other hand, there are the resonance effects previously discussed whereby large bodies of fill or loose earth tend to shake more severely than rock outcrops. This effect is so pronounced that it may much more than offset the relatively greater ability of hard rocks to transmit the vibrations without absorption of energy. Lastly, certain geologic structures such as faults or contacts under certain circumstances constitute a barrier to the passage of seismic waves. Behind such a structure there may be a shadow zone in which the intensity is less than would otherwise be expected.

An interesting example of this has been reported by Machado (1954). In studying the intensity of the Azores earthquake of August 31, 1926,

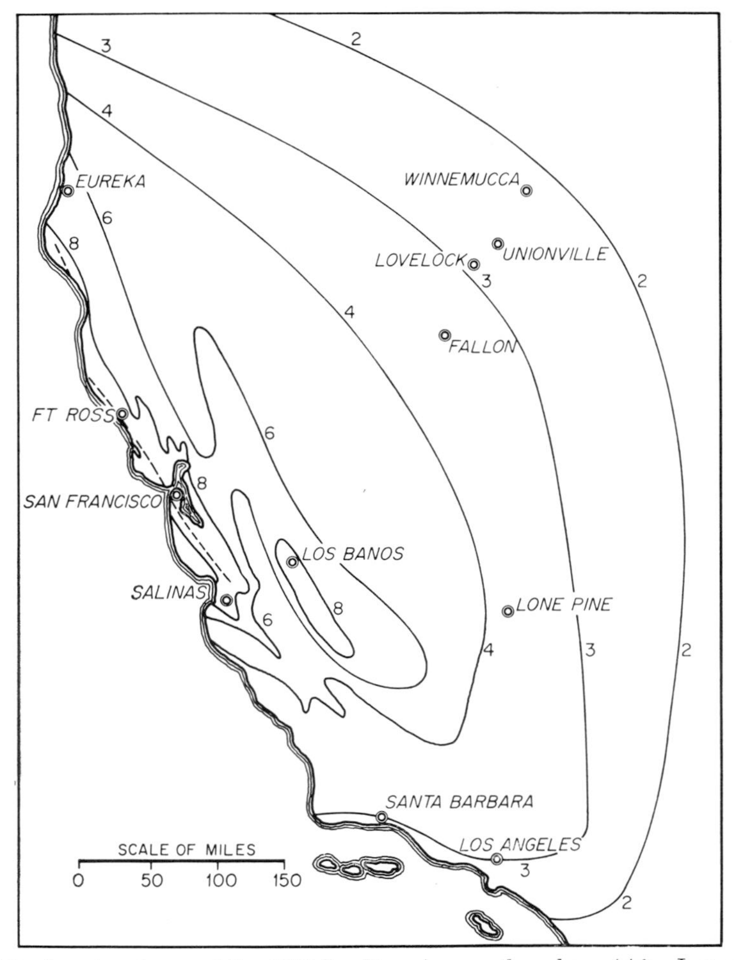

Fig. 7.2 Isoseismal map of the 1906 San Francisco earthquake. (*After Lawson et al., 1908.*)

on Fayal and Pico Islands he noted three areas of abnormally low intensity compared with what would be expected considering the distance from the epicenter (Fig. 7.4). Machado interpreted these anomalies as being due to the presence of liquid magma chambers beneath the islands, both of which are volcanic. The decrease in intensity is to be expected because the shear waves, which usually are the strongest vibrations in an

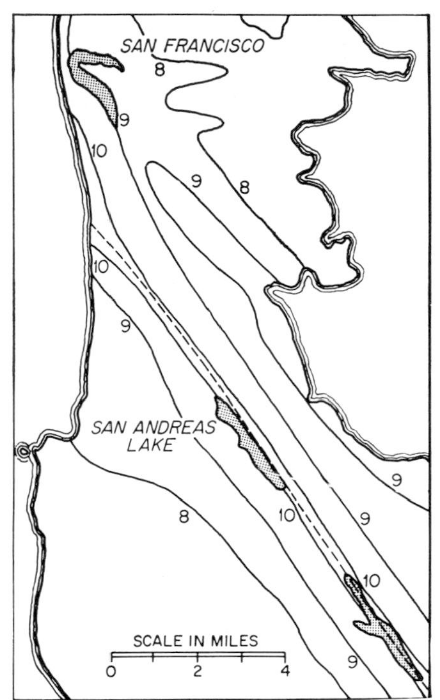

FIG. 7.3 Isoseismal map of the epicentral region, 1906 San Francisco earthquake. (*After Lawson et al., 1908.*)

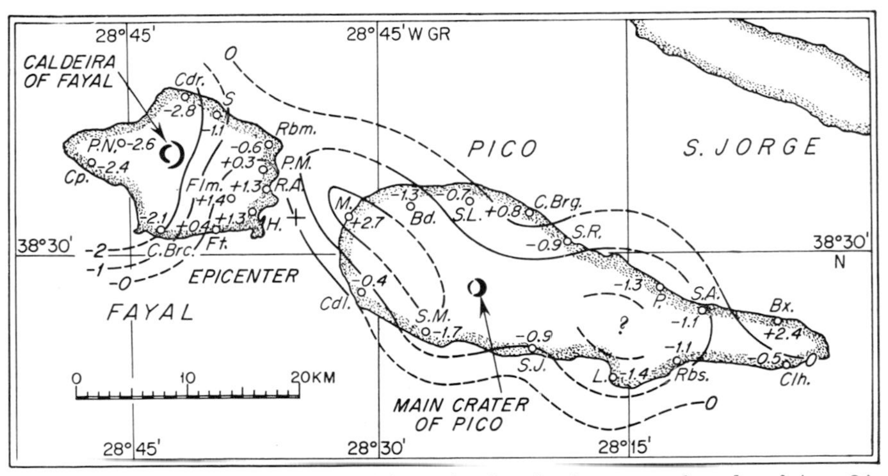

FIG. 7.4 Lines of equal anomaly of intensity for the Azores earthquake of Aug. 31, 1926. (*Courtesy of Machado, 1954.*)

earthquake such as this one, would be in large part blocked off by the liquid, through which shear waves would not be transmitted.

Inhomogeneities of the ground tend to make isoseismal lines quite irregular. At large distances from the epicenter, there tend to be small areas of high intensity entirely surrounded by areas of lower intensity and separated from the main area of maximum damage by a considerable distance. In other cases long peninsulas of severely shaken ground extend out from the central area following bodies of easily shaken soft ground. However, in all known cases some sort of roughly circular or elliptical pattern exists. The center of this pattern, where the intensity is greatest, is usually close to the instrumental epicenter. The making of an isoseismal map is at present the most accurate way of locating the epicenter unless there are several seismic observatories nearby, in which case the location can sometimes be more accurately found from the times of arrival of the earthquake pulses at the observatories.

The more intense the earthquake, the greater is the area over which it is felt. Most earthquakes are felt only over a few tens of square miles at most. Destructive earthquakes (Wood-Neumann intensity VI or greater) are felt over hundreds or thousands of square miles, and the largest earthquakes occurring in historic times have been felt at distances exceeding 800 miles from the epicenter. Davison (1936) states that the Lisbon earthquake of 1755 was reported felt at Falun in Sweden, 1,850 miles from the epicenter, though he questions whether this was actually the case. Deep earthquakes are felt over a much wider area than shallow earthquakes of the same intensity, but this is because the maximum intensity is less in proportion to the total energy of the earthquake owing to the greater depth of focus. The vibrations from a large earthquake are recorded by seismographs all over the world. The surface waves may travel around the world as many as four times before their amplitude is reduced to the microseism level.

Animals, especially birds, are sometimes more sensitive to earthquake vibrations than human beings, and are disturbed when human beings do not perceive the shocks. In a number of cases domestic fowl have been observed to become alarmed just before the person observing them felt the first earthquake waves arrive. This is possibly a result of their greater sensitivity to low-frequency vibrations. Where the seismic waves are dispersed, the low-frequency waves tend to travel fastest and arrive first, though they are usually of lesser amplitude than the maximum of the pulse. Very low-frequency vibrations may not be so readily felt by human beings as higher-frequency vibrations of equal energy, whereas animals may perceive them more readily.

7.5 Seiches. In very large earthquakes in particular a large amount of low-frequency energy is generated. One way in which this manifests itself is in disturbances of lakes, ponds, and bays. If the frequency of the earthquake vibrations corresponds to the natural frequency of oscillation of the body of water, a resonance phenomenon may occur wherein the water moves back and forth in its basin with gradually increasing amplitude until the seismic waves pass, and then continues to oscillate with decreasing amplitude for considerable further time. Such oscillations are called seiches. They are often observed at distances far beyond where the earthquake is felt.

The Lisbon, Portugal, earthquake of 1755 was particularly notable for seiches. This was one of the great earthquakes of all historic time. Actually there were three principal shocks at approximately 9:40, 10:00, and noon on the morning of November 1. Shocks were felt over an area of about a million square miles in southwestern Europe and northeastern Africa. Separate sequences of aftershocks occurred at Lisbon, Algiers, and Mequinez in Morocco, so there probably were earthquakes at several widely separated epicenters at about the same time. About 55,000 out of a total population of 235,000 were killed at Lisbon, many of them when a newly built quay, to which they had fled following the first shock, sank beneath the sea during the second quake. A part of the city was built on soft Tertiary strata, and it was almost completely destroyed, whereas the remainder, built on firm Mesozoic rocks, suffered less serious damage. There were three phases of movement during the shock: first, rapid small vibrations, too small to cause alarm and presumed to be dilatational waves; second, about 30 sec later, violent, rapid vibrations which lasted about 2 min and were presumably the shear waves; and lastly, less than 1 min later, a violent upward jerking of the ground which lasted for about 2½ min, thought to be the surface waves. All three phases were observed widely.

The seiches were not observed near the epicenter, which is believed to have been off the Portuguese coast not far from Lisbon. They began at a distance of about 600 miles. This lack of seiches at short distances from the epicenter is not uncommon. It may be that they are not developed until the surface waves have traveled far enough to become dispersed into a long train of waves. If the pulse of energy is short, there are too few individual oscillations to build up the amplitude of motion to an observable level. The seiches in England exhibited predominantly north-south motion, suggesting that they were generated by the Rayleigh waves, since these have particle motions in this direction. The period varied from 16 sec in small pools to 10 min in Loch Lomond. Many English ponds overflowed. The amplitude was 6 ft in the harbor at Yarmouth (1,090 miles from Lisbon), several feet in some of the Swiss lakes. Ships' moorings were broken at Amsterdam, Rotterdam, and Dartmouth. The most distant seiches reported were in Scandinavian lakes as far as 1,820 miles from Lisbon.

A similar phenomenon is the swinging of chandeliers, which probably results from a like, though higher frequency, resonance. In the case of the Lisbon quake this phenomenon was observed out to 1,350 miles.

7.6 Tunamis. Another phenomenon which occasionally accompanies large earthquakes is the tunami,[1] or seismic sea wave. Tunamis originate sometimes in the vicinity of the epicenter, sometimes at some distance from it. The seismic sea wave which accompanied the Lisbon earthquakes arrived immediately following the second of the three shocks in the group. It had a height variously estimated at 16 to 50 ft at Lisbon. At Tangiers the wave had a height of 50 ft and flowed for a mile and a half inland. It was observed along the south coast of England and Ireland with an amplitude of up to 9 ft, and at Antigua and Martinique in the

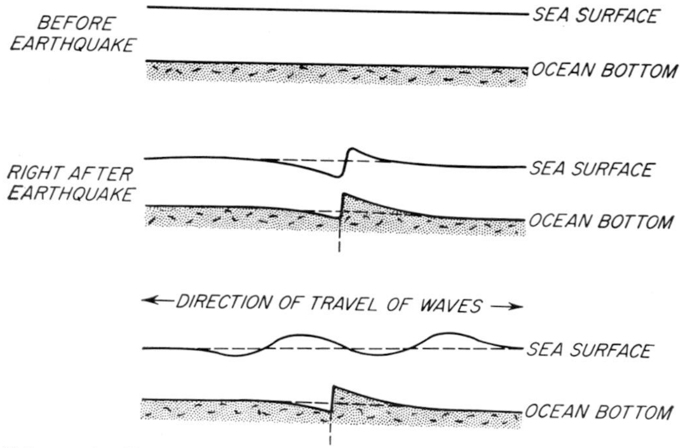

FIG. 7.5 Schematic diagram showing the theory of the formation of a tunami by faulting of the sea floor. Waves spread in both directions from the location of the fault. Vertical scale greatly exaggerated.

West Indies. To have been noticed in England, Portugal, and the West Indies with its observed size, it must have originated at a considerable distance from Lisbon, and hence it is thought to be an effect of the first quake. The first wave was at many places followed by a series of large waves of decreasing amplitude, one every 15 min for 5 hr at Antigua. It is possible that these subsequent oscillations are a form of seich stimulated by the tunami rather than the earthquake itself.

There is considerable uncertainty as to how earthquakes cause tunamis. It is possible that in some cases vertical faulting of the sea floor may produce the initial wave (Fig. 7.5). If this is the case, then on one side of the fault the tunami would arrive first as a recession of the sea, then as a crest. On the other side the order of crest and trough would be reversed. In the case of the Lisbon earthquake, the tunami began as a recession of the sea. Recessions have been reported as the first motion of tunamis in

[1] Also spelled tsunami.

the majority of cases, though there seems to be no theoretical reason why this should be so. It may be that the recession of the sea is more easily observed. It is certain that when the sea retreats, leaving the ocean floor exposed, there is certain to be a correspondingly extreme return of the water soon thereafter. When the wave breaks on a coast line containing long bays which taper toward narrow heads, the height of the wave is magnified as it proceeds up the constricting estuary and commonly results in great loss of life and destruction of property. In the Grand Banks earthquake of November 18, 1929, many people were killed along the south coast of Newfoundland. Not all the villages were as lucky as one where the postmaster, on seeing the sea retreat and leave the

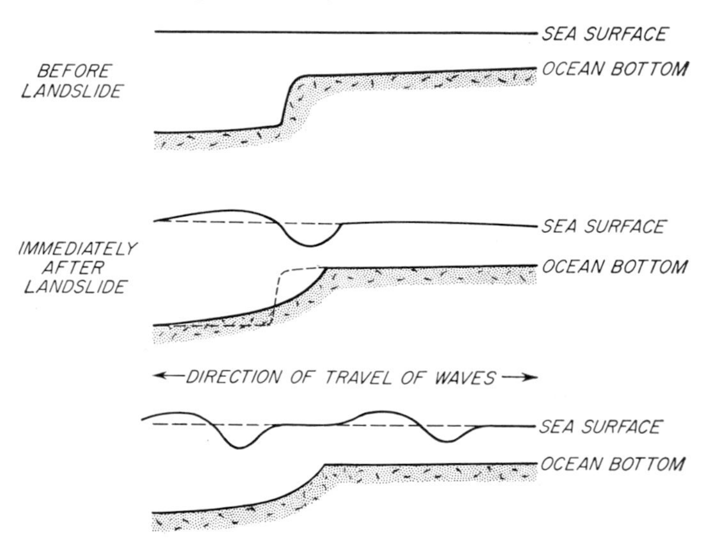

FIG. 7.6 Schematic diagram showing the theory of the formation of a tunami by a submarine landslide. Vertical scale greatly exaggerated.

harbor bottom exposed, realized it would return to a height equal to the depth to which it receded. In the few minutes before this occurred, he had time to run the length of the village's one street, calling to the people to flee to the hills, which they did, so that all were saved.

In some cases it is clear that the tunami originated at some other place than the earthquake epicenter, and hence that it cannot easily be explained as due to faulting. In the case of the 1922 Chilean earthquake the epicenter of the earthquake was inland, and the accompanying tunami proceeded down the coast from some distance to the north. It has been suggested that tunamis may result from landslides caused by the earthquake (Fig. 7.6). Submarine volcanic activity has also been suggested as a major cause. The explosive eruption of Krakatoa volcano in 1883 caused a large sea wave (see Sec. 8.7).

7.7 Study of Earthquake Effects. The Lisbon earthquake is notable as the first shock for which a thorough, systematic study was made of the effects of an earthquake. Following the quake, the Marques de Pombal, the Secretary of State for Portugal, sent a questionnaire to the priest of every parish in that country. The answers to this query have fortunately been preserved in the national archives. De Pombal asked the time of the occurrence of the several quakes; the duration of the shaking in each case; the observed directions of ground motions; the effects on the sea, springs, rivers, and lakes, especially the height and duration of any unusual sea waves; the times of aftershocks; whether any fissures were observed in the ground; the population of each parish; and the deaths, destruction, and fires resulting from the earthquakes. As this was the first questionnaire systematically circulated to study an earthquake, it marks the beginning of the scientific study of seismology.

The procedure followed by de Pombal differs hardly at all from that used today to study the effects of a quake. The U.S. Coast and Geodetic Survey circulates post-card questionnaires to dependable observers following every large earthquake in this country and uses the data so obtained in making isoseismal maps. It is more difficult than at first might be expected to get reliable reports of what has happened during an earthquake. Many people experience considerable emotional stress during even mild shocks, and there is a tendency to exaggerate what has been observed, in some cases perhaps as an unconscious justification of the fear the observer may have experienced. Another difficulty is a tendency for people to see what they expect to see rather than what actually occurs. For this reason it is necessary to seek quantitative answers to questions regarding the amount of disturbance reported and to confirm such data from independent observers or by personal examination of the effects. The most dependable evidence would be a photograph, but most pictures are taken, understandably, only after the earthquake is over.

Our knowledge of what to expect from an earthquake has increased greatly as a result of such studies. Table 7.4 lists the different sorts of effects which have been observed for earthquakes. Many of these have been discussed in the examples previously treated, so only those not already mentioned will be examined here in any detail.

Most easily studied of all effects of earthquakes are those on buildings and other structures built by man. Not merely the presence and degree of damage are important but also its detailed nature. From the direction of fall of walls one can sometimes estimate the direction of ground motion causing the collapse. In some cases, such as the Ischia earthquake of 1883 in Italy, the roofs were frequently caved in but the walls left standing, indicating that the greatest accelerations were in a vertical direction. It is more general for the walls to yield but the roof to be less

TABLE 7.4 DIRECTLY OBSERVABLE EARTHQUAKE EFFECTS

1. Trace phenomena:
   - Amount of displacement
   - Direction of displacement, slickensides, drag
   - Number of breaks
   - Uniformity of character of motion
   - Dip of fault plane
   - Straightness of fault
   - Number of breaks
   - Length of break
   - Relation to older scarps
   - Ridges
   - Troughs
   - Excavation of trace by water
   - Width of gouge zone
   - Mole tracks
   - Arrangement of structural patterns (*en echelon* or parallel to trace)
   - Dammed streams
   - Waterfalls and rapids
   - Offset streams and stream piracy
   - Fences, roads offset
2. Other deformation features:
   - Depressions
   - Ponds formed
   - Height of ridges changed
   - Settling of loose earth
   - Landslides
   - Fissuring (in loose ground)
   - Fractures (in solid rock)
   - Tilting
   - Depths of harbors, etc., changed
   - Sand blows
   - Raised or depressed beaches
   - Waves in ground, cracking along crests
   - Cracks opening and closing in ground
   - Changes in position of geodetically located points
3. Effects on water:
   - Tunamis
   - Seiches
   - Flow of springs and wells
   - Fountains
   - Sand and mud craters
   - Water welling up owing to compacting of soil
   - Agitation of water in containers, pools, rivers, etc.
4. Effects on structures built by man:
   - Direction of fall of walls
   - Collapse of roofs as compared with walls
   - Intensity maps (relation to nature of ground)
   - Chimneys down
   - Plaster cracked
   - Movement of loose objects

TABLE 7.4 DIRECTLY OBSERVABLE EARTHQUAKE EFFECTS (*Continued*)

Chandeliers swing
Clocks stopped
Resulting fires
Roads, railroads, telegraph lines out of line
Bridges and culverts damaged
Damage to underground pipes and cables
Rotation of objects

5. Effects on animals and plants:
   Trees broken off
   Trees uprooted
   Trees sway
   "Waves" in grain
   Damage to roots
   Animals (especially birds) disturbed
   Death or injury
6. Effects on people:
   Deaths and injuries
   Activity vs. perception
   Amount of panic
   Area over which felt (intensity)
   Observed duration and direction of vibration
   Time
   Ability to stand or walk, etc.
   Felt on ships, in cars
   Noises
7. Other effects:
   Foreshocks
   Aftershocks
   Acceleration, movement of objects
   Lights seen
   Associated volcanism
   Changes in magnetic field
   Correlation of formations across a fault
   Geologic features of adjoining fault blocks contrasted

damaged. Following the 1940 Imperial Valley earthquake in California the author saw a two-story building which had been used as a gas station where the first floor walls had collapsed, leaving the upper part of the building almost intact. From a distance, no damage was visible. It looked like a normal structure. Only on coming close to it was it clear what had happened.

The shear patterns in masonry and plaster are particularly worthy of attention, as from a study of these broken materials and of displaced objects one can sometimes estimate the forces involved. Chimneys are particularly subject to damage. In many houses the chimney is not rigidly attached to the rest of the building, often being a long, narrow tower partially or fully surrounded by a more flexible structure. A frame house may bend easily without harm under the stresses caused by a quake, where the same shock will break a masonry structure unless special care is taken in construction to give it extra strength (Fig. 7.7).

Any loose object is likely to be moved, especially heavy objects on casters, which may roll across rooms, injuring other furniture or people. Objects on shelves come tumbling down, sometimes more from one wall than another. Any suspended object can swing. This includes such relatively rigid suspensions as bridges. Bridges and culverts are often foci of earthquake damage (Fig. 7.8). Pendulum clocks are often stopped

FIG. 7.7 Daiwa Department Store, Fukui City, Japan, after the 1948 earthquake. (*U.S. Army photograph.*)

by earthquakes, which is one way of determining roughly when the shock occurred. Tall, slim buildings can act as inverted pendulums, causing extreme damage in the upper stories, where the motion is greatest.

At one time it was thought that the rotation of objects represented the effect of a torsional component of ground vibrations. However, this is not necessarily so, as an object sitting with its weight unevenly distributed on its base can under certain circumstances be rotated by torque-free forces. Gravestones and other monuments are commonly found either rotated or tipped over. Whole houses may move on their foundations in this way. The practice, common in some parts of the world, of building a house on a group of posts driven into the ground is particularly conducive to serious damage. A slight shift of the house with respect to the ground will move the supporting framework off the posts, so that the

Fig. 7.8 Damage to Nakatsuno Bridge, Fukui, Japan, earthquake of 1948. (*U.S. Army photograph.*)

Fig. 7.9 Damage on the Stanford campus caused by the 1906 San Francisco earthquake. (*Lawson et al., 1908. Courtesy of Carnegie Institution of Washington.*)

house drops, leaving the posts protruding through the floor. Underground pipes and cables may be broken or bent even if there is no noticeable surface deformation. More commonly, roads, railroads, telephone lines, or fences are seen to be shifted out of line.

Contrary to popular belief it is not always safest to rush out of doors when an earthquake occurs. In cities, the streets are often filled with masonry which falls from the walls of tall buildings, and persons in the streets may be killed by it (Figs. 7.9 and 7.10).

The first thought in an earthquake should be to stay calm. As soon as it is safe to move about, all open flames should be put out. Often an earthquake is followed by a fire which may be far more serious than the shock itself. This was the case in the 1923 Tokyo earthquake and the 1906 San Francisco earthquake. Broken gas mains and upset stoves start fires at many places simultaneously. Fire fighting is hampered by the general confusion and often panic. Alarm systems may fail, streets become blocked, and sometimes water supplies to fight the fires are unavailable because the mains are broken. In the 1923 Tokyo earthquake 38,000 people who had fled to the relative safety of an open park were burned to death when the inflammable goods they had carried with them from their homes to save them from the flames caught fire and made an inferno of the area.

Fig. 7.10 This statue fell from its mounting at Stanford during the 1906 San Francisco earthquake. (*Lawson et al., 1908. Courtesy of Carnegie Institution of Washington.*)

Plants, especially trees, can be damaged as well as buildings. The waves passing through the ground may be visible as they cause grain to sway. Tilting of the ground during the passage of an earthquake may be shown in magnified form by the swaying of trees. If they bend far enough, they may uproot themselves, and if the ground moves too rapidly for the tops to follow, the trunks may be snapped off. Compression and shear in the ground may damage the roots of plants. Animals may be simply frightened by the vibrations themselves or injured or killed by falling objects or in other ways.

Reports of persons or animals swallowed by fissures which open and close in the ground are common but unconfirmed by reputable witnesses. In the case of the San Francisco earthquake a cow is reported to have fallen into a fissure opened by the quake. The crack closed again on the cow, leaving only her tail above the ground. By the time that the State Earthquake Commission representative came to investigate this remarkable phenomenon, dogs, so it was suggested, had unfortunately eaten off the tail, and the cow's body could not be found. In the 1949 Ecuador quake a woman was reported to have been similarly swallowed by the earth but saved her baby by holding it above her head in her hands, where it was afterward found unharmed (so it is said).

In the case of human beings, not only can death and injury be noted, but the sensations described, from which some idea of the ground motion can be ascertained. In cars the sensation is sometimes similar to driving on a bumpy road, and steering becomes difficult. When the 1940 Imperial Valley earthquake occurred, the author was in an old frame dormitory on the California Institute of Technology campus 175 miles from the epicenter. The shock began as a sharp jerk, which felt as if a large truck had backed into the building. This was followed by a more

FIG. 7.11 Craters formed by fountaining of water during the Assam earthquake of 1897. (*Oldham, 1899. Courtesy of Geologic Survey of India.*)

gentle shaking motion which rattled windows and pipes. Sometimes an optical illusion is created, and buildings appear to sway back and forth to a degree that would be impossible without their being badly damaged. A sound often accompanies or even precedes earthquakes, usually a very low frequency rumbling sound. This phenomenon was widely observed in the Charleston, South Carolina, earthquake of 1886.

If the shaking is violent enough, a person may be unable to walk or even to stand. In the case of weak shocks the activity of the observer has a close connection with whether or not the vibration will be observed. Seated persons are more likely to note it than are active persons. An alert person often thinks to note the time of occurrence of the quake and its duration.

Water, being fluid, has its own peculiar ways of behavior during earthquakes. At sea it may be thrown into a tunami. Lakes, rivers, or bays may be agitated by seiches or less regular disturbances. Water may be squeezed so violently from the ground as to form fountains. Often it brings sand and mud with it, forming craters which may be large enough to remain for years to mark the violence of the quake (Fig. 7.11). Such mounds were formed at many places by the Missouri Valley earthquake of 1811, possibly the most violent on record in the United States. On level land where the water table is shallow, the soil may settle, allowing the water to flow out over wide areas. Underground disturbances may stop the flow of wells or springs or increase it, sometimes forming new springs.

Most striking of all earthquake phenomena are those connected with faulting. Faulting of the surface is common with large shallow shocks (Fig. 7.12). Probably most of the countless faults observed in rocks were formed by earthquake action. However, faulting has been observed without an earthquake, as in the Buena Vista oil field of California (Koch, 1933).

The amount of displacement is believed commonly to increase with depth. In the 1930 Idu earthquake in Japan, the displacement is reported by Suyehiro (1932) to have been about 3 ft on the surface but 8 ft underground in a long railway tunnel. Following the quake the fault continued to move, with gradually decreasing velocity. Ten months after the shock the rate was 0.001 mm per day as measured by a dial gauge.

Where faulting does occur, the amount and direction of the displacement and dip can be measured and compared with that indicated by old slickensides and drag. The motion may be uniform in character or at some places one way and at others another. Along the San Andreas fault in California the northeast side always moves southeast relative to the other side, but this block moves sometimes up, sometimes down with respect to the southwestern one, even during one shock such as the 1906 quake. The break may be quite straight, as it was in the case of the 1857 Fort Tejon, California, earthquake, or sinuous as in the case of the 1940 Imperial Valley shock (Fig. 7.15). Sometimes there is one break; sometimes motion occurs on more than one fault simultaneously. The length along which motion occurred in 1906 was 275 miles. Sometimes the faulting occurs on an existing branch of the fault, and at other times a new branch appears to be formed. In the 1872 Owens Valley earthquake the fault appeared out in the alluvial valley floor about 5 miles from the scarp which fronts the eastern side of the Sierra Nevada, but the range was again raised as much as 23 ft. The breaks in general closely followed the foot of a range of low hills, some coinciding with older fault traces and some not (Hobbs, 1910).

The fault is not always marked by a simple surface displacement. The

1906 San Francisco earthquake exhibited three other types of trace deformation called the ridge, trough, and *en echelon* phases (Fig. 7.13). Their occurrence can be understood if one visualizes the mechanism of their formation. They result from the different ways in which the soft

FIG. 7.12 Fault scarp of the Fairview Peak, Nevada, earthquake of Dec. 16, 1954. (*Courtesy of P. Byerly.*)

surface materials yield under stress as compared with the fracture of more solid rock at greater depths. Because of large local variations in the breaking strength of the ground, it will crack along an irregular surface that only approximately follows the straight line along which one would customarily expect a massive rock to fracture. As the underlying rock continues to be displaced, the stresses at the surface are not all parallel to the trace. For a north-south fault, if the eastern block moves south, there will tend to be compression where the surface trace crosses the principal trend of the fault from west to east, resulting in the ridge phase of deformation. Where it crosses from east to west, the trough phase is developed. Where the surface trace is parallel to the general trend of the shear, there are a compression in a northeast-southwest direction and tension in the southeast-northwest direction. Cracks and ridges form at around 45° to the fault. Unless the ridges are quite large, they may be less easily recognized than the cracks. This *en echelon* pattern is typical and frequently observed. The parallel ridgelets are called "mole tracks" because of their resemblance to the marks made in soft ground by the tunneling of small animals (Fig. 7.14). A similar pattern will be obtained if a sheet of tissue paper is laid on a flat surface, held along one edge, and the opposite edge moved parallel to it.

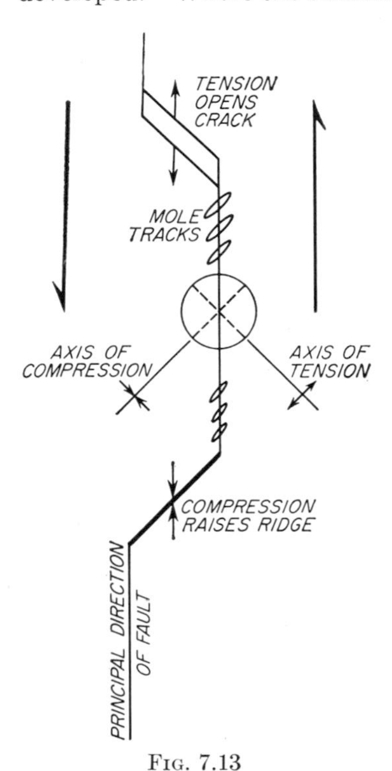

FIG. 7.13

FIG. 7.14 Mole tracks made by the 1940 Imperial Valley earthquake.

Where the fault crosses a stream, pools, rapids, or waterfalls may be formed. Streams, as well as fences and roads, can be offset (Fig. 7.15). The traces of old faults can often be located in this way. Such patterns are most easily recognized from the air. Successive shocks may separate the two parts of a stream on either side of a fault so gradually that it maintains its course, except for a jog at the fault itself. Eventually, if the offset is enough, an adjoining stream may pirate its head. In the meantime the water may have excavated quite a trough along the fault trace. Faults tend to occur in valleys because along the trace the rock is broken and often more easily eroded away than on either side.

Even where there is no surface break, tilting of the land may form enclosed depressions, which usually fill with water in moist climates, or may cause rapids where stream flow is accelerated. Elevations are changed, and points moved horizontally (Fig. 7.16). Harbor depths are altered. Some of this is due to landsliding, which is one of the commonest effects of earthquakes. Fissuring in loose ground may represent incipient landslides, but fracturing in solid rocks without faulting is also observed. In Japan much research has been done indicating that, during earthquakes

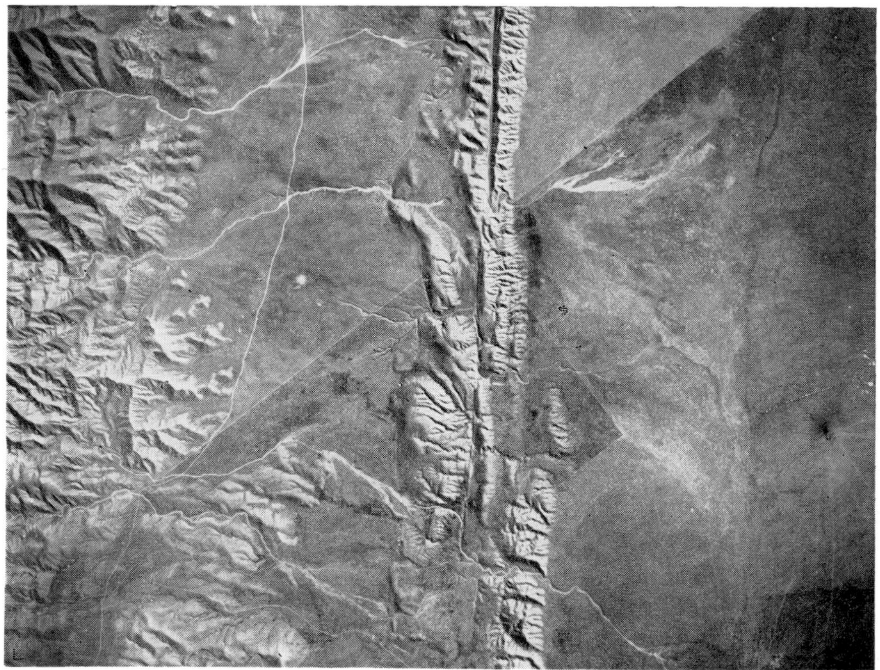

Fig. 7.15 The San Andreas fault from the air. Note the offset streams. (*Courtesy of Fairchild Aerial Surveys, Inc.*)

and at other times, there is tilting of large areas of the ground. Changes in elevation are particularly easy to recognize along the seacoast, where raised or submerged beaches result. The 1899 Yakutat Bay, Alaska, earthquake raised some beaches 47⅓ ft above mean tide level (Tarr and Martin, 1912).

With the 1930 Idu Japanese earthquake peculiar lights appeared in the sky in the vicinity of the epicenter. Their form and color varied. At places they were reported to be bright enough to illuminate objects. The color ranged from blue to reddish yellow. They appeared in such forms as radiating or single rays and fireballs. This has been reported for other earthquakes as well, but no adequate explanation is known for such phenomena. It has been reported also that local changes in the earth's magnetic field have occurred, though this has never been scientifically verified. It seems more likely that the reported magnetic variations

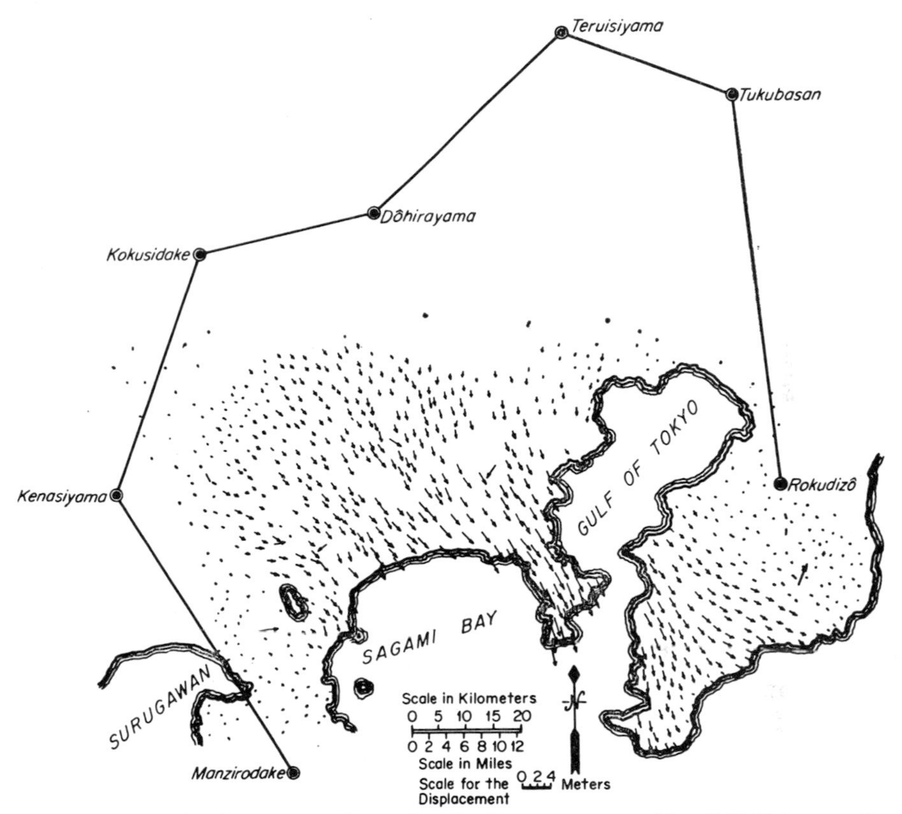

Fig. 7.16 Result of survey to determine displacements caused by 1923 Tokyo earthquake. (*From Suyehiro, 1932, "Engineering Seismology." Courtesy of American Society of Civil Engineers.*)

resulted only from the effect of the ground vibrations on the instruments being used to record the magnetic field.

Volcanic action in certain regions accompanies or is accompanied by earthquakes. It is uncertain which is cause and which effect or if both are the manifestation of some more fundamental, deep-seated activity. This will be discussed further in the next chapter.

CHAPTER 8

CAUSES OF EARTHQUAKES

8.1 The San Andreas Fault. It is generally believed that faulting is one of the major causes of earthquakes. A considerable number of earthquakes have occurred in the neighborhood of known faults. In many cases the intensities of these earthquakes were greatest in elongated strips along the fault traces (Figs. 7.2 and 7.3). In certain cases displacement has occurred on the fault at the time of the earthquake. The correlation between faulting and earthquakes is so good that it is believed that the vast majority of earthquakes are accompanied by faulting at some place, usually deep beneath the earth's surface.

The intimate connection between faulting and earthquakes is well revealed by a study of one of the largest of these breaks known, the San Andreas fault system of western North America (Fig. 8.1). This structure extends the length of California. Its southern end runs into the Gulf of Lower California, whose existence is thought to be the result of the dropping of a block of the earth's crust between two branches of the fault system. Exactly how far north and south it continues cannot be precisely determined, as it lies beneath the ocean for much of its length. Although a belt of seismic activity continues to the south along the west coast of Mexico, Central America, and South America, its relation to the California belt is not clear. It has also been postulated that the volcanic belt which crosses central Mexico from west to east lies along a continuation of the fault and that the volcanoes result from the upwelling of molten rock through this great crack. There is no real evidence that this is so. The southern extent of the fault is unknown.

In California the fault follows the trend of the Imperial Valley. Here it has many branches, which coalesce to the north in the vicinity of San Gorgonio and Cajon Passes, which owe their locations in part to its presence. The first of these two passes occupies a graben between two branches of the fault. In the other, the presence of the fault, crossing the San Gabriel Mountains diagonally from southeast to northwest, has resulted in a zone of weakness through which the Cajon River has cut a deep gap. The main branch of the fault in this region trends N60°W.

In the vicinity of Tejon Pass, 45 miles northwest of Los Angeles, it meets another large break, the Garlock fault, at an angle of about 50°. The latter structure is also active along at least a part of its length, though it is not the locus of so many quakes as is the San Andreas. At the intersection, the trend of the San Andreas changes to N40°W. Northwest of here the break consists of only one main shear zone as far as the south end of San Francisco Bay where it again splits into several branches. One arm passes under the Golden Gate. A main branch continues north along the coast to Pt. Arena, 100 miles to the northwest, where it passes out to sea. It may intersect the land again from Pt. Delgada to Cape Mendocino 105 miles farther north, though it is impossible to tell if the break here is the main one. As in the case of the southern end, it is not known how much farther it extends. There are few suboceanic earthquakes north of 44° off the Oregon and the Washington coasts. The San Andreas fault intersects another major structural feature, the Mendocino fracture zone, off northern California (Menard, 1955). It is possible that it terminates here even though the epicenter belt extends farther northward. The length of the fault exposed on land is over 1,100 km.

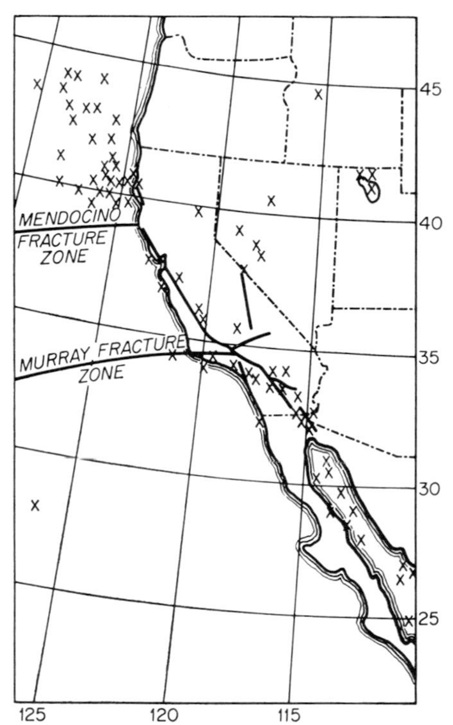

Fig. 8.1 Principal active faults of western North America and main earthquakes. (*Data largely from Gutenberg and Richter, 1949.*)

Fig. 8.2 Idealized cross section of San Andreas fault showing main gouge zone, flanking ridges, and converging auxiliary faults.

In cross section the fault is highly complex. There is present everywhere a zone of gouge from a few to many hundreds of feet wide, merging into a network of branching faults, the principal members of which dip inward toward the center of the fault zone (Fig. 8.2). The trace is generally marked by a depression flanked by ridges. It is notable that nowhere along the exposed length of the break can the rocks be correlated from one side of the fault to the other. Thus the total displacement is not measurable.

Geologists believe that the fault may have been active since the beginning of Miocene time or even earlier. During the last hundred years horizontal displacement of the order of 10 ft has occurred along most of its exposed length. This is an average movement of 0.1 ft per year, which would add up to approximately 400 miles in the roughly 22 million years since the start of Miocene time. These are provocative figures to keep in mind when one is considering the time necessary for observed great deformations of the earth's crust to have occurred. The present rate of deformation on the San Andreas fault is as great as was required to produce the most striking tectonic features which have ever existed on earth.

Because of the complexity of the break, it is impossible to tell how steep its average dip is, though the fault is thought to be close to vertical. Nor are the locations of the earthquake epicenters of much help here. Those associated with surface displacements usually lie, to the accuracy of the measurements, right on the fault. And where there is no surface displacement, it is not possible to tell on which of the many faults of California the earthquake occurred.

8.2 The Tejon Earthquake. Until after the discovery of gold in 1848, California was so lightly populated that the record of earthquake activity is almost certainly very incomplete. Although there are records of many large earthquakes, it is generally impossible to locate their epicenters with useful accuracy. Since 1848, however, many California earthquakes have been studied in detail. There have been three large earthquakes in which displacement was observed on the San Andreas fault. The first of these is known as the Tejon earthquake. It occurred on January 9, 1857.

Fort Tejon, for which the earthquake is named, was situated at the crest of the mountains along the trail from Los Angeles north to the San Joaquin Valley. The cavalry who occupied it were stationed there to stop Indians from the north from raiding the herds of settlers in the San Fernando and Los Angeles basins. As is usual in the case of earthquakes along the San Andreas fault, the earth motion was predominately horizontal. The amount of displacement is unknown but can be estimated as being of the order of a few or several tens of feet. The trace passed beneath a sheep corral, the originally round wall being offset by the break to form an "S" (Wood, 1955). The surface break extended from near San Bernardino for 225 miles northwest to the Cholame Valley, and the quake was felt from Yuma, Arizona, to Sacramento, California. The extreme intensity of the shaking can be judged by the fact that trees were uprooted and broken by the force of the shock. Yet because of the sparseness of the population, only one person was reported killed.

8.3 The 1906 San Francisco Earthquake. This is the most famous of United States earthquakes, probably because it destroyed most of a large and colorful city and because its effects were thoroughly investigated by a group of highly competent geologists. Their report (Lawson et al., 1908) is one of the most complete ever made of an earthquake.

The surface displacement extended from the vicinity of San Juan, San Benito County, to Cape Mendocino, a distance of 270 miles, leaving an unbroken section about 100 miles long between the areas shifted in 1857 and 1906. At least at the surface there has been no movement on this part of the fault since then, but sooner or later one may be certain that a shifting will occur. Geologic evidence shows that there has been repeated movement in the not-too-distant past. The displacement in 1906 was largely horizontal, the maximum measured being 21 ft. The northeast side moved southeast relative to the other blocks. Vertical displacements were uncommon, except north of San Francisco, where they were as great as 3 ft but not consistent in direction. The southwest side was raised more often than the other. Usually the raised portion extended for not over a few hundred yards along the fault.

The surface manifestation was usually not a simple crack but rather a disturbed zone several feet wide. A ridge from 3 to 10 ft wide and up to 18 in. high was the commonest type of deformation, but elsewhere a shallow trench with ragged vertical sides from 2 to 6 ft apart marked the trace. Elsewhere the ground was traversed by a system of roughly parallel cracks inclined at an angle of about 45° to the fault. These three phases are, respectively, the ridge, trough, and *en echelon* phases of the fault (see Sec. 7.7 and Fig. 7.13). The displacement was not always on a single break, but sometimes was distributed over as many as 10 fractures. The blocks on either side did not move as rigid units. A check of the location of points surveyed before the quake compared with their relative positions afterward showed that the amount of movement decreased with distance from the fault (Table 8.1).

The intensity of the shock on the modified Mercalli scale was at least XI (see Table 7.3). The isoseismals closely paralleled the fault along most of the break, showing the close connection of the structural damage to the rock fracture (Figs. 7.2 and 7.3). This pattern was modified by the nature of the ground. Much greater damage occurred to structures located on filled ground and alluvium than to those on solid rock. Landslides were common, and fissuring marked places where landslides started to develop but did not, either because of lack of grade or because the strength of the material was too great. Within a quarter mile of the fault, trees up to 6 ft in diameter were up-rooted or broken, testifying to the intensity in this narrow belt. Fountains of water and sand or mud were reported at places to have spurted as much as 20 ft into the air.

Waves in the ground resembling ocean waves were claimed to have been observed with amplitudes as great as 3 ft and 60 ft from crest to crest. However, such large amplitudes are thought most probably to be an optical illusion produced perhaps by refraction of light by density changes in the air related to the elastic waves in the ground. Omori, a Japanese seismologist, estimated from study of damage caused by the shock that the accelerations of the ground must have been as great as 2 m per sec^2 at a frequency of about 1 cycle per sec.

In spite of its great intensity, the quake caused the death of only about 390 people in San Francisco. The damage was great, estimated at $400,000,000, but it resulted primarily from the fire which started as a result of the shaking. The pressure failed in the city water mains because many of the pipes had been broken, so that the fire could not be fought properly. It took three days to bring it under control, by which time large areas of the city had been completely burned.

8.4 The 1940 Imperial Valley Earthquake. The intensity of this latest of the three great shocks on the San Andreas fault was less than that of the other two, yet the rock displacement was of the same order of magnitude, up to 14 ft 10 in. horizontally but never over 4 ft vertically. Most of what vertical motion was observed may have been due to unequal settling of the unconsolidated rocks underlying the valley, as sometimes one side was down, sometimes the other. The crack began about 10 miles south of the Salton Sea and followed an old fault scarp about 6 to 10 ft high which ran in a southeasterly direction. It had not been recognized as a fault feature until after the quake, possibly because it was so sinuous. On a map its flexures can be seen to be small and its general trend straight (Ulrich, 1941). The break extended about 20 miles across the Mexican border, the total known length being nearly 50 miles. The largest displacement observed occurred where the trace crossed the embankment of the All-American irrigation canal, then under construction. A line of survey stakes provided an accurate, easy way of measuring the horizontal displacement. The bank here was displaced very little vertically.

One of the major causes of property damage was the collapse of the embankments of the older Imperial Canal to the south. The whole of the rich Imperial Valley agricultural area depended on this for irrigation water during the increasing heat of late May and early June. Every available piece of earth-moving machinery in southern California was rushed to the site to try to get the canal back into operation as soon as possible. The sight of long rows of power shovels and earth movers struggling to get the dikes rebuilt before the crops died was indeed impressive.

The scarp, where there was one, faced northeast. It was up to 4 ft high and either vertical or dipping steeply northeastward. In mud flats south of the Salton Sea at the northwestern extremity of the break, it appeared as a sequence of *en echelon* cracks up to an inch wide and at a small angle to the general fault trend. As one proceeded southeastward, the cracks gradually became more continuous. The size of the ground shift increased to its maximum, then gradually decreased to the southeast. Beyond the irrigated district it was hard to follow, as the ground was very soft. In this district its surface expression was a series of characteristic *en echelon* mole-track ridges and cracks (Fig. 7.14) whose size decreased southeastward.

8.5 Elastic Rebound Theory. One of the significant features of all three of these earthquakes was that the northeast block always moved southeastward. This fact and other evidence indicate that the landward portion of the Pacific Coastal area of California is shifting steadily with respect to the oceanward side. All the evidence indicates that this drift has been going on for a long time and can therefore be expected to continue in the future. Therefore, more large earthquakes along the San Andreas fault are inevitable.

This drift in the case of the 1906 earthquake has been measured. The maximum relative movement of 21 ft, which was observed, was large enough to distort geodetic survey networks a measurable amount. Three such surveys have been run in the San Francisco region, one in 1851 to 1866, one in 1874 to 1892, and one immediately after the quake in 1906 to 1907. The relative displacements between the second and third surveys are shown in Table 8.1. In computing this it was assumed that the area

TABLE 8.1 DISPLACEMENTS OF GEODETIC STATIONS DURING AND PRECEDING THE SAN FRANCISCO EARTHQUAKE*

Distance from fault, km	Displacement, m	Number of points averaged to get displacement
6.4 east	0.58 south	1
4.2 east	0.86 south	3
1.5 east	1.54 south	10
2.0 west	2.95 north	12
5.8 west	2.38 north	7
37.0 west	1.78 north	1

* Data from Reid, 1910.

northeast of a line passing through Mount Diablo, 53 km northeast of the fault, was unmoved. Points on this line were not moved relative to other stations east of them in the geodetic survey network, so that they provide a dependable reference line. However, it cannot be proven that the whole set of stations did not move, leaving the area southwest of the fault fixed in position. When large blocks of the crust shift, our surveying is only accurate enough to determine the relative motion. Eventually shifts of areas may be measured by comparing the variation in latitude at many places all over the earth. Measurements of latitude are accurate enough to detect relative north-south motions of the order of a few meters.

Between 1851 to 1866 and 1874 to 1892, the San Francisco area moved northwestward about 5.2 ft, but between 1874 to 1892 and 1906 to 1907, the direction of the shift was reversed. The process involved can best be visualized with the aid of a diagram (Fig. 8.3). Points lying on a straight line AOB'' surveyed across the fault in 1851 to 1866 had all shifted to the northwest by 1874 to 1892, the westerly points moving most (line

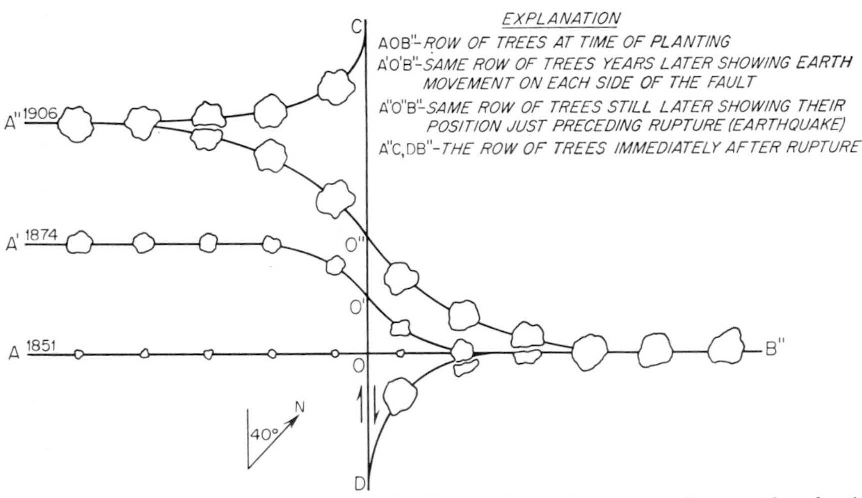

FIG. 8.3 Idealized deformation on the San Andreas fault according to the elastic rebound theory, 1851 to 1906.

$A'O'B''$). Following the earthquake, the third survey showed that points west of the fault had continued to move north but that points east of it had moved south (line $A''C,DB''$). It is clear that immediately before the earthquake the position of the line must have been $A''O''B''$ and that this line was split by the fault in 1906. In other words, the western block moved north until the shear along the fault became so great that the rock broke, causing the earthquake. The curvature of the line $A''C,DB''$ in Fig. 8.3 indicates that the motion began previous to 1851. Since the distance CD is greater than AA'', the motion in 1906 must have relieved more stress than that accumulated between 1851 and 1906. This sort of deformation was named elastic rebound by H. F. Reid, one of the commission of scientists employed by the state of California to study the 1906 earthquake. It is impossible to determine from geodetic measurements how large the blocks affected by this motion are, whether they are continental in size or of lesser dimensions. The accuracy of the best surveys is not great enough to demonstrate a shift of only a few feet over many hundreds of miles.

8.6 Mechanics of the Break. It appears from the above discussion that earthquake faulting is a result of the gradual accumulation of shearing stress, which builds up until the breaking strength of the rock is exceeded. Such stresses accumulate slowly, the energy released in the quake being stored as elastic energy in the deformed rocks until the time of the break. The principal deformation is the slow, continuous shift of the land. The fault and resulting earthquake are the final events of a long cycle.

It is generally believed that faulting starts at some one specific point and then spreads in all directions along the fault plane with a speed not exceeding that of elastic waves through the rock. The initial slip may involve only a relatively small area of fault, followed after a short interval by a shift over a much larger surface. In this case there may be two earthquakes so close together that no observer can distinguish one from the other. If the time between the two is large enough to distinguish both of them, the first one is classed as a foreshock. In general one would expect the pulse of energy radiated from an earthquake fault to consist of a series of vibrations arising from the complex original motion. Even if there were no other mechanism complicating the ground motion during a shock, shaking would have to continue for as long a time as the two blocks of the earth took to complete their shift relative to each other. Because energy travels through the ground at several different velocities and can travel along various paths from one point to another, the duration of an earthquake will be much longer than the causative movement. In general the greater the distance from the fault, the longer the motion lasts. Large earthquakes cause disturbances which are recorded by seismographs all over the world, the energy from one quake sometimes taking several hours to die out. Near the epicenter, where the shock can be felt, the duration is usually from a few seconds to several minutes. In the case of the San Francisco shock, the motion observed at Berkeley is in general typical of the area near the fault. The shaking began with feeble motion which lasted for 30 sec. After a lull of about 10 sec a more violent vibration commenced, rising in intensity, then dying away after about 25 sec (Davison, 1936).

In general, the motion from a natural earthquake is more complicated than that from an explosion. In the latter case the motion starts with a single sudden heave, followed by a rolling vibration of the ground. In the case of surface explosions the pressure wave in the air, which arrives toward the end or after the ground motion, is usually the most violent phase of the shakings.

The shift of the rock along the principal break at the time of an earthquake, although it relieves the main stress in the rocks, is likely to set up new stresses in adjoining places. Furthermore, it is unlikely that the stress is everywhere evenly relieved, so that following the main shock, a series of minor adjustments, some of them on the main fault plane, others at some distance from it, result in sequences of aftershocks of gradually decreasing intensity and frequency. Once a relatively stable state is achieved, it is believed that the fault surface seals itself by the lithification of the crushed gouge zone due to deposition or recrystallization of minerals.

8.7 Classification of Earthquakes. It is generally believed today that the majority of earthquakes are caused by elastic rebound. However, many other possible causes have been suggested, and some of them are known to be the source of certain quakes. The plausible explanations can be divided on the basis of mechanism into three classes: tectonic, volcanic, and impact. These can be divided into 13 specific causes (Table 8.2). The subdivisions are not necessarily mutually exclusive. Some of them may overlap one another, the dividing lines being difficult to define.

TABLE 8.2 CLASSIFICATION OF EARTHQUAKES

1. Tectonic
   a. Elastic rebound
   b. Sudden shearing during plastic flow
   c. Folding
2. Volcanic
   d. Explosions due to accumulated underground pressure
   e. Crystallization
   f. Tension cracking
   g. Magma intrusion
   h. Stoping
   i. Stopping of flow
3. Impact
   j. Surface explosions
   k. Meteors, etc., falling
   l. Cave-ins
   m. Rockslides and similar phenomena

The tectonic class includes all earthquakes resulting from deformation of the rocks, such as that involved in mountain building. Elastic rebound is the principal member of this class. Deep within the earth, rocks are thought to be plastic, yielding predominately by flow rather than by fracture. Plastic rocks can both flow and fracture if the stress is great enough, so that we have as the second proposed cause the sudden shearing of plastic rocks at depth, either along one plane or throughout an extended volume. The mechanism in this case is generally similar to elastic rebound in more rigid rocks, only the rock is different (see Chap. 16).

The last member of the class is sudden tensional cracking and crushing, which, it is theorized, can result when rocks are being folded, independent of any elastic shear rebound of the same formations. Since such cracks are usually small, this is probably a very minor cause if it is not completely insignificant.

Earthquakes commonly accompany volcanic eruptions. In some cases shocks are thought to be caused by the volcanism, though most such vibrations are probably tectonic. The mechanisms by which volcanism can set off an earthquake are largely a matter of speculation, the only definitely known cause being volcanic explosions.

The most famous example of this is the eruption of Krakatoa, which occupies an island in the Sunda Strait between Java and Sumatra. The East Indian volcanoes are in general noted for the extreme violence of their outbreaks. The history of Krakatoa is little known. It was active in 1680. From then until 1883 it was relatively quiescent. In May of 1883 a cloud of steam appeared over the vent, and in August a series of gigantic explosions destroyed two-thirds of the island. The sound of the largest of these was heard in Australia, and the resulting barometric pressure wave reached Berlin in 10 hr. No lava was emitted, only fragmental material. Pumice covered the surrounding seas to such an extent that navigation was impeded, and ashes fell over a 300,000-square-mile area. Fine dust was blown into the upper atmosphere where it remained diffused for over a year, causing sunsets to be exceptionally red and sometimes green. A year later, measurements of the sun's heat penetrating the atmosphere showed it to be reduced to 87 per cent of normal. Although there was little direct loss of life from the explosion, a large sea wave was caused, which drowned 36,000 people in Java.

Five other ways have been suggested by which volcanism may be capable of causing earthquakes, though none has been shown to have caused an actual earthquake. At depths where pressure is great and temperature conditions uniform, it has been suggested that magmas can supercool without freezing until large volumes suddenly crystallize with a consequent decrease in volume which causes a contraction of extreme violence and which constitutes an earthquake. Though very rapid crystal growth can be produced in the laboratory under certain conditions, there is no evidence that it can occur in nature with such rapidity as to result in any appreciable earth vibrations.

A logical cause of shocks is tension cracking. As lavas cool, they crack. If a large enough crack was formed at any one time, the event might release enough energy to cause a quake. Similarly, the pressure of intruding magma breaking its way through the rock might split apart large rock bodies. It has been suggested that stoping, the process whereby blocks of rock break loose from the roof of a batholith and sink into the magma, may occur with such violence that the roof, springing back on the release of a large block, may cause an earthquake. Lastly, if a large hollow cavern within the earth was being filled with magma, as the cavern became completely filled, the flowing mass of liquid rock would act as a plunger striking the walls of the cavern and causing an earthquake. All these hypotheses are pure speculation.

Whatever the cause, certain earthquakes which occur in volcanic regions are sufficiently characteristic to be thought to belong to a special group. Such shocks are characterized by their extreme violence locally but by a rapid decrease in ground motion with distance, indicating an unusually shallow focus. They often accompany volcanism in the region of their origin. Examples are certain earthquakes felt on Ischia, a volcanic island in the mouth of the bay of Naples, Italy. The last eruption there was from a vent in the side of the mountain in 1302. In 1762 the volcano showed signs of again becoming active but did not do so. However, there was a series of violent earthquakes, at least 50 in one night, followed by a series of aftershocks of diminishing intensity. Another bad shock occurred in 1828. In 1881, 127 persons were killed by a quake which was not even recorded in Naples, 20 miles away. In 1883 a more violent shock killed over 2,000 people. This shock was felt on the mainland, but not strongly. It was notable for the presence of largely vertical forces which threw down ceilings while the walls were left standing. There is no proof that these shocks were not tectonic, but their peculiar characteristics suggest that they belong to a special class. Earthquakes which can definitely be considered volcanic are extremely rare.

Earthquakes of the impact class result from superficial causes. Many large explosions have been recorded over wide areas. The explosion at Oppau, Germany, on September 21, 1921, was recorded throughout western Europe, and the resulting air wave did considerable damage. Most of the energy from a surface explosion goes into heat and into air oscillations. It is estimated that the chemical energy released by the Oppau explosion was about 6×10^{19} ergs, while the energy radiated as ground vibrations was only 5×10^{16} ergs.

It is believed that large meteorites striking the earth also cause earthquakes, though the distance to which the resulting vibrations can be recorded is usually small. On June 30, 1908, a giant meteorite (Podkamennaya Tunguska meteorite) landed about 150 miles north of Lake Baikal in Siberia. The air waves were recorded in Europe, but it is uncertain if the seismic pulse recorded at that time came from the meteorite or some other cause.

It has also been suggested that the collapse of the roofs of caverns and the fall of large landslides release enough energy to constitute an earthquake, though there is no proof of this. The inverse is commonly true, as earthquakes frequently cause caverns to collapse and landslides to flow.

8.8 Pseudoseisms. From the above it will be clear that explosions and other sources of earthquakes also result in air vibrations in many cases. Human beings are more sensitive to air motion than to ground motion. In many cases low-frequency sounds, which are felt but not truly heard, are mistaken for ground movements. Thus, it is often reported by observers that the ground shook from an explosion when all that actually happened was that an air vibration was felt. Such disturbances are called pseudoseisms.

In some cases the distance from the explosion to the point where it is observed is large. Under certain barometric conditions, sounds are focused by the air at a large distance from their source, being unheard over most of the intervening distance. During the early morning of January 28, 1930, residents of southern California from Los Angeles to Bakersfield were disturbed by what they thought were a series of light earthquakes accompanied by a dull roar. Windows were rattled, and doors swung near Bakersfield. Actually, these were pseudoseisms resulting from target practice by a battleship at sea 150 miles away.

8.9 Periodicity of Earthquakes. The majority of earthquakes are believed to be tectonic. Since such shocks result from the slow accumulation of stress over long periods of time, one might expect them to occur most often when the earth is under stress from such external forces as air pressure or the tides. It is not supposed that these forces in themselves are great enough to produce earthquakes, but added to the larger causative stresses, which arise from unknown sources, they might act as triggering forces, raising the stress by a little extra increment that the material is unable to withstand. They might thus control the time of occurrence of the shocks. Many statistical analyses of the time of occurrence of earthquakes have been made without any well-marked periodicity being observed (Bullen, 1947; Jeffreys, 1952). This must mean either that such periodic forces as exist are insignificant compared with the quake-causing stresses, or that they are not directed in such a manner as to cause local accumulation of strain of the type involved in earthquakes. The principal exception to this rule is the prevalence of aftershocks following a large earthquake. Recently, also, some evidence has been accumulated which suggests a correlation between the rate of energy released by earthquakes and the amplitude of the Chandler motion of the poles (Sec. 12.8). There may also be a correlation in certain limited areas with earth tides.

In some parts of the world there is a belief that earthquakes are commonest in hot, sultry weather. There is no scientific support of this. Statistical examination of the times of occurrence of earthquakes has failed to establish any correlation with weather conditions.

CHAPTER 9

INSTRUMENTAL SEISMOLOGY

9.1 What Is Measured. Up to this point we have treated seismology primarily from the point of view of what can be directly observed during and following an earthquake. Such information is limited by the presence or absence of reliable observers at the scene of events. Because knowledge of when and where an earthquake will occur is lacking, it is impossible to have observers always present to make the desired observations. And even if this were not the case, events happen so quickly and are of such a varied nature that no observer could record them all completely and faithfully.

It is well known that a man sees in part what he expects to see, and can never escape completely the bias of his own preconceptions no matter how hard he tries to be completely objective. Therefore, it is desirable to secure as much data as possible by machines, whose records can be preserved and studied. For superficial effects a camera could be used, though few pictures of events have been taken during earthquakes. At such a time not many people have the self-control to devote themselves to obtaining them.

The principal direct records we get of earthquakes are seismograms. The purpose of a seismogram is to give a written record of the ground motion—displacement, velocity, or acceleration—and to indicate the times at which each event occurred. Because of mechanical limitations, no seismometer[1] makes a perfect reproduction of the ground vibrations. Usually only a limited spectrum of frequencies is reproduced, and often the behavior of the instrument is such that the recording pen or light beam goes through a longer series of oscillations than the ground.

In a well-designed instrument three pieces of information are generally available. The time of each event can usually be determined to an accuracy of 1 sec from comparison with time marks recorded at regular intervals, usually every minute. The direction of motion of the beginning of each pulse can be determined from the directions of deflection of the recording traces, and if the seismometer is properly calibrated, the

[1] See Sec. 6.4 for a discussion of seismometers.

approximate amplitude of the ground motion can be calculated for any time during the arrival of the quake. The use of measurements of the time of seismic events will be the subject of Chap. 11. Amplitude and the direction of first motion will be examined here.

9.2 Magnitude. The intensity of an earthquake varies from place to place, depending not only on the amount of energy released and on the distance from the focus but also on the nature of the intervening ground. It is, therefore, not a good measure of the size of the shock, though large shocks tend to have greater intensities than do small ones. However, the measurement of ground-motion amplitudes gives us a relatively precise method of measuring the size of an earthquake.

C. F. Richter (1935) designed a magnitude scale to compare the energies released in earthquakes in southern California and adjoining regions. He defined magnitude as the logarithm of the largest amplitude, measured in microns (0.001 mm), on the record made by a standard Wood-Anderson torsion seismometer[1] at a distance of 100 km from the epicenter of the earthquake. The magnitudes of earthquakes recorded at other distances can be determined if it is known how the largest amplitude varies with distance. For shallow earthquakes in southern California in the range 200 to 1,500 km an empirical relation between magnitude M and maximum trace amplitude A is

$$M = \log A + 3 \log \Delta - 3.37 \tag{9.1}$$

where Δ is the distance measured in kilometers.

For larger distances, the relation is more complicated, though magnitude can sometimes be determined from a nomograph such as Fig. 9.1. Other nomographs and formulas have been developed which depend on calculated ground amplitude rather than seismogram amplitude (Gutenberg and Richter, 1936*b*, 1942, 1955, 1956; Gutenberg, 1956*b*). In some cases surface-wave amplitudes are used, and in other cases body-wave amplitudes. The rates of attenuation of these two types of waves are different (see Sec. 9.6), and they depend differently on many factors besides epicentral distance and the size of the earthquake. These factors include the nature of the ground between the focus and the recorder, the azimuth of the recorder relative to the strike of the fault on which the earthquake originated, the duration of the shaking, and the frequencies of the oscillations. Thus, values of magnitude calculated at different observatories, using different seismometers at one observatory, or even different phases (body or surface waves) on the same seismogram, may be different. For this reason care must be used in comparing magnitudes to be sure that the figures being considered were all calculated in a similar manner.

[1] The standard Wood-Anderson seismometer has a free period of 0.8 sec, a magnification of 2,800 times, and a damping factor of 0.8.

One of the most important uses of magnitude is in getting a rough estimate of the energy released by earthquakes. To see how the magnitude is related to the energy, assume that all the energy of the earthquake is radiated as elastic waves and that it spreads equally in all directions from the focus. Suppose that at the seismometer the principal part of the

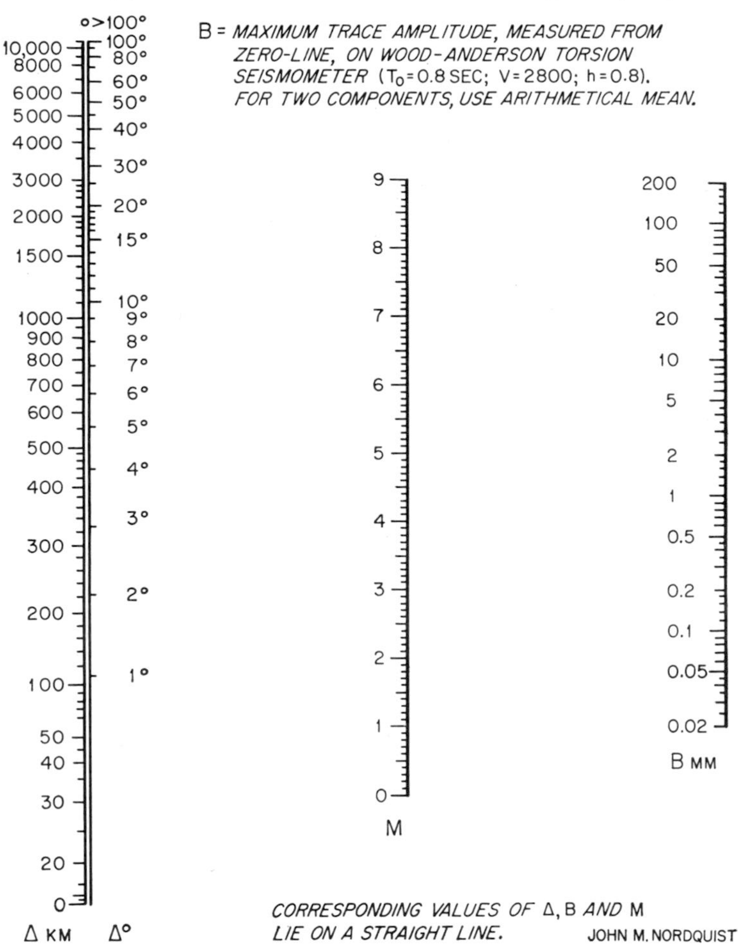

FIG. 9.1 Nomogram for determining earthquake magnitudes from trace amplitudes. (*Gutenberg and Richter, 1942.*)

energy arrives as a series of n equal sinusoidal waves of length λ, amplitude A_0, and period T_0. The kinetic energy of a unit particle will be $0.5mv^2$, where v is the instantaneous particle velocity and m is its mass. The position of a particle at any time can be given by the equation

$$x = A_0 \cos \frac{2\pi t}{T_0} \tag{9.2}$$

Therefore the velocity is

$$v = \frac{dx}{dt} = -\frac{2\pi A_0}{T_0} \sin \frac{2\pi t}{T_0} = v_0 \sin \frac{2\pi t}{T_0} \tag{9.3}$$

and the acceleration is

$$a = \frac{d^2x}{dt^2} = -\frac{4\pi^2 A_0}{T_0^2} \cos \frac{2\pi t}{T_0} = -\frac{4\pi^2 x}{T_0^2} \tag{9.4}$$

The instantaneous kinetic energy will be

$$E_i = 0.5 m v_0^2 \sin^2 \frac{2\pi t}{T_0} \tag{9.5}$$

The average kinetic energy for a unit volume of a rock of density ρ will be

$$\begin{aligned} E &= 0.5 \rho v_0^2 T_0^{-1} \int_0^{T_0} \sin^2 \frac{2\pi t}{T_0}\, dt \\ &= 0.25 \rho v_0^2 = 0.25 \rho \left(\frac{2\pi A_0}{T_0}\right)^2 = \frac{\pi^2 \rho A_0^2}{T_0^2} \end{aligned} \tag{9.6}$$

Within a spherical shell of thickness $n\lambda$ and radius h, with the focus as a center, the kinetic energy will be

$$E_T = 4\pi h^2 n \lambda E \tag{9.7}$$

If the energy is traveling with velocity V, then $\lambda = VT_0$ and

$$E_T = \frac{4\pi^3 h^2 n V \rho A_0^2}{T_0} \tag{9.8}$$

But from Eq. (9.4) we can see that the average acceleration is

$$a_0 = \frac{-4\pi^2 A_0}{T_0^2} \tag{9.9}$$

so (9.8) becomes

$$E_T = \frac{4\pi^3 h^2 n V \rho}{T_0} \frac{T_0^4 a_0^2}{16\pi^4} = \frac{h^2 n V \rho T_0^3 a_0^2}{4\pi} \tag{9.10}$$

The length t_0 of the pulse of energy will be nT_0, so

$$E_T = \frac{h^2 V \rho t_0 T_0^2 a_0^2}{4\pi} \tag{9.11}$$

From this we get

$$\log E_T = 2 \log h + \log t_0 + 2 \log T_0 + 2 \log a_0 + \log \frac{V\rho}{4\pi} \tag{9.12}$$

where E_T is in ergs, h in centimeters, t_0 and T_0 in seconds, a_0 in centimeters per second per second, V in centimeters per second, and ρ in grams per cubic centimeter. If we assume that ρ is approximately 3 gm per cm^3 and V is about 3.3 km per sec, log $V\rho/4\pi$ is about 4.9, and if we express h in kilometers, we must add 10 to Eq. (9.12), making it

$$\log E_T = 14.9 + 2 \log h + \log t_0 + 2 \log T_0 + 2 \log a_0 \quad (9.13)$$

This neglects absorption, which appears to be small except very near the source of the energy. It also assumes that the energy is radiated as a relatively simple pulse and that the vibratory motion represents all the radiated energy, which is not the case. (On the average, in theory, half the energy will be in the form of kinetic energy of vibration of the particles and half in the form of potential energy in the stressed state of the medium.)

By considering all the factors involved, Gutenberg and Richter (1956*a*) have been able to evaluate the various terms of the equation, obtaining the empirical formula

$$\log E_T = K_1 + K_2 M - K_3 M^2 \quad (9.14)$$

where K_1, K_2, and K_3 are constants whose value depends on how M is determined. Richter originally defined the magnitude scale for local earthquakes in California using a Wood-Anderson torsion seismometer to determine M. In this case the best determination of Eq. (9.14) gives

$$\log E_T = 9.4 + 2.14M - 0.054M^2 \quad (9.15)$$

It is now common practice to determine M at any distance and using a wide variety of seismometers. Different values of M are often obtained, depending on whether the maximum-amplitude body or surface waves are used to calculate the magnitude. Using body waves to find magnitude M_B, Gutenberg and Richter (1955, 1956*b*) have obtained the tentative relation

$$\log E_T = 5.8 + 2.4M_B \quad (9.16)$$

Earlier studies (e.g., Gutenberg and Richter, 1942, 1949), based largely on surface waves for epicentral distances greater than 1,000 km, gave the following relation between energy and magnitude M_s:

$$\log E_T = K_1 + 1.8M_s \quad (9.17)$$

Various values in the range 9 to 12 were found for K_1.

Equation (9.16) is believed to give more accurate values of energy than (9.17), though to date more work has been done using the latter formula. The data presented below are based on formula (9.17) except where otherwise noted. Energies calculated using this tend to be high, especially for the largest earthquakes. (M_s tends to be a little larger than M_B for large earthquakes, but this is more than counterbalanced by the difference in the two values of K_2.) The errors introduced by using the less accurate formula generally do not affect qualitative conclusions based on magnitude studies.

The magnitude scale was designed so that the smallest natural earthquake likely to be recorded would have a magnitude of 0. Using Eq. (9.16), its energy is seen to be 6.3×10^5 ergs. An earthquake such as the 1906 San Francisco earthquake, $M_B = 7.8$, must have released about 3.3×10^{24} ergs (Gutenberg, 1956*a*). The largest earthquake known to have occurred since modern seismometers came into use, the Colombian earthquake of 1906, with a magnitude M_B of 8.1 or 8.2, released approximately 2×10^{25} ergs.

As pointed out earlier, magnitude and intensity are not directly related. However, since a large percentage of all shocks appears to originate at a depth of 15 to 20 km, and since ground conditions everywhere usually include much the same range of conditions, there is a very rough correlation between earthquake intensity and magnitude. Gutenberg and Richter (1942) have obtained the empirical relation

$$M_s = 1.3 + 0.6I_{\max} \tag{9.18}$$

[M_s in this equation is the same as in (9.17)]. The smallest shocks felt are usually of magnitude about 1.5, which would correspond to intensity I on the modified Mercalli scale (Table 7.3). Ordinarily perceptibility begins at about magnitude 2.5 or intensity II. Damage begins with magnitude 4.5, intensity V to VI. Shocks of magnitude 6 are destructive in a limited region, where the greatest intensity would likely be about VIII. Shocks of magnitude 7 are usually recorded over the whole earth, often are accompanied by fissuring and cracking of the ground, are thought of as "major" earthquakes, and correspond to a maximum intensity of at least IX. The most intense shocks known, degree XII, where the ground accelerations at the surface probably exceed gravity, are probably of magnitude M_s about 8.5 (magnitude M_B of 8.0+).

9.3 Frequency of Earthquakes. Only six earthquakes of magnitude $M_s = 8.4$ or more are known to have occurred during the period from 1904, when instruments of the accuracy necessary to estimate magnitude were first put into operation, to June, 1957. These earthquakes occurred along the Colombia-Ecuador border on January 31, 1906; in central Chile on August 17, 1906; in the province of Tien Shan, China, on January 3, 1911; in Kansu province, China, December 16, 1920; off the northeast coast of Honshu, Japan, on March 2, 1933; and in northern Assam on August 15, 1950. There were 59 shocks of magnitude 8.0 or larger during the same period, giving a yearly average of 1.1 of this size. According to Gutenberg and Richter (1949), about 18 shocks of magnitude between

7 and 7.9 occur annually (Table 9.1). In a typical year there would be about 120 of magnitude between 6 and 6.9. Smaller earthquakes than this can easily occur without being recorded at a seismic observatory anywhere in the world, so it is impossible to tell the total number of shocks which occur annually.

TABLE 9.1 FREQUENCY OF OCCURRENCE OF EARTHQUAKES*

	Magnitude	Average number annually
Great earthquakes	8 or more	1.1
Major earthquakes	7–7.9	18
Destructive shocks	6–6.9	120
Damaging shocks	5–5.9	800
Minor strong shocks	4–4.9	6,200
Generally felt	3–3.9	49,000
Potentially perceptible	2–2.9	300,000+

* Largely after Gutenberg and Richter, 1949.

The number undoubtedly continues to increase rapidly for each step downward in the magnitude scale. Gutenberg and Richter (1949) have shown that the frequency N of earthquakes of magnitude M_s (range $\pm$ 0.1) can be approximated by the equation

$$\log N = a + b(8 - M_s) \tag{9.19}$$

where $a = -0.48$, $b = 0.90$ for shallow shocks; $a = -1.2$, $b = 1.2$ for shocks at intermediate depth; and $a = -1.9$, $b = 1.2$ for deep shocks. In southern California and New Zealand b has, as nearly as it can be determined for all shocks larger than magnitude 2.5, the same value 0.90 as for world-wide shallow shocks. (The value of a is naturally different for each region, -2.04 for California, -1.88 for New Zealand.) Therefore, it seems reasonable to suppose that Eq. (9.19) is a good approximation for world-wide shocks of magnitude 2.5 and larger. This would mean that there are about 800 shocks of magnitude 5.0 to 5.9 annually, 6,200 of 4.0 to 4.9 and 49,000 of 3.0 to 3.9. Shocks of magnitude 2.5 or less are so local that they are consistently recorded only if they occur within a radius of about 25 miles from some seismic station. In any region this small the occurrence of earthquakes might not be typical of the earth as a whole, so that it is difficult to carry the frequency study down to such low magnitudes. Ordinary quarry blasts can be as large as magnitude 2, and the Bikini atom bomb test has an estimated magnitude of 5.5 (Gutenberg and Richter, 1946). There may well be as many as a million earthquakes a year.

Since there is one shock of magnitude $M_s = 8$ or more every year on the average, one might expect from extrapolation of Table 9.1 a shock of magnitude 9 every decade or so. However, no shock of greater size than the Colombian earthquake of 1906, magnitude $M_s = 8.6$, is known to have occurred. Certainly there has been none in the last 50 years. Even the Lisbon earthquake of 1855, possibly the most violent to have been recorded in history, probably was not over magnitude 9 and may have been 8.5 or less. It seems probable that there is an upper limit to the amount of stress which can be built up in any limited region of the earth, corresponding closely to magnitude 8.5.

In the case of deep-focus shocks, the upper limit of size is at an even lower magnitude, 8.2 for intermediate-depth shocks and 8.0 for deep shocks. This may mean that as depth within the earth increases, the rocks break under lesser stress, or it may mean that the stresses are

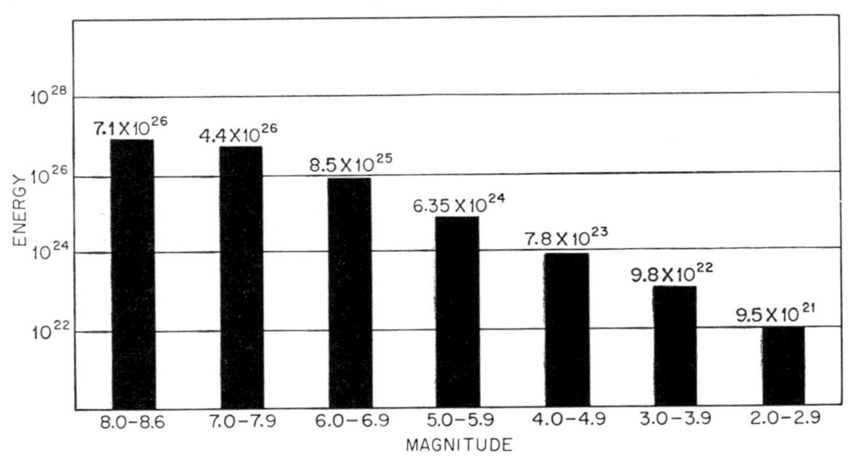

FIG. 9.2 Approximate energy released by earthquakes annually.

relieved too fast by other means to allow sufficient energy to accumulate for larger shocks to take place. Either condition is consistent with the absence of any earthquakes beneath 700 km in depth.

If one considers the amount of energy being released by earthquakes annually, it is found that the largest earthquakes account for the greatest part of the energy. This is shown graphically in Fig. 9.2. The vertical scale is logarithmic. Shocks of magnitude 8 or more release 7.1×10^{26} ergs of energy annually [assuming that K_1 in (9.17) equals 12]; magnitude 7 to 7.9, 4.4×10^{26} ergs; and so on. Shocks of magnitude 2 to 2.9 release only 9.5×10^{21} ergs a year. Thus, shocks of magnitude 7 and larger represent over 90 per cent of all seismic energy.

9.4 Benioff's Rule. According to Benioff (1949) the potential energy E_p of a volume W possessing a coefficient of shear μ strained an average amount s immediately before an earthquake is

$$E_p = 0.5\mu W s^2 \tag{9.20}$$

The energy of the released seismic waves is

$$E_T = 0.5f\mu W s^2 \tag{9.21}$$

where f is the fraction of the energy released as seismic waves. If the strain is reduced to zero during the earthquake by movement along a fault, then s is proportional to the fault displacement x_f:

$$s = Cx_f \tag{9.22}$$

where C is a constant of proportionality. Substituting this in (9.21),

$$E_T = 0.5f\mu WC^2x_f^2 = C_1^2x_f^2 \tag{9.23}$$

where

$$C_1 = (0.5f\mu WC^2)^{1/2} \tag{9.24}$$

Thus, the displacement on the fault is seen to be proportional to the square root of the energy released as seismic waves, all factors on which C_1 depends being equal.

Using Eq. (9.17), with a value of 9 for K_1,

$$\log C_1x_f = \log E_T^{1/2} = 4.5 + 0.9M_s \tag{9.25}$$

$$x_f = \frac{1}{C_1}10^{4.5+0.9M_s} \tag{9.26}$$

This gives the relation of fault displacement to magnitude. Thus, if we know the magnitudes of all earthquakes occurring on any one fault over a period of years, we can plot the displacement occurring during that time. Benioff has done this for two groups of earthquakes (Figs. 9.3 to 9.8).

Figure 9.3 is a graph of the cumulative strain factor $E_T^{1/2}$ in (ergs)$^{1/2}$ given by Eq. (9.25), against time for all shallow earthquakes in the Tonga-Kermadec area. Each rod represents one earthquake, the relation between rod height and magnitude being shown in the diagram. Plotted in this manner, the rate of release of energy is made clear. The duration of the observations is too brief to give a comprehensive picture of the rate of strain relief, though it appears that following the earthquake of April 30, 1919, the rate suddenly decreased.

Figure 9.4 shows the corresponding data for deep plus intermediate earthquakes. Until May 26, 1932, the strain appears to have been building up asymptotically toward a maximum, but then something happened which caused the displacement to accumulate linearly with time. The suggested interpretation is that two blocks of the earth were moving as shown in Fig. 9.5. Until 1932 the fault was so tightly locked at the point X that no shift could take place there. Faulting could and did occur elsewhere, but because of the attachement of the two blocks at X, the amount was gradually decreasing. On May 26, 1932, fracture occurred at X, and thereafter the release of energy was at a constant rate.

The sequence of earthquakes on the west coast of South America shows similar patterns, as shown in Figs. 9.6 to 9.8. In the case of shallow

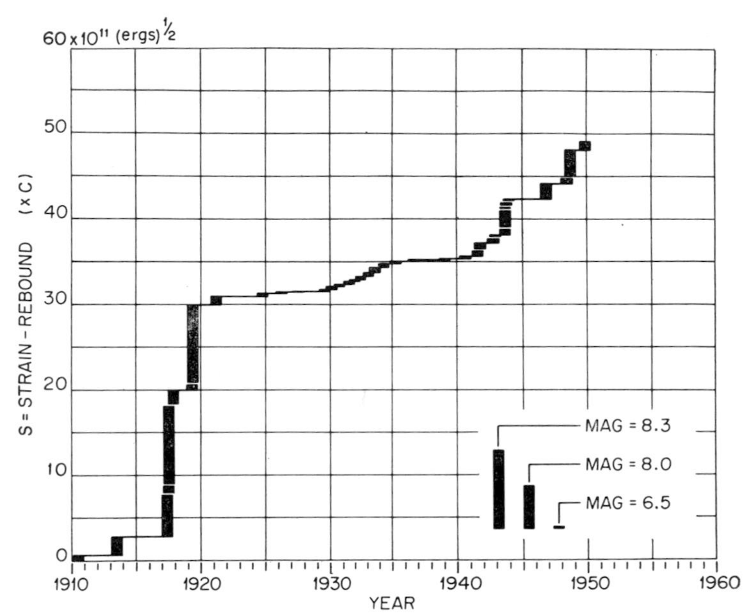

FIG. 9.3 Strain-rebound increments of Tonga-Kermadec shallow earthquakes. (*Benioff, 1955.*)

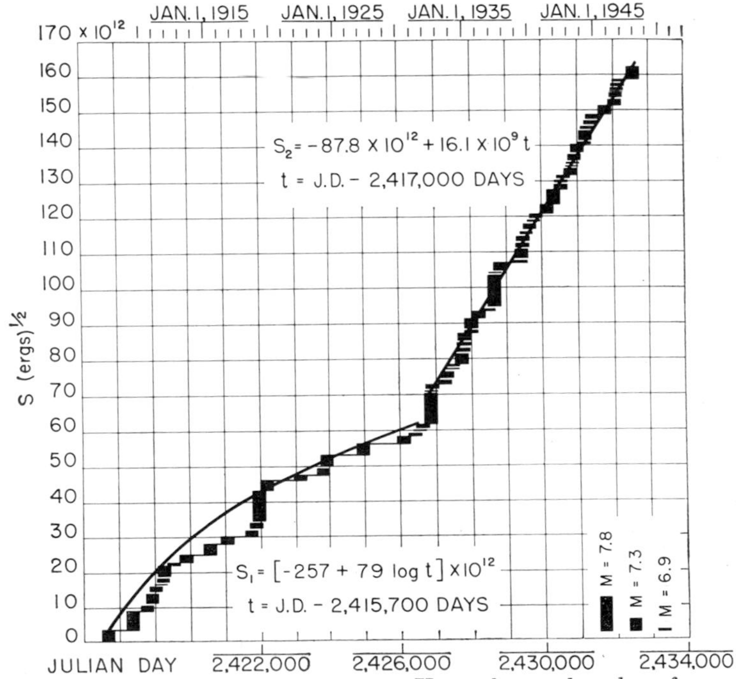

FIG. 9.4 Strain-rebound increments of Tonga-Kermadec earthquakes of over 70-km focal depth. (*Benioff, 1955.*)

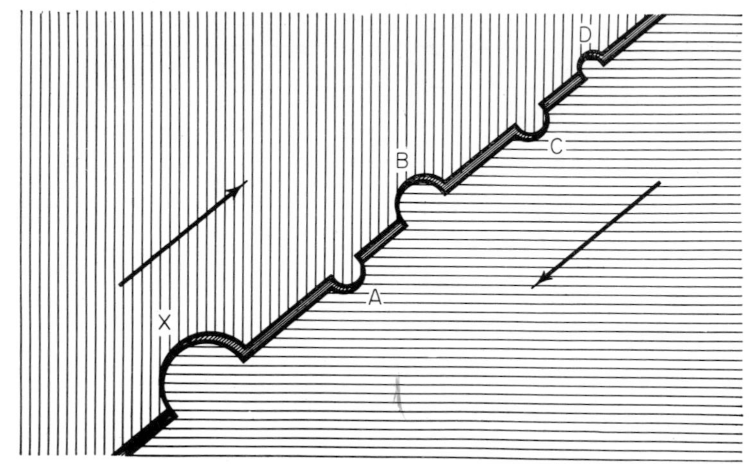

FIG. 9.5 Tonga-Kermadec fault mechanism suggested by strain-rebound curve of the deep sequence. (*Benioff, 1949.*)

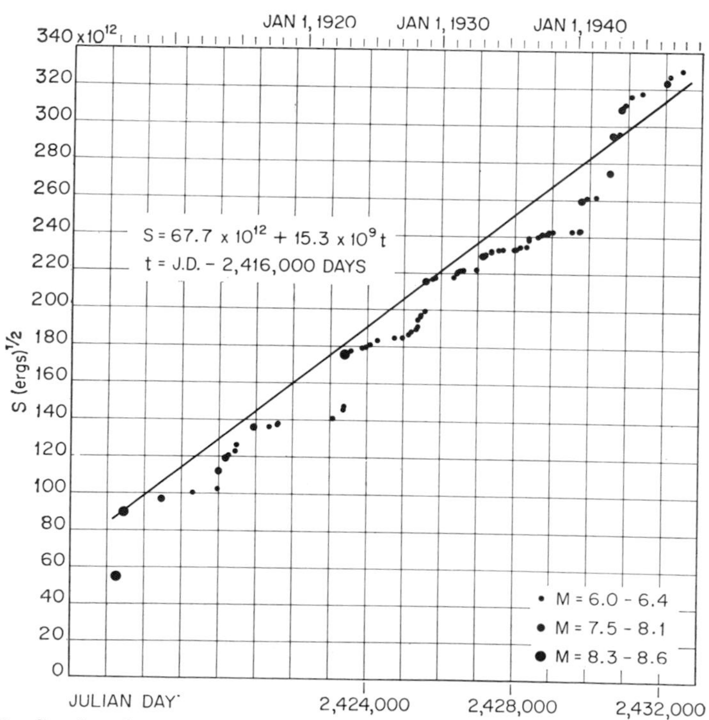

FIG. 9.6 Strain-rebound increments of South American shallow earthquakes. (*Benioff, 1949.*)

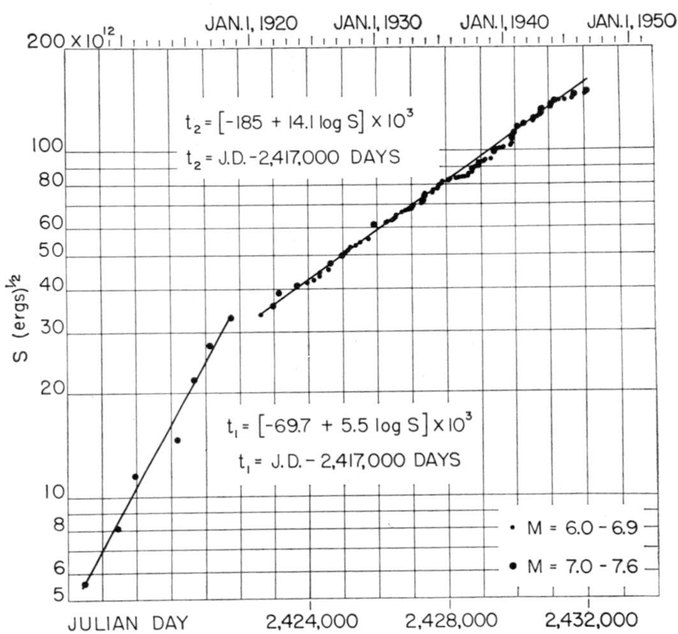

FIG. 9.7 Strain-rebound increments of South American intermediate-depth earthquakes. (*Benioff, 1949.*)

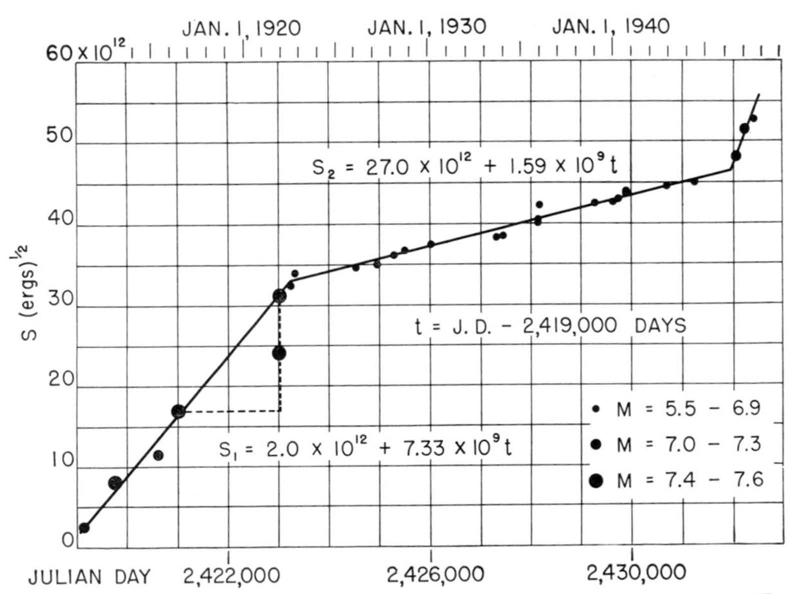

FIG. 9.8 Strain-rebound increments of South American deep earthquakes. (*Benioff, 1949.*)

shocks the average rate of release of energy is approximately constant, quiescent periods being followed by large shocks. In the case of intermediate shocks, there appears to be a change in the rate of release of energy around 1920. At that time the frequency of shocks increased, but the size and rate of energy release decreased. Deep shocks were similarly affected, though the change may not have been permanent.

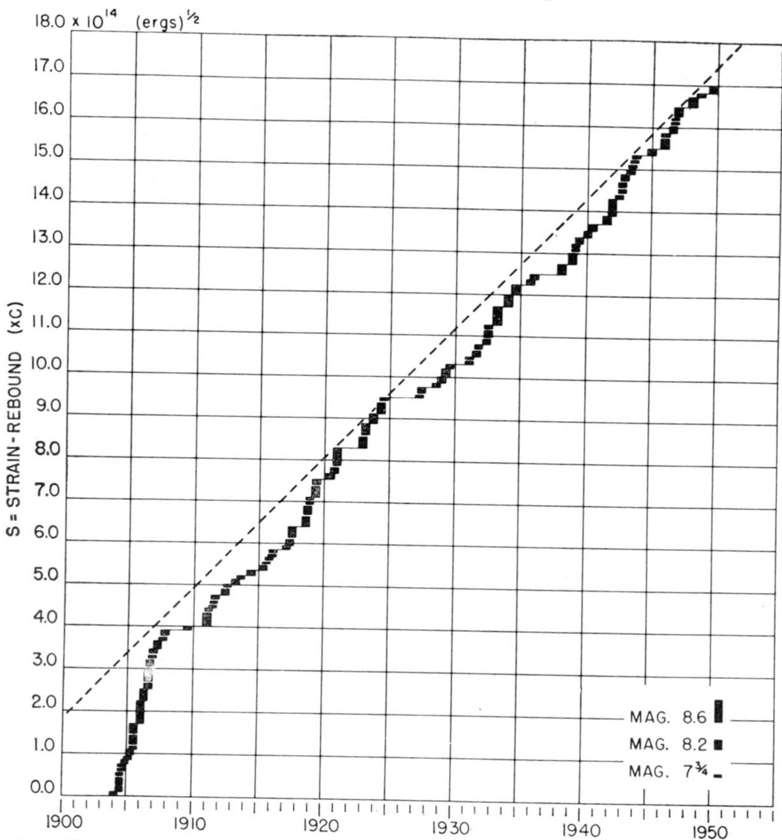

Fig. 9.9 Strain-rebound increments of magnitude 7¾ and larger shallow earthquakes. (*Benioff, 1951.*)

The conclusion to be drawn from these data is that whole large regions seem to be linked in some manner whereby the average rates of release of energy throughout the regions are constant over long periods of time. It is as though displacements were slowly taking place on a single fault. Occasionally, however, changes occur which result in sudden, marked alterations in the rate of release of energy. Furthermore, the structures are limited in the depth to which they extend. Although in some cases earthquakes at two depth ranges belong to the same pattern, in other cases each depth range is characterized by its own pattern. Therefore, it is concluded that the large faults or other structures along which the quakes occur have greater horizontal than vertical continuity.

Interesting relationships are also found if we examine the rate of release of energy thoughout the earth as a whole. Figure 9.9 shows cumulative strain released by large shallow earthquakes. The rate of release over the whole earth appears to have been approximately constant since 1907. This must mean either that the source of energy for these earthquakes

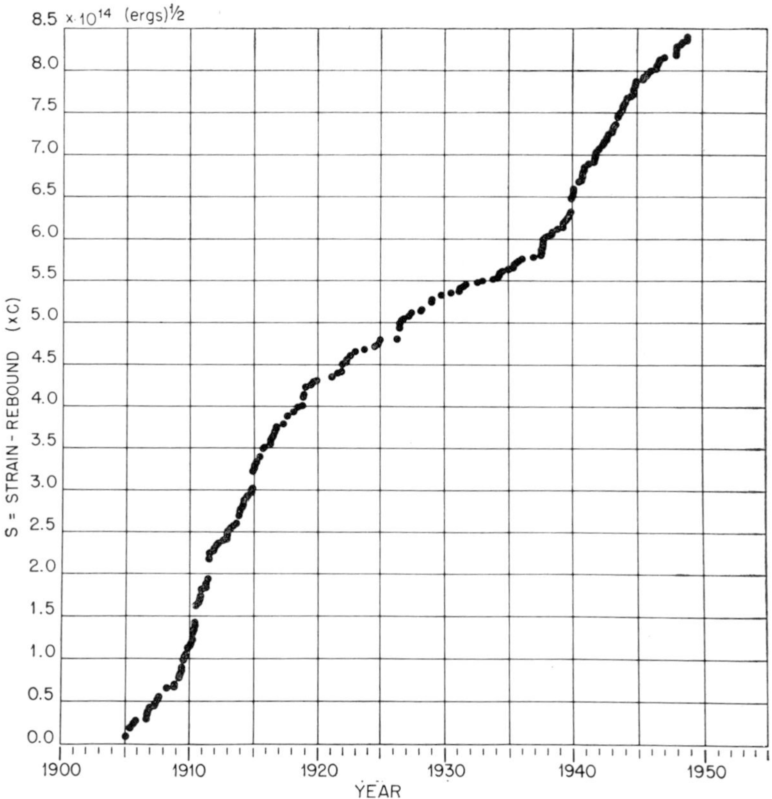

FIG. 9.10 Strain-rebound increments of magnitude 7.0 and larger intermediate-depth earthquakes. (*Benioff, 1951.*)

involves a world-wide stress system, or that in every region individually there are processes acting at constant rates. If shocks of magnitude 8.0 and larger only are considered, a slight but irregular periodicity is apparent (Benioff, 1951, 1955). It has been suggested that this is related either to the Chandler motion of the poles or to suspected but unproved periodic variations in the earth's radius. The same conclusions cannot be drawn for intermediate and deep earthquakes, where the processes involved result in different patterns. For intermediate shocks there appears to be a different periodic variation in rate (Fig. 9.10). The pattern for deep earthquakes does not exhibit any clear periodicity. Thus earthquake generation appears to be a function of depth, there being three distinct layers in which different sets of conditions exist. The shallow layer extends to about 70 km, the intermediate from 70 to 300 km, and the deep from 300 to 700 km. These layers may not be everywhere independent of one another (see Chaps. 19 and 20). Benioff (1955) has suggested that under the oceans the intermediate and deep layers are part of one system, while under the continents the intermediate and shallow earthquake zones are related. Since earthquakes do not occur at greater depths than 700 km, we must suppose either that the rock lying beneath these three tectonic units has different physical properties allowing relief without large shocks or that large stresses are not generated here.

The figures show that the individual shocks are parts of long-continuing sequences. It is entirely possible that the little more than 50 years for which usable data are available for studying this phenomenon is too short a period to reveal the long-term trends. It should be clearly realized that the layers determined from these studies are distinct because of their mechanical behavior. It is not required that they differ in composition from one another or that each be of uniform composition, only that each respond in a characteristic manner to the stresses existing within the earth, or that distinctly different stress patterns be generated in each.

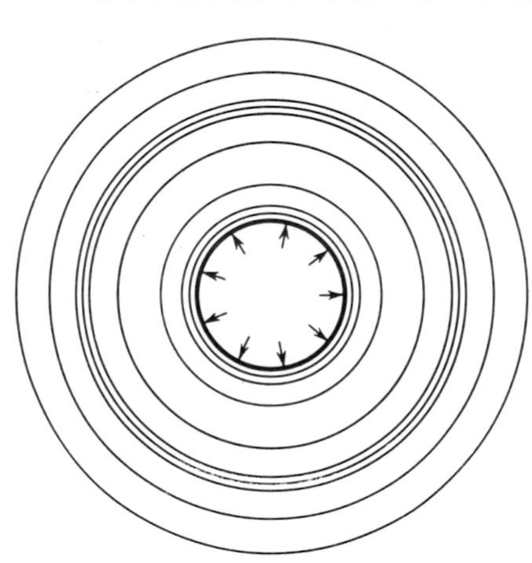

Fig. 9.11 In a homogeneous, isotropic, elastic medium the walls would be expected to vibrate radially around a spherical source of wave motion.

9.5 Significance of First Breaks. The direction of the first motion spreading from a shock also gives us definite information about the cause of a shock. Consider an explosion of dynamite set off in a homogeneous, isotropic, elastic medium. The detonation of the explosion produces an outward pressure on the walls of the chamber containing it (Fig. 9.11). The particles of the walls move radially outward. The compression of the surrounding rock is followed by a rarefaction as elastic forces resist the motion. Waves of compression and rarefaction spread in all directions from the shock.

On the other hand consider a sudden displacement horizontally along a fault (Fig. 9.12). If we choose Cartesian axes parallel and perpendicular to the fault, and think of an elastic rebound displacement on it, then in quadrants II and IV the first arrivals will be a motion away from the epicenter, and in the other two toward it. At right angles to the fault the motion would be expected to be a minimum, while at small angles to it, as parallelism to the ground motion is approached, the motion would be a maximum. There will be a rapid but continuous reversal in the direction

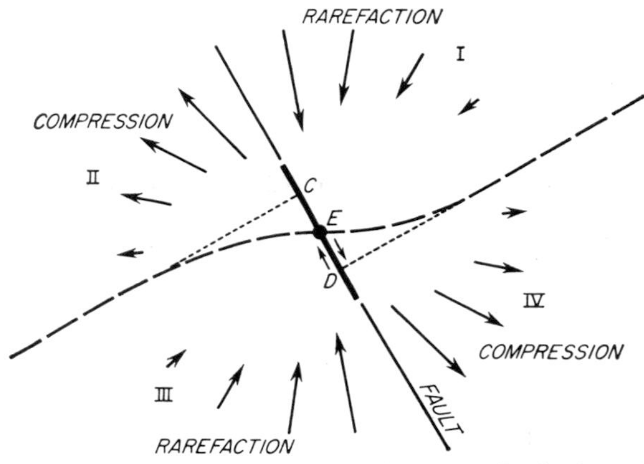

FIG. 9.12 Direction of first ground motion around a horizontal shear.

of first motion as one crosses the trend of the fault. Exactly on the projection of it the impulses from opposite sides would be expected to cancel each other. The case for a vertical fault can be visualized by turning Fig. 9.12 on end as shown in 9.13. Quadrants I and II lie on either side of the epicenter, while quadrants III and IV extend from the horizontal plane through the focus to the far side of the earth. Similar patterns can easily be visualized for cases where the fault motion has both a horizontal and vertical component. In the actual earth, allowance will have to be made for the fact that the rays are bent owing to refraction.

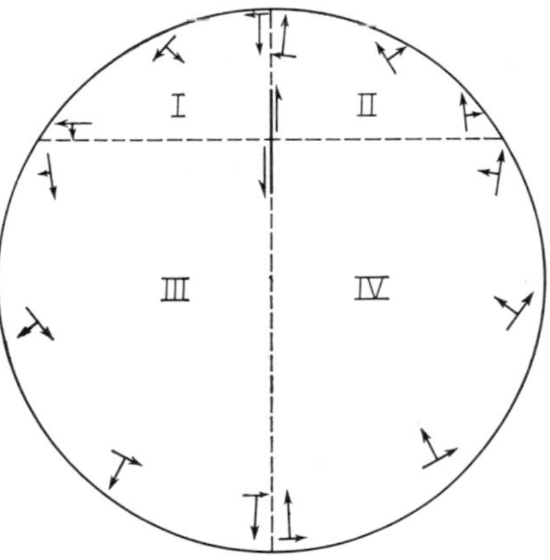

FIG. 9.13 Direction of first motion of dilatational and shear waves caused by a vertical fault in a homogeneous earth.

Byerly (1955) and Hodgson (1957) have studied 75 earthquakes in this fashion to determine the nature of the faulting. In 67 of these cases the motion was predominently strike-slip. These data combined with observed fault motions and geologic observations show that there are consistent trends in the deformations of large areas. The first motions of earthquakes on the San Andreas fault system in southern California indicate a persistent tendency of the continentward side to move southeast relative to the adjoining block (Gutenberg, 1941*a*). Byerly (1955) observed a similar sense (continentward side south) in four out of five South American earthquakes studied. In New Zealand, the western block moves north relative to the Pacific basin. Benioff (1957) suggests that the whole Pacific basin may be rotating in a counterclockwise direction relative to the adjoining land with a period of 10^9 years. On the other hand, Gutenberg (1951*f*) states that Tsuboi has presented evidence that the motion in Japan is in the opposite sense, and Willis (1944) mentions similar motion on the great Visayan rift zone in the Philippine Islands.

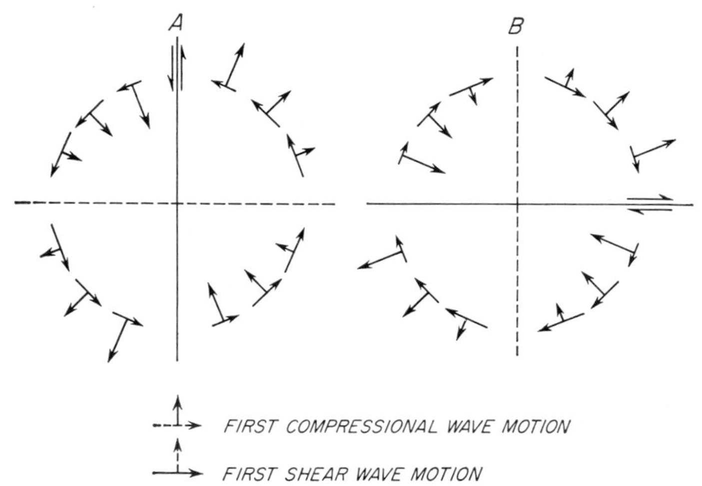

FIG. 9.14 Use of shear arrivals to settle ambiguity of interpretation of dilatational arrivals.

If the fault trend is unknown but the direction of first motions observed at various azimuths from the epicenter, then the trend of the fault may be either one of two directions as shown in Fig. 9.14. The choice of direction can sometimes be made from knowledge of local geologic conditions. At other times the direction of first motion of the later-arriving shear waves is theoretically capable of serving to distinguish between the two cases, as can be seen by comparing the left-hand diagram with the right-hand one in Fig. 9.14. In practice this may be difficult, as the first shear-wave motion may be hard to distinguish on the records.

In the case of an explosion, since the generating force is predominantly radial, the energy is radiated largely as dilatational waves. In an elastic rebound earthquake, shear waves will also be generated. The nature of the causative motion being a shearing, it is logical to expect that the shear waves will be strong in comparison with the dilatational. This is usually the case for an earthquake.

9.6 Attenuation with Distance. As the distance from the epicenter increases, the amplitude of ground motion decreases. This is owing in part to the radial spreading of the energy but is also the result of three other factors. At each boundary encountered, part of the energy is reflected and part transmitted into the new medium, causing a division of the original pulse. Furthermore, within each medium there is absorption of energy from the pulse. Lastly, the length of the seismic pulse, especially surface waves, tends to increase with distance, with a corresponding decrease in amplitude at any instant.

In the case of body waves generated near the earth's surface, since the pulses spread in all directions through the rock, the energy is distributed over a hemispherical area whose size is proportional to the square of the distance from the focus. In general, absorption by the ground is an exponential function of distance, so that for any body wave,

$$E_\Delta = E_{b1}\Delta^{-2}e^{-\alpha\Delta} \tag{9.27}$$

where E_Δ is the energy in the waves at distance Δ, E_{b1} is the energy at unit distance, and α is the coefficient of absorption.

For a pulse of a given shape, energy is proportional to the square of amplitude A, so that

$$A_\Delta = A_{b1}\Delta^{-1}e^{-\frac{1}{2}\alpha\Delta} \tag{9.28}$$

A_{b1} (or E_{b1}) can be eliminated from the equations by using values of A_Δ (or E_Δ) at two Δ's:

$$A_{b1} = A_{\Delta 1}\Delta_1 e^{\frac{1}{2}\alpha\Delta_1} = A_{\Delta 2}\Delta_2 e^{\frac{1}{2}\alpha\Delta_2} \tag{9.29}$$

This can be solved for α:

$$\alpha = \frac{2}{\Delta_2 - \Delta_1}\ln\frac{A_{\Delta 1}\Delta_1}{A_{\Delta 2}\Delta_2} = \frac{1}{\Delta_2 - \Delta_1}\ln\frac{E_{\Delta 1}}{E_{\Delta 2}}\left(\frac{\Delta_1}{\Delta_2}\right)^2 \tag{9.30}$$

For observed earthquake body-wave pulses α is usually too small to measure, indicating that the interior of the earth is nearly perfectly elastic. In the near surface layers α is larger, typical values for body waves being as great as 0.062 per meter.

TABLE 9.2 TYPICAL VALUES OF α IN NEAR-SURFACE MATERIALS, WAVES PRODUCED BY SMALL EXPLOSIONS*

Pulse	α/m	Conditions
Dilatational	0.062	In weathered layer
Dilatational	0.00033	Refracted through near-surface solid layer
Coupled waves	0.036	
Pseudo-Rayleigh waves	0.017	

* Data from Howell and Kaukonen, 1954, and Howell and Budenstein, 1955.

Earthquake surface waves are absorbed more rapidly than the corresponding body waves, though the rate of absorption is still not large in solid rock. Since surface waves spread in only two dimensions instead of three, the corresponding equations are

$$E_{\Delta s} = E_{s0}\Delta^{-1}e^{-\alpha_s\Delta} \tag{9.31}$$

$$A_{\Delta s} = A_{s0}\Delta^{-1/2}e^{-1/2\alpha_s\Delta} \tag{9.32}$$

$$\alpha_s = \frac{2}{\Delta_2 - \Delta_1} \ln \frac{A_{\Delta s1}}{A_{\Delta s2}} \left(\frac{\Delta_1}{\Delta_2}\right)^{1/2} = \frac{1}{\Delta_2 - \Delta_1} \ln \frac{E_{\Delta s1}\Delta_1}{E_{\Delta s2}\Delta_2} \tag{9.33}$$

Observed values of α_s for earthquakes are of the order of 5×10^{-6} per kilometer, depending greatly on frequency, type of surface wave, and geographic location (Gutenberg, 1932). For explosion-generated surface waves in soft soil α_s can be as great as 0.036 per meter. This is probably much higher than the average for surface waves in shallow formations.

In spite of this greater rate of absorption, the amplitude of surface waves falls off more slowly with distance from their source than does the amplitude of body waves. This is because A_Δ decreases as Δ^{-1} but $A_{\Delta s}$ decreases as $\Delta^{-1/2}$. Near the epicenter the body and surface waves often have nearly equal amplitudes, but at greater distances the surface waves become increasingly strong in comparison.

The problem of surface-wave attenuation is greatly complicated by the broadening of the pulse as it travels. The velocity of surface waves depends generally on frequency. This dependence of velocity on frequency is called dispersion. This means that high-frequency surface-wave vibrations travel at a different velocity from low-frequency vibrations (see also Sec. 10.8). The coefficient of absorption α_s generally increases with frequency. In some cases, the rate of increase may be so rapid that α_s increases with the square of frequency. The result of this is a rapid loss of high-frequency energy in seismic waves with distance from the source. At large distances the principal wavelengths of the observed motions are generally greater than near the source. This phenomenon is so striking that local shocks can sometimes be recognized from teleseisms simply by the higher predominant frequency of ground vibration.

One must be careful not to confuse the effect of absorption on frequency with the effect of the size of the shock. Small explosions have a tendency to generate a greater percentage of high-frequency vibrations in the ground than do large explosions, and the same is true for earthquakes. Gutenberg and Richter (1942) have shown empirically that in southern California

$$\log T_0 = 0.22M - 1.5 \tag{9.34}$$

where M is the magnitude and T_0 is the predominant period of an earthquake.

9.7 Prediction. The subject of earthquake prediction has long been of popular interest. Many individuals claiming psychic or other occult powers have attempted to predict shocks. To date none has been consistently correct. The occasional successes of some individuals are easy to understand if one recalls that there are probably in excess of a million potentially perceptible shocks yearly, of which perhaps as many as 100,000 are felt though not always reported, or over 250 per day somewhere in the world. In an average day about three of these would be capable of doing appreciable damage. Furthermore, these shocks occur largely in certain regions of the world where earthquakes are common (see Chap. 19). Therefore, if one is vague as to exact time and place in predicting the event, not too much risk of error is involved. Analyzed scientifically such predictions always turn out to be of no value.

There are, however, four general approaches which yield useful results, though none give exact predictions. One of these is Benioff's rule (Sec. 9.4) that in certain areas the rate of release of energy is constant. In such an area, the longer the period of time without a shock, the larger the shock to be expected. Present knowledge indicates that the areas involved are large, so the rule is not yet of much help in anticipating shocks.

A similar rule, more useful locally, is that the oftener earthquakes have occurred in the past, the oftener they can be expected in the future. Insurance companies use this rule in determining the cost of insurance against losses incurred through damage due to earthquakes as illustrated in Table 9.3. These figures are not a true indication of the expectable

TABLE 9.3 EXPECTABLE AVERAGE EARTHQUAKE DAMAGE AS RECOMMENDED BY J. R. FREEMAN (1932) FOR COMPUTING INSURANCE PREMIUMS IN THE UNITED STATES

Regions	*Premiums per* $100, *cents/year*
California:	
Coastal area and Imperial Valley	10
Sierra Nevada region	7
San Joaquin Valley	5
Washington and Oregon coasts	6
Eastern Washington and Oregon	4
Rocky Mountains	3
Great Plains and Mid-Continent	1
Great Lakes-Mississippi Valley region, bottom land	2
Great Lakes-Mississippi region, 10 miles beyond bottom land	1
Atlantic Coast	1
Atlantic region over 50 miles from coast	0.5

damage, which is much less than this, being of the order of magnitude of 0.01 cent per $100 valuation per year in the United States east of the Rocky Mountains.

Absence of earthquakes in the past, however, is no guarantee that there will be none in the future. Charleston, South Carolina, had no past history of earthquakes up to 1886. Yet on August 31 of that year at 9:51 in the evening a violent earthquake occurred, killing 27 people out of a population of 50,000 and driving many persons from their homes. The total casualty list was increased to about 100 persons by later deaths attributed to exposure. Except for a few foreshocks the week preceding the earthquake, there was almost no record of seismic activity previous to that time. Nor has there been comparable activity since, though the shock was followed by a series of aftershocks extending over several years. Total damage amounted to $50,000,000, $100 for every person in the city. The shock itself was preceded by a widely heard roaring sound, and earth noises were heard occasionally with the aftershocks. Within an area of about 600 square miles sand blows and fountains were common and the ground was deformed, twisting railroad tracks and other structures. In this area the maximum intensity was about X on the Rossi-Forel scale and probably IX or X on the Mercalli scale. C. E. Dutton, who studied the earthquake effects in the field, concluded that there appeared to be two epicenters about 22 km apart and that the shocks originated at shallow depths of 13 and 20 km at the two places, which are between 16 and 32 km west and northwest of Charleston. However, the methods he used to estimate the depths are open to question.

The shock was notable also because of the wide area over which it was felt (see Fig. 9.15). This included most of the Mississippi Valley and points as far away as Boston, Bermuda, and Cuba. Among the interesting features of this map are the low intensities which are observed in a part of the north-central Appalachians. Apparently the rock structures here are such that the area is unusually insensitive to earthquake vibrations. The occurrence of this earthquake, striking as it did a region thought to be free of strong seismic activity, is proof that no region can consider itself immune to catastrophe of this sort.

Another way in which the occurrence of earthquakes can be predicted is from the study of the strains being built up. We observed in the last chapter that before the San Francisco earthquake the two blocks on either side of the fault were gradually shifted a measurable amount with respect to each other. This strain was observed to have occurred between the 1851 to 1866 and 1874 to 1892 surveys, but at the time was thought to have represented errors in the earlier survey. Such deformation is direct evidence that the rocks are under stress and, if observed, could serve as an accurate means of prediction. An instrument capable of measuring strains of 1 micron (10^{-6} m) out of 25 m, or 1 part in 2.5×10^7, has been built by the California Institute of Technology (Benioff et al., 1953). The sensitivity of this instrument is equivalent to noting a change of 6 in.

in the distance from New York to Los Angeles. Since we can estimate the strength of rocks, perhaps someday we can tell, by measuring the strain they are under, when the rocks have reached the maximum elastic deformation they can stand without fracturing, and hence when they are

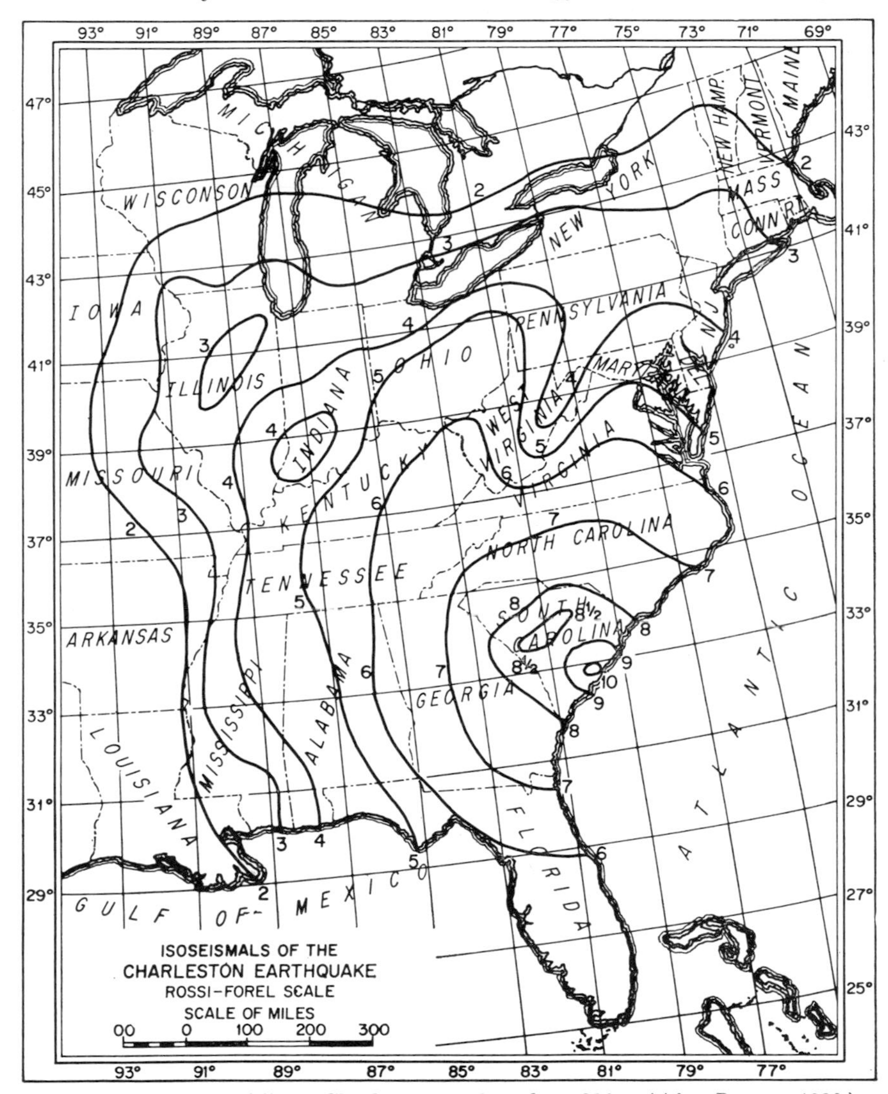

Fig. 9.15 Isoseismal lines, Charleston earthquake, 1886. (*After Dutton, 1889.*)

about to break, causing an earthquake. In any case, observed earth motions should be recognized as tectonic phenomena of interest to geologists and geophysicists, and not dismissed as errors in measurement, as is often done, without good reason to believe them to be such.

The Japanese have pioneered in the study of block movements by geodetic and level surveys (Fig. 7.16). They have recognized and measured the amount of movement of many parts of Japan which are currently being deformed. One of the results of detailed studies of seismic activity is the discovery that in certain cases large earthquakes are preceded by an increase in the frequency of small shocks. Such activity may in some cases be a warning, but suffers the disadvantage that it is often instead a false alarm. More often than not, temporary increases in minor activity are entirely independent of any large earthquake.

At our present stage of understanding of seismic phenomena, prediction with any reasonable degree of accuracy seems to be impossible. We can only hope that continued detailed study of earthquakes will make us better able to see into the future.

CHAPTER 10

TRANSMISSION OF SEISMIC WAVES

When an earthquake occurs, there is a sudden sharp movement of the ground. As the rock snaps from one position to another, parts of the earth at successively greater distances from the focus are drawn along. The disturbance thus spreads throughout the whole earth at a velocity which depends on the nature of the rocks. Where the earth approximates a homogeneous, elastic solid, the energy is transmitted as elastic body waves, of which there are two types: dilatational and shear waves, as discussed in Chap. 6. Inhomogeneities cause reflection and refraction of the elastic waves. Several types of surface waves can be generated along boundaries.

Near the surface, at least, the earth is not perfectly elastic. The manner of transmission of seismic waves through inelastic substances is not well understood, but in general the same types of pulses appear to be involved. The main effects are to increase absorption greatly, to distort the pulse shape, and to spread the pulse in time.

Near a source of seismic waves, where the energy is spreading radially, special types of pulses whose amplitudes fall off rapidly with distance are to be expected but have never been observed (Fu, 1947). At large distances from the source, it is satisfactory to treat seismic waves as though they were plane instead of spherical waves. This is done in the following section.[1]

10.1 Derivation of Basic Equations. Consider the forces acting on an infinitesimal cube of density ρ and dimensions dx, dy, dz in an infinite, homogeneous, isotropic, elastic body. According to Newton's second

[1] Sections 10.1 to 10.6 may be omitted by students having inadequate mathematical background to comprehend their significance. In these sections the equations for the velocity of propagation V_p and V_s of dilatational and shear waves are derived

$$V_p = \left(\frac{\lambda + 2\mu}{\rho}\right)^{1/2}$$

$$V_s = \left(\frac{\mu}{\rho}\right)^{1/2}$$

where λ and μ are Lamé's constants and ρ is the density of the rock.

law, the acceleration of a particle in the body must be related to the forces acting on it. In the x direction

$$\int_V \rho a_x \, dx \, dy \, dz = \int_V \rho X \, dx \, dy \, dz + \int_S X_n \, dS \tag{10.1}$$

where a_x = the component of acceleration in the x direction, x = the x component of the body forces such as gravity, and X_n = the x component of the surface forces per unit area. X_n must be summed over the whole surface area S of the cube. Similarly:

$$\int_V \rho a_y \, dV = \int_V \rho Y \, dV + \int_S Y_n \, dS \tag{10.2}$$

$$\int_V \rho a_z \, dV = \int_V \rho Z \, dV + \int_S Z_n \, dS \tag{10.3}$$

where $dV = dx \, dy \, dz$.

To see more clearly what we mean by X_n, consider Fig. 10.1. F_x is a stress across the back face of the cube perpendicular to the x axis. It has three components, X_x, Y_x, and Z_x, all acting on the x face but directed parallel to the three coordinate axes. Such a stress is called a traction. There are two other tractions on the y and z faces having the components X_y, Y_y, Z_y, X_z, Y_z, and Z_z. On the opposite faces of the cube the x components of the tractions are

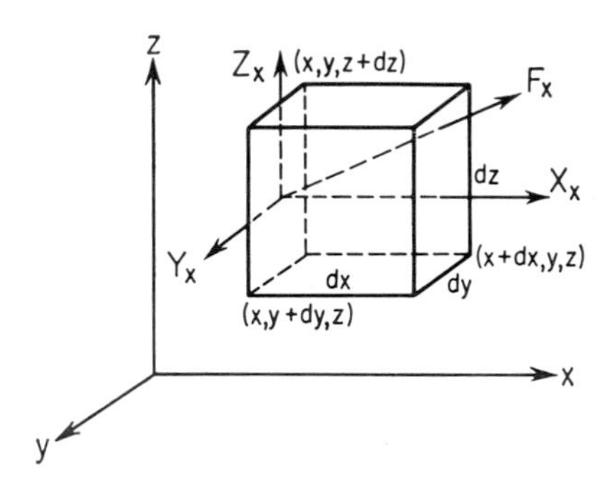

Fig. 10.1

$X_x + (\partial X_x/\partial x)\,dx, X_y + (\partial X_y/\partial y)\,dy$ and $X_z + (\partial X_z/\partial z)\,dz$, where $\partial X_x/\partial x$ is the rate of increase of X_x in the x direction, etc. There are similar components of the y and z tractions.

If the cube is very small and the forces are continuous functions, on one set of faces the force will be directed inward, on the other set outward. If we consider the components of an outward-directed force to be positive and an inward one negative, we get

$$\begin{aligned}\int_S X_n \, dS &= \int \left(X_x + \frac{\partial X_x}{\partial x} dx\right) dy \, dz - \int X_x \, dy \, dz \\ &+ \int \left(X_y + \frac{\partial X_y}{\partial y} dy\right) dx \, dz - \int X_y \, dx \, dz \\ &+ \int \left(X_z + \frac{\partial X_z}{\partial z} dz\right) dx \, dy - \int X_z \, dx \, dy \\ &= \int_V \left(\frac{\partial X_x}{\partial x} + \frac{\partial X_y}{\partial y} + \frac{\partial X_z}{\partial z}\right) dx \, dy \, dz \end{aligned} \tag{10.4}$$

This can be abbreviated

$$\int_S X_n \, dS = \int_V \operatorname{div} X_n \, dV \tag{10.5}$$

where

$$\operatorname{div} X_n = \frac{\partial X_x}{\partial x} + \frac{\partial X_y}{\partial y} + \frac{\partial X_z}{\partial z} \tag{10.6}$$

Equation (10.5) is one form of the divergence theorem, a very important physical law. It is true for any force system of the type being discussed here. Thus if A is any vector having the components A_x, A_y, A_z,

$$\operatorname{div} A = \frac{\partial A_x}{\partial x} + \frac{\partial A_y}{\partial y} + \frac{\partial A_z}{\partial z} \tag{10.7}$$

Equations (10.1) to (10.3) can now be rewritten:

$$\int_V \rho a_x \, dV = \int_V (\rho X + \operatorname{div} X_n) \, dV \tag{10.8}$$

$$\int_V \rho a_y \, dV = \int_V (\rho Y + \operatorname{div} Y_n) \, dV \tag{10.9}$$

$$\int_V \rho a_z \, dV = \int_V (\rho Z + \operatorname{div} Z_n) \, dV \tag{10.10}$$

where

$$\operatorname{div} Y_n = \frac{\partial Y_x}{\partial x} + \frac{\partial Y_y}{\partial y} + \frac{\partial Y_z}{\partial z} \tag{10.11}$$

and

$$\operatorname{div} Z_n = \frac{\partial Z_x}{\partial x} + \frac{\partial Z_y}{\partial y} + \frac{\partial Z_z}{\partial z} \tag{10.12}$$

Since the integration must be valid over any small volume within the solid, these equations can be satisfied only if the expressions being integrated are equal at every point in the body. Therefore,

$$\rho a_x = \rho X + \operatorname{div} X_n \tag{10.13}$$

$$\rho a_y = \rho Y + \operatorname{div} Y_n \tag{10.14}$$

$$\rho a_z = \rho Z + \operatorname{div} Z_n \tag{10.15}$$

These equations can be written in another way. For very small motion,

$$a_x = \frac{\partial^2 u}{\partial t^2} = \ddot{u} \tag{10.16}$$

$$a_y = \frac{\partial^2 v}{\partial t^2} = \ddot{v} \tag{10.17}$$

$$a_z = \frac{\partial^2 w}{\partial t^2} = \ddot{w} \tag{10.18}$$

where u, v, w are the displacements and t is the time. Rewriting Eqs. (10.13) to (10.15) in terms of the displacements,

$$\rho \ddot{u} = \rho X + \operatorname{div} X_n \tag{10.19}$$

$$\rho \ddot{v} = \rho Y + \operatorname{div} Y_n \tag{10.20}$$

$$\rho \ddot{w} = \rho Z + \operatorname{div} Z_n \tag{10.21}$$

These are the equations of motion of a point in a body such as we are considering here.

Now consider the moments about the three axes. These will be of the form

$$\int_V \rho(xa_y - ya_x)\, dV = \int_V \rho(xY - yX)\, dV + \int_S (xY_n - yX_n)\, dS \tag{10.22}$$

By substituting Eqs. (10.13) and (10.14) into (10.22) we get

$$\int_V [x(\rho Y + \text{div } Y_n) - y(\rho X + \text{div } X_n)]\, dV = \int_V \rho(xY - yX)\, dV + \int_S (xY_n - yX_n)\, dS \tag{10.23}$$

which simplifies to

$$\int_V (x \text{ div } Y_n - y \text{ div } X_n)\, dV = \int_S (xY_n - yX_n)\, dS \tag{10.24}$$

As before X_n has six values corresponding to the six faces: X_x, X_y, X_z, $X_x + (\partial X_x/\partial x)\, dx$, $X_y + (\partial X_y/\partial y)\, dy$, $X_z + (\partial X_z/\partial z)\, dz$, and y has the values Y_x, Y_y, Y_z, $Y_x + (\partial Y_x/\partial x)\, dx$, $Y_y + (\partial Y_y/\partial y)\, dy$, $Y_z + (\partial Y_z/\partial z)\, dz$. By use of the divergence theorem and Eq. (10.7), the right-hand side of Eq. (10.24) can be turned into a volume integral:

$$\begin{aligned}\int_S (xY_n - yX_n)\, dS &= \int_V \text{div } (xY_n - yX_n)\, dV \\ &= \int_V \left[\frac{\partial}{\partial x}(xY_x - yX_x) + \frac{\partial}{\partial y}(xY_y - yX_y) + \frac{\partial}{\partial z}(xY_z - yX_z)\right] dV \\ &= \int_V \left(Y_x + x\frac{\partial Y_x}{\partial x} - y\frac{\partial X_x}{\partial x} + x\frac{\partial Y_y}{\partial y} - X_y - y\frac{\partial X_y}{\partial y} + x\frac{\partial Y_z}{\partial z} - y\frac{\partial X_z}{\partial z}\right) dV\end{aligned} \tag{10.25}$$

On regrouping terms,

$$\begin{aligned}\int_S (xY_n - yX_n)\, dS &= \int_V \left[x\left(\frac{\partial Y_x}{\partial x} + \frac{\partial Y_y}{\partial y} + \frac{\partial Y_z}{\partial z}\right) - y\left(\frac{\partial X_x}{\partial x} + \frac{\partial X_y}{\partial y} + \frac{\partial X_z}{\partial z}\right) + Y_x - X_y\right] dV \\ &= \int_V (x \text{ div } Y_n - y \text{ div } X_n + Y_x - X_y)\, dV\end{aligned} \tag{10.26}$$

For (10.26) to be the equivalent of (10.24),

$$\int_V (Y_x - X_y)\, dV = 0 \tag{10.27}$$

For this integral to be zero for any small volume in the body,

$$Y_x = X_y \tag{10.28}$$

It can be shown in a similar manner that

$$Z_y = Y_z \tag{10.29}$$
$$X_z = Z_x \tag{10.30}$$

Thus, the nine components of the traction at a point in a body reduce to six.

10.2 Strains Resulting from Dilatation. Consider an infinitesimal cube as shown in Fig. 10.2, in which only dilatational (tensional and compressive) stresses X_x, Y_y, Z_z are acting, as shown. The change in length Δl_{xx} of the x side of the cube due to the stress X_x is given by Hooke's law:

$$\frac{\Delta l_{xx}}{l_x} = \frac{X_x}{E} \tag{10.31}$$

where E is Young's modulus. The changes in length due to Y_y and Z_z are

$$\frac{\Delta l_{xy}}{l_x} = -\sigma \frac{\Delta l_{yy}}{l_y} = -\sigma \frac{Y_y}{E} \tag{10.32}$$
$$\frac{\Delta l_{xz}}{l_x} = -\sigma \frac{\Delta l_{zz}}{l_z} = -\sigma \frac{Z_z}{E} \tag{10.33}$$

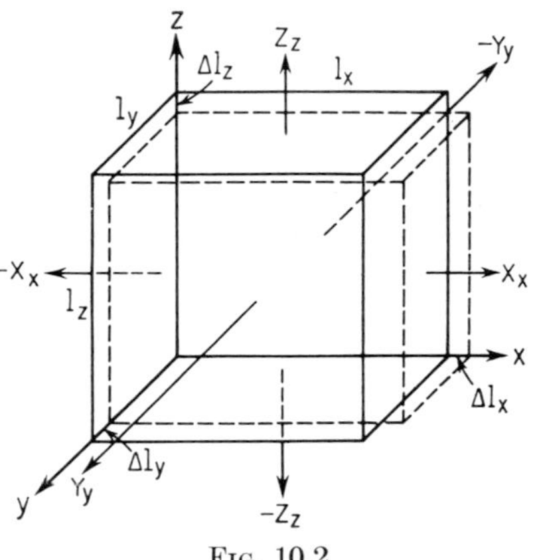

FIG. 10.2

where σ is Poisson's ratio. The total change in length of the x side is

$$\frac{\Delta l_x}{l_x} = \frac{1}{E}[X_x - \sigma(Y_y + Z_z)] \tag{10.34}$$

At any point in the cube, the x dimension is changing at the rate $\partial u/\partial x$ in the x direction. The total change in the distance l_x is $(\partial u/\partial x)l_x$. Therefore

$$\frac{\Delta l_x}{l_x} = \frac{(\partial u/\partial x)l_x}{l_x} = \frac{\partial u}{\partial x} = \frac{1}{E}[X_x - \sigma(Y_y + Z_z)] \tag{10.35}$$

In a similar manner it can be shown that

$$\frac{\partial v}{\partial y} = \frac{1}{E}[Y_y - \sigma(X_x + Z_z)] \tag{10.36}$$
$$\frac{\partial w}{\partial z} = \frac{1}{E}[Z_z - \sigma(X_x + Y_y)] \tag{10.37}$$

Equations (10.35) to (10.37) can be solved for X_x, Y_y, and Z_z in terms of

σ, E, and the partial derivatives of displacement. First add the three equations together.

$$\theta = \frac{\partial u}{\partial x} + \frac{\partial v}{\partial y} + \frac{\partial w}{\partial z} = \frac{1}{E}[(X_x + Y_y + Z_z) - 2\sigma(X_x + Y_y + Z_z)]$$
$$= \frac{1}{E}(1 - 2\sigma)(X_x + Y_y + Z_z) \tag{10.38}$$

θ is called the cubical dilatation. It is a measure of the change in volume ΔV of the body being stressed, for

$$\Delta V = dx\left(1 + \frac{\partial u}{\partial x}\right) dy\left(1 + \frac{\partial v}{\partial y}\right) dz\left(1 + \frac{\partial w}{\partial z}\right) - dx\,dy\,dz$$
$$= \left(\frac{\partial u}{\partial x} + \frac{\partial v}{\partial y} + \frac{\partial w}{\partial z} + \frac{\partial u}{\partial x}\frac{\partial v}{\partial y} + \frac{\partial u}{\partial x}\frac{\partial w}{\partial z} + \frac{\partial v}{\partial y}\frac{\partial w}{\partial z} + \frac{\partial u}{\partial x}\frac{\partial v}{\partial y}\frac{\partial w}{\partial z}\right) dx\,dy\,dz \tag{10.39}$$

which becomes, for very small displacements where the products of two small quantities can be neglected,

$$\Delta V = \left(\frac{\partial u}{\partial x} + \frac{\partial v}{\partial y} + \frac{\partial w}{\partial z}\right) dx\,dy\,dz \tag{10.40}$$

Now add $0 = (\sigma/E)X_x - (\sigma/E)X_x$ to (10.35):

$$\frac{\partial u}{\partial x} = \frac{1}{E}[(1 + \sigma)X_x - \sigma(X_x + Y_y + Z_z)] \tag{10.41}$$

Use (10.38) to clear this of $X_x + Y_y + Z_z$:

$$\frac{\partial u}{\partial x} = \frac{1}{E}\left[(1 + \sigma)X_x - \sigma\frac{E}{1 - 2\sigma}\theta\right] \tag{10.42}$$

which can be solved for X_x:

$$X_x = \frac{\sigma E}{(1 + \sigma)(1 - 2\sigma)}\theta + \frac{E}{1 + \sigma}\frac{\partial u}{\partial x} \tag{10.43}$$

Now let us define two abbreviations

$$\lambda = \frac{\sigma E}{(1 - 2\sigma)(1 + \sigma)} \tag{10.44}$$

$$\mu = \frac{E}{2(1 + \sigma)} \tag{10.45}$$

λ and μ are called Lamé's constants. In terms of them,

$$X_x = \lambda\theta + 2\mu\frac{\partial u}{\partial x} \tag{10.46}$$

And similarly,

$$Y_y = \lambda\theta + 2\mu \frac{\partial v}{\partial y} \tag{10.47}$$

$$Z_z = \lambda\theta + 2\mu \frac{\partial w}{\partial z} \tag{10.48}$$

In a liquid, pressure P is uniform in all directions; so $X_x = Y_y = Z_z = P$. Adding Eqs. (10.46) to (10.48),

$$X_x + Y_y + Z_z = 3P = 3\lambda\theta + 2\mu\left(\frac{\partial u}{\partial x} + \frac{\partial v}{\partial y} + \frac{\partial w}{\partial z}\right)$$
$$= (3\lambda + 2\mu)\theta \tag{10.49}$$

or

$$P = (\lambda + \tfrac{2}{3}\mu)\theta = k\theta \tag{10.50}$$

k is called the bulk modulus, or coefficient of incompressibility. It is the ratio of stress to resulting volume change.

10.3 Shearing Strains. Consider one face of an infinitesimal cube distorted by the pair of tractions X_y and Y_x as shown in Fig. 10.3:

$$\phi_{xy} = \frac{1}{2n} X_y \tag{10.51}$$

$$\phi_{yx} = \frac{1}{2n} Y_x \tag{10.52}$$

where n is the coefficient of shear, called the rigidity. From Eq. (10.28), $X_y = Y_x$; therefore

$$\phi_{xy} = \phi_{yx} \tag{10.53}$$

For very small distortions, tan $\phi = \phi$, so in the limit as the square becomes very small,

$$\phi_{xy} = \frac{\Delta u}{\Delta y} = \frac{\partial u}{\partial y} \tag{10.54}$$

$$\phi_{yx} = \frac{\Delta v}{\Delta x} = \frac{\partial v}{\partial x} \tag{10.55}$$

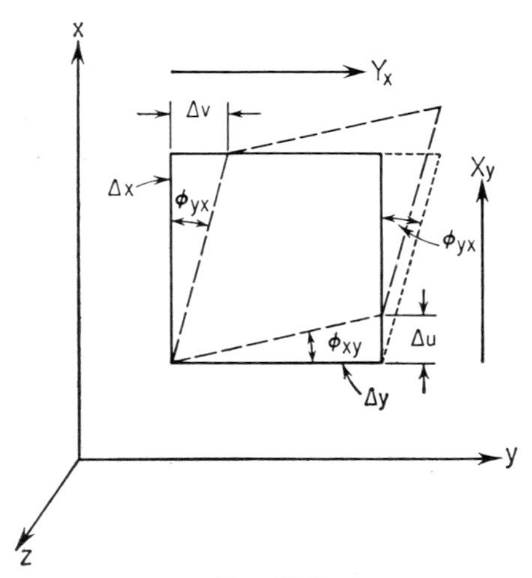

FIG. 10.3

The change in angle between two perpendicular lines in the xy plane is

$$\phi^*_{xy} = \phi_{xy} + \phi_{yx} = \frac{\partial u}{\partial y} + \frac{\partial v}{\partial x} = \frac{1}{2n}(X_y + Y_x) = \frac{1}{n}X_y \tag{10.56}$$

or

$$X_y = n\phi^*_{xy} = n\left(\frac{\partial u}{\partial y} + \frac{\partial v}{\partial x}\right) \tag{10-57}$$

similarly

$$Y_z = n\phi^*_{yz} = n\left(\frac{\partial v}{\partial z} + \frac{\partial w}{\partial y}\right) \tag{10.58}$$

$$Z_x = n\phi^*_{zx} = n\left(\frac{\partial w}{\partial x} + \frac{\partial u}{\partial z}\right) \tag{10.59}$$

Equations (10.46) to (10.48) and (10.57) to (10.59) give the relations between very small stresses and the resulting strains in an isotropic, elastic body in terms of the elastic constants λ, μ, and n. If the body is not isotropic, similar but more complex equations apply.

Actually μ and n are identical. To prove this we have only to perform a rotation of the axes and observe the relation of the tractions in the two sets of coordinate systems. Consider the tractions in the xy plane as shown in Fig. 10.4. The two sets of coordinate axes are at an angle of 45°

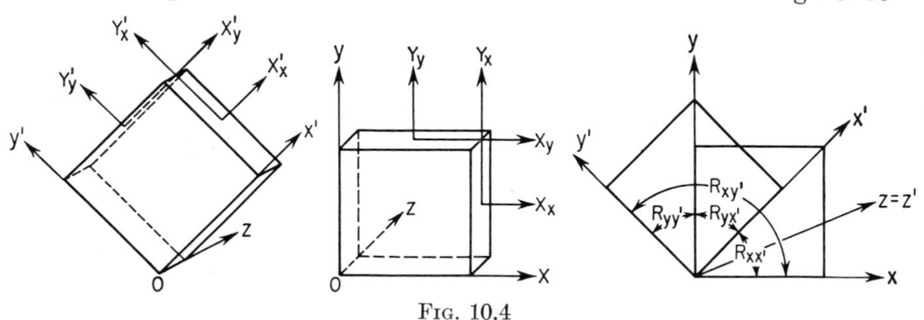

Fig. 10.4

to each other. Each traction in the new coordinate system receives a contribution from each of four tractions in the original system. The fraction of itself that each contributes is the product of the cosine of the angle between the old and new stress vectors and the cosine of the angle between the surfaces on which they act. Thus, using primes to represent the new system,

$$
\begin{aligned}
X'_y &= X_x \cos R_{xx'} \cos R_{xy'} \\
&\quad + X_y \cos R_{xx'} \cos R_{yy'} \\
&\quad + Y_x \cos R_{yx'} \cos R_{xy'} \\
&\quad + Y_y \cos R_{yx'} \cos R_{yy'}
\end{aligned}
\tag{10.60}
$$

From inspection of Fig. 10.4,

$$\cos R_{xx'} = \cos 45° = (0.5)^{1/2} \tag{10.61}$$
$$\cos R_{xy'} = \cos 135° = -(0.5)^{1/2} \tag{10.62}$$
$$\cos R_{yx'} = \cos -45° = (0.5)^{1/2} \tag{10.63}$$
$$\cos R_{yy'} = \cos 45° = (0.5)^{1/2} \tag{10.64}$$

Substituting these values in 10.60,

$$X'_y = 0.5(-X_x + X_y - Y_x + Y_y) \tag{10.65}$$

and since $X_y = Y_x$, using (10.46) and (10.47),

$$
\begin{aligned}
X'_y &= 0.5(Y_y - X_x) \\
&= 0.5\left(\lambda\theta + 2\mu \frac{\partial v}{\partial y} - \lambda\theta - 2\mu \frac{\partial u}{\partial x}\right) \\
&= \mu \left(\frac{\partial v}{\partial y} - \frac{\partial u}{\partial x}\right)
\end{aligned}
\tag{10.66}
$$

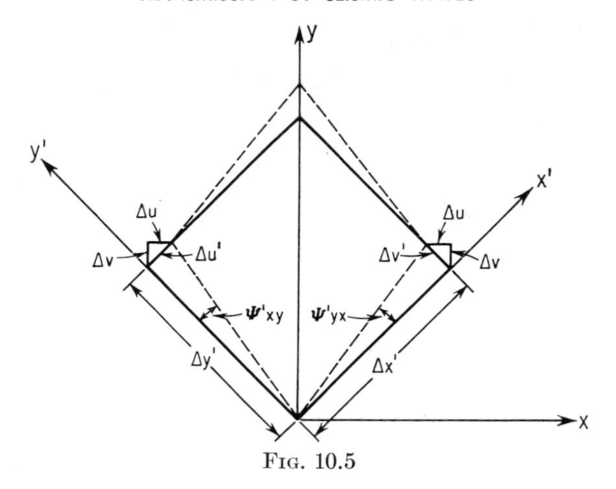

Fig. 10.5

Now consider Fig. 10.5. By analogy with Eq. (10.56),

$$\phi_{xy}^{*\prime} = \psi_{xy}' + \psi_{yx}' = \frac{\partial u'}{\partial y'} + \frac{\partial v'}{\partial x'} \tag{10.67}$$

$$\begin{aligned}
\frac{\partial u'}{\partial y'} &= \frac{\partial}{\partial y'}\,(u \cos R_{xx'} + v \cos R_{yx'}) \\
&= \cos R_{xx'} \frac{\partial u}{\partial y'} + \cos R_{yx'} \frac{\partial v}{\partial y'} \\
&= \cos R_{xx'} \left(\frac{\partial u}{\partial y} \cos R_{yy'} + \frac{\partial u}{\partial x} \cos R_{xy'}\right) \\
&\qquad + \cos R_{yx'} \left(\frac{\partial v}{\partial x} \cos R_{xy'} + \frac{\partial v}{\partial y} \cos R_{yy'}\right) \\
&= \frac{1}{2}\left(\frac{\partial u}{\partial y} - \frac{\partial u}{\partial x} - \frac{\partial v}{\partial x} + \frac{\partial v}{\partial y}\right)
\end{aligned} \tag{10.68}$$

$$\begin{aligned}
\frac{\partial v'}{\partial x'} &= \frac{\partial}{\partial x'}\,(v \cos R_{yy'} + u \cos R_{xy'}) \\
&= \cos R_{yy'} \frac{\partial v}{\partial x'} + \cos R_{xy'} \frac{\partial u}{\partial x'} \\
&= \cos R_{yy'} \left(\frac{\partial v}{\partial x} \cos R_{xx'} + \frac{\partial v}{\partial y} \cos R_{yx'}\right) \\
&\qquad + \cos R_{xy'} \left(\frac{\partial u}{\partial x} \cos R_{xx'} + \frac{\partial u}{\partial y} \cos R_{yx'}\right) \\
&= \frac{1}{2}\left(\frac{\partial v}{\partial x} + \frac{\partial v}{\partial y} - \frac{\partial u}{\partial x} - \frac{\partial u}{\partial y}\right)
\end{aligned} \tag{10.69}$$

Substituting (10.68) and (10.69) in (10.67),

$$\phi_{xy}^{*\prime} = \frac{\partial v}{\partial y} - \frac{\partial u}{\partial x} \tag{10.70}$$

By analogy with Eq. (10.57),

$$X'_y = n\phi^{*\prime}_{xy} \tag{10.71}$$

and using (10.70),

$$X'_y = n\left(\frac{\partial v}{\partial y} - \frac{\partial u}{\partial x}\right) \tag{10.72}$$

Comparison of (10.66) and (10.72) shows that

$$n = \mu \tag{10.73}$$

Equations (10.57) to (10.59) can be rewritten:

$$X_y = \mu\left(\frac{\partial u}{\partial y} + \frac{\partial v}{\partial x}\right) \tag{10.74}$$

$$Y_z = \mu\left(\frac{\partial v}{\partial z} + \frac{\partial w}{\partial y}\right) \tag{10.75}$$

$$Z_x = \mu\left(\frac{\partial w}{\partial x} + \frac{\partial u}{\partial z}\right) \tag{10.76}$$

10.4 Equations of Motion. Substitute (10.46) to (10.48) and (10.74) to (10.76) into (10.19) to (10.21):

$$\begin{aligned}\rho\ddot{u} &= \rho X + \frac{\partial X_x}{\partial x} + \frac{\partial X_y}{\partial y} + \frac{\partial X_z}{\partial z} = \rho X + \frac{\partial X_x}{\partial x} + \frac{\partial X_y}{\partial y} + \frac{\partial Z_x}{\partial z} \\ &= \rho X + \lambda\frac{\partial \theta}{\partial x} + 2\mu\frac{\partial^2 u}{\partial x^2} + \mu\left(\frac{\partial^2 u}{\partial y^2} + \frac{\partial^2 v}{\partial x\,\partial y}\right) + \mu\left(\frac{\partial^2 w}{\partial x\,\partial z} + \frac{\partial^2 u}{\partial z^2}\right) \\ &= \rho X + \lambda\frac{\partial \theta}{\partial x} + \mu\left(\frac{\partial^2 u}{\partial x^2} + \frac{\partial^2 u}{\partial y^2} + \frac{\partial^2 u}{\partial z^2}\right) + \mu\left(\frac{\partial^2 u}{\partial x^2} + \frac{\partial^2 v}{\partial x\,\partial y} + \frac{\partial^2 w}{\partial x\,\partial z}\right)\end{aligned} \tag{10.77}$$

If we introduce the abbreviation

$$\nabla^2 = \frac{\partial^2}{\partial x^2} + \frac{\partial^2}{\partial y^2} + \frac{\partial^2}{\partial z^2} \tag{10.78}$$

which is a convenient operator called the Laplacian operator, nabla (or del) squared, (10.77) becomes

$$\begin{aligned}\rho\ddot{u} &= \rho X + \lambda\frac{\partial \theta}{\partial x} + \mu\nabla^2 u + \mu\frac{\partial}{\partial x}\left(\frac{\partial u}{\partial x} + \frac{\partial v}{\partial y} + \frac{\partial w}{\partial z}\right) \\ &= \rho X + (\lambda + \mu)\frac{\partial \theta}{\partial x} + \mu\nabla^2 u\end{aligned} \tag{10.79}$$

Similarly

$$\rho\ddot{v} = \rho Y + (\lambda + \mu)\frac{\partial \theta}{\partial y} + \mu\nabla^2 v \tag{10.80}$$

$$\rho\ddot{w} = \rho Z + (\lambda + \mu)\frac{\partial \theta}{\partial z} + \mu\nabla^2 w \tag{10.81}$$

Equations (10.79) to (10.81) are the equations of motion for an isotropic, elastic solid where the amount of stress is small in amplitude.

10.5 Dilatational Waves. In the absence of body forces ($\rho X = \rho Y = \rho Z = 0$), Eqs. (10.79) to (10.81) are easily solved. Differentiate (10.79) with respect to x, (10.80) with respect to y, (10.81) with respect to z, and add:

$$\rho \frac{\partial^3 u}{\partial x\, \partial t^2} + \frac{\partial^3 v}{\partial y\, \partial t^2} + \frac{\partial^3 w}{\partial z\, \partial t^2}$$
$$= (\lambda + \mu) \frac{\partial^2 \theta}{\partial x^2} + \mu \nabla^2 \frac{\partial u}{\partial x}$$
$$+ (\lambda + \mu) \frac{\partial^2 \theta}{\partial y^2} + \mu \nabla^2 \frac{\partial v}{\partial y}$$
$$+ (\lambda + \mu) \frac{\partial^2 \theta}{\partial z^2} + \mu \nabla^2 \frac{\partial w}{\partial z} \tag{10.82}$$

which simplifies to

$$\rho \frac{\partial^2 \theta}{\partial t^2} = (\lambda + \mu)\nabla^2\theta + \mu\nabla^2\theta$$
$$= (\lambda + 2\mu)\nabla^2\theta \tag{10.83}$$

It is easy to show that the following relationship satisfies this equation:

$$\theta = \theta_0 e^{i(cr - pt)} \tag{10.84}$$

where $i = (-1)^{1/2}$, provided that

$$V_p = \frac{p}{c} = \left(\frac{\lambda + 2\mu}{\rho}\right)^{1/2} \tag{10.85}$$

and

$$r = c_x x + c_y y + c_z z \tag{10.86}$$

c_x, c_y, c_z are the direction cosines of the transmission direction angles.

Equation (10.84) represents a pure change in volume θ traveling with period $2\pi/p$ and wavelength $2\pi/c$. Thus, V_p is the velocity of transmission of dilatational waves.

10.6 Shear Waves. Differentiate (10.80) with respect to x, (10.79) with respect to y, and subtract, again neglecting body forces:

$$\rho\left(\frac{\partial^3 v}{\partial x\, \partial t^2} - \frac{\partial^3 u}{\partial y\, \partial t^2}\right) = (\lambda + \mu)\left(\frac{\partial^2 \theta}{\partial x\, \partial y} - \frac{\partial^2 \theta}{\partial x\, \partial y}\right) + \mu\nabla^2\left(\frac{\partial v}{\partial x} - \frac{\partial u}{\partial y}\right) \tag{10.87}$$

$$\rho \frac{\partial^2}{\partial t^2}\left(\frac{\partial v}{\partial x} - \frac{\partial u}{\partial y}\right) = \mu\nabla^2\left(\frac{\partial v}{\partial x} - \frac{\partial u}{\partial y}\right) \tag{10.88}$$

From (10.54) and (10.55),

$$\frac{\partial v}{\partial x} - \frac{\partial u}{\partial y} = \phi_{yx} - \phi_{xy} = \omega_z \tag{10.89}$$

where ω_z is the rotation of the body about the z axis under the influence of the shearing tractions. Equation (10.88) can be written

$$\rho \ddot{\omega}_z = \mu \nabla^2 \omega_z \tag{10.90}$$

Similarly,

$$\rho \ddot{\omega}_x = \mu \nabla^2 \omega_x \tag{10.91}$$

$$\rho \ddot{\omega}_y = \mu \nabla^2 \omega_y \tag{10.92}$$

These have the solution

$$\omega = \omega_0 e^{i(c_s r - p_s t)} \tag{10.93}$$

where

$$V_s = \frac{p_s}{c_s} = \left(\frac{\mu}{\rho}\right)^{1/2} \tag{10.94}$$

This represents a pure shear distortion of wavelength $2\pi/c_s$ and period $2\pi/p_s$ traveling with the velocity V_s.

It can be shown that in an infinite, homogeneous, elastic, isotropic body, in the absence of body forces and subject to only small stresses, these are the only two types of waves which can be transmitted. It is important to note that the compressional waves always travel faster than the shear waves and that both travel more slowly the denser the medium. Density increases with depth within the earth owing to compaction and changes in composition. As a result of this, one would expect a decrease in the velocity of seismic waves with depth. However, Lamé's elastic constants λ and μ increase with depth more rapidly than density decreases. Hence, in most places, there is an increase in velocity with depth.

In fluids μ is zero. Hence liquids and gases will not transmit shear waves. In this case λ equals k, the bulk modulus, and

$$V_p = \left(\frac{\lambda}{\rho}\right)^{1/2} = \left(\frac{k}{\rho}\right)^{1/2} \tag{10.95}$$

Solids also have a bulk modulus as defined by Eq. (10.50). For solids Eq. (10.95) becomes

$$V_p = \left(\frac{\lambda + 2\mu}{\rho}\right)^{1/2} = \left(\frac{k + 4\mu/3}{\rho}\right)^{1/2} \tag{10.96}$$

Although fluids lack rigidity, they possess viscosity. Because viscosity offers resistance to shear, a highly viscous fluid behaves much like a solid to high-frequency vibrations, even to the extent of transmitting waves similar to shear waves.

The transmission of seismic waves in viscous media and in the presence of body forces is treated in advanced treatises on seismology such as Bullen (1947), Love (1911), and Ewing et al. (1957).

10.7 Reflection and Refraction. Up to this point it has been assumed that the medium through which the waves are progressing is homogeneous. If there is a boundary of some sort, transmission is altered. To understand what happens in such a case, consider a series of waves striking a thin, rigid wall in which there are one or more small holes (Figs. 10.6 to 10.8). The waves pass through the holes and beyond the barrier spread in all directions. This phenomenon led the Dutch mathematician

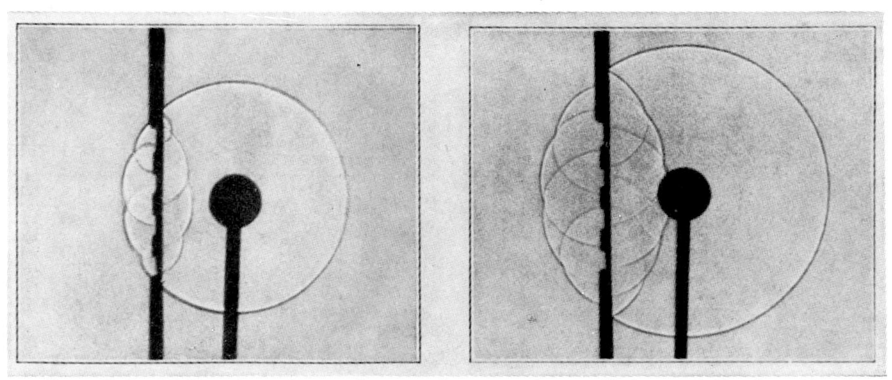

FIG. 10.6 Diffraction of sound waves by a grating. (*Foley and Souder, 1912.*)

and physicist Christian Huygens to postulate that each point on an advancing wave front acts as a new source of waves, which spread in all directions. All the infinitesimal wave fronts combine to form the single one observed. The energy transmits at right angles to the wave fronts, since the lateral components cancel one another.

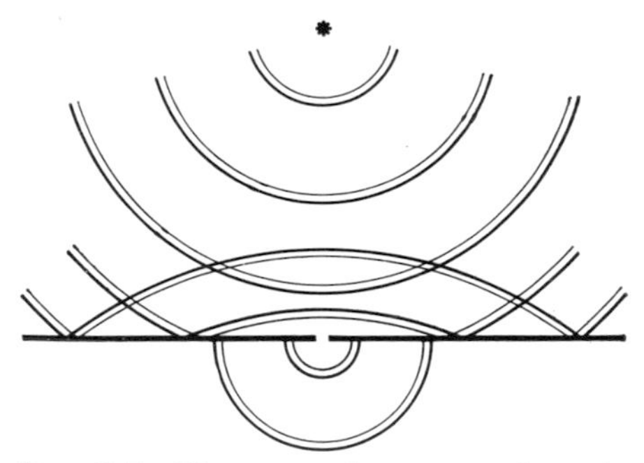

FIG. 10.7 Waves entering a space through a narrow opening spread radially as though the opening were a source.

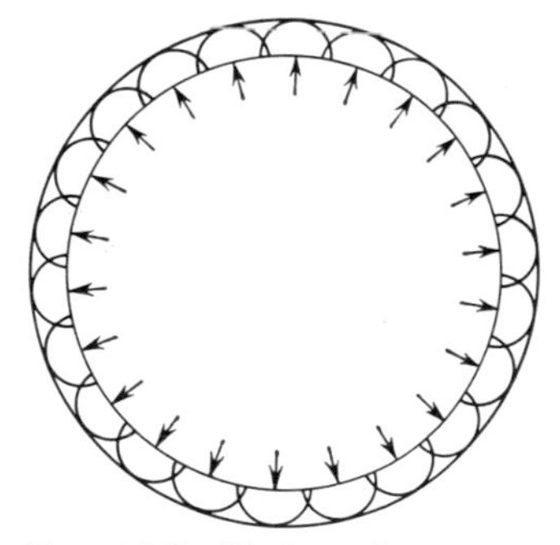

FIG. 10.8 Each point on an advancing wave front acts as a new source of waves.

In this way waves can go around corners. A wave which has entered the area shadowed from the source in this manner is spoken of as diffracted. The energy density in a diffracted pulse is always much less than in a direct pulse because it is scattered over such a wide area. In general, the longer the wavelength, the more easily a wave is diffracted.

When a wave strikes a rigid boundary, it bounces back as an echo. If we think of the energy traveling along rays perpendicular to the wave fronts, then the rays reflect in such a manner that the angle of reflection i_r in Fig. 10.9 equals the angle of incidence i_i.

If the boundary separates two materials both of which will transmit waves, then only part of the energy if reflected, the rest passing into the second medium (Fig. 10.10). In the second medium, the direction of

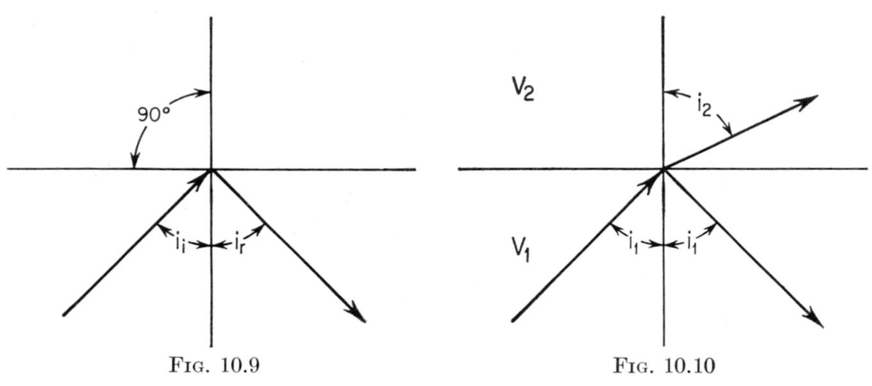

Fig. 10.9 Fig. 10.10

transmission will be changed. To see how great this change is, consider a ray traveling from a point Q_1 in a medium of velocity V_1 to a point Q_2 in a medium of velocity V_2 (Fig. 10.11). Energy spreads radially from Q_1 until it strikes the boundary at points P_a, P_b, P_c, ... According to Huygens' principle each of these points will act as a source, forming a new family of rays in medium 2. Since the energy spreads radially from each P_a, P_b, P_c, . . . , some must flow from each of these toward Q_2. But all except one of these will be canceled out by energy spreading sidewise from adjoining rays. The French mathematician Pierre de Fermat has pointed out that the path along which energy will actually flow from Q_1 to Q_2 is the minimum time path, as along this route the energy will always be a little bit ahead of energy flowing in from either side and so it will not be canceled out.

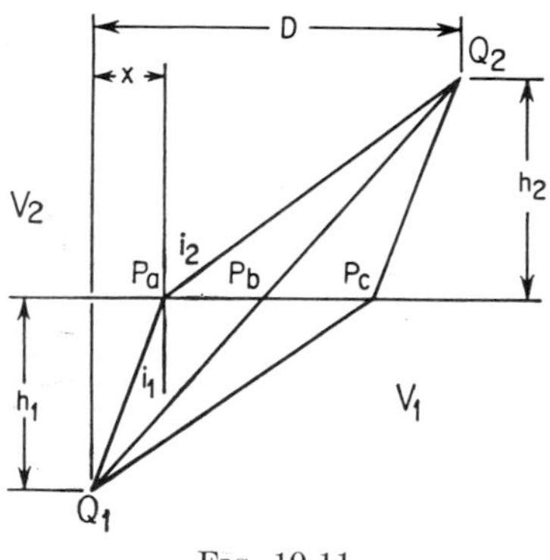

Fig. 10.11

Fermat's principle can be expressed mathematically as follows. The time for the energy to travel from Q_1 to Q_2 is

$$T = \frac{Q_1P}{V_1} + \frac{PQ_2}{V_2}$$
$$= \frac{(h_1^2 + x^2)^{1/2}}{V_1} + \frac{[h_2^2 + (D - x)^2]^{1/2}}{V_2} \qquad (10.97)$$

For T to be a minimum

$$\frac{dT}{dx} = \frac{x}{V_1(h_1^2 + x_2)^{1/2}} - \frac{D - x}{V_2[h_2^2 + (D - x)^2]^{1/2}} = 0 \qquad (10.98)$$

But

$$\frac{x}{(h_1^2 + x^2)^{1/2}} = \sin i_1 \qquad (10.99)$$

and

$$\frac{x}{[h_2^2 + (D - x)^2]^{1/2}} = \sin i_2 \qquad (10.100)$$

So (10.98) is the equivalent of

$$\frac{\sin i_1}{V_1} = \frac{\sin i_2}{V_2} \qquad (10.101)$$

Equation (10.101) is known as Snell's law. It can be derived directly from Huygens' principle as shown in Fig. 10.12. If the velocity of the

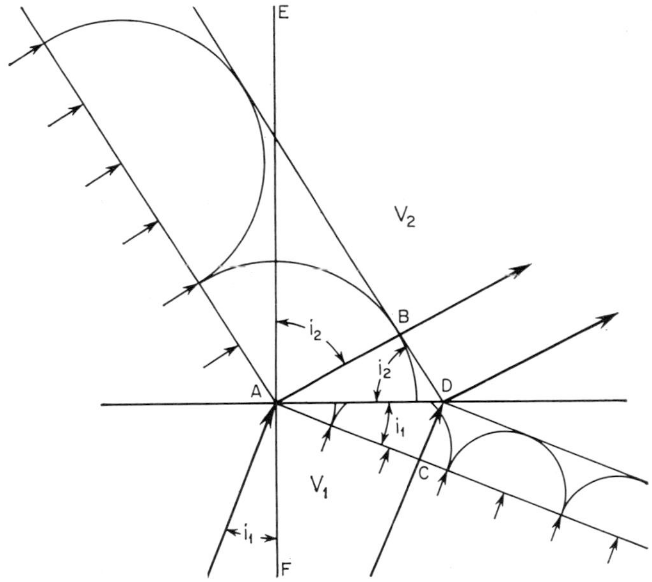

FIG. 10.12 AB and CD are perpendicular to the wave fronts BD and AC. EF is perpendicular to AD.

waves in the second medium exceeds that in the first, energy starting from A will travel the distance AB in the second medium while energy starting from C will travel the distance CD in the first medium. Since the wave fronts must be continuous across the boundary, AC and BD represent their relative directions in the two media. If T is the time required to travel this distance,

$$AB = TV_2 \qquad (10.102)$$

$$CD = TV_1 \qquad (10.103)$$

Since the rays are perpendicular to the wave fronts,

$$\frac{V_1}{V_2} = \frac{CD}{AB} = \frac{AD \sin i_1}{AD \sin i_2} = \frac{\sin i_1}{\sin i_2} \tag{10.104}$$

The process of changing the direction of transmission of the energy is called refraction. If there is a gradual change in velocity from one place to another, the rays are refracted gradually, but always according to Snell's law.

Now consider a compressional wave striking an immovable boundary at an angle of incidence i_i of 45° (Fig. 10.9). The angle of reflection must also be 45°, and all the energy will be reflected. The direction of motion of the particles excited by the incident ray is at right angles to the motion of the particles in the reflected ray. Right at the point of reflection the motion would appear to turn suddenly through a 90° angle. At an immovable boundary the particle motion at any instant must be zero. This can be expressed mathematically as

$$\Sigma u = 0 \tag{10.105}$$

$$\Sigma w = 0 \tag{10.106}$$

where u and w are the components of particle motion parallel to and perpendicular to the boundary, and the sum is taken of the incident and reflected waves. To satisfy (10.105) and (10.106) there must be something more than just an incident and a reflected compressional wave. What happens is that a reflected shear wave is also generated (Fig. 10.13). The relative amplitudes of the two reflected waves in relation to the incident wave will be such that (10.105) and (10.106) are satisfied.

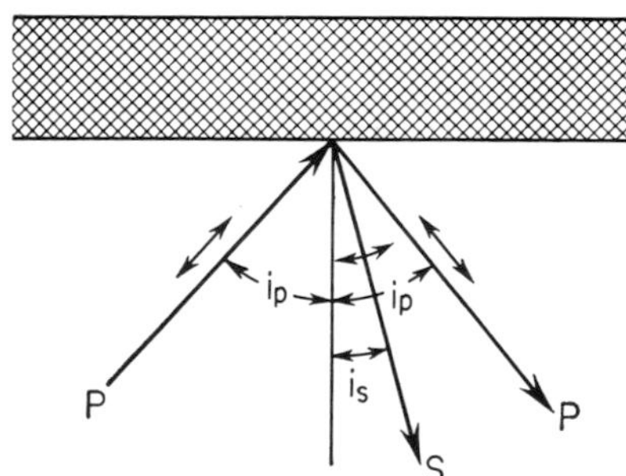

FIG. 10.13 An incident pulse produces two reflected pulses.

In the more general case of two elastic media adjoining along a plane boundary, the sum of the motions parallel to the boundary on one side must be the same as those on the other side, or there will be slipping along the boundary

$$\Sigma u_1 = \Sigma u_2 \tag{10.107}$$

Similarly for motion perpendicular to the boundary, if no gap is to open up along the boundary,

$$\Sigma w_1 = \Sigma w_2 \tag{10.108}$$

In this case four pulses can be expected (Fig. 10.14): reflected dilatational and shear waves and refracted dilatational and shear waves. Their directions of transmission are given by Snell's law:

$$\frac{\sin i_{P1}}{V_{P1}} = \frac{\sin i_{P2}}{V_{P2}} = \frac{\sin i_{S1}}{V_{S1}} = \frac{\sin i_{S2}}{V_{S2}} \tag{10.109}$$

where V_{P1}, V_{P2}, V_{S1}, V_{S2} are the compressional- and shear-wave velocities in the two media. Note that since the velocity of shear waves is always

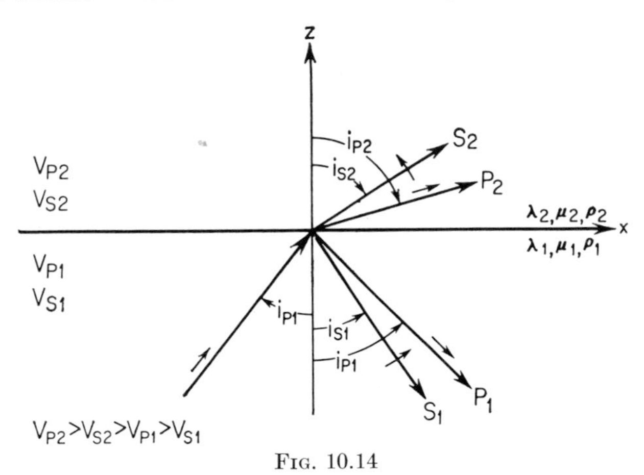

Fig. 10.14

less than that of compressional waves, they always have lesser angles of reflection and refraction.

Now consider two adjoining layers in which $V_{S1} < V_{P1} < V_{S2} < V_{P2}$. If the angle of incidence at which a shear wave strikes the boundary going from layer 1 to layer 2 is gradually increased, there will come a time when i_{P2} equals 90° (Fig. 10.15). The compressional wave in the second layer then travels parallel to the boundary. The angle of incidence at which this occurs is called the critical angle. For i_{S1} greater than the critical angle no compressional wave is produced in layer 2.

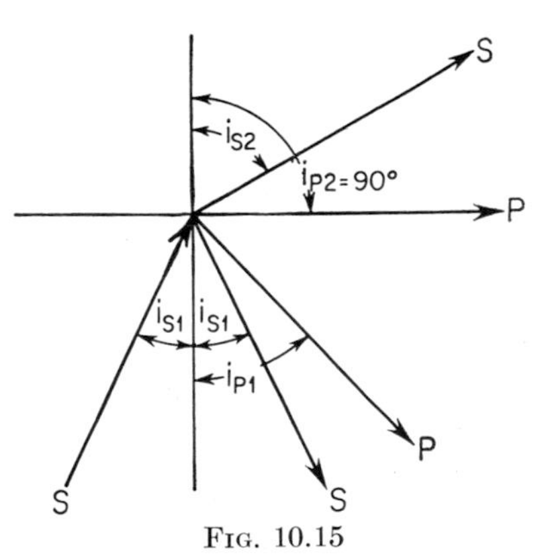

Fig. 10.15

As the angle of incidence is increased further, a second critical angle is reached at which i_{S2} becomes 90°. There are six critical angles for a boundary: the two described above, one which is reached by further increase of i_{S1} to the point where i_{P1} reaches 90°, and two for incident P waves where i_{P2} and i_{S2} are 90°. The sixth occurs for a shear wave in the second medium striking the boundary with i_{S2} so large that no reflected P wave is possible. If V_{P1} exceeds V_{S2} ($V_{S1} < V_{S2} < V_{P1} < V_{P2}$), four are reached by incident rays in layer 1 causing reflection or refraction parallel to the boundary as before. The other two cases are then for an incident S wave in layer 2 producing 90°-refracted waves in layer 1 or 90°-reflected waves in layer 2.

The critical angles are better visualized as properties of the boundary rather than the rays. They exist regardless of which direction the energy is flowing, from the high- to the low-velocity medium or in the opposite direction. Critical-angle refraction is involved in the case of a very important wave in seismology. Consider a ray which strikes a boundary at the critical angle so that it travels in the second medium parallel to the boundary (Fig. 10.16). Energy flow is possible in either direction along the ray path. Therefore, from symmetry, energy traveling parallel to a

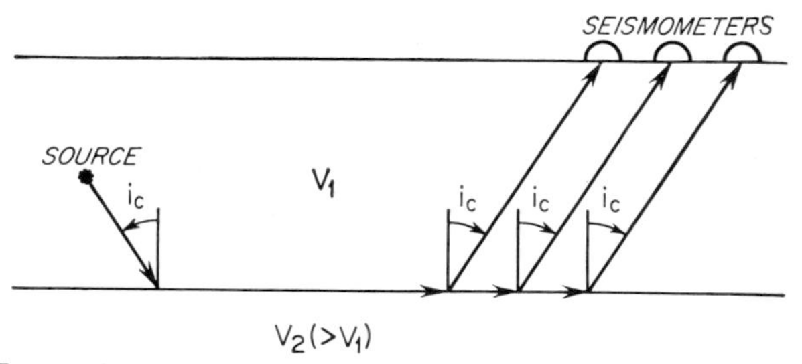

FIG. 10.16 Energy from the critically refracted ray is fed back continuously into the low-velocity medium.

boundary in a high-speed layer must be gradually fed into the low-speed layer by refraction at the critical angle. One might expect that the energy in such a pulse would be small, since the ray parallel to the boundary must divide its energy over an infinite number of rays returning to the surface. However, consideration of Huygens' principle will show that in such a case energy is fed to this ray from adjoining rays in the high-velocity medium, keeping up the strength of the ray along the boundary.

10.8 Division of Energy. Consider a dilatational wave in the xz plane incident on a plane boundary between two media as shown in Fig. 10.14. The small arrows beside the rays represent the supposed directions of particle motion in the original and each of the four resulting pulses. The amplitudes of the five rays are

$$\text{Incident } P \text{ ray} = A \exp\left[ip\left(t - \frac{x \sin i_{P1} + z \cos i_{P1}}{V_{P1}}\right)\right] = Ae^{a} \qquad (10.110)$$

$$\text{Reflected } P \text{ ray} = B_1 \exp\left[ip\left(t - \frac{x \sin i_{P1} - z \cos i_{P1}}{V_{P1}}\right)\right] = B_1 e^{b_1} \qquad (10.111)$$

$$\text{Refracted } P \text{ ray} = B_2 \exp\left[ip\left(t - \frac{x \sin i_{P2} + z \cos i_{P2}}{V_{P2}}\right)\right] = B_2 e^{b_2} \quad (10.112)$$

$$\text{Reflected } S \text{ ray} = C_1 \exp\left[ip\left(t - \frac{x \sin i_{S1} - z \cos i_{S1}}{V_{S1}}\right)\right] = C_1 e^{c_1} \quad (10.113)$$

$$\text{Refracted } S \text{ ray} = C_2 \exp\left[ip\left(t - \frac{x \sin i_{S2} + z \cos i_{S2}}{V_{S2}}\right)\right] = C_2 e^{c_2} \quad (10.114)$$

And the x and z components of the motion are

$$u_1 = Ae^a \sin i_{P1} \qquad w_1 = Ae^a \cos i_{P1} \quad (10.115)$$

$$u_2 = B_1 e^{b_1} \sin i_{P1} \qquad w_2 = -B_1 e^{b_1} \cos i_{P1} \quad (10.116)$$

$$u_3 = B_2 e^{b_2} \sin i_{P2} \qquad w_3 = B_2 e^{b_2} \cos i_{P2} \quad (10.117)$$

$$u_4 = C_1 e^{c_1} \cos i_{S1} \qquad w_4 = C_1 e^{c_1} \sin i_{S1} \quad (10.118)$$

$$u_5 = -C_2 e^{c_2} \cos i_{S2} \qquad w_5 = C_2 e^{c_2} \sin i_{S2} \quad (10.119)$$

At the boundary, the displacements on either side are given by Eqs. (10.107) and (10.108). Also the tractions Z_z and Z_x must be equal in the two media at the interface. Therefore, from (10.48) and (10.76),

$$\sum \left(\lambda_1 \theta + 2\mu_1 \frac{\partial w}{\partial z}\right)_{\mathrm{I}} = \sum \left(\lambda_2 \theta + 2\mu_2 \frac{\partial w}{\partial z}\right)_{\mathrm{II}} \quad (10.120)$$

$$\sum \mu_1 \left(\frac{\partial u}{\partial z} + \frac{\partial w}{\partial x}\right)_{\mathrm{I}} = \sum \mu_2 \left(\frac{\partial u}{\partial z} + \frac{\partial w}{\partial x}\right)_{\mathrm{II}} \quad (10.121)$$

Where for motion confined to the xz plane, as is the case here,

$$\theta = \frac{\partial u}{\partial x} + \frac{\partial w}{\partial z} \quad (10.122)$$

Substituting Eqs. (10.115) to (10.119) into (10.107) and (10.108), at $x = z = 0$, $t = 0$,

$$A \sin i_{P1} + B_1 \sin i_{P1} + C_1 \cos i_{S1} = B_2 \sin i_{P2} - C_2 \cos i_{S2} \quad (10.123)$$

$$A \cos i_{P1} - B_1 \cos i_{P1} + C_1 \sin i_{S1} = B_2 \cos i_{P2} + C_2 \sin i_{S2} \quad (10.124)$$

Substituting (10.115) to (10.119) into (10.120) and (10.121) for the same conditions,

$$-\frac{A + B_1}{V_{P1}} (\lambda_1 + 2\mu_1 \cos^2 i_{P1}) + \frac{C_1}{V_{S1}} (2\mu_1 \sin i_{S1} \cos i_{S1})$$
$$= -\frac{B_2}{V_{P2}} (\lambda_2 + 2\mu_2 \cos^2 i_{P2}) - \frac{C_2}{V_{S2}} (2\mu_2 \sin i_{S2} \cos i_{S2}) \quad (10.125)$$

$$-\frac{A - B_1}{V_{P1}} (2\mu_1 \sin i_{P1} \cos i_{P1}) + \frac{C_1}{V_{S1}} \mu_1(\cos^2 i_{S1} - \sin^2 i_{S1})$$
$$= -\frac{B_2}{V_{P2}} (2\mu_2 \sin i_{P2} \cos i_{P2}) + \frac{C_2}{V_{S2}} \mu_2(\cos^2 i_{S2} - \sin^2 i_{S2}) \quad (10.126)$$

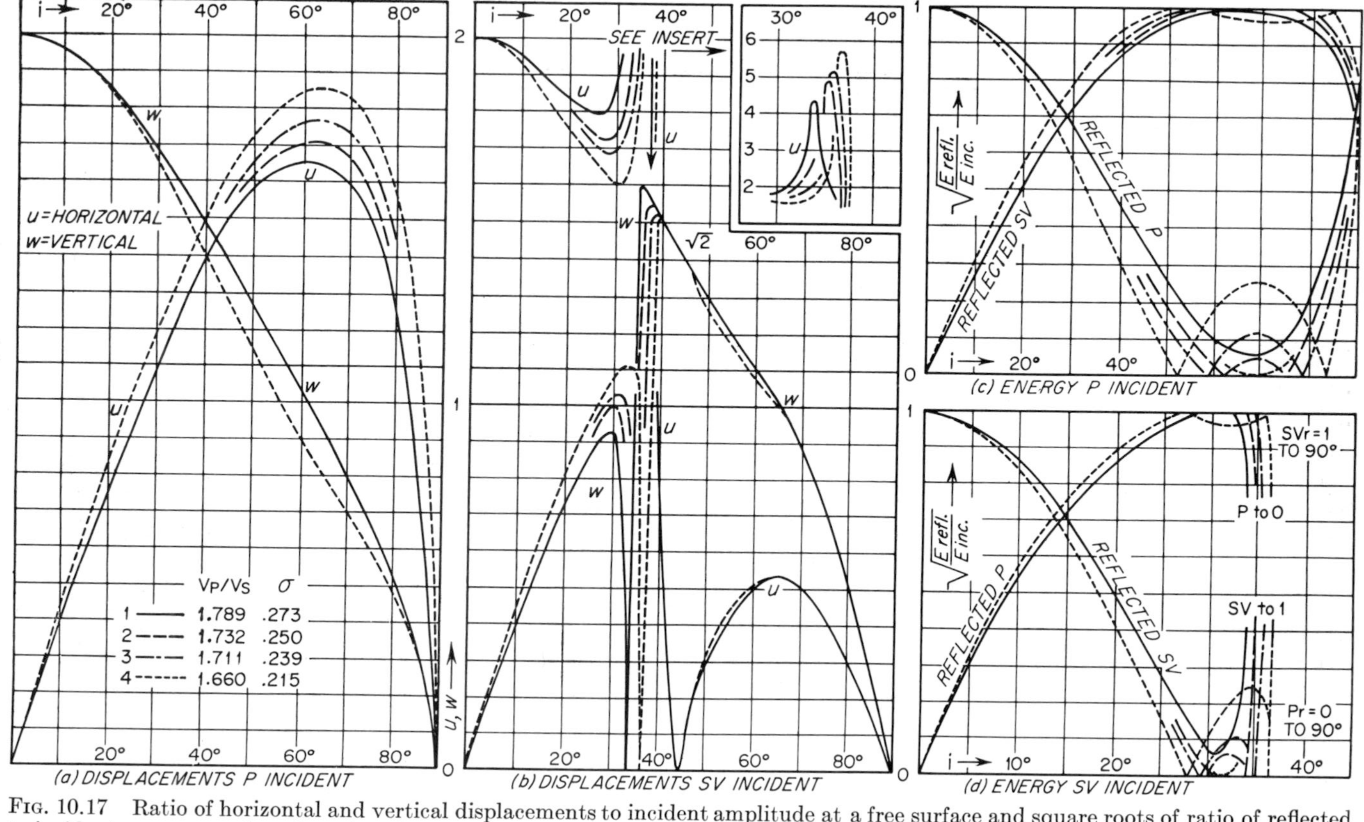

Fig. 10.17 Ratio of horizontal and vertical displacements to incident amplitude at a free surface and square roots of ratio of reflected to incident energy as a function of angle of incidence for various values of Poisson's ratio. (*Gutenberg, 1944.*)

With the use of (10.85) and (10.94) these equations can be cleared of λ and μ:

$$\frac{A + B_1}{V_{P1}} (\rho_1 V_{P1}^2 - 2\rho_1 V_{S1}^2 \sin^2 i_{P1}) - C_1\rho_1 V_{S1} \sin 2i_{S1}$$
$$= \frac{B_2}{V_P^2} (\rho_2 V_{P2}^2 - 2\rho_2 V_{S2}^2 \sin^2 i_{P2}) + C_2\rho_2 V_{S2} \sin 2i_{S2} \qquad (10.127)$$

$$\frac{-A + B_1}{V_{P1}} \rho_1 V_{S1}^2 \sin 2i_{P1} + C_1\rho_1 V_{S1} \cos 2i_{S1}$$
$$= -\frac{B_2}{V_{P2}} \rho_2 V_{S2}^2 \sin 2i_{P2} + C_2\rho_2 V_{S2} \cos 2i_{S2} \qquad (10.128)$$

Using (10.109) to simplify the terms involving $\sin^2 i_P$, (10.127) becomes

$$(A + B_1)\rho_1 V_{P1} \cos 2i_{S1} - C_1\rho_1 V_{S1} \sin 2i_{S1}$$
$$= B_2\rho_2 V_{P2} \cos 2i_{S2} + C_2\rho_2 V_{S2} \sin 2i_{S2} \qquad (10.129)$$

Equations (10.123), (10.124), (10.128), and (10.129) are four simultaneous equations in which B_1/A, B_2/A, B_3/A, and B_4/A are the unknowns. Given any set of values for the densities, the velocities, and the angle of incidence, the amplitude of the separate components can easily be computed.

Gutenberg (1944) has calculated the energy which each pulse would carry and plotted it as a function of the angle of incidence for several different ratios of velocities of the two media under a number of different conditions (Fig. 10.17).

10.9 Surface Waves. In deriving the above equations it was assumed that the wave fronts were plane and that the motions of the ground were so small that boundaries were undisturbed by the passage of the waves. In actuality neither condition is perfectly fulfilled. There are many types of waves which can exist in the vicinity of a boundary, and some of these will be generated by the incidence of dilatational or shear waves on a boundary. By definition, a surface wave is one whose amplitude dies off as a function of distance from an interface along which it travels. The first type of surface wave to be recognized was predicted by Lord Rayleigh in 1885. It consists of an elliptical particle vibration, usually retrograde in sense and with the vertical component stronger than the horizontal. Lamb (1904) showed that if a free surface of a semi-infinite elastic solid is disturbed, relatively weak dilatational and shear pulses and a strong Rayleigh pulse will be generated in the medium. Later investigators (Love, 1911; Stoneley, 1924; Fu, 1947; Ewing et al., 1957) showed that the Rayleigh pulse at a free surface is only one of a large family of waves which can travel along nearly any boundary separating elastic media. Such pulses along nonfree surfaces are called

Stoneley waves. Stoneley waves can be considered to be either retrograde or direct, depending on how you view them (Fig. 6.7). The equation for the existance of Rayleigh waves is

$$S_R^3 - 8S_R^2 + (24 - 16P_S)S_R - 16(1 - P_S) = 0 \qquad (10.130)$$

where $S_R = V_R^2/V_S^2$ and $P_S = V_S^2/V_P^2$.

For Stoneley waves and various types of pseudo-Rayleigh waves which it has been shown can exist along the surface of layered media such as the earth, the equations are more complex.

The whole Rayleigh wave class consists of motion in a plane perpendicular to the surface and parallel to the direction of transmission. On seismograms, motion at right angles to this is equally common. One such type of wave has been described by Love (1911). Love waves are

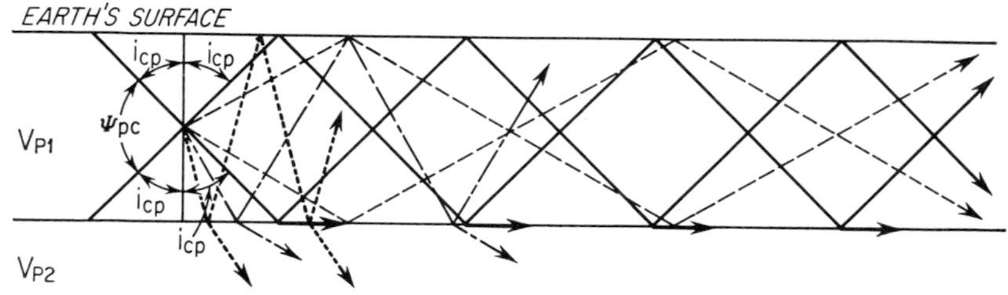

FIG. 10.18 Energy radiated in the segment ψ_{pc} is confined to the layer.

surface shear waves which travel in a thin surface layer and the vicinity of its lower boundary. Their equation of existence is

$$\tan sH = \frac{\rho_2 V_{S2}}{\rho_1 V_{S1}} \left(\frac{V_{S2}^2 - V_L^2}{V_L^2 - V_{S1}^2} \right)^{1/2} \qquad (10.131)$$

where

$$s = \frac{2\pi}{L} \left(\frac{V_L^2}{V_{S1}^2} - 1 \right)^{1/2} \qquad (10.132)$$

H is the thickness of the layer, L is the wavelength, V_L is the velocity of Love waves, and ρ_1, ρ_2, V_{S1}, and V_{S2} are the densities and shear-wave velocities in the surface layer and underlying medium, respectively.

One reason that surface waves are so strong in the earth is that much of the energy generated in a near surface layer can never escape to the deeper layers. This is caused by the rapid increase in seismic-wave velocity with depth. If energy is generated in a low-velocity layer, only that cone of rays striking the boundaries at not greater than the critical angle is fed into the second medium (Fig. 10.18). For compressional rays, the fraction of the energy completely confined is ψ_{pc}/π, where

$$\psi_{pc} = \pi - 2i_{cp} \qquad (10.133)$$

Snell's law, (10.109), can in this case be written in the form

$$\sin i_{cp} = \frac{V_{P1}}{V_{P2}} \tag{10.134}$$

so that (10.133) becomes

$$\psi_{pc} = \pi - 2 \sin^{-1} \frac{V_{P1}}{V_{P2}} \tag{10.135}$$

Similarly for shear waves, an even larger fraction of the generated energy is confined to the surface layer. Even the waves striking the boundary at less than the critical angle contribute substantially to the waves in the layer, as only part of their energy refracts into the deeper layer at each incidence on the boundary, the rest being reflected up toward the surface. Thus, even if no surface waves were produced at the boundary, there would be a family of pulses spreading outward along the layer.

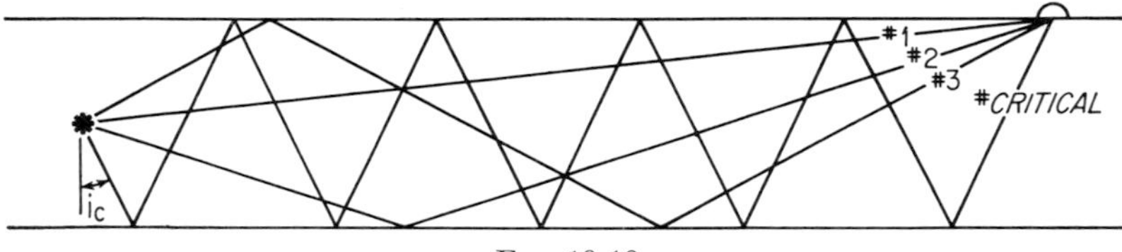

Fig. 10.19

At a large distance Δ from the source, this family of pulses would begin with the direct pulse from the source. It would be followed by a series of pulses, each having undergone one more reflection than the preceding one (Fig. 10.19). Finally, there would arrive a pulse whose angle of incidence at each encounter with the surface was close to the critical angle. Later-arriving pulses would be weak because of their loss of energy into the deeper layer. Toward the end of the arrival of this series of pulses, the individual arrivals would overlap so as to be indistinguishable from one another, and their paths and velocities would be such that they would arrive together with the surface waves generated by their striking the boundaries of the layer. The particle motions of the body waves would also be similar to the surface-wave motions, so that for practical purposes they may be considered to be the same waves.

Because they must be formed by multiple reflections as described above, surface waves will arrive as an extended series of ground motions in contrast to the sharper beginnings and endings of conventional body waves. This spreading of the pulses would be expected for another reason. Surface waves travel near the surface, but the energy is actually distributed over an appreciable depth into the earth. Because of this, energy of long wavelength must penetrate to greater depth than short-wavelength energy. As velocity increases with depth in the earth, the longer-wavelength energy will travel faster than the short-wavelength energy and will arrive first at a distant station. The variation of velocity with wavelength is called dispersion. The observed dispersion of surface waves can be used to investigate the variation of velocity with depth at the earth's surface (Jeffreys, 1952). Dispersion is so pronounced a characteristic of surface waves that they can often be recognized from body waves because of it.

CHAPTER 11

DATA DERIVED FROM SEISMOLOGY

11.1 Travel-time Curves. In the last chapter we saw something of how seismic waves are transmitted. The purpose of this chapter will be to show how that knowledge has been used to gain information on the interior of the earth. Let us consider for a moment what would be observed if the earth were a homogeneous, elastic, isotropic sphere and an earthquake originated at some point on its surface (Fig. 11.1*a*). Lamb

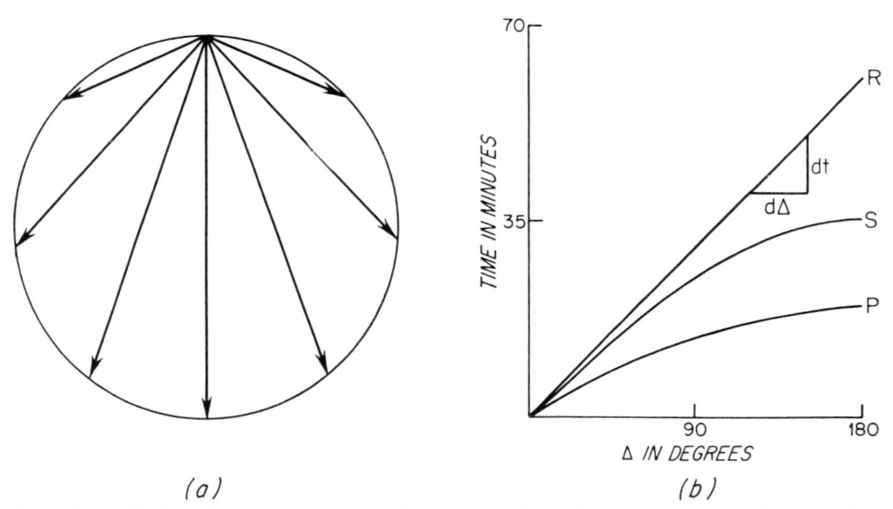

Fig. 11.1 Paths of rays and travel-time curves for a homogeneous earth assuming that the velocities of seismic waves are $V_P = 11$ km/sec, $V_S = 6$ km/sec, $V_R = 5.5$ km/sec.

(1904) has shown that the elastic waves would spread in all directions through the earth as dilatational P and shear S pulses and over the surface as a Rayleigh R pulse. If we make a plot of arrival time versus great-circle distance along the surface measured in degrees from the line joining the center of the earth and the epicenter, it will look like Fig. 11.1*b*. Such a graph is called a travel-time or time-distance curve.

Travel-time plots of this sort play an important role in seismology. Note that the slope of the travel-time curve of R represents its velocity:

$$\frac{d\Delta}{dt} = V_R \tag{11.1}$$

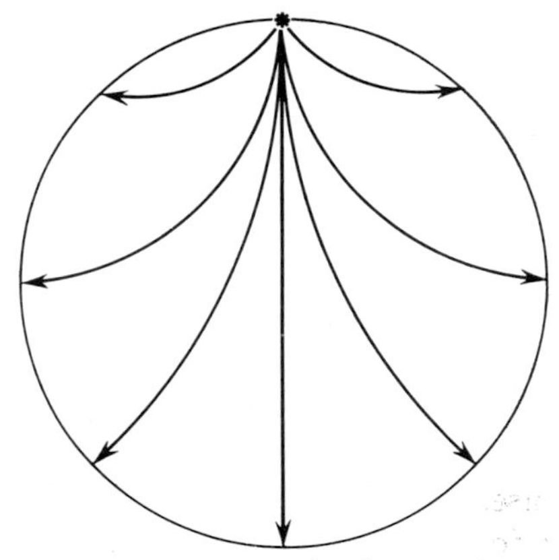

FIG. 11.2 Ray paths in a sphere where velocity increases with depth.

Similarly, the slopes of the P and S graphs correspond to the apparent velocities of these pulses, but only at the origin to their true velocities.

11.2 Paths in the Earth. The actual earth is not so simple as this. For one thing the velocity of transmission in general increases with depth. As a result the ray paths are curved as shown in Fig. 11.2. The pulses arriving at the largest distances have penetrated most deeply into the earth. The velocities at each depth can be calculated from the times of transmission. The actual variation of velocity with depth is shown in Fig. 11.3.

When a seismogram is studied, it is seen to consist of many more pulses than simply P, S, and R. When certain of these pulses are examined,

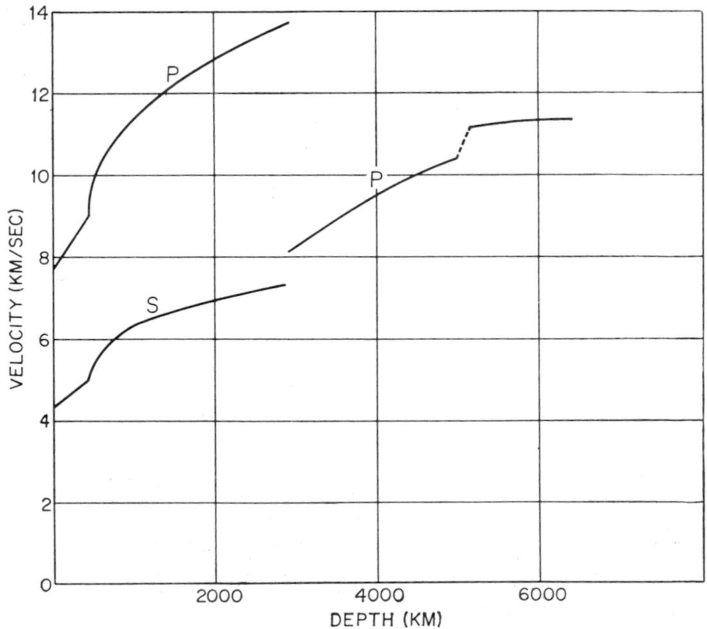

FIG. 11.3 Variation of V_P and V_S with depth in the earth. (*After Bullen, 1947.*)

they are found to arrive at about twice the time of similar pulses arriving at half the distance and hence are concluded to be once reflected at the earth's surface (Fig. 11.4). Such a pulse is given the symbol *PP* if compressional, *SS* if shear, and *PS* or *SP* if compressional before or after reflection and shear over the other half of its journey. Two once-reflected compressional pulses are possible at any point, one reflected between the epicenter and recording point and the other reflected at the antipode of this point. Although no generally accepted designation exists for the second of these pulses, the designation (*PP*), (*SS*), and (*PS*) or (*SP*) will be used here. The parentheses represent transmission the long way around the earth. Twice- and thrice-reflected pulses such as *PPP*, (*PPP*), *PPPP*, *PPS*, etc., are also observed.

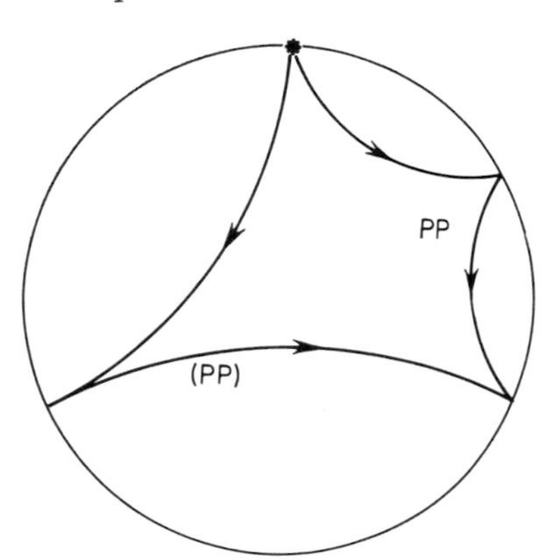

FIG. 11.4 Paths of once-reflected seismic rays.

11.3 Core of the Earth. The *P* pulse is not recorded everywhere. At distances larger than about 103° it is generally absent. At lesser distances a pulse is observed arriving at a time which corresponds to reflection at 2,900 km, the maximum depth of penetration reached by the *P* arriving at 103°. The conclusion is that there is a core within the earth about 3,470 km in radius, and that its elastic properties are markedly different from those of the rocks which surround it (Fig. 11.5). The boundary of the core is known as the Gutenberg-Wiechert discontinuity. Wiechert was the first man to predict the existence of this boundary, which he did in 1897, and Gutenberg first determined its depth in 1912. The symbol *c* is used to represent reflection at the outer side of the boundary of the core. Thus *PcP* is a *P* pulse reflected as a *P* at this discontinuity. *PcS* is a *P* reflected as an *S*. More complicated pulses such as *PcPPcP* are occasionally observed.

The part of the earth outside the core with the exception of the uppermost layers is called the mantle. The uppermost layers are separately designated as the crust of the earth. The evidence for the existence of a boundary separating the mantle from the crust will be given in Sec. 11.5.

Waves diffracted around the core are occasionally observed at greater than 103°, but with only very low amplitudes. The area behind the core where *P* is rarely observed is called the shadow zone (Fig. 11.6).

Where the initial pulse strikes the boundary of the core, only part of the energy is reflected. The rest is refracted into the core. At the far side it again divides, part staying in the core and part being refracted back into the mantle (Fig. 11.5). The symbol K is used for transmission through the core. Thus a P pulse refracted into the core at its first incidence on the Gutenberg-Wiechert discontinuity and out again at its second incidence is PKP. This is usually abbreviated P'. K is a compressional pulse. Shear waves which have traveled through the outer part of the core have never been observed. It can therefore be concluded that the core more nearly resembles a liquid than a solid, except for its central part, about which little is known. The pressures and temperatures which are believed to exist in the core are so much greater than what can be reproduced at the earth's surface that one is not justified in assuming that the rock is what we call fluid under surface conditions. It is better to say that the core behaves like a liquid with respect to the transmission of elastic waves, and not say specifically that it is a liquid.

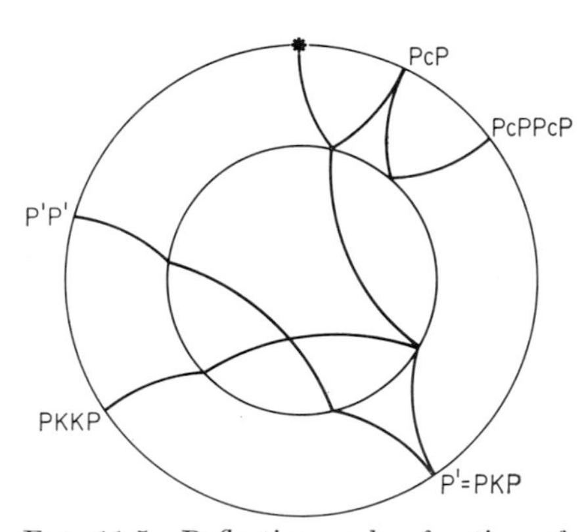

FIG. 11.5 Reflection and refraction of seismic waves at the Gutenberg-Wiechert discontinuity.

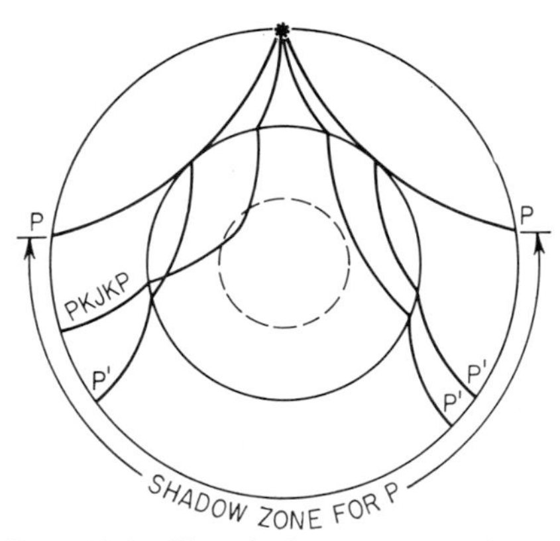

FIG. 11.6 The shadow zone produced by the core and the paths of typical rays penetrating it.

Pulses traveling through the mantle as S may be refracted as K through the core and reach the far side of the earth as SKS or SKP. $PKKP$ is a pulse which has been reflected once inside the core. Pulses such as PKS, $P'P'$, $SKKP$, and $PcPP'$ are also observed.

The velocity of compressional waves just inside the boundary of the core is less than that in the mantle; therefore, the refraction is of such a nature that the shadow zone of P is not filled in by P' pulses (Fig. 11.6). There is a focusing effect at certain distances which increases the intensity of P', the core behaving like a lens. At other distances P' is weak or unobserved.

Within the core there are at least two layers, perhaps more than this. The nature and effects of the inner core are still not entirely understood. It is probable that most or all of this central body is solid (Bullen, 1950). The symbols I and J have been proposed for compressional and shear pulses in the inner core. Their whole paths are indicated by such symbols as *PKIKP* and *PKJKP*.

11.4 Paths for Deep-focus Sources. Up to this point it has been assumed that the source of the rays was on the surface of the earth. If the source is deep enough, three pulses are frequently observed for every one listed so far. For each direct pulse recorded there is a corresponding pulse reflected from the earth's surface near the epicenter, starting as either a compressional or a shear wave (Fig. 11.7). This initial pulse is known as *p* or *s*, the lower case letters being used to distinguish pulses which leave the focus going upward instead of downward. At short distances there may be no *P*, only a *p* pulse, since a ray starting horizontally from a focus must travel some distance before it strikes the surface. There is also a minimum distance for *pP*, *sP*, *PP*, and all other reflected pulses.

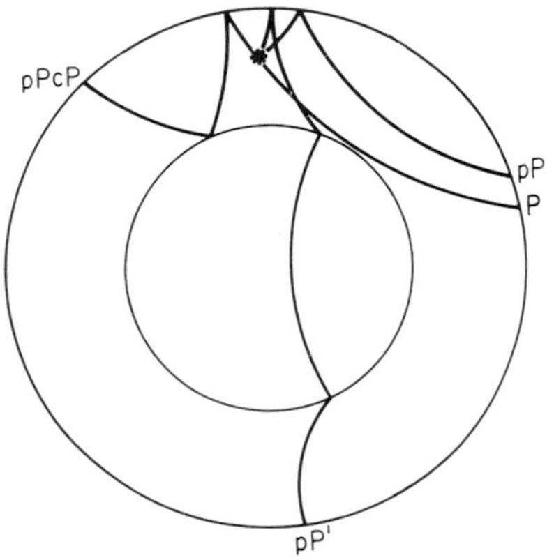

Fig. 11.7 Typical ray paths for a focus at greater than normal depth.

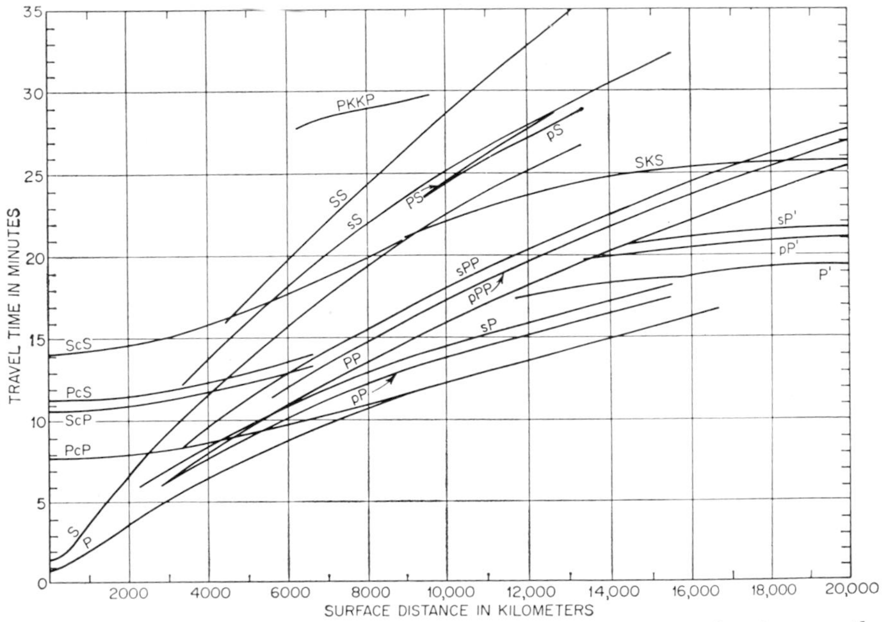

Fig. 11.8 Calculated travel-time curves of some of the commonest pulses for an earthquake at 400-km focal depth. (*After Gutenberg and Richter, 1936a.*)

As there is no limit to the number of times a pulse can be reflected and refracted, there is no theoretical limit to the possible pulses. However, each time a ray strikes a boundary, its energy divides among the several pulses formed, and the farther it travels, the more it is absorbed, so that in practice only a limited number of pulses are observed (Fig. 11.8).

11.5 Surface Layers. At the surface of the earth, the rocks are varied in nature. Beneath the sedimentary veneer the igneous and metamorphic basement consists of a complicated assemblage of formations. Although more uniform in their elastic properties than the surface rocks, the various igneous and metamorphic rocks still differ greatly from one another. There is no evidence that a tendency to greater simplicity exists as depth is increased. Nevertheless, because of our inability to examine the interior of the earth in detail, we are forced to overlook most

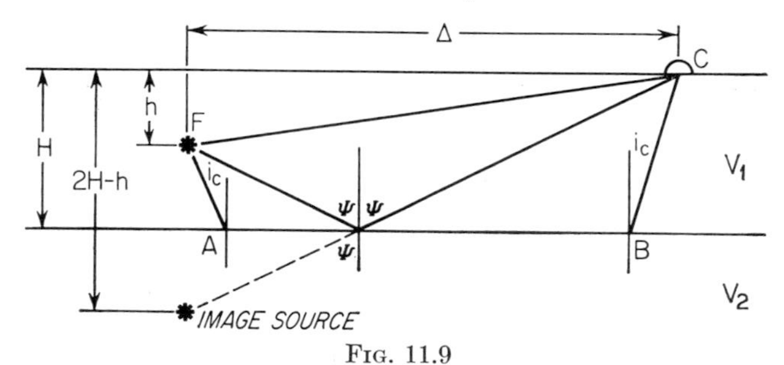

FIG. 11.9

of the structural relationships which presumably exist, and lump the rocks together in large units which can be distinguished by the methods at present at our disposal.

If the earth outside the core were uniform in composition and the velocity of seismic waves depended only on depth, near the epicenter there would be only one unreflected compressional pulse recorded from any earthquake and its time of arrival would be a function of epicentral distance and focal depth only. If the earth's curvature and the velocity variation with depth are neglected, the time of arrival of a pulse traveling with velocity V_1 at a distance Δ and starting from a depth of focus h would be

$$T_D = \left(\frac{\Delta^2 + h^2}{V_1^2}\right)^{1/2} \tag{11.2}$$

For actual earthquakes the travel-time curves of both P and S are more complex than this. It is apparent that the outermost part of the earth is composed of several layers. Consider what would be observed if an earthquake occurred at a depth h within a layer of thickness H and velocity V_1, overlying a layer of velocity V_2 (Fig. 11.9). (The shear waves will be neglected in this discussion. The arguments presented apply to them in the same manner as to the dilatational waves.) Not only would there be a direct P pulse observed arriving at the time given by Eq. (11.2), but also a reflected pulse at time

$$T_{RL} = \frac{[\Delta^2 + (2H - h)^2]^{1/2}}{V_1} \tag{11.3}$$

As Δ increases, the difference between T_D and T_{RL} decreases, until the two pulses become indistinguishable, so that the reflected pulse is rarely recognized. On the seismograms even near the epicenter it tends to be obscured by the earlier arriving P, S, and surface-wave pulses.

Consider, however, the ray striking the interface at the critical angle i_c. In the second medium it must be refracted at 90°, parallel to the interface, and hence must be continuously being refracted back to the surface all along the boundary. Such pulses are observed from earthquakes.

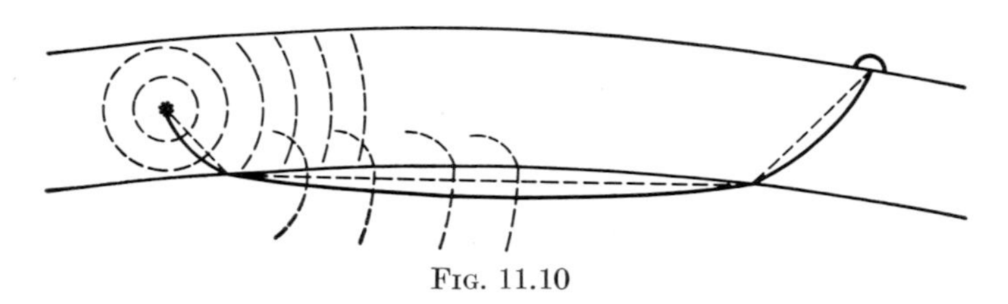

FIG. 11.10

One may wonder why the single ray which arrives at exactly the critical angle is able to provide enough energy to be fed back to the surface with appreciable amplitude over any considerable distance. There are three factors which may explain this. First, because of the velocity gradient within the earth, the rays do not travel in straight lines, but along arcs, so that the refracted rays do not strike the interface at exactly the critical angle of incidence (Fig. 11.10). Also since the earth is round, the rays travel along chords, and not exactly along the interface. Third, as shown in Sec. 10.6 Huygens' principle provides for a continuous feeding of energy into the ray parallel to the boundary.

The time of the refracted pulse will be (Fig. 11.9)

$$\begin{aligned} T_{RR} &= \frac{FA}{V_1} + \frac{AB}{V_2} + \frac{BC}{V_1} = \frac{H - h}{V_1 \cos i_c} + \frac{\Delta - (2H - h)\tan i_c}{V_2} + \frac{H}{V_1 \cos i_c} \\ &= \frac{2H - h}{V_1 \cos i_c} + \frac{\Delta}{V_2} - \frac{(2H - h)\sin i_c}{V_2 \cos i_c} \end{aligned} \tag{11.4}$$

But from Snell's law,

$$\frac{\sin i_c}{V_1} = \frac{\sin 90°}{V_2} = \frac{1}{V_2} \tag{11.5}$$

Therefore,

$$T_{RR} = \frac{2H - h}{V_1 \cos i_c} + \frac{\Delta}{V_2} - \frac{(2H - h)\sin^2 i_c}{V_1 \cos i_c} = \frac{\Delta}{V_2} + \frac{(2H - h)\cos i_c}{V_1}$$
$$= \frac{\Delta}{V_2} + \frac{2H - h}{V_1}\left(1 - \frac{V_1^2}{V_2^2}\right)^{1/2} \qquad (11.6)$$

Figure 11.11 gives the travel-time curve for such a pulse. Note that at large distances the slope of the travel-time curve for the direct pulse approaches $1/V_1$ whereas the slope of the curve for the refracted pulse is $1/V_2$. There is no refracted pulse at short distances. The refracted travel-time curve starts at the distance where the reflected pulse arrives from a reflection at the critical angle. At this critical distance the two have identical paths. At short distances the direct pulse arrives first. The term "critical distance" is also sometimes used to designate the distance at which the refracted pulse starts being the first arrival.

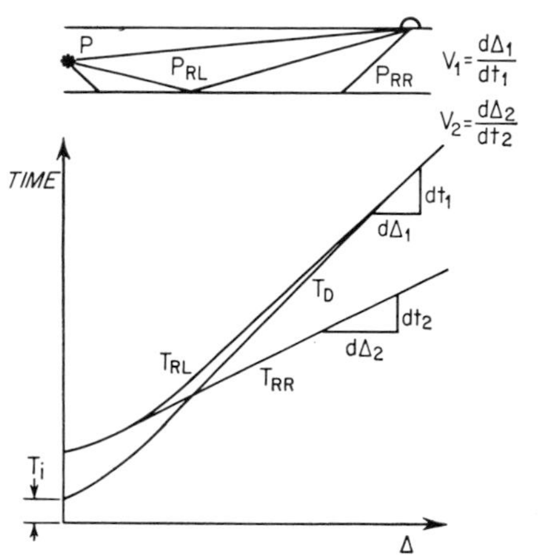

FIG. 11.11 Ray paths and travel-time curve for pulses from a source within a surface layer.

In theory, the depth of focus can be calculated from the arrival time of the direct pulse. Unfortunately, Eq. (11.2) is sensitive to the value of h only where Δ is small. Since earthquakes rarely occur close to a seismic observatory, and since their distance can rarely be found with great exactness, the value of h is usually hard to determine. Most earthquakes occur within 50 km of the surface. Estimates of the average depth for shallow earthquakes vary. Gutenberg (1951) gives 18 km; Jeffreys (1952), 35 km. Knowing h, Eq. (11.6) can be solved for H.

The situation becomes more complicated if more than one layer is present (Fig. 11.12). In this case, if the waves originate in the upper layer, equations giving H and h can be derived as before. It is common for the focus to be in the second layer. In this case h is even more difficult to find, but H_1 and H_2 are easier to get. If V_2 is considerably greater than V_1 and Δ greatly exceeds H_1, ψ_2 will be close to 90°. Then the time of the once-refracted pulse will be almost exactly the same as if the earthquake had been at a depth H_1. From Eq. (11.6),

$$T_{RR} = \frac{\Delta}{V_2} + \frac{H_1 \cos \psi_1}{V_1} = \frac{\Delta}{V_2} + \frac{H_1}{V_1}\left(1 - \frac{V_1^2}{V_2^2}\right)^{1/2} \qquad (11.7)$$

from which H_1 can be found. When H_1 is known, h can be found from the intercept time T_i where the travel time cuts the zero time axis (Fig. 11.11). This is the time for the pulse to travel straight upward from the focus to the surface:

$$T_i = \frac{H_1}{V_1} + \frac{h - H_1}{V_2} \tag{11.8}$$

In practice, sufficient data are rarely available to determine T_i accurately.

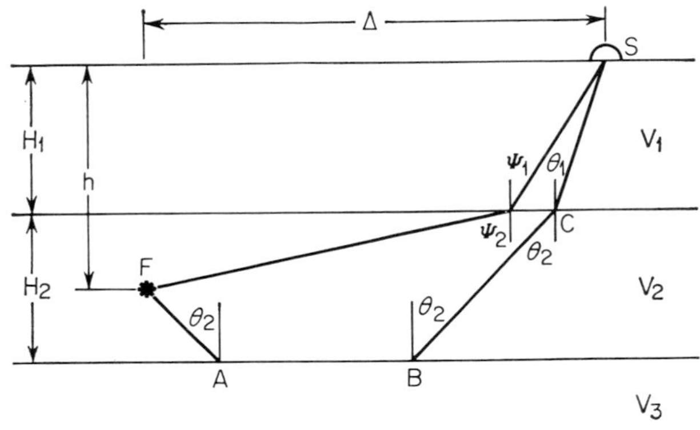

FIG. 11.12

The pulse penetrating to the third layer will arrive after a time

$$\begin{aligned} T_{RR} &= \frac{FA}{V_2} + \frac{AB}{V_3} + \frac{BC}{V_2} + \frac{CS}{V_3} \\ &= \frac{H_1 + H_2 - h}{V_2 \cos \theta_2} + \frac{\Delta - (2H_2 + H_1 - h) \tan \theta_2 - H_1 \tan \theta_1}{V_3} \\ &\qquad + \frac{H_2}{V_2 \cos \theta_2} + \frac{H_1}{V_1 \cos \theta_1} \end{aligned} \tag{11.9}$$

which, as in the case of (11.6), reduces to

$$\begin{aligned} T_{RR} &= \frac{\Delta}{V_3} + \frac{H_1 \cos \theta_1}{V_1} + \frac{(2H_2 + H_1 - h) \cos \theta_2}{V_2} \\ &= \frac{\Delta}{V_3} + \frac{H_1}{V_1}\left(1 - \frac{V_1^2}{V_3^2}\right)^{1/2} + \frac{2H_2 + H_1 - h}{V_2}\left(1 - \frac{V_2^2}{V_3^2}\right)^{1/2} \end{aligned} \tag{11.10}$$

From this, H_2 can be found knowing H_1 and h. The travel-time curve is similar to Fig. 11.11, except that the slopes of the two curves are $1/V_2$ and $1/V_3$ instead of $1/V_1$ and $1/V_2$. It should be noted than any error in h is carried forward and produces a corresponding error in the computed value of H_2.

Using the principles outlined above, it has been found that there is a crust on the outside of the mantle of the earth up to 50 km thick. Its thickness varies, generally being greatest under mountain ranges. Under the continents where it is most easily measured the thickness is most commonly from 25 to 40 km. Because of the difficulty of making measurements at sea, relatively few have been made there until recently, but these few indicate that the crust is thinner under the oceans than on land (see, for instance, Ewing et al., 1950, 1954; Officer and Ewing, 1954; Gutenberg, 1955).

The crust is distinguished from the mantle by its lower seismic-wave velocities. At short distances the earliest waves to arrive from earthquakes indicate a velocity of compressional waves beneath the sedimentary veneer of around 6.0 $\pm$ 0.5 km per sec. Because this velocity closely approximates what would be expected for granite at temperatures and pressures expected at shallow depth, this upper layer has been called granitic, or sometimes sialic after silicon and aluminum, two of the principal elements in granite. There is much doubt whether the basement is predominantly granite in composition, as where it is exposed, it is seen to contain a large percentage of more basic rocks. At intermediate distances a refracted pulse with a velocity of 6.5 to 7.0 km per sec is often observed (Gutenberg, 1955). This has been interpreted as representing a deeper layer of different material, and the corresponding layer is called basaltic or simatic (for silicon and magnesium), largely because basaltic composition rocks have higher seismic-wave velocities than granite. This layer is not always recognized on travel-time profiles, and there is some question if it even exists as a separate entity. The alternative hypothesis is that there may be a gradual change in the basicity of the crustal rocks going downward without any sharp, uniformly distributed boundary.

At large distances (beyond about 100 km on the continents) the first arrival is a ray refracted through a deeper layer with a velocity in the range 7.6 to 8.4 km per sec, but at most places having a value of 8.1 $\pm$ 0.1 km per sec. The existence of this layer is well established. It has been recognized all over the world, and its upper surface is known as the Mohorovicic discontinuity, after its discoverer. By analogy with the change in composition from the granitic to the basaltic layers, it has been suggested that beneath this boundary the rocks are predominantly ultrabasic. There is, however, little reason to suppose that the rocks at these depths are any less variegated than at the surface. It would be better to think of the layers by names which infer less as to their composition. The Mohorovicic discontinuity is the bottom of the crust. Beneath this point velocity is believed to increase to the boundary of the core without any additional jumps, with the possible exception of one change at about 950 km (Birch, 1952; Macelwane, 1951).

Within the crust there is a further difficulty in delineating the layers which are present. Gutenberg (1952) has pointed out that the first arrivals from explosions indicate a near-surface velocity of 5.9 to 6.5 km per sec. This is inconsistent with data obtained from natural earthquakes, whose first arrivals at short distances come in at around 5.6 km per sec. The principal difference in the paths involved is that the earthquakes originate at a depth, on the average, of about 18 km while the explosions are on the surface. Gutenberg has suggested that this anomalous condition may result from the presence of a low-velocity layer in the crust. Such a layer would form a channel along which seismic waves would travel without losing energy by refraction (Fig. 11.13). If an earthquake originated in such a layer, rays striking the upper or lower boundary with angles of incidence greater than the critical angle would be unable to leave the layer. Thus, most of the energy of the shock would spread out horizontally in the layer. Some energy would be lost from this bound wave by reflection and refraction at inhomogeneities within the layer; and since the layer is thin, it would vibrate as a whole, and thus disturb the surface to a certain extent, accounting for the observed velocity of waves from earthquakes of 5.6 km per sec. Rays refracted into the surface layer near the source might be quickly dispersed and absorbed in the inhomogeneous surface layer, whereas those penetrating to the 7.0 km per sec layer would be frequently observed when they are refracted back to the surface.

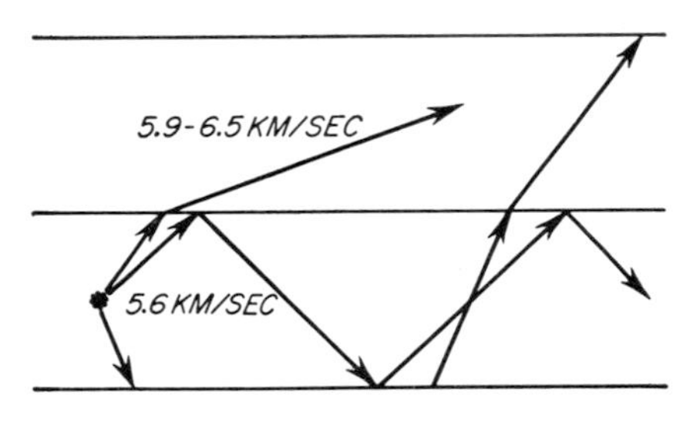

FIG. 11.13 A low-velocity layer between two high-velocity layers would form a channel for the transmission of seismic energy.

11.6 "Sofar" Channel. A low-velocity layer with discontinuous boundaries is not necessary for this type of phenomenon. If the velocity has a minimum at some depth, any seismic energy generated at a depth close to this will tend to be confined to the channel (Fig. 11.14). Because of the increase in velocity going either upward or downward, every ray tends to be returned to the minimum velocity level, and after crossing it tends to be returned again.

Such a minimum-velocity layer exists in the oceans at a depth of about 4,000 ft (Ewing and Worzel, 1948). The velocity V of compressional waves in water depends on the temperature T and pressure P, which vary with the depth D. From Eqs. (10.95) and (10.50)

$$V = \left(\frac{k}{\rho}\right)^{1/2} = \left(\frac{P}{\theta\rho}\right)^{1/2} \tag{11.11}$$

where k is bulk modulus, ρ is density, and θ is the cubical dilatation, the change of volume of the water produced by the pressure P. To a first approximation, P is a linear function of depth while ρ depends only on temperature, so that for small-amplitude pressure fluctuations at any depth,

$$\begin{aligned} V &= \left[\frac{P_0(1 + fD)}{\theta\rho_0/(1 + T/273)}\right]^{1/2} \\ &= \left[\frac{P_0}{\theta\rho_0}(1 + fD)\left(1 + \frac{T}{273}\right)\right]^{1/2} \\ &= V_0(1 + fD)^{1/2}\left(1 + \frac{T}{273}\right)^{1/2} \end{aligned} \tag{11.12}$$

where P_0, ρ_0, and V_0 are the pressure, density, and velocity at the surface (at 0°C) and f is the coefficient giving the rate of increase of pressure with

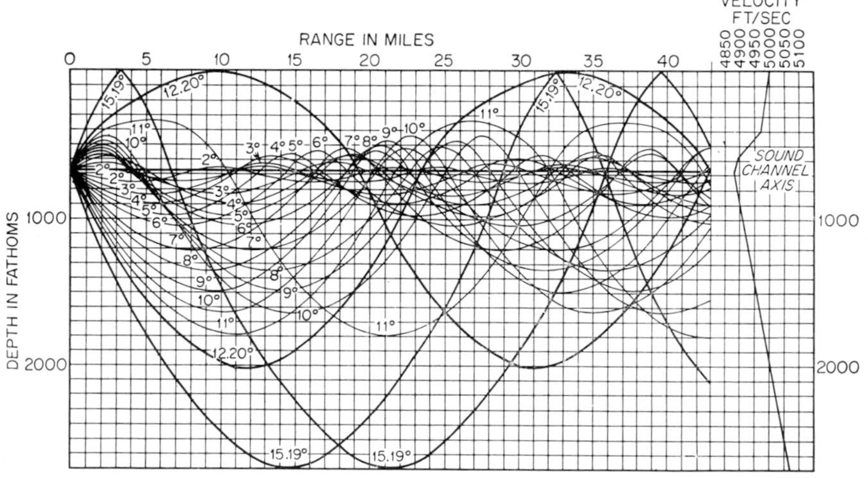

Fig. 11.14 Ray diagram for typical Atlantic Ocean sound channel. *(Ewing and Worzel, 1948.)*

depth. In the ocean T decreases with depth, rapidly at first and then more slowly. As a result V decreases at first, and then, when the decrease in T becomes more gradual, the effect of increase in pressure becomes predominant and V increases.

It has been proposed that this *sofar* (standing for *so*und *f*ixing *a*nd *r*anging) channel be used as an emergency signaling medium for ships at sea. Explosions of 4 lb of TNT at a depth of 4,000 ft have been recorded at distances as great as 2,300 miles, and it is believed that they would be observable out to 10,000 miles. The signals received are characteristic and have a minimum velocity of 4,888 ft per sec. It is estimated that the source of such signals could be located to within 30 miles out of 1,000 using this method. Lifeboats or downed planes would have only to drop a charge overboard, set to explode at the pressure existing at a depth of 4,000 ft. Permanent listening posts would then report to a central station which would compute the location from the arrival times and dispatch assistance to the scene.

A similar velocity variation could exist in the earth owing to the effect of quartz (Gutenberg, 1951*b*). There are two types of quartz known as α- and β-quartz. These differ slightly in their crystal structure. β-quartz is formed under higher temperatures than α-quartz. The elasticity of α-quartz is a function of temperature, decreasing as the inversion temperature is approached. Thus in the earth one might expect the velocity of seismic waves to decrease with temperature in a quartz-rich rock up to the inversion depth and then suddenly increase owing to the presence of β- instead of α-quartz. The rate of change of velocity would depend not only on temperature and pressure but also on the amount of quartz present as well as on the elastic properties of any other minerals present. Other minerals exhibiting similar phase changes may also be involved.

11.7 Evidence from Surface Waves. As a result of dispersion (see Sec. 7.1) the frequency of ground vibration generally increases during the arrival of a train of surface waves of any type from an earthquake. Surface waves of a period of 1 min or longer travel with velocities of 4.0 to 4.8 km per sec (Gutenberg, 1951*b*). The velocities of shorter period surface waves vary greatly from place to place over the earth. In the case of those of a period of 15 to 30 sec, they are highest under the Pacific Ocean (4.1 to 4.4 km per sec) and lowest on the continents (3.1 to 3.8 km per sec). The Indian Ocean exhibits velocities nearly as great as the Pacific (4.0 to 4.2 km per sec). Velocities under the Atlantic generally resemble those under the Pacific and Indian Oceans, though velocities as low as 3.4 km per sec have been reported. The best explanation for these variations is that they are due to variations in the thickness of the surface layers. The so-called granitic layer appears to be absent under almost the whole of the ocean basins.

This picture is consistent with the results obtained from refraction studies. Ewing (Ewing et al., 1950 and 1954) detonated explosions on the bottom of the Atlantic and recorded refracted pulses which indicate a layer of sediments of very variable thickness, thousands of meters on the continental shelves thinning to as little as 1.5 km in the central parts of the basins. This is underlain by about 5 km of rock of a compressional-wave velocity of 6.5 km per sec and beneath this the Mohorovicic discontinuity. Raitt (1954) reports similar conditions in the Pacific, with 5 to 10 km of material with a velocity of 6.8 km per sec above the Mohorovicic discontinuity. Press and Ewing (1955) have shown that thicknesses such as these are just about right to explain the observed dispersion of both Rayleigh and Love waves under the Pacific and at least a large part of the Atlantic Ocean. This suggests that granitic material is absent or nearly so under the oceans.

Jeffreys (1952) has analyzed the data on dispersion of surface waves for many parts of the world and concluded that under the continents it is consistent with a picture of about 15 km of granitic material and 30 km of intermediate composition overlying the Mohorovicic discontinuity. These are rough, average figures, which is the best that can be obtained considering the uncertainties as to the body-wave velocities at different places.

Rothé (1951) has postulated that the mid-Atlantic ridge is the true western boundary of the Eurasian continent and that a thicker layer of sialic rocks is present east of here than beneath the western Atlantic basins. This would explain observed low surface-wave velocities. At one time it was thought that the surface waves under the Atlantic were too slow for typical oceanic conditions to exist here. It is now known that this is not the case (Press and Ewing, 1950). Berckhemer (1956) has shown that the observed dispersion in the eastern Atlantic is consistent with a crustal thickness of only 10 km over at least most of this area. Another of Rothé's reasons for adopting his hypothesis is the distribution of earthquake epicenters in the Atlantic Ocean. Shocks are common along the mid-Atlantic ridge and in a belt running from the region of the Azores east to the Mediterranean. This pattern is similar to that which surrounds the Pacific Ocean, the bottom of which is also almost free of earthquakes (see Chap. 19).

11.8 Andesite Line. The Pacific basin especially seems to be in marked contrast to the adjoining land. Within the basin only rocks of basic composition are found, while on the surrounding islands and continental masses acidic rocks are also common. Figure 11.15 shows how the limit of occurrence of andesites outlines the Pacific area. The surface waves of earthquakes traveling close to parallel to the andesite line and striking it at large angles of incidence are strongly attenuated, sometimes by as much as 90 per cent, indicating that the line is a marked discontinuity in seismic wave velocity. The boundaries of the Atlantic and Indian Oceans do not have such a strong effect on surface waves (Gutenberg, 1951*b*). The location of the andesite line is well defined on the west side of the Pacific basin. On the east side, the reverse is true, and it is thought that it may swing out to sea following the Easter Island rise rather than following the coast of South America as shown in Fig. 11.15.

11.9 Evidence from Reflection Amplitudes. Another line of evidence on the nature of the oceanic floors is provided by the amplitudes of the once-reflected pulses *PP* and *PS*. Consider a compressional pulse striking a free surface at an angle of incidence of about 45° (Fig. 11.16*A*). For

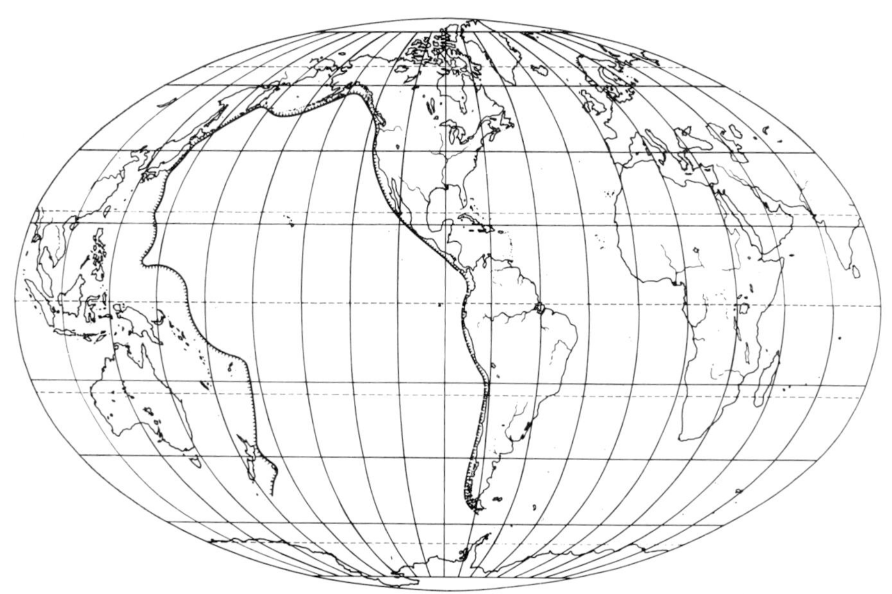

Fig. 11.15 The andesite line. *(After Chubb, 1934; Gutenberg and Richter, 1949; Marshall, 1912; Umbgrove, 1947.)*

the reflected pulses to have a combined particle motion equivalent to that of the incident pulse, *PS* must be stronger than *PP*. On the other hand, if the angle of incidence is small the reverse will be true: *PP* will be relatively stronger compared with *PS* (Fig. 11.16*B*). In the case of reflection at the earth's surface, if there is a low-velocity (granitic) layer present, the surface reflection will be at a low angle of incidence owing to the effect of refraction into this layer (Fig. 11.16*C*). If no such layer is present, the angle of incidence will be greater. Thus the ratio of the amplitudes A_{PP}/A_{PS} will be considerably greater when a low-velocity surface layer is present than when it is not.

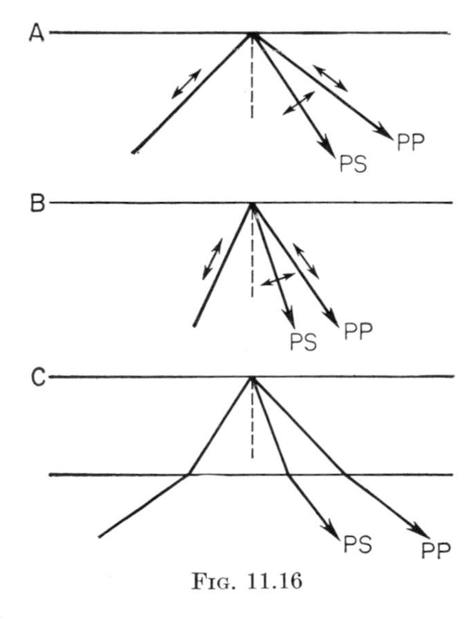

Fig. 11.16

The earth can be divided into areas of large and small A_{PP}/A_{PS}. Large ratios suggest the presence of a low-velocity surface layer; small ones suggest its absence. Pulses reflected under the continents have large ratios, indicating that a low-velocity surface layer is present.

Pulses reflected under most of the Pacific basin have low ratios, suggesting that it is absent or much thinner than one wavelength. There is, however, a large area off of the west coast of South America, the Albatross Plateau, where continental-type reflections occur.

11.10 Deeper Layering. So far the earth has been shown to be divided into three principal layers: the core, the mantle, and the crust, with a probable fourth layer, the inner core. The crust is thought by some to be divisible into the sedimentary veneer, a low-velocity layer, and a high-velocity layer. At some places intermediate- and minimum-velocity layers have also been postulated. It is clear from direct observation of the basement rocks and from the detailed examination of the seismograms of large explosions that these layers, if they exist at all, are not homogeneous but are complex in character (Tatel et al., 1953). Their thicknesses vary from place to place.

The detailed structure of the rocks beneath the Mohorovicic discontinuity is unknown. Moreover, it is unlikely that it can be determined by the methods discussed to date, which depend on studying the paths and times of travel of seismic pulses. Structures whose dimensions are of the order of a wavelength or less of the seismic waves being used to study them cannot be delineated. Beneath the Mohorovicic discontinuity, compressional pulses travel 8 km per sec or more and periods of greater than 1 sec predominate. Thus, the wavelength is usually 8 km or more. Therefore, present methods can never give a picture of detailed structure at these depths.

Furthermore, if at any depth there is a decrease instead of an increase in seismic-wave velocity, rays will be refracted downward and returned to the surface only when they reach a depth where the velocity is again increased. The determination of the velocity profile with depth is based on calculations of the velocity at the deepest point of penetration of rays emerging at successive distances. Since the deepest point never lies in a low-velocity layer, such bodies cannot be discovered by the refraction method. Reflections from the upper or lower surface of such a layer could be used to map it if such were observed. However, none has been as yet.

The core or mantle may be layered without there being sharp boundaries between the subdivisions. Examination of the velocity against depth profile (Fig. 11.3) shows that more often than not there is a gradual rather than a sudden change in velocity from one depth to the next, and in this case no reflected pulse will be generated. Thus there may be layers within the earth whose existence is not clearly marked. In the mantle at a depth probably near 400 km, there is a relatively sudden increase in the rate of increase in velocity with depth. Such a change constitutes a second-order discontinuity in contrast to a first-order discontinuity, which occurs where there is a jump in the velocity against depth profile. Below this depth the rate of increase gradually falls off until about 1,000 km, below which the rate of increase becomes much more gradual (third-order discontinuity). Shortly before the core is reached, another slight but sudden decrease in the rate of increase has been recognized.

The causes of these second- and third-order discontinuites are unknown. Since there is no discontinuous step in the velocity profile, they probably do not represent a sudden change in composition, though they may represent a gradual one. Birch (1952) suggests that changes in mineral phases are important. On the other hand, the velocity changes may represent only alterations in elastic and other physical properties resulting from changes in pressure and temperature with depth. Mineral-phase changes could conceivably explain even the discontinuous steps in the curve, as an inversion from one crystal form to another of some common mineral might cause a sudden alteration of elastic properties.

11.11 Depth of Focus. Depth of focus is in some ways easier to calculate for deep shocks than for shallow ones, though great accuracy is still difficult (see Sec. 11.5). This is possible because of the presence of pulses such as *pP* and *sP* reflected from the surface near the epicenter. Consider the two pulses *P′* and *pP′* arriving at epicentral distances close to 180° (Fig. 11.17). The *pP′* pulse has traveled farther than *P′* by an amount approximately equal to twice the depth of focus. Thus the time interval between the arrival of these two pulses is a measure of depth of focus, and if the velocity profile with depth is known, the depth of focus is easily found (Gutenberg and Richter, 1936*a*).

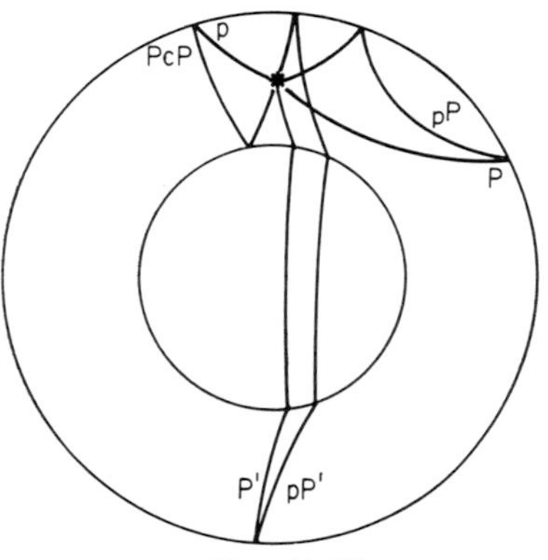

Fig. 11.17

Similarly at short distances the times of *p* and *PcP* can be used, since the core radius is known. At intermediate distances the time between *P* and *pP* is useful in the same manner. The accuracy of depth determinations using these methods is about ±25 km, which corresponds to 3 sec on the seismograms where the velocity of transmission is 8.3 km per sec.

The different pulses on a seismogram are usually identified by noting their times of arrival and comparing these with the times as given on a standard travel-time curve such as Fig. 11.8. The travel-time curves are different for each depth of focus. Therefore, determination of focal depth is the first step in identifying the pulses on a seismogram.

There are six characteristics by which deep-focus earthquakes can be distinguished from shallow in addition to the difference in the travel-time curves. First, the surface waves are weak or absent. This is expectable, since an earthquake at large depth causes little disturbance of the earth's surface compared with a shallow shock of the same size.

The second distinguishing feature is the lack of such pulses as *PP* and *pP* at short distances. Similarly, the arrival of pulses in groups of three, a principal *P* and *S* pulse preceded by surface reflection as a *pP* or *pS*, then as an *sP* or *sS*, is characteristic.

Fourth, the intensity changes only slowly with distance, especially near the epicenter. The reason for this is clear if we visualize isoseismal lines as the intersection of isoseismal surfaces with the earth's surface. The less steeply the two surfaces intersect, the broader the areas of equal intensity (Fig. 11.18). Thus the ratio of the areas of maximum intensity to those of lesser intensity is a measure of the depth of focus.

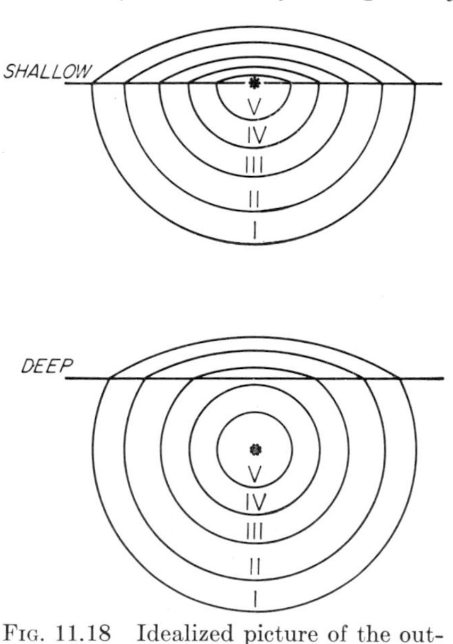

FIG. 11.18 Idealized picture of the outcrop of the isoseismal surfaces for a shallow and a deep earthquake.

Next, if the arrival times are noted at several places near the epicenter, they will be observed to differ from one another very little for a deep shock but a great deal for a shallow one, since the total distance traveled for a deep shock changes only slowly at short epicentral distances. Thus the apparent acceleration (rate of change of apparent velocity) as determined from the travel-time curve for short distances is less for deep than for shallow earthquakes.

Last, the beginnings of the pulses are sharper for deep shocks. This may be because the rays do not have to pass through the surface layers in the early part of their paths, thus being divided, or because the deeper layers of the earth are more uniform in composition and hence cause less scattering. Other factors may be that the surface-reflected pulses *pP*, *sP*, etc., arrive well after the direct pulses and hence do not interfere with them, and that the surface waves are relatively weak.

11.12 Location of Epicenters. Only in case an earthquake occurs in an inhabited region can the epicenter be located by a study of its surface intensity, and then only if it is strong enough to be widely felt. However, if it is recorded at several seismic observatories, the epicenter can be calculated from the times of arrival of the various pulses. On a flat, homogeneous earth wherein the velocities of transmission of seismic waves V_p and V_s are constant, if T_0 is the time of occurrence of an earthquake, the times of arrival of P and S at distance Δ will be

$$T_p - T_0 = \frac{\Delta}{V_p} \tag{11.13}$$

$$T_s - T_0 = \frac{\Delta}{V_s} \tag{11.14}$$

Subtracting (11.13) from (11.14) gives

$$T_s - T_p = \Delta\left(\frac{1}{V_s} - \frac{1}{V_p}\right) \tag{11.15}$$

or

$$\Delta = \frac{T_s - T_p}{1/V_s - 1/V_p} \tag{11.16}$$

Using the arrival times at any three or more stations the location of the shock can be determined by drawing circles of the calculated radius on a map and noting their intersection (Fig. 11.19).

If (11.13) and (11.14) are cleared of Δ instead of T_0, the time the earthquake occurred can be found:

$$T_0 = \frac{T_pV_p - T_sV_s}{V_p - V_s} \tag{11.17}$$

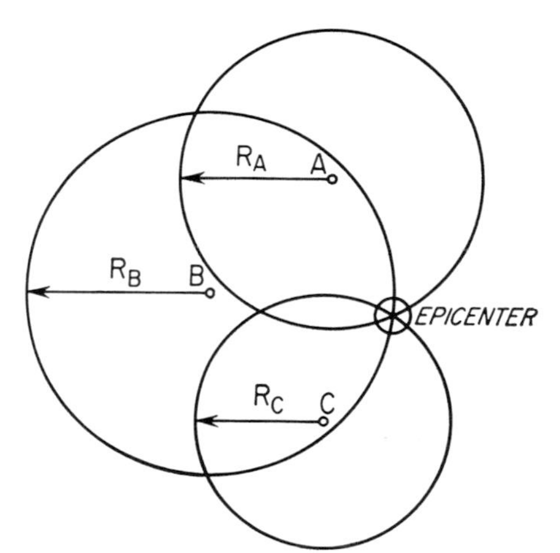

Fig. 11.19 Location of epicenter knowing distances from stations A, B, and C.

The real earth is not flat, nor is it homogeneous. Nevertheless, the time difference between T_p and T_s is still characteristic of distance and origin time. By noting at what distance the P and S arms of the travel-time curve of Fig. 11.8 are separated by the observed time interval $T_s - T_p$, both distance and T_0 can be directly determined.

The Russian seismologist Galitzin proposed a method of locating an earthquake from the records of one seismic observatory. If the two horizontal seismometers are identical in sensitivity, then the amplitudes of first motion of P on the corresponding seismograms can be used to tell the direction to the source.

$$\tan\theta = \frac{A_{EW}}{A_{NS}} \tag{11.18}$$

where θ is the direction, measured clockwise, of the source with respect to north; A_{EW} is the east-west amplitude, east being positive, west negative; and A_{NS} is the north-south amplitude, north being positive, south negative. θ is the direction to the source if the first motion is a rarefraction, from it if it is a compression. Which case applies can be determined from inspection of the vertical trace. If first motion is up, it is a compression; if down, it is a rarefaction. Distance and origin time are determined as described above. Galitzin's method is rarely applied because it is often difficult to recognize the earliest motion clearly and few stations have calibrated seismometers with approximately like sensitivities.

The location of epicenters is carried out by government and scientific organizations as a part of routine scientific research. Most of the stations throughout the world report their observations of pulse arrival times to central bureaus in the United States operated by the U.S. Coast and Geodetic Survey in Washington, D.C., and the Jesuit Seismological Association in Saint Louis, Missouri; to the International Seismological Summary at Kew, England; and to the International Union of Geodesy and Geophysics at Strasbourg, France. These organizations publish a great part of the data thus collected, including locations of the epicenters, origin times, focal depths, and the arrival times of the principal pulses at observatories all over the world. The individual stations publish their own data in the form of bulletins which they circulate to one another to aid in seismic investigations, an exemplary illustration of scientific cooperation on a world-wide scale.

11.13 Tunami Warning System. In some cases the rapid instrumental determination of epicenters immediately after an earthquake can be put to practical use. An example is the tunami warning system developed by the U.S. Coast and Geodetic Survey. Destructive tunamis commonly follow large earthquakes which occur in certain places such as the Aleutian Islands region. The times of large earthquakes recorded at several Pacific stations are quickly reported to a central station at Honolulu, Hawaii. If the epicenter lies in a region known to be a common source of tunamis, oceanographic stations nearer the epicenter than Hawaii are alerted. If a sea wave if observed, it is reported at once to Honolulu. In this way it is hoped that the coastal towns in Hawaii can be warned in time to prepare for the wave and that disasters such as that resulting from the April 1, 1946, tunami, which killed 173 persons and did $25,000,000 property damage, can be lessened.

CHAPTER 12

MASS, MOMENT, SHAPE, AND SIZE OF THE EARTH

12.1 Universal Law of Gravitation. Today nearly everyone knows that the weight of an object results from the gravitational pull of the mass of the earth. This was not always realized. The discovery of the universal law of gravitation by Newton is one of the great discoveries of all time. There is a story told that this great man was walking one day in an orchard, and just as he passed under a tree an apple fell, striking him on the head. As he ruefully considered what had befallen him, he suddenly conceived the universal law of gravitation.

It is doubtful if Newton had such a sudden revelation of the law. More likely he came to it by a gradual process. It can be derived from Kepler's laws, which were already known in Newton's time. Kepler's laws are empirical; that is, they are based on observation alone and are not derived from more fundamental considerations or from other empirical observations. Studying the motions of the planets, Kepler observed that:

1. All planets revolve about the sun in elliptical orbits with the sun as the focus:

$$\frac{(x + a\epsilon)^2}{a^2} + \frac{y^2}{b^2} = 1 \qquad (12.1)$$

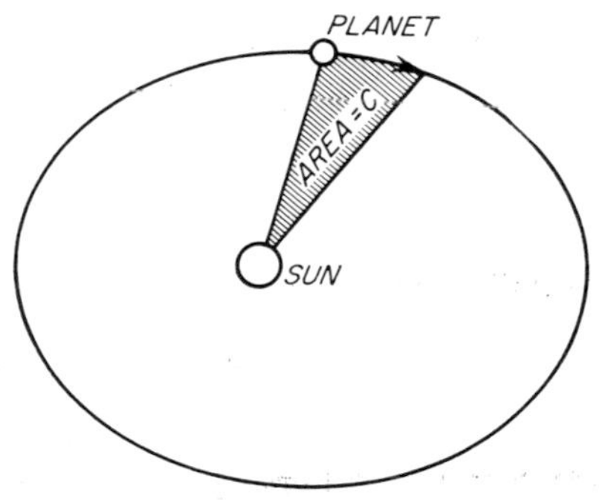

FIG. 12.1 A planet sweeps out a constant area per unit time.

where a and b are the major and minor half-axes and ϵ is the eccentricity.

2. A line drawn from the sun to any planet sweeps a constant area per unit time (Fig. 12.1):

$$\frac{dS}{dt} = C \qquad (12.2)$$

3. The square of the period of revolution is proportional to the cube of the length of the major half-axis of the ellipse of the planetary orbit:

$$T^2 \sim a^3 \qquad (12.3)$$

To derive the universal law of gravitation from these laws, let us first change to polar coordinates:

$$x = r \cos \theta \tag{12.4}$$
$$y = r \sin \theta \tag{12.5}$$

Equation (12.1) becomes

$$\frac{r^2 \cos^2 \theta}{a^2} + \frac{2\epsilon r \cos \theta}{a} + \epsilon^2 + \frac{r^2 \sin^2 \theta}{b^2} = 1 \tag{12.6}$$

On dividing through by r^2, this can be solved for $1/r$, giving

$$\frac{1}{r} = \frac{-\dfrac{2\epsilon \cos \theta}{a} \pm \left[\dfrac{4\epsilon^2 \cos^2 \theta}{a^2} - 4(\epsilon^2 - 1)\left(\dfrac{\cos^2 \theta}{a^2} + \dfrac{\sin^2 \theta}{b^2}\right)\right]^{1/2}}{2(\epsilon^2 - 1)} \tag{12.7}$$

Since for an ellipse $1 - \epsilon^2 = b^2/a^2$ and representing $1/r$ by u, this simplifies to

$$\begin{aligned} u = \frac{1}{r} &= \frac{\dfrac{\epsilon \cos \theta}{a} \pm \left[\dfrac{\cos^2 \theta}{a^2}\left(1 - \dfrac{b^2}{a^2}\right) + \dfrac{b^2}{a^2}\left(\dfrac{\cos^2 \theta}{a^2} + \dfrac{\sin^2 \theta}{b^2}\right)\right]^{1/2}}{b^2/a^2} \\ &= \frac{a\epsilon \cos \theta \pm a}{b^2} \end{aligned} \tag{12.8}$$

From Newton's second law, the force which acts on a planet in radial coordinates would be (Houston, 1934, p. 26)

$$F_R = ma_R = m\left[\frac{d^2r}{dt^2} - r\left(\frac{d\theta}{dt}\right)^2\right] \tag{12.9}$$

radially and

$$F_T = ma_T = m\left(2\frac{dr}{dt}\frac{d\theta}{dt} + r\frac{d^2\theta}{dt^2}\right) \tag{12.10}$$

tangentially, where a_R and a_T are the radial and tangential accelerations. The area swept out in unit time is

$$S = 0.5 \int_0^{\theta'} r^2 \, d\theta \tag{12.11}$$

where θ' is the angular motion per unit time. Therefore from Eq. (12.2)

$$\frac{dS}{dt} = 0.5r^2 \frac{d\theta}{dt} = C \tag{12.12}$$

On rearranging terms,

$$\frac{d\theta}{dt} = 2Cr^{-2} = 2Cu^2 \tag{12.13}$$

from which it is seen that

$$\frac{d^2\theta}{dt^2} = -4Cr^{-3}\frac{dr}{dt} = -4Cu^3\frac{dr}{dt} \tag{12.14}$$

Substituting (12.13) and (12.14) into (12.10),

$$F_T = m\left(4Cu^2\frac{dr}{dt} - 4Cu^3r\frac{dr}{dt}\right) = 0 \tag{12.15}$$

This means that the tangential force is zero and the planet is acted on only by a force directed toward the sun of amount [from (12.9)]

$$F_R = m\left(\frac{d^2r}{dt^2} - 4C^2u^4r\right) = m\left(\frac{d^2r}{dt^2} - 4C^2u^3\right) \tag{12.16}$$

Now note that, using (12.8) and (12.13),

$$\frac{dr}{dt} = \frac{du^{-1}}{dt} = -u^{-2}\frac{du}{dt} = \frac{a\epsilon \sin\theta}{u^2b^2}\frac{d\theta}{dt} = 2Cb^{-2}a\epsilon \sin\theta \tag{12.17}$$

$$\frac{d^2r}{dt^2} = 2Cb^{-2}a\epsilon \cos\theta\frac{d\theta}{dt} = 4C^2b^{-2}u^2a\epsilon \cos\theta \tag{12.18}$$

Substituting this in (12.16) and using (12.8) to get rid of $\cos\theta$,

$$F_R = m\left[4C^2u^2\left(u \pm \frac{a}{b^2}\right) - 4C^2u^3\right] = -\frac{4mC^2u^2a}{b^2} \tag{12.19}$$

The negative solution only is kept, as the positive solution corresponds to an outward force, which would lead to instablilty.

Since the area of an ellipse is πab, the amount swept out in unit time is $\pi ab/T$. From Kepler's second law this is equal to the constant here called C. Therefore,

$$T = \frac{\pi ab}{C} \tag{12.20}$$

But from Kepler's third law T^2 is proportional to a^3 or

$$\frac{\pi^2a^2b^2}{C^2} \sim a^3 \tag{12.21}$$

and Eq. (12.19) becomes

$$F_R \sim -\frac{4mC^2u^2}{b^2}\frac{\pi^2b^2}{C^2} = -\frac{4\pi^2m}{r^2} \tag{12.22}$$

Therefore the sun exerts an attractive force on all planets which is directly proportional to the mass of the planet and inversely to the square of its radial distance. If the sun exerts such a force on any planet, then it should exert it on any mass m_1, and since action and reaction are equal and opposite, m_1 must exert a similar force on the sun or on a third mass m_2, so

$$F = \frac{\gamma m_1 m_2}{r^2} \tag{12.23}$$

γ is called the universal constant of gravitation.

12.2 Cavendish's Experiment. The most famous experiment to determine γ was made by Henry Cavendish at Cambridge, England, in 1798 using a torsion balance, as shown in Fig. 12.2. He measured the torque required to prevent rotation of the m_2 masses when the m_1's were moved from position I to II. The force between m_1 and m_2 is

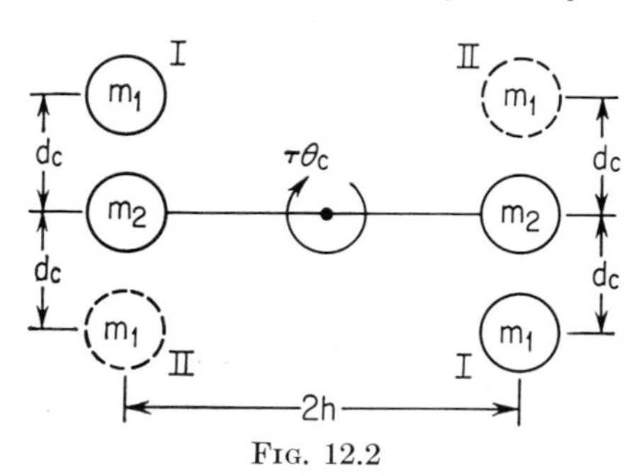

FIG. 12.2

$$F = \frac{\gamma m_1 m_2}{d_c^2} \tag{12.24}$$

If the upper end of the torsion wire is twisted an amount θ_c and its torsion modulus is τ, then the difference in torque when m_1 is moved from I to II will be

$$\tau\theta_c = 2hF - (2h)(-F) = 4hF = \frac{4h\gamma m_1 m_2}{d_c^2} \tag{12.25}$$

To determine the value of τ the m_1 masses were removed and the m_2 mass system was set in oscillation in a horizontal plane about its axis of suspension. The equation of motion in this case is

$$I\frac{d^2\theta}{dt^2} + \tau\theta = 0 \tag{12.26}$$

The solution of this equation is

$$\theta = \theta_0 \cos\left(\frac{\tau}{I}\right)^{1/2}(t + \psi) \tag{12.27}$$

which corresponds to simple harmonic motion with the period

$$T_c = 2\pi\left(\frac{I}{\tau}\right)^{1/2} \tag{12.28}$$

ψ is a phase angle.

Solving (12.25) for γ and substituting the value of τ obtained from (12.28),

$$\gamma = \frac{\pi^2 I\theta_c d_c^2}{T_c^2 h m_1 m_2} \tag{12.29}$$

Since all the terms at the right are measurable, γ can be calculated. The most accurate measurements made to date were made by Heyl and Chrzanowski (1942) at the National Bureau of Standards. They found γ to be $6.673 \pm 0.003 \times 10^{-8}$ cgs unit.

12.3 Acceleration of Gravity. Equation (12.23) gives us a way of weighing the earth. Assuming that the earth approximates a sphere, its attraction on a unit mass at a point on its surface a distance R_e from the center would be

$$g = \frac{\gamma M_e}{R_e^2} \qquad (12.30)$$

where M_e is the mass of the earth. The term g is called the acceleration of gravity. It can be found by swinging a pendulum. For a simple pendulum as is shown in Fig. 12.3 the equation of motion is

$$I \frac{d^2\theta}{dt^2} = -mgL \sin\theta \qquad (12.31)$$

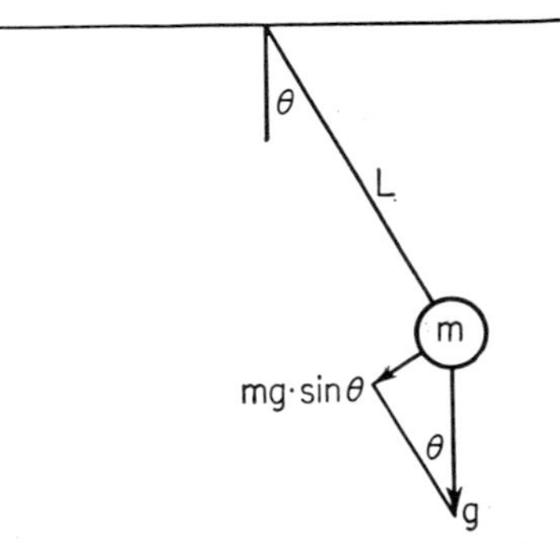

FIG. 12.3

where I is the moment of inertia of the system, m the mass of the bob, and L the length of the suspension. If the amplitude of vibration is very small, $\sin\theta$ approximately equals θ and (12.31) becomes

$$I \frac{d^2\theta}{dt^2} = -mgL\theta \qquad (12.32)$$

for which the solution is

$$\theta = \theta_0 \cos \left(\frac{mgL}{I}\right)^{1/2} (t + \psi) \qquad (12.33)$$

For a mass suspended by a weightless suspension, such as assumed here, I is equal to mL^2. The period of such a pendulum would therefore be

$$T_P = 2\pi \left(\frac{I}{mgL}\right)^{1/2} = 2\pi \left(\frac{L}{g}\right)^{1/2} \qquad (12.34)$$

Since T_P is easily measured, g can be determined to as great an accuracy as L can be measured.

A simple pendulum is impossible to construct, as no suspension is weightless. This difficulty was overcome in an ingenious manner by Henry Kater. It is a theorem of mechanics that any system of parallel forces, such as gravity, acting on a rigid body can be resolved into a single force acting at the center of mass. Thus, for any pendulum of whatever shape there will be a point, the center of mass, at a distance h_1 from the axis of suspension at which the gravitative force can be considered as concentrated (Fig. 12.4). The equation of motion of such a pendulum is

$$I_1 \frac{d^2\theta}{dt^2} = -mgh_1 \sin \theta \tag{12.35}$$

And using the same approximation as before, its period is

$$T_1 = 2\pi \left(\frac{I_1}{mgh_1}\right)^{1/2} \tag{12.36}$$

This is the period of a simple pendulum of length

$$L_1 = \frac{I_1}{mh_1} \tag{12.37}$$

Now if the body is swung about another parallel axis at distance h_2 beyond

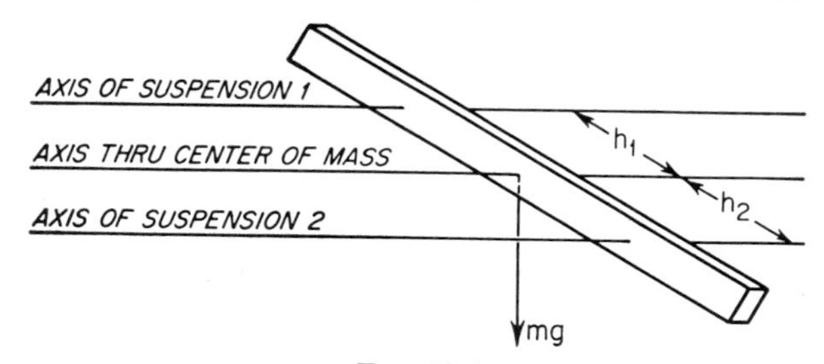

FIG. 12.4

the center of mass from the first suspension, its moment of inertia being I_2, its equivalent length L_2 will be

$$L_2 = \frac{I_2}{mh_2} \tag{12.38}$$

There is a theorem in mechanics which says that the moment of inertia of a mass about any axis is equal to the moment of inertia I_0 about a parallel axis through the center of mass plus the moment of inertia of a particle of mass equal to that of the body placed at the center of mass:

$$I_1 = I_0 + mh_1^2 \tag{12.39}$$

$$I_2 = I_0 + mh_2^2 \tag{12.40}$$

Substituting into (12.37) and (12.38),

$$L_1 = \frac{I_0}{mh_1} + h_1 \tag{12.41}$$

$$L_2 = \frac{I_0}{mh_2} + h_2 \tag{12.42}$$

If the period of the pendulum is the same about both axes, then L_1 must equal L_2 or

$$\frac{I_0}{mh_1} + h_1 = \frac{I_0}{mh_2} + h_2 \tag{12.43}$$

which can be solved for I_0/m, giving

$$\frac{I_0}{m} = h_1 h_2 \tag{12.44}$$

Therefore, from (12.41) and (12.42),

$$L_1 = L_2 = h_1 + h_2 \tag{12.45}$$

This means that if a compound pendulum is swung about two parallel axes and is found to have the same period in both cases, this period is the same as that of a simple pendulum whose length is the separation of these axes and whose mass is the same as that of the compound pendulum. Substituting (12.45) in (12.34) gives

$$T_P = 2\pi \left(\frac{h_1 + h_2}{g}\right)^{1/2} \tag{12.46}$$

$$g = \frac{4\pi^2(h_1 + h_2)}{T_P^2} \tag{12.47}$$

Kater's pendulum provides the most accurate way known of determining gravity. The best measurements made up to the present time indicate that the average value of gravity at sea level at the equator is 978.0373 gals (Jeffreys, 1952, p. 184). The gal is a unit of acceleration equal to 1 cm per sec^2.

12.4 Radius of the Earth. The one remaining quantity which is needed to calculate the mass of the earth from Eq. (12.30) is its radius. That the earth was round was recognized by Pythagoras about 540 B.C., and two centuries later Aristotle mentions that its circumference was believed to be about 74,000 km. However, the earliest known actual measurement was made by Eratosthenes, librarian at Alexandria, in the second or third century before Christ. He observed that at noon on a certain day the sun fully illuminated the bottom of a well at Aswan, Egypt (then called Syene). A year later at noon on the same day he observed that the length of a shadow of a vertical pole at Alexandria subtended one-fiftieth of a circle (360°/50 = 7.2°). Since the distance from Aswan to Alexandria was known to be roughly 5,000 stadia (925 km), he was able to calculate the circumference C_e of the earth, assuming that the rays of the sun are parallel (Fig. 12.5):

$$\frac{L_e}{C_e} = \frac{\theta_e}{2\pi} = \frac{1}{50} \tag{12.48}$$

In this manner Eratosthenes found the earth's circumference to be 46,250 km, which is only about 15 per cent too large, reasonably close considering the lack of accurate measuring instruments in his time.

Eratosthenes' method is basically the one still used today. It was used also by the Egyptian-Greek philosopher Ptolemy in the second century of our era. His accuracy was less than Eratosthenes'. He found the circumference to be only about 32,000 km. This was the figure Columbus knew when he set out to travel west to Cathay and is one of the reasons why he expected that country to be much nearer Europe than it is. Had he known the true distance, he might not have been so eager to sail westward.

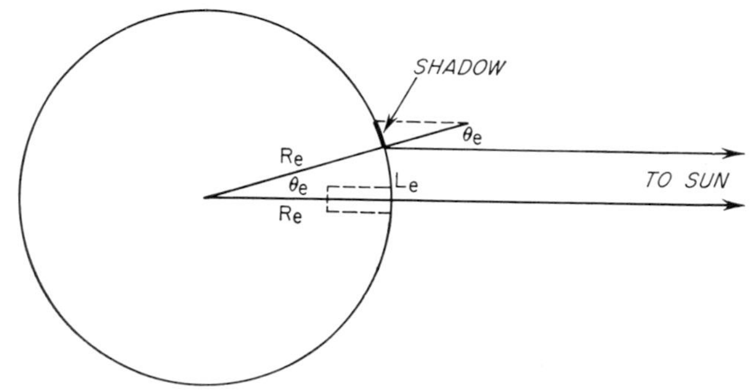

FIG. 12.5 Eratosthenes' experiment.

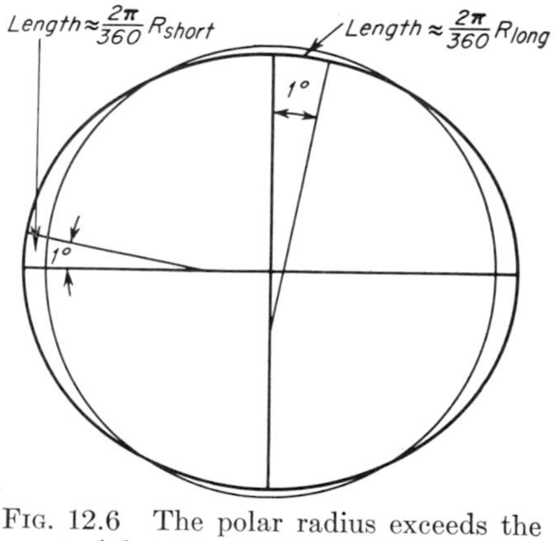

By the middle of the eighteenth century the determinations of the earth's radius were sufficiently accurate that it was recognized that the earth was not perfectly spherical. The French government sent two expeditions, one to the far north in Lapland and the other to the equator in what is now Ecuador but was then a part of the Spanish colony of Peru. Each expedition measured the length of 1 degree of arc. The arc in Lapland was longer than that in Peru, proving that the earth was an oblate spheroid, flattened at the poles (Fig. 12.6).

FIG. 12.6 The polar radius exceeds the equatorial.

Since the eighteenth century there have been numerous determinations of the ellipticity of the earth, along both latitude and longitude lines. Degrees are measured by taking the angle between the vertical and the direction to the sun or a star at two points simultaneously. Until the advent of the telegraph the principal uncertainty was the time difference between the two observations, one at either end of the arc. This affects the length of a degree of longitude, as any difference in the times of measurement corresponds to an error in angle of the amount the earth rotated during this interval. To a first approximation the earth is an ellipsoid of revolution (spheroid). Its dimensions are (Jeffreys, 1952)

$$R_{eq} = \text{equatorial radius} = 6{,}378{,}099 \text{ m}$$
$$R_p = \text{polar radius} = 6{,}356{,}631 \text{ m}$$
$$\text{Ellipticity (geometric flattening)} = \frac{R_{eq} - R_p}{R_{eq}} = \frac{1}{297}$$

The radius of a sphere with the same volume R_v is 6,371,200 m (Gutenberg, 1951*d*).

12.5 Variation of Gravity with Latitude and Longitude. The value of gravity given in Sec. 12.3 is approximately correct only for points on the equator. Since the radius of the earth increases from the poles to the equator, gravity must decrease as one moves in this direction. The effect of centrifugal force, which opposes gravity, must be included in this decrease. Indeed, it is centrifugal force which causes the earth to bulge at the equator and prevents its being a nearly perfect sphere. It can be shown that the shape of the earth is very close to that which a fluid of the same volume would assume. There is also a mass effect due to the attraction of the extra material in the equatorial bulge (Hammer, 1943).

The variation of gravity with latitude can be expressed to a first approximation by

$$g_I = 978.049(1 + 5.2884 \times 10^{-3} \sin^2 \theta - 5.9 \times 10^{-6} \sin^2 2\theta) \text{ gal} \tag{12.49}$$

where θ is the latitude. This equation was adopted by an international commission as best expressing the normal gravity field of the earth to the approximation of an ellipsoid of revolution. It is known as the "International Formula of 1930." This equation depends critically on the absolute value of gravity. Most measurements of gravity are only relative (see Chap. 14). Equation (12.49) is based on an absolute value measured at Potsdam, Germany, which is now believed to be in error in the fifth significant figure. Jeffreys (1952), using more recent data, gives the following approximation:

$$g_J = 978.0373(1 + 5.2891 \times 10^{-3} \sin^2 \theta - 5.9 \times 10^{-6} \sin^2 2\theta) \tag{12.50}$$

Other observers have described the gravity variation on the assumption that the earth is a triaxial ellipsoid. Heiskanen (1938), using world-wide data, has obtained the equation

$$g_H = 978.052[1 + 5.297 \times 10^{-3} \sin^2 \theta - 5.9 \times 10^{-6} \sin^2 2\theta + 2.76 \times 10^{-5} \cos^2 \theta \cos 2(\Lambda + 25°)] \text{ gal} \tag{12.51}$$

where Λ is the longitude measured west from Greenwich, England. Niskanen (1945), using only the presumably more accurate stations on level land, obtained

$$g_N = 978.047[1 + 5.2978 \times 10^{-3} \sin^2 \theta - 5.9 \times 10^{-6} \sin^2 2\theta + 2.3 \times 10^{-5} \cos^2 \theta \cos 2(\Lambda + 4°)] \text{ gal} \quad (12.52)$$

Daly (1940) has summarized the history of attempts to determine the variation of gravity.

12.6 Mean Density of the Earth. We are now ready to calculate the mass of the earth. Substituting into (12.30) the value of g at $\theta = 45°$ from Eq. (12.49), Heyl and Chrzanowski's value of γ (Sec. 12.2), and R_v from Sec. 12.4, M_e is found to be 5.965×10^{27} gm. Gutenberg (1951*d*) gives the mass as 5.975×10^{27} gm, based on slightly different values for the basic quantities used. Jeffreys (1952) gives 5.977×10^{27} gm. The average density ρ_{av} can be obtained by dividing the mass by $4\pi R_e^3/3$ or directly from the basic quantities by substituting $4\pi R_e^3 \rho_{av}/3$ for M_e into (12.30) and solving for ρ_{av}:

$$\rho_{av} = \frac{3g}{4\pi\gamma R_e} \quad (12.53)$$

Using the same figures as before, a value of 5.51 gm/cm^3 is found for ρ_{av}. Lambert and Darling (1951) have calculated a value of 5.5145 gm per cm^3.

12.7 Moment of Inertia. The other principal dimensional constant of the earth is its moment of inertia. This is not directly measurable. However, it can be determined from the earth's dimensions, mass, gravity, and angular velocity. Helmert has shown that for a spheroidal earth if I_p and I_e are the moments of inertia about the polar and an equatorial axis, respectively (Lambert and Darling, 1951, p. 342),

$$\frac{I_p - I_e}{M_e R_{eq}^2} = \frac{2e_f}{3} - \frac{\omega^2 R_{eq}}{3g_{eq}} + \xi \quad (12.54)$$

where M_e = mass of earth, R_{eq} = equatorial radius of the earth, e_f = ellipticity (flattening) = $1/297$, ω = angular velocity of earth, g_{eq} = gravity at the equator, ξ = a small correction for higher order terms omitted in the equation. Furthermore, the mechanical ellipticity e' can be calculated from observations of the precession and nutation of the earth and is approximately (Lambert and Darling, 1951)

$$e' = \frac{I_p - I_e}{I_p} = 3.2724 \times 10^{-3} \quad (12.55)$$

Combining Eq. (12.54) and (12.55),

$$I_p = \frac{M_e R_{eq}^2}{e'} \left(\frac{2e_f}{3} - \frac{\omega^2 R_{eq}}{3g_{eq}} + \xi \right) \quad (12.56)$$

Lambert and Darling (1951, p. 342) have shown that I_p approximately equals $0.3337M_eR_{eq}^2$. Gutenberg (1951*d*) gives the values of I_p and I_e as $I_p = 8.08 \times 10^{44}$ gm cm^2 and $I_e = 8.05 \times 10^{44}$ gm cm^2.

The moment of inertia of a sphere of uniform density of radius r and mass m about an axis is $0.4mr^2$. Thus the earth, with a moment of only $0.3337M_eR_{eq}^2$, has less moment of inertia than a uniform sphere. This means that the density must increase with the depth. The rate of increase will be the subject of the next chapter.

The earth's moment of inertia is subject to small variations. Changes in the rate of rotation of the earth of the order of 1 part in 10^8 have been measured (Runcorn, 1954; see also Sec. 23.5). Since angular momentum must be conserved, variations in the moment of inertia would be expected in the opposite sense to the changes in the rate of rotation.

12.8 Motion of the Poles. Position on the earth is commonly referred to in terms of latitude and longitude. Longitude is measured in terms of angular distance east or west of a plane through the axis of rotation of the earth and Greenwich, England. Geocentric latitude is the angle between a line from the center of the earth to a point on the earth's

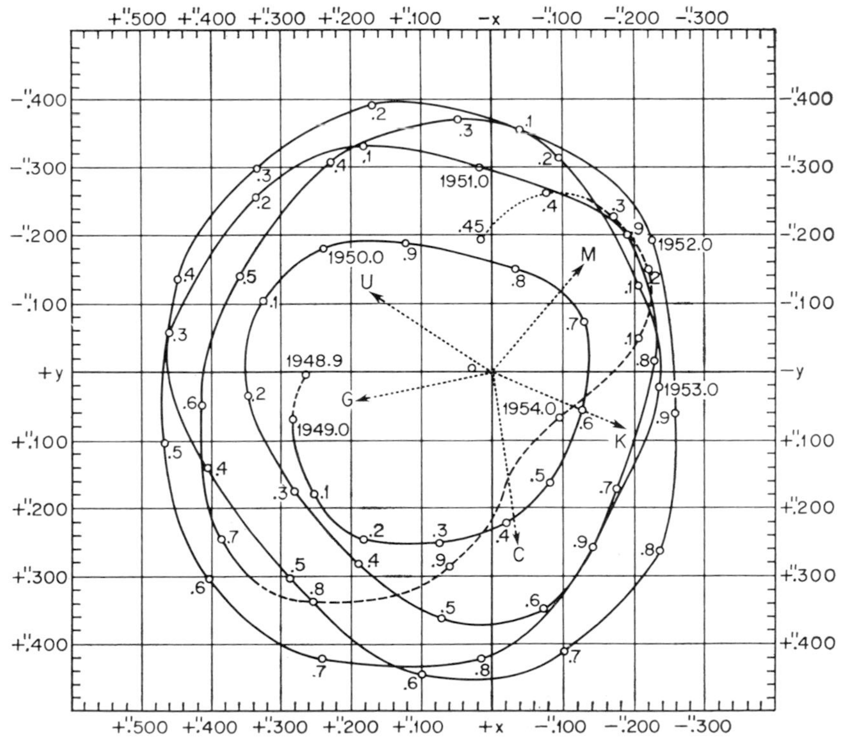

FIG. 12.7 Observed movement of the North Pole. *(Courtesy of G. Cecchini, 1954.)*

surface and the equatorial plane. Astronomic latitude is the angle between the vertical at a point and the equatorial plane. The equatorial plane is the plane through the earth's center perpendicular to the axis of rotation. Because of the ellipticity of the earth geocentric and astronomic latitude are not everywhere the same. There are also small deflections of the vertical of the order of a few seconds of arc due to the gravitational pull of mountains and density variations in the earth.

Furthermore, latitude varies a small amount with time. This is owing in part to use of the axis of rotation of the earth as a reference line. The earth does not always rotate about the same axis. To an observer looking down from the north, the pole of instantaneous rotation describes a counterclockwise orbit about the axis of figure. This is called the Chandler motion of the poles and is illustrated in Fig. 12.7. The motion is not entirely regular, being made to vary by unknown causes. Any tectonic deformation of the earth would tend to have an effect of this kind. So might the variations in the earth's rate of rotation referred to in Sec. 12.7. The amplitude of the motion is only of the order of a few meters, the maximum separation of the two axes being about 4 sec, or 12 m at the earth's surface. This is comparable in size to the largest displacements involved in earthquakes and is so small that only the most accurate observations of the latitude of a point can detect it.

Nonperiodic variations of position of points on the earth's surface have also been postulated. Very large motions of this sort have never been proved to occur, in terms either of a shift of the whole surface with respect to the axis of rotation or of one part of the crust with respect to another. The latter motion is called continental drift and will be the subject of Chap. 18.

CHAPTER 13

DENSITY AND ELASTIC CONSTANTS

13.1 Uniformity of Layering. In discussing the transmission of seismic waves in Chap. 10 we saw that the velocities of propagation, and hence the paths of the waves through the earth, depend on three quantities: the rigidity μ, Lamé's constant λ, and the density ρ. In most crystals μ and λ are different in different directions in the crystal, but in isotropic media both these constants and density are independent of direction. They are constants for any given material under one set of environmental conditions (temperature and pressure). To the accuracy of our present knowledge, the materials of which the earth is composed are usually isotropic if considered in large masses (dimensions much larger than the size of single crystals). To a first approximation, beneath the crust we can assume that the earth is completely uniform at any depth, and hence we can think of λ, μ, and ρ as being functions of depth also.

At the surface, direct observation shows us that the rocks of the earth are complexly arranged and no simple sequence of horizontal layers exists except very locally. At places the surface sediments are almost or completely level, but as one goes down or horizontally from such a location, their attitudes become more irregular. Beneath the sediments a basement of igneous and metamorphic rocks appears to be present everywhere. This basement is in places more complex than the sediments, but elsewhere igneous rocks of one composition outcrop over wide areas. Batholiths are of the latter nature. These bodies are the only type of rock which are not observed to overlie rocks of a different nature. In general where they outcrop, batholiths show evidence that their horizontal extent increases with depth. For this reason, geologists have long thought that some batholiths represent surface outcrops of certain of the layers of the earth postulated by seismologists. There is no real evidence to support this view. Recent seismic studies (Tatel et al., 1953) indicate that at least to the bottom of the crust the earth retains some of its complexity. The large volumes of the observed batholiths suggest that the size of individual bodies may become larger as one goes down into the earth, but how far this simplification of the structure continues is unknown.

The assumption of a uniform layering of the earth is justified, however, because of two facts. First we know that the earth is at least this complex. Second, our present ability to distinguish structural details will locate boundaries among rocks only if the boundaries extend over large areas and separate rocks of very different elastic properties. Therefore, only the most extensive and sharp boundaries can be located. Thus, though we do not have a detailed picture of the earth's interior, we can observe the main features.

13.2 Poisson's Ratio. In Chap. 11 it was shown that the interior of the earth consists of three principal layers, all of which can be further subdivided. No factual evidence is available as to their compositions, though speculation suggests that the core is composed of nickel and iron, that the upper mantle is composed of basic silicates, and that the lower mantle is either transitional between these compositions or possibly composed largely of metallic oxides and sulfides. The boundaries can be defined by describing the variations of the seismic-wave velocities with depth. They have been located, as pointed out above, by study of the travel-time curves of earthquakes.

Thus we know two properties of the rocks at each depth within the earth: the velocities of compressional and of shear waves (Fig. 11.3). From these two variables can be calculated a third: Poisson's ratio σ. If we take the ratio of V_p/V_s we get

$$\frac{V_p}{V_s} = \left[\frac{(\lambda + 2\mu)/\rho}{\mu/\rho}\right]^{1/2} = \left(\frac{\lambda + 2\mu}{\mu}\right)^{1/2} \tag{13.1}$$

Substituting for λ and μ their values from (10.44) and (10.45) and squaring gives

$$\left(\frac{V_p}{V_s}\right)^2 = \frac{\lambda}{\mu} + 2 = \frac{\sigma E/(1+\sigma)(1-2\sigma)}{E/2(1+\sigma)} + 2$$
$$= \frac{2\sigma}{1-2\sigma} + 2 = \frac{2-2\sigma}{1-2\sigma} \tag{13.2}$$

Solving this for σ gives

$$\sigma = \frac{(V_p/V_s)^2 - 2}{2(V_p/V_s)^2 - 2} \tag{13.3}$$

13.3 Variation in Density with Depth. One other independent property, the density ρ, can be determined using the information developed in Chap. 12. For the approximate determination of its variation with depth we are indebted to K. E. Bullen (1947). Suppose that everywhere at a distance r from the center of the earth, the density is ρ, the bulk modulus is k, the pressure is P, and the gravitational attraction is g.

Let m be the total mass within the sphere of radius r. Assume that the earth is spherical, a good first approximation, and that it behaves like a liquid, a common assumption for which there is also some justification. At any given point the pressure will be increasing with depth at the rate

$$\frac{dP}{dr} = -g\rho \tag{13.4}$$

The minus sign comes from the increase in pressure as r decreases. It can be shown that inside a spherical shell of uniform density, the shell causes no gravitational field, while outside the shell, the force is the same as though the mass of the shell were concentrated at its center. Therefore, under the assumptions made, only the material inside the radius r acts at the point under consideration, and

$$g = \frac{\gamma m}{r^2} \tag{13.5}$$

where γ is the universal constant of gravitation. By definition the bulk modulus of a fluid is the ratio of the pressure differential required to cause a given fractional change in volume V under adiabatic conditions (no gain or loss of heat). In our notation this becomes

$$k = \frac{dP}{dV/V} = \frac{dP}{d\rho/\rho} \tag{13.6}$$

But from (10.50), (10.85), and (10.94),

$$k = \lambda + \tfrac{2}{3}\mu = \rho(V_p^2 - \tfrac{4}{3}V_s^2) \tag{13.7}$$

Therefore, using (13.4) through (13.7), density is seen to vary with depth according to the equation

$$\frac{d\rho}{dr} = \frac{dP}{dr}\frac{d\rho}{dP} = -g\rho\frac{\rho}{k} = \frac{-g\rho^2}{\rho[V_p^2 - (4V_s^2/3)]} = \frac{-\gamma m\rho}{r^2[V_p^2 - (4V_s^2/3)]} \tag{13.8}$$

Since ρ is a function of r, we cannot integrate this equation directly. However, if the value of ρ is known at any particular depth, Eq. (13.8) gives the rate at which it is changing at that depth, and if it is assumed that density changes linearly with depth for a unit distance downward, density can be found at this distance inward. When this new density is known, a new rate of increase can be calculated, and hence one can proceed layer by layer toward the center of the earth until a discontinuous change in density is reached. The continuity of the curve of velocity against depth (Fig. 11.3) suggests that from the bottom of the crust to the outside of the core the density increases continuously except possibly in the region around a depth of 412 km. Thus, if we assume that immediately beneath the Mohorovicic discontinuity the density is 3.32 gm per cm³, we get the density variation from here to 412 km as shown in Fig. 13.1.

A more rapid increase in density beneath 412 km is necessary to satisfy other requirements. Density discontinuities probably occur also at the boundary of the core and at one or more places within it. There are two reasons why these sudden density changes are postulated. First, it is logical to suppose that where the velocity of compressional waves changes suddenly, as at the core boundary, density changes also, since the velocity

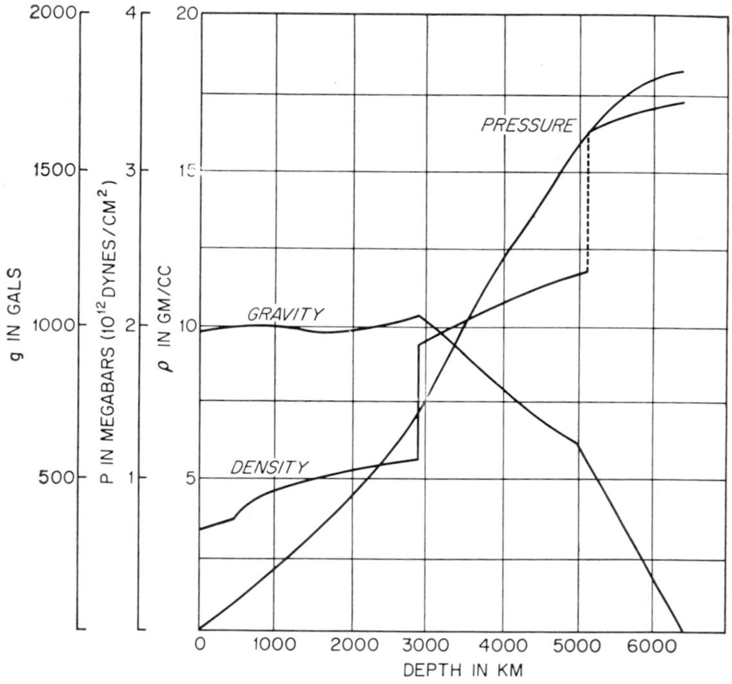

FIG. 13.1 Variation of density, gravity, and pressure with depth. (*After Birch, 1952; Bullard, 1954; and Bullen, 1947.*)

is a function of density. Second, if one were to continue to use formula (13.8) to find the density distribution below 412 km neglecting the probable discontinuous increases in density, the resulting mass distribution would not be dense enough to account for the known moment of inertia of the earth or even to provide for its total mass.

Reasonable assumptions appear to require a substantial increase in density on entering the core. As was shown in Sec. 12.7, the earth's low moment of inertia requires that there be a large concentration of mass toward the center. Within the core there is considerable latitude in the range of values possible, especially as one approaches the center. The simplest hypothesis to use in calculating core densities is to assume that there are no discontinuities below a depth of 3,000 km. On this assumption, the restriction of finding a density distribution which gives a total angular momentum of about 8.1×10^{44} gm per cm^2 requires a density increase of from 9.7 to 12.3 gm per cm^3 going from the outside to the center of the core. If discontinuities are present, the density may be considerably higher at the center. Within the core there is still no generally

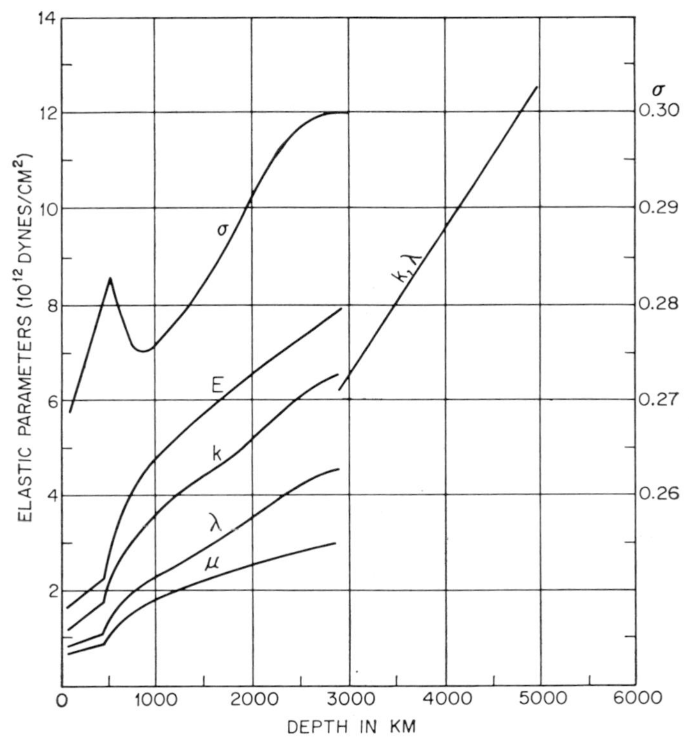

FIG. 13.2 Variation of the elastic constants. *(Bullen, 1947. Courtesy of Cambridge University Press.)*

accepted distribution, and Fig. 13.1 must be looked upon as showing only one possible hypothesis. Lambert and Darling (1951) discuss others.

13.4 The Other Elastic Constants. From density and the seismic-wave velocities, all the other elastic constants, λ, μ, k, σ, and Young's modulus E, can be calculated. From (10.94), (10.85), (10.45), and (13.3),

$$\mu = \rho V_s^2 \tag{13.9}$$

$$\lambda = \rho V_p^2 - 2\mu = \rho(V_p^2 - 2V_s^2) \tag{13.10}$$

$$E = 2\mu(1+\sigma) = 2\rho V_s^2 \left(1 + \frac{(V_p/V_s)^2 - 2}{2(V_p/V_s)^2 - 2}\right) = \rho V_s^2 \left(\frac{3V_p^2 - 4V_s^2}{V_p^2 - V_s^2}\right) \tag{13.11}$$

Bulk modulus is given by Eq. (13.7), and Poisson's ratio by (13.3). Values for these elastic constants can be calculated and are presented in Fig. 13.2, computed from values of density from Fig. 13.1 and values of seismic-wave velocity from Fig. 11.3.

13.5 Pressure and Gravity. Once we know the density at each depth, we can calculate the acceleration of gravity at any radius R using Eq. (13.4):

$$g = \gamma m R^{-2} = \gamma R^{-2} \int_0^R 4\pi r^2 \rho \, dr \qquad (13.12)$$

Using this equation, the value of g would be approximately as shown in Fig. 13.1. As one gets nearer the center of the earth, gravity tends to increase because of the decrease in distance. On the other hand, since the shells outside the point under consideration cause no gravitational pull, the decrease in attracting mass tends to lessen gravity. Down to 2,400 km gravity varies relatively little. It then slowly increases to the boundary of the core, inside of which it steadily drops to zero at the earth's center, the rate being sensitive to the variations in density.

When gravity and density are known, the pressure can be calculated for any radius R, under the assumption of fluidity, by integrating Eq. (13.4), inasmuch as the pressure is simply the weight of the overlying material:

$$P = \int_{R_V}^{R} - g\rho \, dr \qquad (13.13)$$

where R_V is the earth's radius (radius of a sphere of volume equal to the earth). This also is shown in Fig. 13.1.

These figures on the variation of V_p, V_s, ρ, the elastic constants, pressure, and gravity, with depth represent just about all that is known with any certainty about the deep interior of the earth. Any speculations which one makes concerning these regions must be consistent with these facts to be acceptable.

CHAPTER 14

MEASUREMENT OF GRAVITY

14.1 The Gravity Pendulum. In Chap. 12 it was shown that gravity can be measured using a pendulum. The accuracy of measuring gravity with Kater's pendulum is only 1½ parts in a million (Clark, 1940). It is limited by the accuracy with which the length of the pendulum can be determined. The relative gravity at two different stations can be compared with a greater accuracy by swinging a pendulum first at one place and then at the other and comparing the periods at the two locations. In Chap. 12 it was shown that the period of a simple pendulum is

$$T_P = 2\pi \left(\frac{L}{g}\right)^{1/2} \tag{14.1}$$

where g is the acceleration of gravity and L the length of the pendulum. Where the pendulum is not a simple one, L can be defined as the length of the equivalent simple pendulum. Solving this equation for g gives

$$g = \frac{4\pi^2 L}{T_P^2} \tag{14.2}$$

If one pendulum is swung at two locations, assuming the length of the pendulum is unchanged (neglecting any stretch of the pendulum caused by gravity), the ratio of gravity at the second station to that at the first station will be

$$\frac{g_2}{g_1} = \frac{T_1^2}{T_2^2} \tag{14.3}$$

The rate of change of gravity with change in period is given by

$$\frac{dg}{dT_P} = -\frac{8\pi^2 L}{T_P^3} = -\frac{2g}{T_P} \tag{14.4}$$

Thus for small changes in period

$$\Delta g = -\frac{2g\,\Delta T_P}{T_P} \tag{14.5}$$

FIG. 14.1 Gulf pendulum apparatus. Top: Complete apparatus with cover removed. Bottom: Quartz pendulums and knife-edge flats. (*Courtesy of Gulf Research and Development Co.*)

Using either Eq. (14.3) or (14.5), the relative gravity at two places can be determined more accurately than gravity itself can be conveniently measured at either one, since the accuracy of Δg in this case depends primarily on that of ΔT. Since L does not appear in either equation, the relative magnitude of the gravitational attraction at several points can be accurately compared even though the pendulum length is unknown.

The U.S. Coast and Geodetic Survey has compared gravity at 1,185 points in the United States with gravity at three base stations in Washington, D.C., using this method (Duerksen, 1949). The survey allows their pendulums to swing for 6 hr in order to get values of T accurate to 1 part in a million (Swick, 1942). With the use of the most modern exploration-geophysics pendulum apparatus the time has been reduced to as little as 30 min to obtain an accuracy of 1 part in 4 million in comparative gravity values (Nettleton, 1940). For this purpose, the period of two identical quartz pendulums at a field station is compared with that of a similar base station instrument (Fig. 14.1). The pairs of pendulums are mounted on one stand and swung 180° out of phase to decrease the effect of sway of the support as the pendulums swing.

FIG. 14.2 Worden gravimeter in use. (*Courtesy of Houston Technical Laboratories.*)

14.2 The Gravimeter. Even 30 min is an undesirably long time to take for a measurement of gravity. A faster operating type of instrument is the gravimeter (Fig. 14.2). Its operation is simple. The basic element is a weight suspended from a spring. In Fig. 14.3, m is the mass. It stretches the spring a length s which is measured on a scale. The stretch will be proportional to gravity

$$mg = \kappa s \tag{14.6}$$

where κ is called the spring constant. As in the case of the dependence of gravity on the period of a pendulum, a simple relation can be found between g and s by taking the derivative

$$\frac{\Delta g}{\Delta s} \approx \frac{dg}{ds} = \frac{\kappa}{m} \tag{14.7}$$

Within the elastic limit of the spring

$$\Delta g = \frac{\kappa}{m} \Delta s \tag{14.8}$$

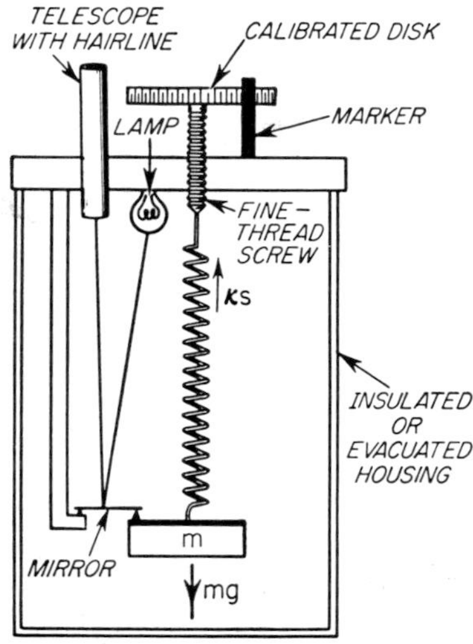

FIG. 14.3 Operating principle of a gravimeter. The dial is rotated raising or lowering the mass until the mirror reflects the lamp filament right on the hairline in the telescope.

The gravimeter constant κ/m can be determined by noting Δg and Δs at two places whose gravity was previously determined by pendulum. Then, since the instrument sensitivity is known, Δg can be found for any other location. Gravimeters can be built to have a measurable response to 10^{-8} of gravity, which means that relative gravity can be observed to a precision of 0.01 milligal.[1] However, because of the various corrections (discussed below) which must be made on the observed values, uncertainties in leveling the instrument, and effects of temperature on the system, the accuracy of measurement of gravity differences is rarely this great.

In order to get this great sensitivity gravimeters depend on extremely delicate springs. The Hoyt (Gulf Oil Co.) gravimeter, an exceptionally sensitive one, has a flat ribbon spring of helical shape (Fig. 14.4). As this spring stretches under a small increase in gravity, the lower end to which the gravimeter mass is attached rotates an amount which is proportional to the stretch. This rotation can be very accurately observed by regarding a fine line reflected by a mirror attached to the mass. A readable deflection of 0.0001 in. corresponds to 0.01 mg (Wyckoff, 1941).

Many gravimeters depend on being operated in a condition which is made very nearly unstable to provide high sensitivity. The principle of such an instrument is illustrated in Fig. 14.5. The mass m is pivoted at point P. Spring A supports the mass against gravity. A slight increase

[1] A milligal is one-thousandth part of a gal, which is a centimeter per second per second.

in gravity will cause the arm to rotate about P. But as the arm moves, not only does the length of spring A increase but also the angle θ it makes with the arm decreases. If θ and the spring length and strength are adjusted, the restoring moment can be made to increase only very slowly as the beam is deflected. Such a spring system, where deflection causes a change in the suspension system assisting gravity (in this case the change is θ), is said to be astatized. Such suspension systems are unstable, since if too great a deflection is allowed, the spring will be unable to support the mass.

In contrast to stable gravimeters such as the Hoyt gravimeter, in an astatized instrument the deflection may not be proportional to the change in gravity. To make the instrument response linear, a second spring B is commonly used (Fig. 14.5). The pull on this weak, auxiliary spring necessary to return m to its normal position is measured (the image of a lamp filament F is returned to a fixed point on the scale

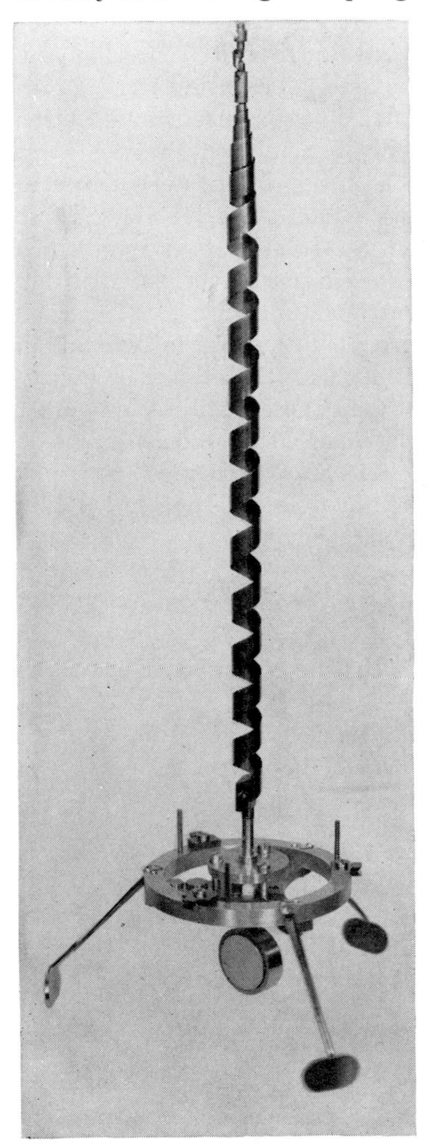

FIG. 14.4 Spring system of a Hoyt (Gulf Oil Co.) gravimeter. (*Courtesy of Gulf Research and Development Company.*)

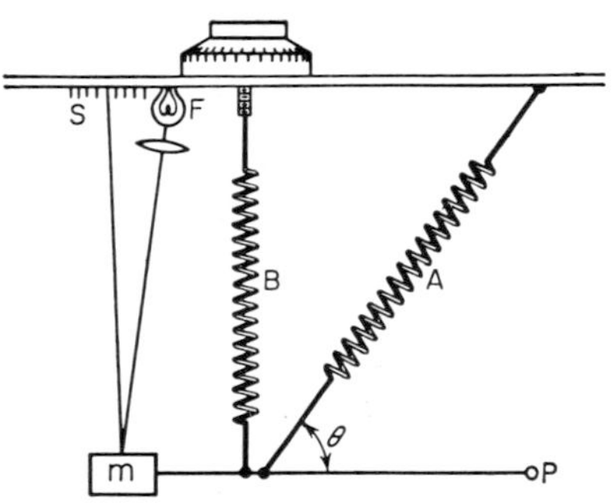

FIG. 14.5 Operating principle of an astatized gravimeter.

S). Since B does not have the main job of supporting m in the gravitational field, it can be very weak, and hence a large change in the length of B corresponds to a small change in gravity, which makes for great sensitivity in the instrument.

14.3 Gravity Corrections: Free Air. If the earth were a perfect sphere whose density varied only with distance from its center, at any point outside its surface gravity could be determined using Eq. (12.30), since all the mass would attract as though it was concentrated at the center. The earth departs from such a body in a number of ways. First it is ellipsoidal instead of spherical. The result is the dependence of gravity on position given in Eqs. (12.49), (12.50), and (12.51). These formulas give what is called normal gravity, the value at sea level which would exist if none of the inhomogeneities discussed below occurred. Normal gravity includes the effect of centrifugal force.

Another obvious departure from uniform conditions is the variation in elevation of the surface. The first result of this is that values of gravity measured at high elevations will be less than those made at low, other things being equal. This results from the inverse square dependence on distance in Newton's law [Eq. (12.23)]. To a first approximation we can get the dependence of gravity on elevation by differentiating Eq. (12.30) with respect to R_e:

$$\frac{dg}{dR_e} = \frac{d(\gamma M_e/R_e^2)}{dR_e} = -\frac{2\gamma M_e}{R_e^3} = -\frac{2g}{R_e} \tag{14.9}$$

where g is gravity and R_e is the earth's radius. For small elevation differences,

$$(\Delta g)_F = -\frac{2gh}{R_e} \tag{14.10}$$

where $(\Delta g)_F$ is the change in gravity on rising the distance h from a point at radius R_e, where gravity has the value g. Table 14.1 gives values of $(\Delta g)_F/\Delta h$ at various latitudes at sea level and at an elevation of 10 km, based on Jeffreys' (1952) figures for the earth's radius and on gravity values of the International Ellipsoid of 1930. The gradient is a function of elevation as well as latitude. Table 14.1 is based on theoretical considerations. The actual vertical gradient of gravity is difficult to measure accurately. However, Hammer's (1938) measurements of the gradient check theoretical figures within 1 per cent.

TABLE 14.1 RATE OF CHANGE OF GRAVITY WITH ELEVATION

Latitude	$-2g/R_e$ at sea level, mg/m	$-2g/R_e$ at h = 10,000 m, mg/m
0°	−0.3067	−0.3062
45°	−0.3080	−0.3075
90°	−0.3093	−0.3088

The Δg given by Eq. (14.10) is called the free-air correction. If it is subtracted [algebraically, $(\Delta g)_F$ is usually negative so the correction is positive] from the value of g given by Eq. (12.49), (12.50), or (12.51), letting h be the elevation above sea level, and this sum subtracted from the observed value of gravity g_0, the difference is called the free-air anomaly (Fig. 14.6).

$$g_F = g_0 - (g_I,\ g_J,\ \text{or}\ g_H) - (\Delta g)_F \tag{14.11}$$

The free-air anomaly is a measure of how much the earth departs from a uniform ellipsoid in which the rocks are of one density in any ellipsoidal layer from the earth's center outward. Making the elevation correction reduces all observations to what they would be if they were made at one elevation, in this case sea level.

14.4 Combined Topographic Correction. A part of the free-air anomaly results from the attraction of the continents and oceanic islands, which rise above sea level in some areas and not in others, and from the lack of attraction of the sea water, which replaces rock in the ocean basins. Since this land and water have been mapped, their effect can be calculated. Consider a small volume of matter ΔV of density ρ at a distance D from a gravity station. If D is large compared with the dimensions of the mass, then the matter can be treated as being concentrated at a point. In Fig. 14.7 gravity is being measured at Q, the mass $\rho\Delta V$ is concentrated at B and is an elevation z above Q. C is the center of the earth, and R_e is its radius.[1] The angles are as shown. The vertical component of the attraction of $\rho\Delta V$ will be

$$\Delta g = \frac{\gamma\rho \sin \beta}{D^2} \Delta V \tag{14.12}$$

Note that

$$BAQ = 180° - CAQ = 90° - \frac{\theta}{2} \tag{14.13}$$

From the law of sines and (14.13)

$$\frac{\sin \beta_c}{z} = \frac{\sin BAQ}{D} = \frac{\cos (\theta/2)}{D} \tag{14.14}$$

Note also that

$$\beta_h = \frac{\theta}{2} = \beta + \beta_c \tag{14.15}$$

[1] Strictly, R_e is the radius of curvature, which in an ellipsoidal body is not usually exactly equal to the geometric radius. Assuming the two are the same introduces negligible error (Hayford and Bowie, 1912).

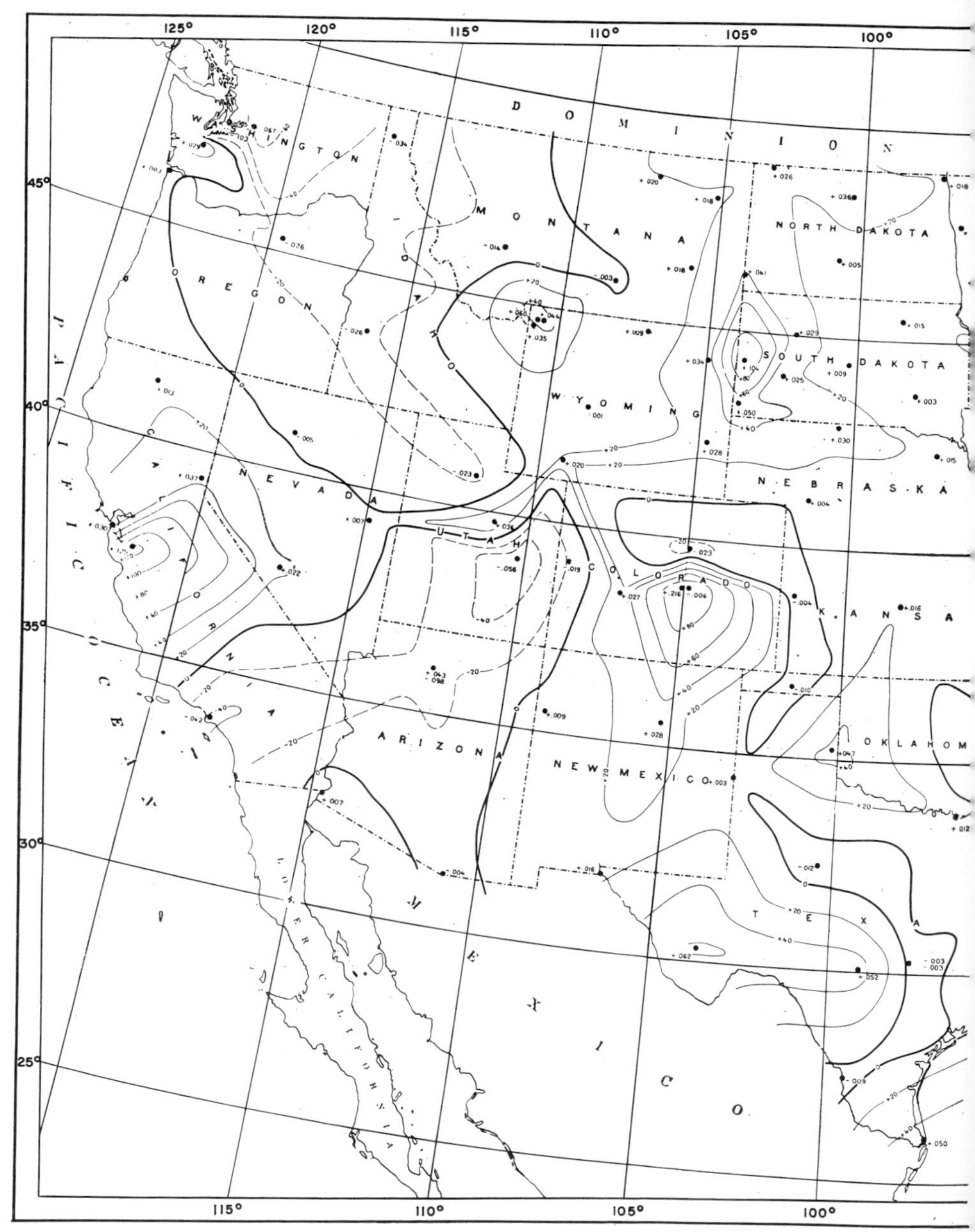

FIG. 14.6 Free-air anomalies in the

United States. (*After Bowie, 1917.*)

Using (14.14) and (14.15) to clear (14.12) of β one obtains

$$\Delta g = \frac{\gamma\rho \sin[(\theta/2) - \beta_c]}{D^2}\Delta V$$
$$= \frac{\gamma\rho \sin\{(\theta/2) - \sin^{-1}[z\cos(\theta/2)/D]\}}{D^2}\Delta V \qquad (14.16)$$

where, from the law of cosines,

$$D^2 = D_1^2 + z^2 + 2D_1z\cos BAQ \qquad (14.17)$$

From Fig. 14.7

$$D_1 = 2R_e \sin\frac{\theta}{2} \qquad (14.18)$$

From (14.13), (14.17), and (14.18)

$$D_2 = 4R_e^2\sin^2\frac{\theta}{2} + z^2 + 4R_ez\sin^2\frac{\theta}{2} = 4R_e(R_e + z)\sin^2\frac{\theta}{2} + z^2 \qquad (14.19)$$

The total effect at Q of all the mass excesses and deficiencies above and below sea level all over the area A of the world is

$$(\Delta g)_T = \int_A \int_{z=-h_Q}^{z=h_B} \frac{\gamma\rho\sin\{(\theta/2) - \sin^{-1}[z\cos(\theta/2)/D]\}}{D^2}\,dz\,dA \qquad (14.20)$$

where h_B is the elevation of B above Q and h_Q is the elevation of Q above sea level.

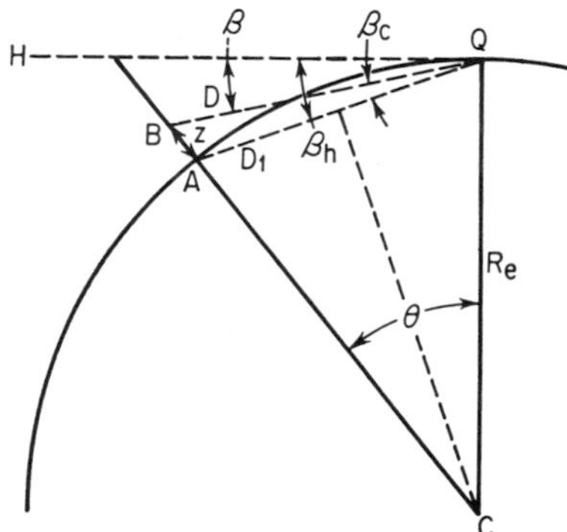

FIG. 14.7 Effect of mass irregularities on a spherical surface. (*After Hayford and Bowie, 1912.*)

This equation is too complex to integrate simply, so it must be solved numerically by summing up the effects of blocks of finite dimensions, treated as though they were concentrated at their centers. Hayford and Bowie (1912) used this method to compute the effect of topography for surveys run in the United States. To facilitate the calculations they made tables based on division of the earth into 33 zones surrounding a station and subdivision of each zone by radial lines into a total of 317 compartments. For each compartment they computed the effect of the mass present above sea level or missing beneath sea level for a wide range of average elevations of the compartment above or below sea level and for a wide range of elevations of the compartment above or below the station. They assumed the density of the surface rocks, ρ in Eq. (14.20), to be everywhere the same, 2.67 gm per cm^3. In the case of the oceans, they subtracted this from the density of sea water, 1.027 gm per cm³, giving a negative density representing the mass deficiency.

14.5 Bouguer Correction. At short distances, where the earth can be considered flat, a simpler formula than (14.20) can be used. Consider the attraction at the center S of a cylindrical ring reaching to a depth H_2 beneath the station and with its top H_1 below it, whose inner and outer radii are R_1 and R_2 (Fig. 14.8). The vertical component of the attraction

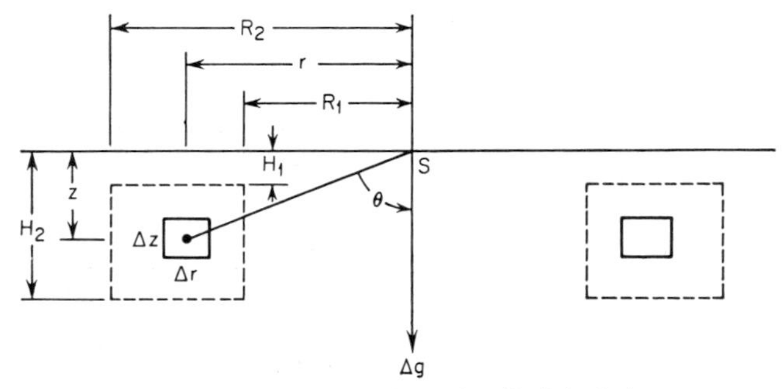

FIG. 14.8 Sectional view of cylindrical ring.

of any small ring-shaped element of the whole ring, of cross-sectional dimensions Δr and Δz at radius r and height z, is

$$\Delta g = \frac{2\pi\gamma\rho r \cos\theta \, \Delta z \, \Delta r}{r^2 + z^2} = \frac{2\pi\gamma\rho r z \, \Delta z \, \Delta r}{(r^2 + z^2)^{1\frac{1}{2}}} \tag{14.21}$$

The effect of the whole ring can be found by integrating this over the cross section of the cylinder:

$$\begin{aligned} \Delta g &= 2\pi\gamma\rho \int_{r=R_1}^{r=R_2} \int_{z=H_1}^{z=H_2} \frac{rz \, dz \, dr}{(r^2 + z^2)^{1\frac{1}{2}}} \\ &= 2\pi\gamma\rho[(R_1^2 + H_2^2)^{\frac{1}{2}} - (R_2^2 + H_2^2)^{\frac{1}{2}} - (R_1^2 + H_1^2)^{\frac{1}{2}} + (R_2^2 + H_1^2)^{\frac{1}{2}}] \end{aligned} \tag{14.22}$$

The effect of any compartment lying between two radial planes will be the appropriate fraction of what is given in (14.22). The effect of such a compartment is to increase gravity if an excess mass lies below the station and to decrease it if the mass lies above the station. The effect of a mass deficiency is the negative of this.

Now it becomes important to remember that for purposes of comparison the observations are to be reduced to what they would be if all the measurements were made at sea level or some other convenient reference elevation. The material between sea level and the station elevation contributes to the downward pull of gravity at the station. If the compartment under consideration is higher than the station, then its upper part exerts an upward pull, reducing gravity (Fig. 14.9). Since H_1 and

H_2 appear in (14.22) only to the second power, no distinction is made between the case when H_1 is positive and when it is negative. Therefore, (14.22) can be used only where H_1 and H_2 are of the same sign. In other cases, the topographic correction must be made in two steps, one to correct for the effect of the material between the elevation of the station and sea level and the other to correct for the effect of peaks and valleys referred to the station elevation.

The first of these two corrections is called the Bouguer correction after Pierre Bouguer, one of the leaders of the French gravity expedition to Peru which proved that the earth approximates an oblate spheroid (see Sec. 12.4). Out to the distance where the effect of the curvature of the earth's surface becomes significant, the effect of the slab between sea level and the station elevation can be found by substituting $H_1 = R_1 = 0$ into (14.22), obtaining

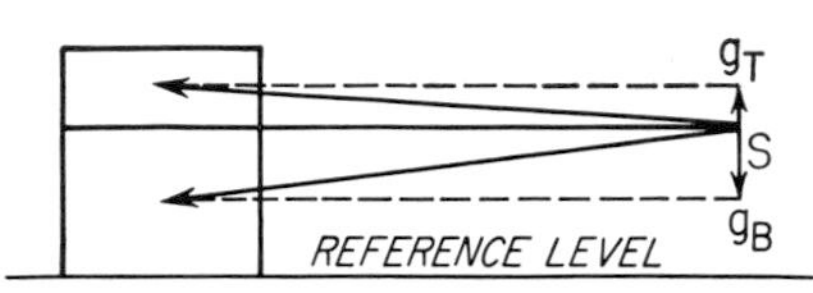

FIG. 14.9 Why topographic correction is made in two parts at short distances.

$$(\Delta g)_B = 2\pi\gamma\rho[R_2 + H_2 - (R_2^2 + H_2^2)^{1/2}] \tag{14.23}$$

H_2 must always be considered positive for purposes of calculation. The Bouguer correction is subtracted from the gravity anomaly for stations above sea level and added to it for stations below sea level.

14.6 Simple Topographic Correction. In the same region for which (14.23) is used to make the Bouguer correction, the remaining simple topographic correction can be found by substituting $H_1 = 0$, $H_2 = h_B$ in (14.22), obtaining

$$(\Delta g)_S = 2\pi\gamma\rho[R_2 - R_1 + (R_1^2 + h_B^2)^{1/2} - (R_2^2 + h_B^2)^{1/2}] \tag{14.24}$$

Although the Bouguer correction can be made in one step for all compartments out to R_2 simultaneously, the topographic correction must be determined for each compartment separately, and the individual corrections summed.

The topographic effect represented by (14.24) always decreases the observed gravity compared with what it would be if the land were level, regardless of whether the irregularities lie above or below the station or whether the station is above or below sea level (Fig. 14.10). A mountain rising above the station causes an upward component of gravity, while a valley results in a

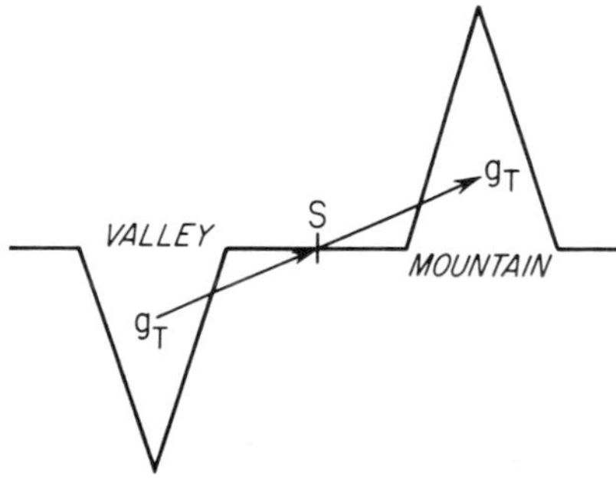

FIG. 14.10 Valleys and mountains both decrease observed gravity.

deficiency in downward attraction, which is equivalent to an upward pull. For this reason the topographic effect must be computed with care for a compartment which has nearly the same elevation as the station, or not enough will be measured. Averaging out the elevations of high and low land areas may give an average elevation for the compartment so near that of the station that most of the topographic effect is missed. For stations above sea level, the small topographic and Bouguer corrections are of opposite sign. For stations below sea level, the Bouguer correction changes sign but the topographic correction does not.

Equation (14.11) gave the gravity anomaly which resulted from all mass excesses and deficiencies throughout the earth. To eliminate that part of this anomaly due to topography, the topographic effect, including the Bouguer effect, must be subtracted from the free-air anomaly [using Eqs. (14.20) or (14.23) and (14.24)]. What remains is called the Bouguer anomaly (Fig. 14.11):

$$\begin{aligned} g_B &= g_F - (\Delta g)_T \text{ or } g_F \pm (\Delta g)_B + (\Delta g)_S \\ &= g_0 - (g_I,\ g_J, \text{ or } g_H) - (\Delta g)_F \pm (\Delta g)_B + (\Delta g)_S \end{aligned} \tag{14.25}$$

Remember that $(\Delta g)_B$ is subtracted for stations above sea level and added for stations below sea level. $(\Delta g)_F$ is a negative quantity if the station is above sea level, so $-(\Delta g)_F$ is usually positive. The free-air and Bouguer corrections are always of opposite sign.

The Bouguer anomaly represents the attraction of buried rocks of greater than normal density less the lack of attraction which results from abnormally low rock densities. When the effects of all known variations in rock density have been subtracted from the Bouguer anomaly, what remains can be used as a means of predicting other structures involving rocks of contrasting densities. Such studies of gravity anomalies have been extremely useful in determining crustal structure and will be discussed further in later chapters.

14.7 Simple Elevation and Bouguer Corrections for Local Surveys. Where gravity values are to be compared for stations within a limited area only, corrections for distant topography can be neglected and a simplified Bouguer correction used. In this case it is a common practice to correct for the Bouguer effect by assuming that it is equal to the attraction of an infinite horizontal plate immediately beneath the station. The effect of such a slab can be found by integrating Eq. (14.21):

$$(\Delta g)_b = 2\pi\gamma\rho \int_{r=0}^{r=\infty} \int_{z=0}^{z=h} \frac{rz\,dr\,dz}{(r^2 + z^2)^{1\frac{1}{2}}} = 2\pi\gamma\rho h \tag{14.26}$$

where h is the elevation of the station above the reference elevation. The effect of topography is found using (14.24) as before. Tables for making

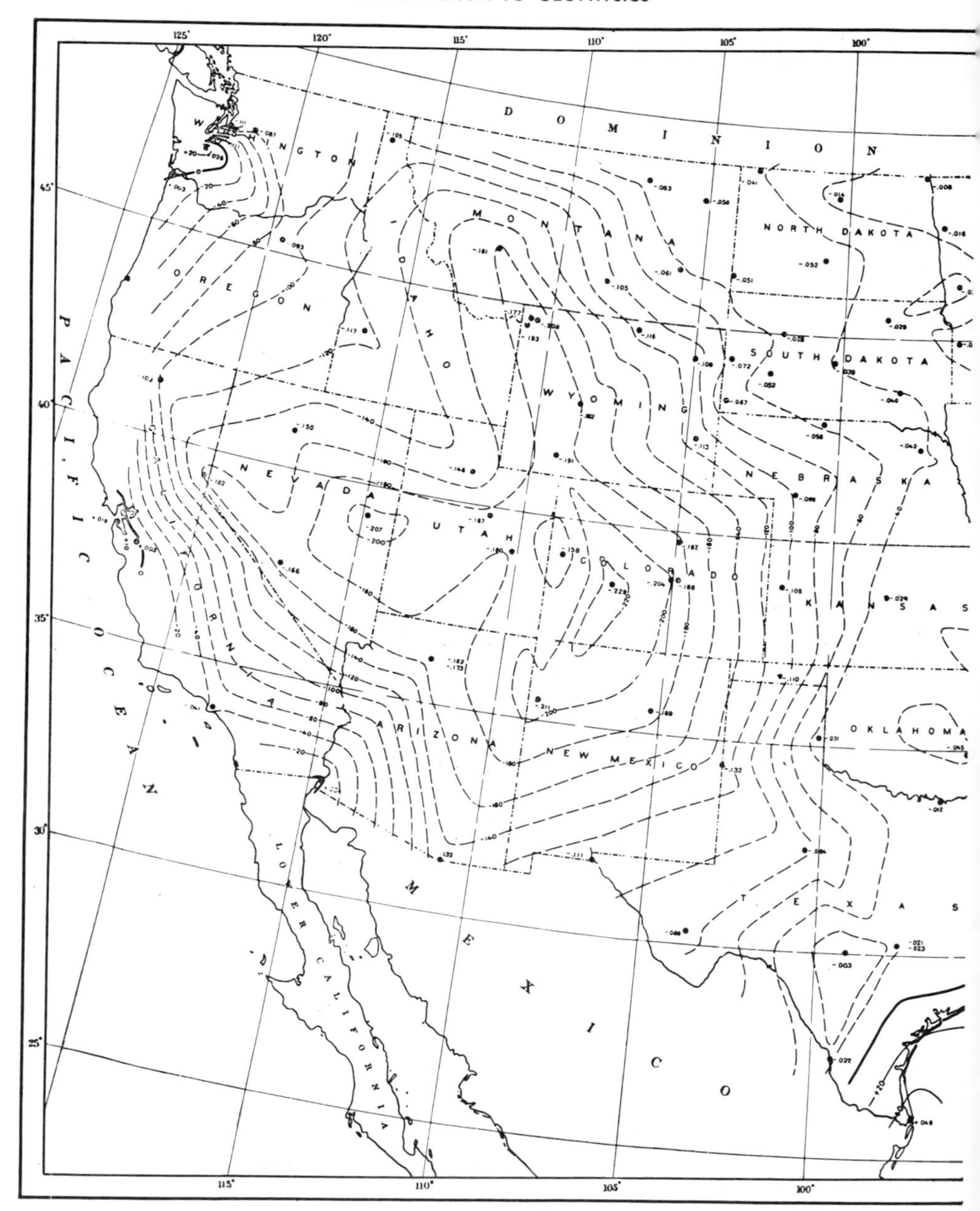

FIG. 14.11 Bouguer anomalies in the

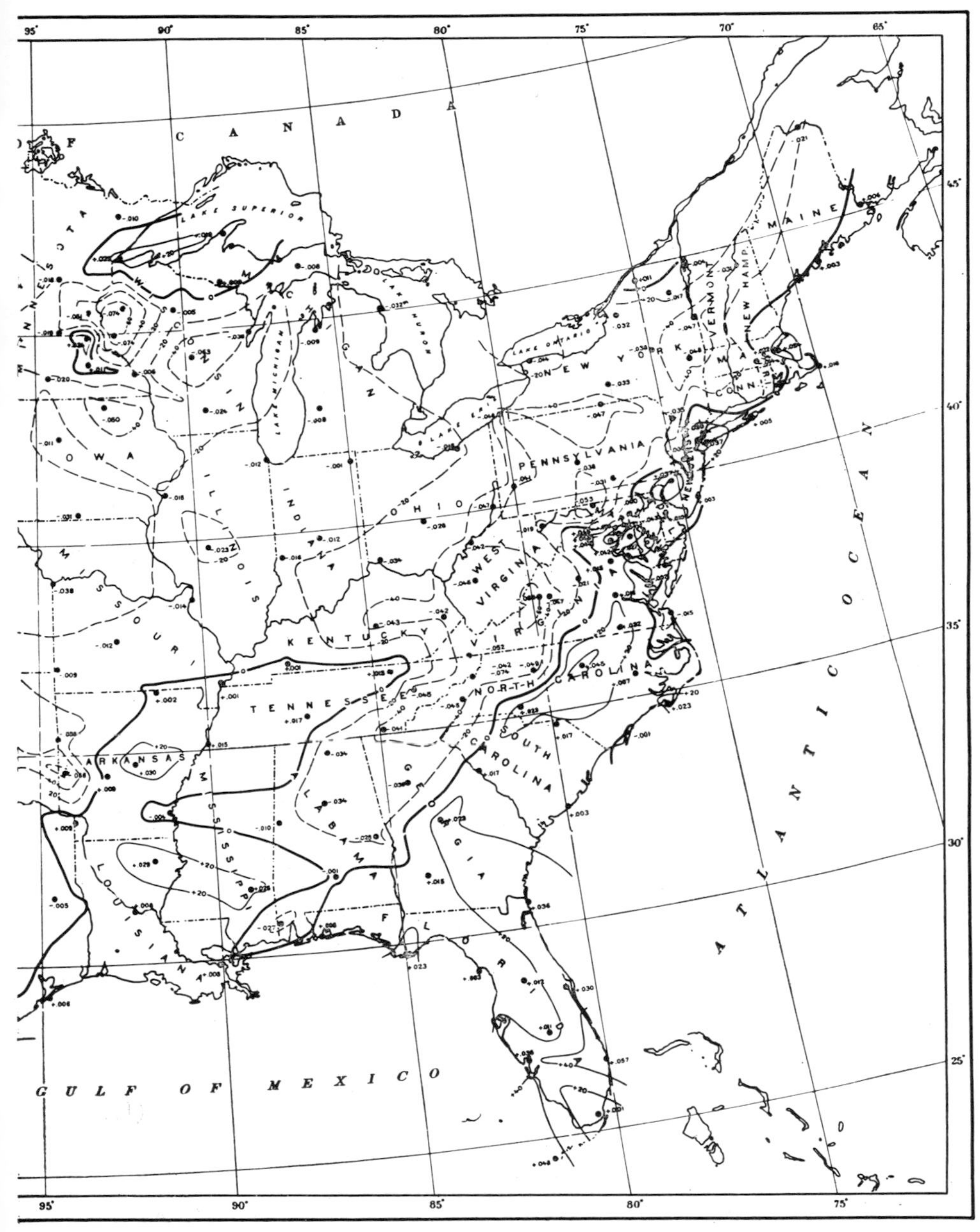

United States. (*After Bowie, 1917.*)

topographic corrections at short distances by this method are given by Nettleton (1940).

When this method is used, the Bouguer and free-air effects can be calculated simultaneously. From (14.10) and (14.26),

$$(\Delta g)_c = -\frac{2gh}{R_e} + 2\pi\gamma\rho h \tag{14.27}$$

Using (12.53) to clear this of γ,

$$(\Delta g)_c = -\frac{2gh}{R_e} + (2\pi\rho h)\frac{3g}{4\pi\rho_{av}R_e} = -\frac{2g}{R_e}\left(1 - \frac{3\rho}{4\rho_{av}}\right)h \tag{14.28}$$

where ρ_{av} is the average density of the earth and ρ is the density of the surface rock. The combined Bouguer and free-air correction is called the elevation correction. In this case the Bouguer anomaly as generally used is given by

$$g_b = g_0 - g_I - (\Delta g)_c + (\Delta g)_S \tag{14.29}$$

where g_0 is observed gravity, g_I is gravity given by the International Ellipsoid formula (12.49), $(\Delta g)_c$ is the combined elevation correction, and $(\Delta g)_S$ is the topographic correction given by (14.24).

The Bouguer gravity anomaly found by this method is not the true Bouguer gravity. Equation (14.24) can be used only for distances where the effect of the curvature of the earth's surface is small. The effects of more distant topography are neglected. These effects do not vary rapidly from place to place, so that the simplified method is useful in locating small, sharp gravity anomalies due to local irregularities in density. If a map of gravity values is contoured like a topographic map, such anomalies stand out as pimples on the slowly changing regional pattern. On such a chart, lines of equal gravity are called isogals.

If a correction for a sheet of material of thickness h were to be made for a spherical shell instead of a flat plate, the world-wide Bouguer correction would be twice that found from (14.26), since in this case, using (12.30),

$$\Delta g = \frac{\gamma M_{\text{shell}}}{R_e^2} = \frac{\gamma 4\pi R_e^2 h\rho}{R_e^2} = 4\pi\gamma\rho h \tag{14.30}$$

Using (14.30) in place of (14.26) would not increase the interpretability of local gravity surveys unless world-wide topographic corrections were also made. The labor of doing this would not be justified by the small improvement in accuracy of gravity anomalies which would result.

14.8 Earth Tides. Although gravity has been treated up to this point as though it were a constant at any point on the earth's surface, this is only approximately true. If gravity is measured as a function of time at any place, it will be found to rise and fall in a manner analogous to the rise and fall of the oceanic tides (Fig. 14.12). Since the tides are a result of the attraction of the moon and the sun, it is obvious that these bodies must contribute slightly to the gravitational attraction at the earth's surface. Wyckoff (1936) has calculated that their contribution is of

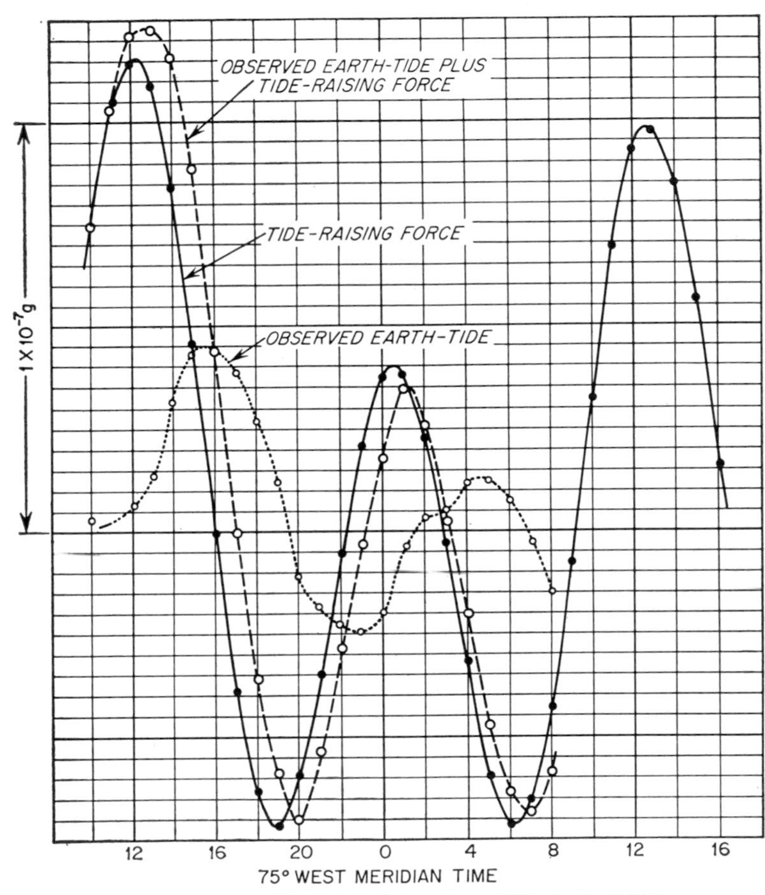

FIG. 14.12 Tidal variations of g. (*Wyckoff, 1936.*)

the order of ± 0.15 milligal, changing with the earth's position with respect to the sun and moon. Wyckoff observed variations of this order of magnitude, but found that the actual gravity fluctuation was delayed about 50 min, on the average, behind the calculated pull of the sun and moon.

This delay can be explained as being due to the deformation of the solid body of the earth by the tidal forces. The size of the component not explained by the lunar and solar attraction is of the order of magnitude of

0.045 mg. If the gravitational attraction of the shifting oceanic and atmospheric tidal bulges is neglected and the variation assumed to be due solely to a rise in the height of the land surface, the height of the solid tide can be estimated from Eq. (14.10) to be 0.073 m. Gutenberg (1951*c*) states that it is as great as twice this at times.

The size of the solid tide is controlled by the rigidity of the earth. Tidal measurements indicate that the average rigidity of the earth is about 1.53×10^{12} dynes per cm^2 (Jeffreys, 1952). This is nearly twice that of steel, which is about 0.8×10^{12} dynes per cm^2. Within the mantle, rigidity varies from about 0.63×10^{12} at the bottom of the crust to 3.03×10^{12} dynes per cm^2 at the core boundary (Fig. 13.2). The core is either liquid or so plastic that shear waves are too rapidly attenuated in it to be observed. The average rigidity of the earth is in reasonable agreement with the concept of a fluid core, though a plastic core of lower rigidity than the mantle is possible.

CHAPTER 15

ISOSTASY

When world-wide Bouguer anomalies are considered, it is found that there is a systematic relation between the average elevation of a region and the computed gravity anomaly (Fig. 14.11). In high areas the gravity is less than average, and over the oceanic areas it is greater. A similar discrepancy is found in the deviations of the plumb line from the vertical. A mountain range would be expected to pull the plumb bob toward itself, but actual deflections are not nearly so great as would be expected from the visible mass of the mountain. This means that beneath high areas the rocks are of below average density and beneath ocean basins they are above average.

15.1 Pratt's Theory. This observed relation between Bouguer gravity and elevation can be explained if we suppose that everywhere on the earth there is the same weight of material in a vertical column of rock:

$$\int_0^R g\rho \, dh = \text{constant} \tag{15.1}$$

Here R is the distance of the surface of the earth from its center, g is gravity and varies with depth; ρ is the density of the rock and varies both horizontally and vertically.

If beneath a certain level at radius R_c, called the level of compensation, the earth is composed of concentric shells of uniform composition, (15.1) can be rewritten

$$\int_{R_c}^R g\rho \, dh = \text{constant} \tag{15.2}$$

If R_c and R are not too different, to a first approximation the variation of g with depth and latitude can be ignored and gravity treated as a constant. (The range of variation of g with latitude is only 0.5 per cent, and within the first 100-km depth the increase is also only 0.5 per cent.)

Although there is a large variation in the density of rocks, most of the observed Bouguer anomaly can be explained by a simple density distribution first proposed by J. H. Pratt in 1859 (Fig. 15.1). According to this hypothesis, each column of rock at the earth's surface may be visualized as consisting of material having a uniform density equal to the weighted average of the density of all the rocks in the column and extending down to the depth of compensation. This density can be easily calculated. It is inversely proportional to the height of the column above the level of compensation:

$$\frac{\rho_n}{\rho_0} = \frac{H}{H_n} = \frac{H}{H + h_n} \tag{15.3}$$

where ρ_n is the density of any column rising a height h_n above sea level, ρ_0 is the density of a column whose top is at sea level, and H is the depth to the level of compensation. If h_n is always much smaller than H, ρ_n varies very little.

The mass M_n of the column between the level of compensation and the reference elevation (sea level is normally used as a reference) would be

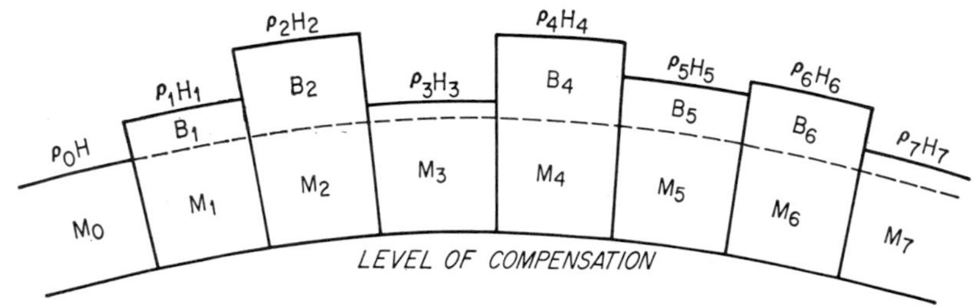

FIG. 15.1 Pratt's theory of isostatic compensation.

decreased by the mass B_n above this height. But in calculating the Bouguer gravity the effect of B_n on the gravity anomaly was taken care of by the combined topographic correction (see Chap. 14). To correct for the equivalent lack of mass in M_n, another correction must be made. This is called the isostatic correction. It can be calculated using Eq. (14.16) or, near the station, (14.21). Obviously, the isostatic correction must very nearly equal the combined topographic correction. They differ only because of the difference in the elevations of the masses involved.

J. F. Hayford and W. Bowie (1912) tested this theory by computing the isostatic correction for 89 stations in the United States, assuming the depth of compensation to be 113.7 km. When they subtracted the isostatic correction from the Bouguer anomaly, the remainder, called the isostatic anomaly, was in almost all cases substantially smaller than either the free-air or Bouguer anomalies (Fig. 15.2). Later studies included a total of 1,185 stations and compared the isostatic anomalies for eight different depths of compensation (Bowie, 1917, 1924; Duerksen, 1949). On the basis of studies of both gravity and plumb-line variations, Bowie concluded that the most probable depth of the level of compensation based on Pratt's hypothesis is 96 km.

Bowie (1927) found the mean of 585 world-wide isostatic anomalies without regard to sign (+ or −) to be only 19 milligals. This corresponds to the gravitative attraction of an infinite slab of density 2.67 gm per cm^3 and 170 m thick. The mean anomaly with regard to sign is 5 milligals, which is therefore what should be subtracted from all his observations to bring them to the reference level for which the average of all anomalies is zero. Local gravity anomalies of as much as −204 milligals have been observed, but the average for regions several hundred kilometers in diameter are always much smaller than this. The largest anomalies are associated with other large nearby anomalies of opposite sign, making the regional anomalies small (Umbgrove, 1947; see also Chaps. 19 to 21). The fact that the vast majority of isostatic anomalies are much smaller than the free-air and Bouguer anomalies in the same regions is evidence that the original assumption of hydrostatic equilibrium at some depth is justified, and that Pratt's concept of the variation of density in different columns of rock is a good first approximation to reality. The concept of a surface layer essentially floating on the underlying part of the mantle is called the theory of isostasy, and the surface layers are spoken of as being in isostatic equilibrium.

On the other hand, the fact that the isostatic anomalies are not zero shows that Pratt's conception is not a perfect approximation. The isostatic anomalies which remain must be the result either of departures from uniformity of the densities in the columns beneath the gravity stations or of failure of hydrostatic equilibrium to be obtained at the level of compensation. The average difference in density of an individual column from that assumed by Pratt would be 170 m per 96 km, or 0.18 per cent, or 0.05 gm per cm^3 out of about 3.00 gm per cm^3. Some anomaly is to be expected at most places because of the extreme complexity of geologic conditions in almost all areas.

15.2 Airy's Theory. The assumption of uniform density in any column above the level of compensation is obviously only a rough first approximation. All that we know from surface geologic and seismologic studies indicates that the distribution of rocks is very complex. In Chap. 11 it was pointed out that beneath mountains there is a root of low-density rocks and that beneath the oceans the granitic layer of the continents is thin or absent.

Pratt's theory may be thought of as a first approximation to existing conditions. G. B. Airy in 1855 proposed a better approximation (Fig. 15.3). He postulated that the surface rocks of the earth may be likened to a series of logs of different diameter but the same density floating in water. The larger the log, the higher its upper surface would be, since each displaces its own weight of water. Airy supposed the crust to be composed of blocks of one density but different thicknesses floating in a

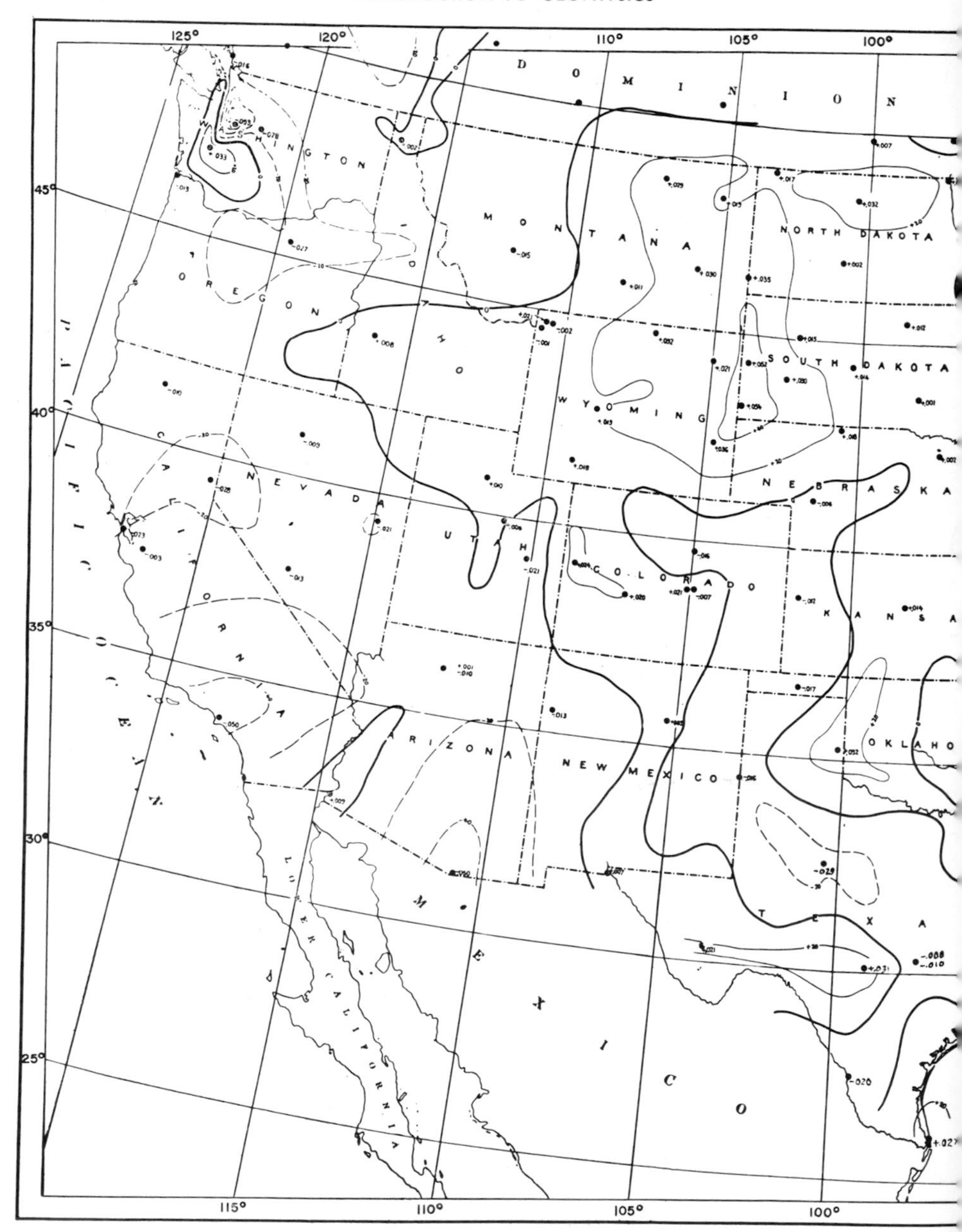

Fig. 15.2 Isostatic anomalies in the United States based on

Pratt's theory, depth of compensation 113.7 km. (*Bowie, 1917.*)

heavier substratum. The weight of the part of the block above sea level is held up by the buoyancy of a root extending below the normal depth of the low-density surface layer:

$$D_n(\rho_b - \rho_a) = h_n\rho_a \tag{15.4}$$

where D_n is the length the block extends beneath the bottom of a block whose top rises just to sea level, h_n is the elevation of its top above sea

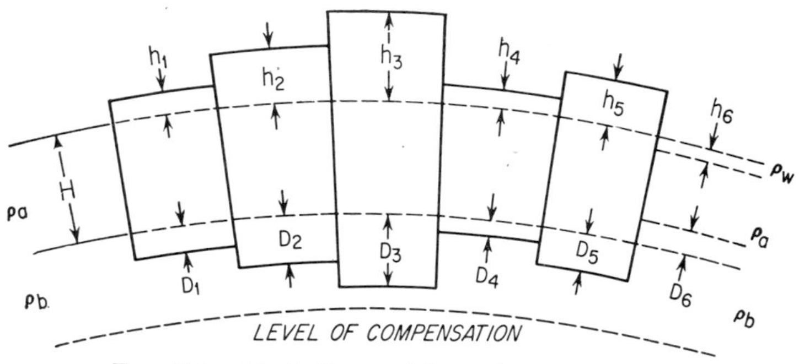

FIG. 15.3 Airy's theory of isostatic compensation.

level, ρ_a is the density of the surface layer, and ρ_b is the density of the underlying material. Using (15.4), the total length of the block is found to be

$$H_n = H + D_n + h_n = H + \left(\frac{\rho_a}{\rho_b - \rho_a} + 1\right) h_n = H + \frac{\rho_b h_n}{\rho_b - \rho_a} \tag{15.5}$$

For oceanic blocks, (15.4) and (15.5) become

$$D_n(\rho_b - \rho_a) = h_n(\rho_a - \rho_w) \tag{15.6}$$

$$H_n = H - \frac{\rho_b - \rho_w}{\rho_b - \rho_a} h_n \tag{15.7}$$

where ρ_w is the density of sea water.

This theory differs from Pratt's in that the depth of the compensating mass is different. Equation (15.2) still holds if R_c is defined as at or below the bottom of the longest column, number 3 in Fig. 15.3. The isostatic correction can be found as before using Eqs. (14.16) and (14.21).

W. A. Heiskanen has compared isostatic anomalies using the Airy hypothesis with those obtained using the Pratt-Hayford-Bowie system. In general the average anomaly without regard to sign is lower for the Airy-type density distribution, though for many individual stations and even regions the reverse is true (Daly, 1940). Heiskanen tried various thickness for H, ranging from 20 to 100 km, and values for $\rho_b - \rho_a$ ranging from 0.2 to 0.6 gm per cm³. For 296 stations in the United States, the mean Hayford isostatic anomaly without regard to sign was 9.1 mg, the mean Airy anomaly assuming $H = 60$ km was 7.8 mg; and assuming $H = 40$ km it was 7.4 mg. In order to eliminate any bias resulting from greater concentration of stations in some parts of the country than in others, he also made a comparison using the average values of the anomalies in seven large regions. The range of the average anomalies in the United States in this case was slightly less for a 60 km Airy-type surface layer than for the other two assumptions.

15.3 Heiskanen's Method. The next step is to assume blocks of different length and different density. Heiskanen has tried this also

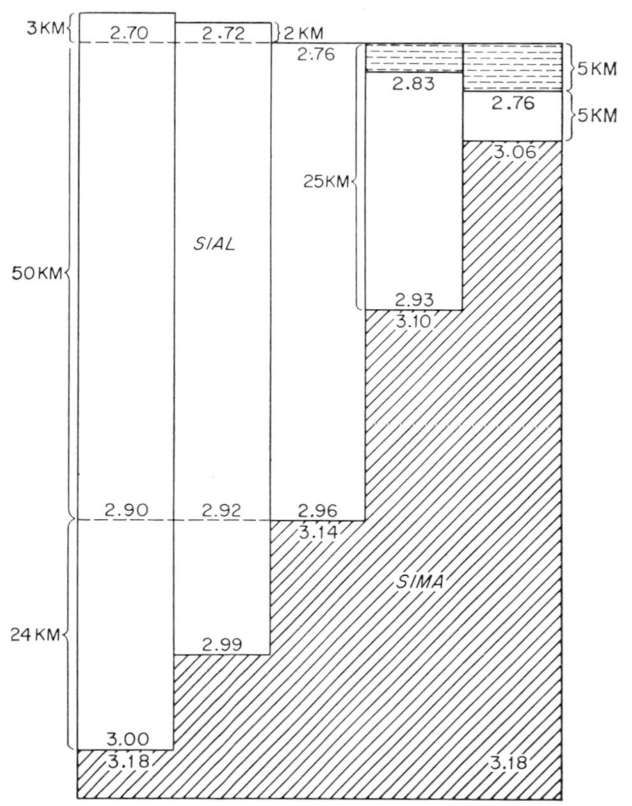

FIG. 15.4 Heiskanen's theory of isostatic compensation. (*After Heiskanen, 1933.*)

(Fig. 15.4). His method combines both Pratt's and Airy's assumptions and allows also for the known increase in density with depth. The surface density is assumed to vary with elevation, decreasing upward from 2.76 gm per cm^3 at sea level to 2.70 gm per cm^3 at 3 km elevation. In any column, density is assumed to increase downward 0.004 gm per cm^3 per km of depth in the light surface rocks and at half this rate in the underlying denser material. The resulting anomalies are slightly, but only very slightly, smaller than those obtained for the Airy distribution. For the 296 American stations, the average Heiskanen isostatic anomaly was 7.1 mg. The range of the anomalies was slightly larger than for the simple Airy assumption.

From the geological point of view, the Heiskanen model is clearly the best, since it is based on knowledge of density variations obtained independently of gravity measurements. The fact that it yields low anomalies not only supports the theory of isostasy but shows also that the density variations assumed are a reasonable approximation to what actually exists.

The amount of information which can be obtained from gravity studies such as described above is limited. There is no unique mass distribution which is required by the observed gravity variations. Rather, there are an infinite number of possible distributions. Other geological and geophysical information must be used to choose which ones are most reasonable. The simple pattern of density distribution which gives the least average anomaly is not necessarily the most nearly correct, though it is likely to be, as all lines of evidence indicate that the structure of the earth is not simple but complex. To the geologist the patterns of anomalies are more interesting than their smallness, as comparing the effects of postulated local density irregularities with local anomalies is a means of testing hypotheses concerning the earth's structure. Furthermore, there is no reason to suppose that the assumption of hydrostatic equilibrium at some depth of the order of magnitude of 96 km is any more than a rough first approximation to the truth.

15.4 Indirect Correction. There is one small, systematic error that was introduced in all the gravity corrections described above and in Chap. 14. In them all elevations were referred to sea level, which was assumed to be spheroidal in shape. Actually, sea level is not quite so symmetrical. The attraction of the land masses draws the water up onto the shore, leaving the ocean surface slightly basin-shaped. The surface from which elevation is actually measured is called the geoid. It is the equipotential surface which most nearly approximates mean sea level. It may be visualized as the surface passing through the continents which the water table would assume if the rock were a porous, permeable mass which exerted no capillary or other forces on the water other than purely gravitational forces.

Beneath the oceans the geoid falls below the spheroid; beneath the land it rises above it. The amount of distortion is small, rarely if ever exceeding 10 m. Its position can be calculated well enough that an additional correction can be made on the gravity anomaly to take it into account. This is called the indirect correction.

15.5 Glacial Disturbances. The fact that large isostatic anomalies do exist makes it necessary to qualify the assumption of hydrostatic equilibrium and to consider what geologic processes might tend to force the earth out of equilibrium if this condition once existed. In areas where there is current tectonic activity, as evidenced by frequent earthquakes and volcanic activity, there are often also strong gravity anomalies (see Chap. 19), showing that tectonic forces can push parts of the crust out of equilibrium. In areas where it is known that the earth was until recently covered by a heavy cap of ice, as in Scandinavia and Ontario, the earth's surface is rising today and gravity anomalies are frequently negative (Figs. 15.2 and 15.5), showing that a readjustment to hydrostatic equilibrium is still going on. Gutenberg (1954) estimates the maximum rate of uplift in both areas to be about 1 m per century. He estimates that in Fennoscandia about 250 m of uplift have occurred since the removal of the icecap 9,000 years ago, and 200 m more of uplift must occur to reestablish equilibrium. This readjustment requires that beneath the crust material flows into the region of uplift from surrounding areas.

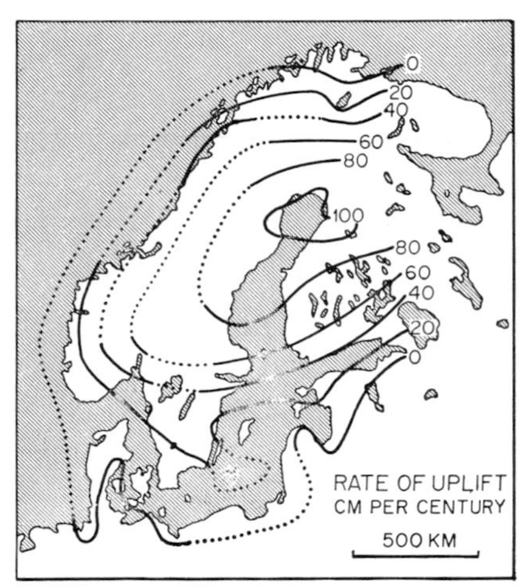

FIG. 15.5 Present rate of uplift in Fennoscandia. (*Gutenberg, 1954.*)

15.6 Effects of Erosion and Deposition. The processes of erosion and sedimentation likewise would produce anomalies if it were not for compensating subcrustal mass transfers. That such processes occur is proved by measurements of gravity in regions of rapid deposition of sediments such as the Nile and Mississippi deltas (Daly, 1940). Here positive gravity anomalies would be expected unless the crust sinks as fast as the sediments accumulate. Lack of such anomalies proves that the crust does sink into the substratum. Ewing and associates (1950) have shown that along the Atlantic Coast of the United States, the bottom of the continental shelf sediments is below the level of the adjoining ocean floor (Fig. 17.6). The bottom of the wedge rises oceanward. This situation is most easily explained by supposing that the wedge of sediments sank under its own weight as it accumulated. The rock surface in central Greenland dips to form a basin beneath the glacier in a similar manner (Gutenberg, 1954).

Large negative anomalies are not found in most mountain regions, even where it is clear from the geologic evidence that thousands or even tens of thousands of meters of rock have been eroded away. The mountains must rise as their summits are removed, tending to maintain their topographic eminence over long periods of time. There may even be a tendency for isostatic adjustment to increase the prominence of mountains. The average height of the land will change only as the average density of the underlying rock column changes. If the downcutting in valleys exceeds the rate of erosion on mountain peaks, the height of the peaks will increase relative to the average elevation of the area. Thus, until the relief of the land is past maturity, the highest mountains may rise solely owing to erosion combined with isostatic adjustment.

An estimate of the rate of mass transfer necessary to compensate for erosion can be obtained by noting the amount of sediment carried to the sea each year. At the present rate, the average elevation of the United States is reduced 0.0013 in. per year, or 0.33 cm per century (Dole and Stabler, 1909). At this rate the whole country will be washed away in only 22.5 million years. Nearly 800 million tons of matter are transported to the sea each year. The volume of rock, however, is only a little over $\frac{1}{16}$ cubic mile, so the compensating flow required is not great.

15.7 Mechanism of Compensation. The mass transfers required to balance the shifting of rock loads at the surface presumably occur at the bottom of the crust or beneath it. There must be some subcrustal flow of matter from regions where material is being accumulated to those where it is being removed by erosion. In as much as there is in general an increase in density with depth, the volume of material shifted at the bottom of the column will be less than that transferred at the surface. Thus if 1 km of granite of density 2.7 gm per cm^3 is eroded from a mountain and deposited as 1.13 km of sediments, average density 2.4 gm per cm^3 in a valley, only 0.90 km of gabbro at 3.0 gm per cm^3 or 0.82 km of dunite at 3.3 gm per cm^3 will have to move to maintain isostatic equilibrium. The height of the mountain will be reduced only by between 0.10 and 0.18 km; the valley filled up by between 0.23 and 0.31 km.

As the elevation difference becomes less, the rate of transfer will decrease because of the reduction in stream gradient. If the material transferred in compensation is of greater density than that shifted at the surface, equilibrium will be asymptotically approached. If there were then no forces acting to disturb the situation, one could expect the surface of the earth today, after billions of years of erosion and sedimentation, to be all ocean without a single island.

Fortunately for us, there are reasons why this equilibrium is never reached. One proposed explanation is that the matter transferred underground has the same density as the surface materials. The weight of accumulating sediments compacts the bottom of the underlying column, so that at a depth of a few kilometers, the sediments are as dense as the crystalline rocks from which they were formed. Metamorphism may be aided by the rise in temperature with depth. The Paleozoic sediments of the Appalachian geosyncline exposed today in the eastern United States have densities close to those of the common crystalline rocks. If the compensating subcrustal currents involved rocks of the same chemical composition as surface rocks, there would be no reason why the mountains could not rise as fast as they were eroded off, and the process go on indefinitely. However, the rigidity of surface rocks suggests that the crust is in general too strong to flow easily and implies that the mass transfers are more likely at greater depth, possibly in the outer mantle, where the rocks are of greater density and of different composition from those common at the surface. Therefore, to prevent all the land from being ultimately worn away, some other process is needed to create new land masses.

The common existence of peneplains in the older rocks suggests that many times in the past great areas have been reduced a good way toward equilibrium. In every case, something has happened to upset conditions and start the cycle anew. Examination of the geologic record shows that the process of peneplanation is terminated by sudden upheavals. The raising of large areas of new land is not a slow, gradual process, like peneplanation. Thus we may look upon isostasy as a process which tries to establish uniform conditions of equilibrium but is repeatedly thwarted by unbalancing disturbances.

15.8 The Law of Isostasy. The theory of isostasy has been so well confirmed that it has become one of the basic laws of geology. In physics a law is usually a precise relationship, often expressible as a mathematical equation. Few geologic laws are so simple. From the above discussions we can attempt to state the law of isostasy in explicit terms as: *All large land masses on the earth's surface tend to sink or rise so that, given time for adjustment to occur, their masses are hydrostatically supported from below, except where local stresses are acting to upset equilibrium.* The term isostasy itself refers to this state of hydrostatic balance, which is never quite achieved. It is a widely used expression. Often, it is used in a vague way to refer to the general phenomena of adjustment. Since it cannot by the nature of the situation be a precise concept, one must be very careful to have a clear understanding of its meaning and use it only to refer to the state of equilibrium which is approached.

Any anomalies which cannot be explained by reasonable density distributions represent departures of the earth from isostatic equilibrium. These are usually very small, but there are exceptions. Where equilibrium does not exist, the earth is under stress. For such anomalies to exist, forces must be acting to hold the earth in this stressed state. The size of the gravity variations is a measure of the size of the forces involved.

CHAPTER 16

TECTONIC FORCES

Isostasy requires that subterranean rock transfers take place to compensate for surface movements of material. These could occur most easily if the interior of the earth were liquid. The existence of perfect isostatic equilibrium would imply that beneath the level of compensation the interior of the earth is fluid, but there are several reasons why it is doubtful if the earth's mantle is in this state. First of all, it transmits shear waves. A perfect liquid will not do this. A viscous liquid might if its viscosity were high enough, but it would have to be higher than is likely. As shown in Chap. 9, the coefficient of absorption for seismic waves through the mantle is less than 0.0001 per km. Absorption in a viscous liquid would be expected to be much greater.

Another point is that earthquakes are common to a depth of 700 km (Fig. 7.1). The pattern of ground motions from deep-focus earthquakes is similar to that of shallow-focus tectonic shocks (see Sec. 9.5), suggesting that both result from similar shearing fractures. In a liquid one would not get such a sudden shearing. Earthquakes originating beneath 700 km have never been observed, so that the evidence for the earth's being solid beyond this depth is less definite. However, it was shown (Chap. 15) that isostatic adjustment took place at a depth of probably less than 150 not 700+ km.

Another piece of evidence comes from the measurement of the tides in the solid earth (Sec. 14.8). From their amplitude, the rigidity of the earth is estimated to be 1.53×10^{12} dynes per cm^2, almost twice that of steel. Such a high rigidity does not seem reasonable for a liquid. All this evidence implies that the outer mantle and crust are largely or entirely solid.

Even those who recognize the impossibility of the mantle being liquid often speak of the earth behaving like a fluid. The answer may be that the earth can behave as a rigid body to forces of short duration but for long-continued stresses acts like a fluid. Just why this should be so or if it is true is unknown. The times involved are too great for laboratory testing. A better idea of the possible nature of the mechanism can be had from study of how materials react to short-duration stresses.

16.1 Elastic Yielding. The simplest form of yielding is elastic. In this case the body is not permanently deformed but only temporarily altered. On removal of the stress it returns to its original size and shape. In the simplest case the strain is at all times proportional to the stress causing it. There are three basic equations which describe this type of behavior. (See Secs. 10.2 and 10.4 for a more detailed treatment.) For shear,

$$\frac{F}{S} = 2\mu\phi \tag{16.1}$$

For dilatation,

$$\frac{F}{S} = E\frac{\Delta L}{L} \tag{16.2}$$

and

$$\sigma = \frac{\Delta D/D}{\Delta L/L} \tag{16.3}$$

where F is the force exerted on the area S, L is length, D is diameter, μ is rigidity, E is Young's modulus, σ is Poisson's ratio, and ϕ, ΔL, and ΔD are the strains (Fig. 16.1).

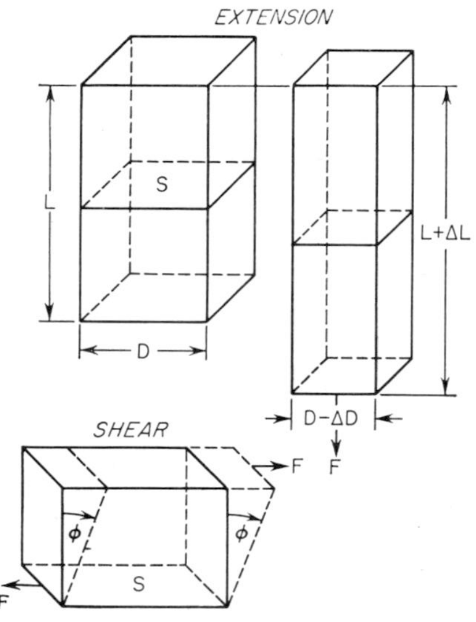

FIG. 16.1 Extension and shear.

Many common materials are elastic under the usual range of stresses. Metals are a good example. Springs are often made of metal because of this property. But if too great a pull is exerted on a spring, the strain will cease being proportional to the stress. The body either will deform in a more complex manner or will break.

16.2 Elastic Afterworking. Equations (16.1) to (16.3) are not the only ones which can describe perfect elastic behavior. The only requirement on an elastic substance is that on removal of the stress the body return to its original shape and size. Thus the strain need not always be proportional to the stress. The type of elasticity described by Eqs. (16.1) to (16.3), where stress is proportional to strain, is called linear or proportional elasticity. Other forms are nonlinear.

In actual practice it takes a finite time to apply a stress and for the resultant straining to occur. If the strain builds up so fast that its lag behind the stress cannot be measured, the response is said to be instantaneous. For noninstantaneous yielding the equations relating stress and strain must involve the time. A simple possibility which agrees to a first approximation with shear observations on many materials is given by Benioff and Gutenberg (1951):

$$s = \frac{P}{\mu} - \frac{\eta}{\mu}\frac{ds}{dt} \tag{16.4}$$

where s is strain, P is force per unit area, μ is rigidity, and η is called the coefficient of internal friction. For constant stress the solution of this equation can easily be seen [by substitution in (16.4)] to have the form (Fig. 16.2)

$$s = \frac{P}{\mu} + s'e^{-t/T} \tag{16.5}$$

where $T = \eta/\mu$ and s' is a constant whose value depends on the initial value of s.

If one starts with no strain and applies a constant stress P, since at time $t = 0$, s must be zero, s' will have to be equal to $-P/\mu$, and

$$s = \frac{P}{\mu}(1 - e^{-t/T}) \tag{16.6}$$

T in this case is the time it takes for the strain to rise to all but $1/e$ of the final value it would have after infinite time.

If the stress P is removed at time $t = 0$ after having been applied for some time, and if the strain at this time is s_0, then substituting $s = s_0$ and $t = 0$ into (16.5) gives

$$s_0 = s' \tag{16.7}$$

and since $P = 0$ at all times t greater than zero, (16.5) must become

$$s = s_0 e^{-t/T} \tag{16.8}$$

T is now the time it takes the strain to fall to $1/e$ of its initial value.

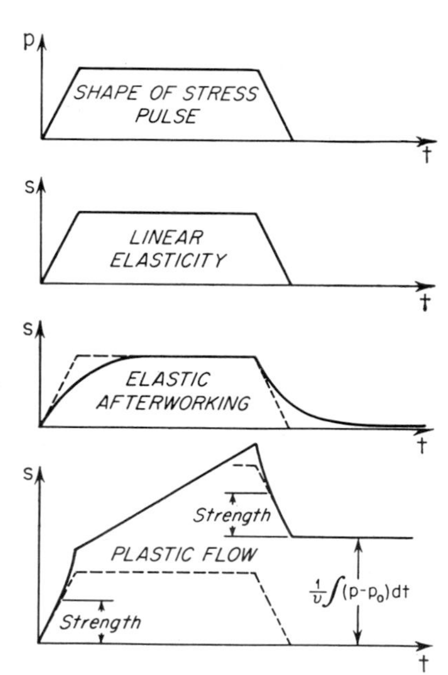

Fig. 16.2 Idealized picture of different types of strain.

When it takes appreciable time for a body to reach its full elastic deformation, this process is called elastic afterworking.

The molecular readjustments which result in elastic afterworking are thought to involve a form of internal friction among atoms, molecules, or small domains in the material. The units of η are poises (1 poise equals 1 dyne-sec per cm^2). The poise represents the ratio of tangential force per unit area between two adjoining layers in a material being sheared to their relative velocity. From studies of the increase in period of seismic waves, on the assumption that this increase is caused by internal friction, η was estimated to be about 5×10^9 poises for the outer part of the mantle (Benioff and Gutenberg, 1951). For the crust it varied from 10^7 poises for seismic pulses from artifical explosions in sediments to 5×10^9 poises as determined from earthquake surface waves.

Elastic afterworking is not always so simple as that described by (16.5) to (16.8). A part of the strain may occur instantaneously, followed by a gradual exponential yielding. Griggs (1939*a*) also describes a type of elastic deformation which obeys a formula of the type

$$s = \frac{P}{\mu} + C \log t \tag{16.9}$$

where C is a constant. In this case the first term represents an instantaneous elastic deformation while the second term represents the elastic afterworking. On removal of the stress, the strain P/μ immediately vanishes, while the remaining deformation disappears more gradually.

16.3 Breaking Strength. If too great a stress is applied to any solid, it will cease to behave elastically and a permanent change will be made in its shape or size. The stress at which this occurs is called the elastic limit.[1] One form that this permanent distortion can take is for the material to break. The stress needed to cause a displacement along some definite surface is called the breaking strength. Breaking strength can be measured in several ways. The ends of a bar of the material can be pulled to find the tensile strength (Fig. 16.3). The ends can be forced together to find the crushing strength, or a plug can be pushed out of a slab of the material to find the shearing strength (Fig. 16.4). Typical values of the breaking strength of rocks are given in Tables 16.1 and 16.2.

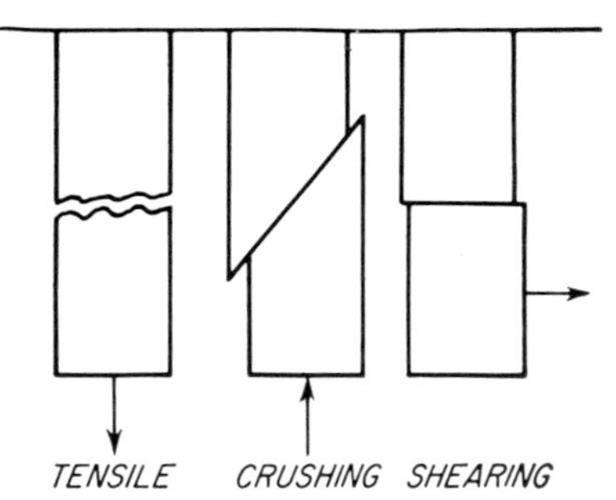

FIG. 16.3 Different types of breaking strength.

The values of breaking strength obtained depend on the method of performing the experiment, including the shape of the specimen tested and the conditions of confining pressure and temperature (Griggs, 1942). Breaking strength may also be a function of time. Some materials such as alabaster will stand a stress for a while but will eventually give way. Griggs (1940) has suggested that such materials may have a fundamental strength which can be defined as the maximum stress that they can with-

[1] Sometimes there is a stress less than the elastic limit up to which strain is proportional to stress but above which nonlinear elastic strain results. The stress at which elastic strain ceases to be proportional to the stress causing it is called the proportional limit. For elastic afterworking of the type described in Sec. 16.2, the proportional limit is zero.

stand indefinitely, but which is different from the stress at which they yield in a particular experiment.

One reason why breaking strength is hard to measure is that, to make the test, a piece of the material must be brought into the laboratory and mounted in the machine which applies the stress. Once separated from the rest of the earth, it may no longer behave as it would in the middle of a

FIG. 16.4 Apparatus used by Kessler, Insley, and Sligh (1940) for measuring shearing strength. (*Courtesy of National Bureau of Standards.*)

rock formation in the ground. Hence, the laboratory measurements are difficult to interpret in terms of natural earth conditions. Care must also be taken to make sure that no natural joints are present in the rock. This is particularly important in the case of measurements of tensile strength. Rocks generally are found to have low tensile strengths compared with other types of breaking strength. This may be because almost all rocks, and particularly sediments, have planes across which the rock is not firmly attached and along which they will part easily under tension. For this reason meaningful figures of the tensile strength of rocks are hard to obtain.

One of the principal problems in interpreting measurements of breaking strength is confinement. In the earth, each piece of rock is surrounded on all sides by more rock. It is impossible to deform one part without at the same time disturbing all the adjoining material. In the laboratory this confinement can be approximated by mounting the laboratory specimen

TABLE 16.1 TYPICAL VALUES OF THE BREAKING STRENGTH OF ROCKS AT ATMOSPHERIC PRESSURE*

Type of rock	Crushing strength, kg/cm^2	Shearing strength, kg/cm^2	Modulus of rupture,† kg/cm^2
Granite	370–3,790		
Syenite	1,000–3,440		
Diorite	960–2,600	277–326	101–368
Gabbro and diabase	460–4,700		
Gneiss	810–3,270		
Quartzite	260–3,200	1,100–3,200	
Marble	310–2,620	560–1,900	42–280
Sandstone	110–2,520	350–1,400	50–160
Limestone	60–3,600	180–2,000	35–140
Slate	600–3,130		420–1,060
Serpentine	630–1,230	780–2,000	92–780
Tuff	100–520		

* Data from Griggs, 1942, and Kessler et al., 1940.

† The modulus of rupture is found from the strength at which a bar breaks when it is supported at two ends and weighted in the center. The convex surface of the bar is thus under tension, and the breaking strength so obtained is a measure of tensile strength.

TABLE 16.2 EFFECT OF CONFINING PRESSURE OF KEROSENE ON SHORT-TIME COMPRESSIVE STRENGTH OF UNJACKETED ROCKS*

Material	At 1 kg/cm^2, kg/cm^2	At 4,000 kg/cm^2, kg/cm^2	At 8,000 kg/cm^2, kg/cm^2	At 10,000 kg/cm^2, kg/cm^2
Marble	810	860	1,650	Over 5,200
Solenhofen limestone	2,560	3,260	5,970	Over 13,000
Calcite	27.9	77	361	540
Quartz (parallel to c axis)	24,000		27,000 (at pressure of 9,000 kg/cm^2)	

* Griggs, 1940.

in some kind of jacket (Fig. 16.5), but unless the jacket has the same elastic properties as the sample, it will still influence the results.

A common practice is to measure the breaking strength at different known hydrostatic confining pressures. In general, the greater the confining pressure, the greater the breaking strength. Thus, the greater the depth beneath the surface, the more difficult it should be to break a rock. Temperature has little effect on dry rocks but in the presence of moisture may assist greatly in reducing breaking strength. Since almost all rocks contain some water, this will tend to lessen breaking strength with depth compared with what it would otherwise be (Griggs, 1942).

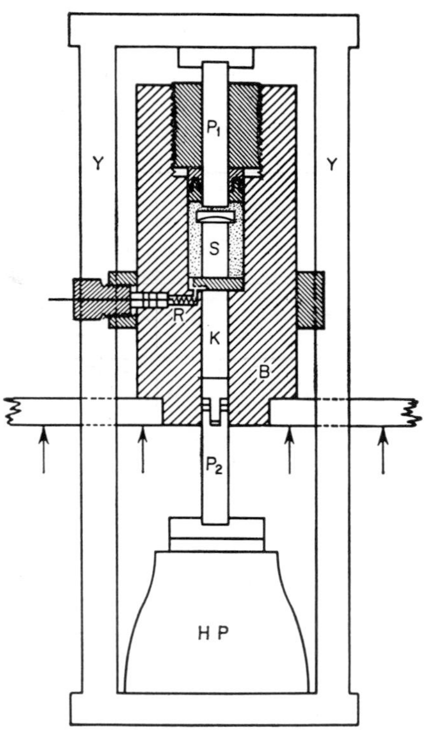

FIG. 16.5 Schematic sketch of Grigg's (1942) high-pressure apparatus.

16.4 Plastic Flow. When the elastic limit is exceeded, a body does not always break. It may take on a permanent change of shape in addition to its elastic deformation without parting anywhere. Nonelastic yielding in which there is no parting along discrete surfaces is called plastic flow. Such deformation (Fig. 16.2) may sometimes be described by an equation of the form

$$s = \frac{P}{\mu} + \frac{1}{\nu} \int (P - P_0)\, dt \quad (16.10)$$

where ν is called the coefficient of viscosity. Equation (16.10) can also be written

$$\frac{ds}{dt} = \frac{1}{\mu}\frac{dP}{dt} + \frac{P - P_0}{\nu} \quad (16.11)$$

P_0 is called the strength of the rock. It is the stress at which plastic flow begins to occur. If stress is applied to a rock of this kind, there is an initial elastic yielding until P reaches P_0; thereafter there is an additional plastic yielding. If the stress is subsequently removed, the rock recovers only the amount of the elastic deformation.

Plastic flow is commonly compared with fluid flow where

$$\frac{ds}{dt} = \frac{P}{\nu_f} \quad (16.12)$$

where ν_f is the coefficient of fluid viscosity. Fluids differ from plastic solids by their lack of any strength.

If a plastic rock is to be given a constant strain s_c, then the stress necessary to produce this will die off with time. The form of this stress can be seen [by substitution into (16.10)] to be

$$P = P_0 + (\mu s_c - P_0)e^{-t/T_p} \tag{16.13}$$

where
$$T_p = \frac{\nu}{\mu} \tag{16.14}$$

Initially a stress μs_c is required, falling off ultimately to the strength P_0. T_p is called the relaxation time. It is the time for which the excess stress beyond P_0 falls to $1/e$ of its initial value.

The above picture of plastic behavior is a considerable simplification of what actually occurs. Viscosity is not in general a constant but itself depends on stress, and may also depend on time or the past history of the material. It depends greatly on temperature. In many materials, if the temperature is raised high enough, relaxation can be speeded up. This is called annealing and is an important property of metals. The temperature at which relaxation time suddenly decreases is called the strain-hardening limit. One possible explanation for the lack of earthquakes beneath 700 km in the earth is that at this depth the temperature has risen to the strain-hardening limit. If this theory is correct, and if (16.10) to (16.14) apply to these rocks, then it must mean that the coefficient of viscosity decreases here, since seismic evidence indicates no sudden increase in μ (Fig. 13.2).

If the stress P is removed at some interval t' after it has been applied, the accumulated strain will be, from Eq. (16.10), $(P - P_0)t'/\nu$. The permanent strain is directly proportional to the amount of excess stress multiplied by the time it has been applied and inversely to the coefficient of viscosity.

In the most general case both plastic flow and elastic afterworking will occur. After a stress P has been applied for a time t, combining (16.6) and (16.10) gives

$$s = \frac{P}{\mu}(1 - e^{-t/T}) + \frac{(P - P_0)t}{\nu} \tag{16.15}$$

If the stress is removed after a time t', the strain will immediately be relieved at the rate given by (16.8), wherein s_0 corresponds to the first term in (16.15):

$$s = \frac{P}{\mu}(1 - e^{-t'/T})e^{-(t-t')/T} + \frac{(P - P_0)t'}{\nu} \tag{16.16}$$

No matter how long a time is allowed to pass, the plastic deformation $(P - P_0)t'/\nu$ remains.

Engineers call the above process creep (Nádai, 1950). In practice the deformation of natural materials is more complicated than would be indicated by any of the above equations. A common phenomenon is for plastic flow to obey Eq. (16.15) for a time, then for the rate to increase, and finally for the rock to fracture, as shown in Fig. 16.6.

Strength should not be confused with breaking strength, which is the stress where parting occurs. Strength is difficult to measure when elastic afterworking occurs, as the completion of elastic deformation and start of plastic yielding are then not clearly separated (Fig. 16.6).

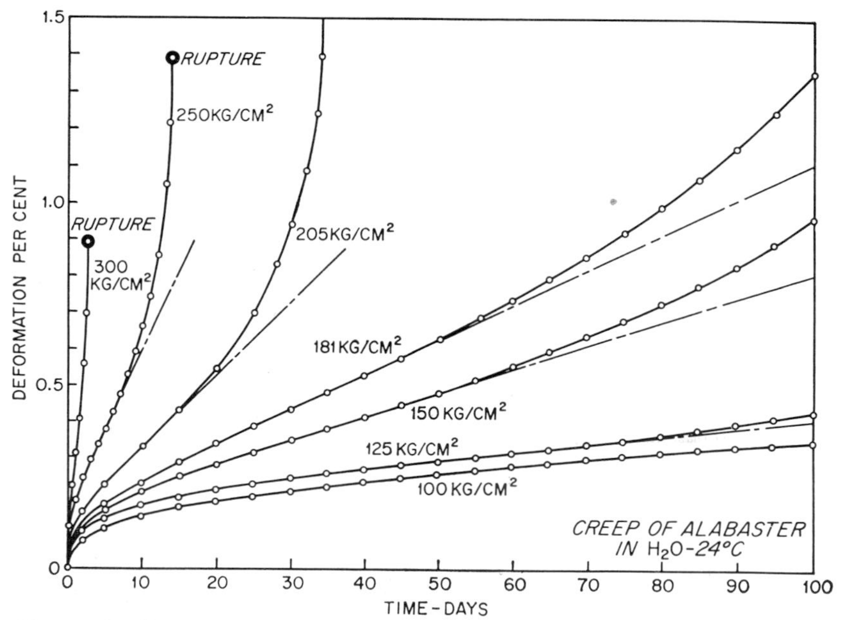

FIG. 16.6 Creep curves of alabaster under compressive stress. (*Griggs, 1942.*)

Where the threshold of plastic flow is at zero stress, a material is said to have no strength. This does not mean that it can be easily broken, as its breaking strength may be high. Amorphous solids are of this nature. It is very difficult to distinguish such materials from liquids. The viscous part of the yielding of a plastic solid of zero strength obeys the same equation (16.12), which describes fluid flow. The constants ν and ν_f are called coefficient of viscosity in both cases. However, in the case of solid flow there is an additional term describing the elastic deformation in (16.11) which is absent in (16.12).

16.5 Deformation of Rocks. If the strength of a material is large enough, it may exceed the breaking strength. In such a case, plastic flow cannot be produced. Solids may be classified as brittle, if they break before they begin to flow, or plastic, if their breaking strength exceeds their strength. Under conditions existing at the surface of the earth most rocks either are brittle or have too large viscosities to measure. As pressure is increased, the breaking strength increases, and at the temperatures and pressures common in the deeper part of the crust and in the mantle of the earth, strength is commonly less than breaking strength, so that the rocks are plastic.

We can speak of three ranges of deformation, depending on the size of the stress: the elastic range, the plastic range, and the fracture range. Small stresses such as those involved in transmission of seismic waves do not drive the rocks out of the elastic range. The gradually created stresses which cause isostatic adjustment build up so slowly that, at the depths where the rocks are plastic, the stress is relieved in large part by flow. Only when stresses build up quickly or where the rocks are brittle solids can tectonic earthquakes occur. If these definitions are a good description of rock behavior within the earth, then we see that beneath 700 km either conditions are more uniform than at shallower depths so that there is less tendency to build up large stresses, or strength is less so that plastic flow starts sooner, or viscosity is small so that relaxation occurs more rapidly than at shallower depths.

It has been postulated that because isostasy is so nearly perfect, there must be some depth at which strength is zero. It is not possible to prove whether this is the case or not, as the variations in the isostatic anomaly from place to place can be due either to imperfections in isostasy or to local density variations which are supported by the strength of the crustal rocks. Even where readjustments are observed to be taking place, it is hard to tell how much of the adjustment is elastic afterworking and how much is plastic flow.

A piece of evidence in favor of a finite strength for rocks comes from the moon. In Chap. 3 it was pointed out that the moon still had the shape which it is believed to have acquired when it was less than one-third its present distance from the earth. The moon is believed to be composed of material similar in composition to the earth's mantle. If it had no strength, any bulge would long ago have disappeared owing to the moon's gravitation. This is proof that rock at the temperatures and pressures in the moon can have some strength and can support a considerable weight permanently. Unless the mantle of the earth is composed of material different from the moon, it is reasonable to expect its outer part to have some strength. On the other hand, the general existence of a high order of isostatic equilibrium makes it certain that the rocks of the earth's mantle, at least those around the depth of compensation, are plastic rather than rigid solids.

To get some idea of the average strength of crustal rocks, consider the heights of mountains and the depths of oceanic troughs. Assuming the average density of surface rocks to be 2.7 gm per cm^3, the pressure increases downward at a rate of approximately 2.6×10^8 dynes per cm^2 per km. At the foot of a cliff 3,500 m (11,480 ft) high, the strength would have to be of the order of 9×10^8 dynes per cm^2, or the foot of the precipice would be crushed. Peak values of elevation such as the height of Mount Everest, 8,440 m, should not be used in such calculations, as the weight of the whole mountain is distributed over its broad base and at no point above sea level does the average pressure reach the weight per unit area of a flat-topped column of the same maximum height. However, large areas of the Himalayas rise 5,000 m above the Ganges basin in distances of only about 100 km. This represents a stress difference beneath them of 1.3×10^9 dynes per cm^2. Similarly, the ocean deeps lie over extensive areas at depths of over 8,000 m. The Ramapo deep off Japan has a maximum depth of 10,550 m. Allowing for the cover of sea water, 8,000 m suboceanic elevation difference also represents a stress difference of 1.3×10^9 dynes per cm^2. Some of the largest local stress differences occur in places like Hawaii, where Mauna Loa rises 4,168 m above sea level and about 9,700 m above the floor of the ocean which surrounds the islands.

All this evidence suggests a strength for crustal rocks of the order of at least 10^9 dynes per cm^2. For the observed isostatic adjustment, at a depth of 100 km it must be only 10^6 to 10^7 dynes per cm^2 at most. Strength has been postulated to increase with depth to a maximum of about 10^{10} dynes per cm^2 at 20 km, decreasing below this (Barrell, 1925).

The viscosity of the rocks in the earth can be only roughly estimated, since their composition is not known with any degree of certainty and temperature and pressure conditions are reproducible in the laboratory only to a depth of a few hundred kilometers, and even then only with great difficulty and on small samples. The best estimates available are from the study of large observed earth deformations. Gutenberg has summarized estimates of the viscosity of the earth (Benioff and Gutenberg, 1951). A value of 4×10^{22} poises was obtained from Vening Meinesz's studies of the rate of uplift of Scandinavia (1 cm per year). Other estimates based on similar studies fall generally in the range 10^{22} to 10^{23} poises. The corresponding values of relaxation time T_p are of the order of magnitude of 10,000 years. Gutenberg believes that to explain the lack of earthquakes below 700 km by a decrease in viscosity, the viscosity would have to be not more than 10^{20} poises at that depth. Even 10^{20} poises is a very large viscosity. The viscosity of soda glass at 575°C is about 11×10^{12} poises. That of glacial ice is 12×10^{13} poises. That plastic flow in rocks is a very slow process can be seen by comparing these values with the fluid viscosities of some common substances. The viscosity of water at 20°C is only 0.010 poise, and machine oils have viscosities of the order of magnitude of only 8 poises.

16.6 Sources of Tectonic Forces. In Chap. 15 it was shown that deposition and erosion changed surface loads and caused isostatic adjustment but that this process could be expected eventually to reach equilibrium unless rejuvenated by the raising of new land masses. The geologic record indicates that high mountains have existed in one place or another during a considerable part of geologic history, if not all of it. There must, therefore, be one or more agents repeatedly or continually upsetting the equilibrium which would otherwise be reached. It is useful to consider what these agents can be from the point of view of energy sources. For the processes to have occurred with comparable violence repeatedly throughout geologic time, energy must have been supplied from some reservoir where it is stored until needed.

If one looks about on the earth's surface, several possible energy sources will be seen. There is the energy involved in the earth's rotation. A point on the equator moves at a velocity of 0.46 km per sec. For material with an average density of 2.67 gm per cm^3 this represents 2.8×10^9 ergs/cm^3 of kinetic energy. Energy is also stored in the earth's revolution about the sun and in the moon's revolution about the earth. In Chap. 2 it was shown that the rate of the earth's rotation is decreasing as a result of tidal friction. Jeffreys (1952) estimates that the energy involved in the transfer of momentum from the earth's rotation to the moon's revolution is of the order of 1.5×10^{19} ergs per sec. The resultant of the tidal forces is a westward pressure on the continental masses. The stresses involved are small, periodic, and irregularly distributed, but their cumulative effect over long periods of time may be great. In addition the resultant decrease in the rate of the earth's rotation causes a decrease in centripetal force which would leave the equatorial bulge unsupported if it did not sink. As there is no tendency for land masses to be more extensive or for isostatic gravity to be larger at low latitudes, it must be concluded that isostasy has allowed the earth to readjust its shape continuously to fit the changing rate of rotation.

If the axis of rotation of the earth were to shift with respect to its body as a whole, large forces would be called into play as the surface elevations adjusted to a new equilibrium. Subcrustal flow by the plastic interior would keep the general spheroidal shape fixed with respect to the axis of rotation. The crust, being more rigid, would behave differently. Stresses would be resisted until breaking occurred, and blocks of land and sea floor could be caused to overlap along the resulting faults and at other places to stretch or to open gaps along cracks. Some shift of the earth's axis has been recognized (see Sec. 12.9). The amplitude by which the axis of rotation and the axis of figure are separated varies, reaching as much as 0.3 second of arc (10 m at the earth's surface, see Fig. 12.6). Gutenberg (1951*c*) estimates that their relative motion will cause horizontal stresses as great as 10^3 dynes per cm^2 in the earth's crust.

Secular changes in latitude have rarely been observed with certainty. Lambert (1922) has measured a movement of the North Pole toward North America amounting to 0.0062 second of arc annually or 1° per 580,000 years. Ukiah, California, seems to be moving northward, which is opposite to the usual San Andreas fault motion. Such a movement, if continued over several geologic periods, would create great stresses. Lambert's measurements were made over a 17-year period in a region known to be tectonically active. Other movements of this magnitude have been noted, but their size is so small as to be hardly beyond the limits of accuracy of the measurements.

Large changes in the position of the earth's axis have been postulated to have occurred in the past (Wegener, 1924; Vening Meinesz, 1947*b*). Such movements will be discussed in Chap. 18. Their existence has not been proved, so their importance cannot be evaluated.

There are known to be other small irregularities in the rate of rotation of the earth. These changes can be correlated with changes in the earth's magnetic field. They are explained by postulating a relative movement of the core with respect to the mantle of the earth, the two being linked electromagnetically. In this way the magnetic field of the earth may be the source of some of the energy for tectonic forces. Since the magnetic field is due at least in part to electrical currents, electrical energy may be one of the ultimate sources of tectonic forces. The magnetic field appears to change greatly with time. It results in part from electrical currents in the atmosphere. These in turn result from radiations which reach the earth from outer space and are believed to originate largely in the sun. Thus radiant energy from extraterrestrial sources may become converted into an effective tectonic agent. (A more detailed discussion of these phenomena is given in Sec. 23.5.)

Tides exist in the solid earth and in the atmosphere as well as in the sea (Sec. 14.8). Tides, tidal waves, and barometric disturbances exert stresses which cause ground tilts as great as 0.05 second of arc (Gutenberg, 1951*c*). Such tilts prove that the earth is continually flexing even under these relatively small stresses.

Another force, which is a direct result of the earth's rotation, is the polfluchtkraft. This results from differences in elevation (Fig. 16.7). Consider two areas of unit cross section at the same latitude ϕ, and as a first approximation assume that the earth is roughly spherical, so that radii are all perpendicular to the surface. (In the case of an ellipsoidal earth, radii are not exactly perpendicular to the surface and the direction of gravity changes with elevation.) Suppose that area II is $2\Delta R$ m higher in elevation than area I. Then the center of mass of the volume above the level of compensation of area II is ΔR higher in elevation than the center of mass of region I. If the mass of each column is m and ω is the angular velocity of the earth, then treating all the force as though it acted at the center of mass the centrifugal force acting on column I is

$$F_1 = m\omega^2 R_1 \cos\phi \quad (16.17)$$

and that acting on column II is

$$F_2 = m\omega^2 (R_1 + \Delta R) \cos\phi \quad (16.18)$$

The difference in force has two components:

$$\Delta F_{\text{vert}} = m\omega^2\,\Delta R \cos^2\phi \quad (16.19)$$

$$\Delta F_{\text{horiz}} = m\omega^2\,\Delta R \cos\phi \sin\phi = 0.5m\omega^2\,\Delta R \sin 2\phi \quad (16.20)$$

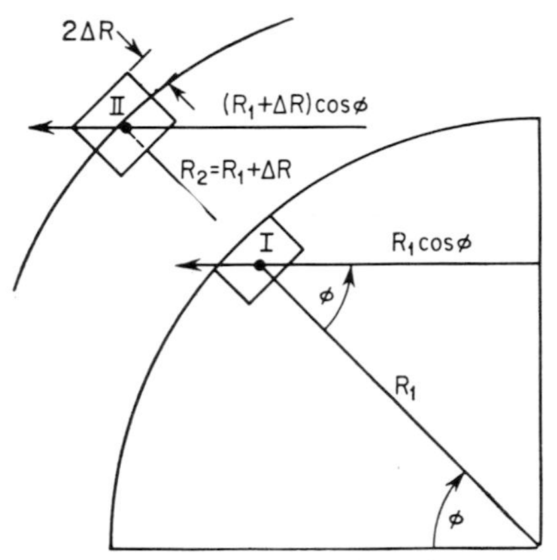

FIG. 16.7 Polfluchtkraft.

ΔF_{vert} results in a distortion of the shape of the geoid, but ΔF_{horiz} must be supported by the strength of the rocks. Polfluchtkraft is strongest at 45° latitude, where (16.20) gives 2.66×10^{-9} dyne per gm per centimeter of difference in height of the center of gravity, or 1.33×10^{-9} dyne per gm per centimeter of elevation difference. The force decreases to zero going to the equator or the poles. For an average rock density of 3 gm per cm^3 and a block 500 km wide, neglecting the effect of the earth's curvature, this amounts to around 0.2 dyne per cm^2 directed toward the equator per centimeter of elevation difference. Even for an elevation difference of 2,000 m this would produce only 4×10^4 dynes per cm^2. The surface layers can withstand such a force easily, but the deeper layers of the earth may be too weak to do so. Actually polfluchtkraft is considerably stronger than the above simplified discussion would indicate. The ellipsoidal shape of the earth results in curvature of a vertical line as shown in Fig. 16.8. The result is that the direction of gravity changes

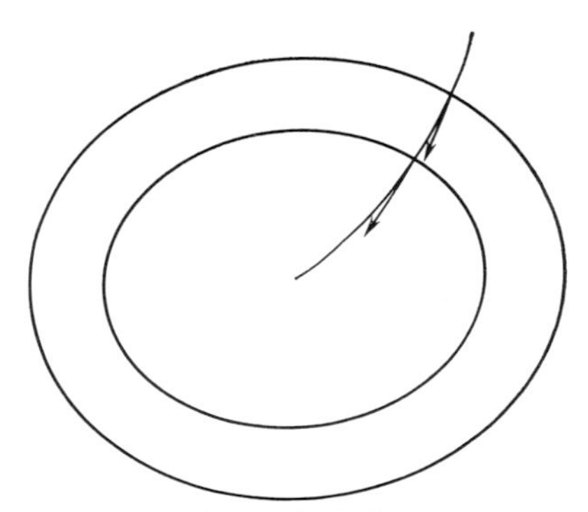
FIG. 16.8 A vertical line is not a straight line on an ellipsoidal earth.

with elevation, and above the geoid there is a small component of gravity which assists centrifugal force in producing the polfluchtkraft.[1]

Another possible energy source is the sun. Solar energy acts upon the earth in a number of ways. It controls surface temperature, resulting in freezing and thawing, which have a superficial effect on stressing the rocks. The forces generated are important in erosion. The sun provides the energy to keep the fluvial cycle going. Evaporation may in time remove the load of an interior lake. In the form of snow, glaciers have been built up and created major deformations of the crust during the Pleistocene. The ice is now retreating, unloading areas it has previously depressed. Assuming an average density of 1.0 gm per cm^3 for ice and 3.0 gm per cm^3 for rock, a glacier would depress the crust about one-third of its thickness. The stresses created are believed to be relieved largely by isostatic adjustment.

Besides the small corpuscles of radiation received, the objects reaching the earth from space grade in size up to large meteorites weighing many tons. The addition of large masses as meteorites can create stresses by the impact of their arrival, by their weight at rest, and by altering the

[1] To calculate the true magnitude of polfluchtkraft it is necessary to consider the gravitational plus the centrifugal potential. This problem has been treated by Lambert (1921), by Epstein (1921), and more briefly by Jeffreys (1952). A simple way of seeing the effect is to assume an approximately spheroidal earth whose surface is in equilibrium so that the gravitational attraction varies with latitude as

$$g = \frac{\partial V}{\partial z} = g_0(1 + \beta \cos^2 \phi) \tag{16.21}$$

where V is the potential, g_0 is gravity at latitude $\phi = 0$ (the equator), and β is a constant. Cartesian coordinates with z directed downward and x equatorward will be used.

Although the horizontal force $X = \partial V/\partial x$ is zero at zero elevation, it will change with elevation at the rate

$$\frac{\partial X}{\partial z} = \frac{\partial}{\partial z}\frac{\partial V}{\partial x} = \frac{\partial g}{\partial x} = \frac{\partial g}{\partial \phi}\frac{\partial \phi}{\partial x} = (2g_0\beta \cos \phi \sin \phi)\frac{\partial \phi}{\partial x} \tag{16.22}$$

or since to a first approximation,

$$\phi = \frac{x}{R} \tag{16.23}$$

where R is the earth's radius,

$$\frac{\partial X}{\partial z} = \frac{g_0\beta}{R} \sin 2\phi \tag{16.24}$$

The difference in force per gram per centimeter difference in elevation of two columns (0.5-cm difference in elevation of centers of mass) at $\phi = 45°$, assuming $g_0 = 980$ cm per sec^2, $R = 6.37 \times 10^8$ cm, and $\beta = 0.00529$ [compare with Eq. (12.47)] is 4.06×10^{-9} dyne compared with the value of 1.33×10^{-9} obtained for a spherical earth. Polfluchtkraft is thus increased by a factor of 3 compared with the case of a spherical earth.

earth's moment of inertia slightly. The distribution of geological formations during the last 500 million years suggests that but little meteoritic material has been added to the earth during this time, and that this was added gradually. Although in the early history of the earth, as in the case of the moon, this may not have been the case, meteoritic acquisition does not appear to be a currently important tectonic process.

The earth's own gravitational field is the means of drawing in the meteoric masses and hence must be considered a major source of energy for tectonic deformations. It is gravity which draws the rivers down the valleys to the sea, eroding away the land. Landslides, density currents in the air and the oceans, and rockfalls of many sorts represent a yielding to such stresses. Low-angle overthrusts may be often only the result of large blocks of rock sliding downhill into depressions, a more reasonable postulate than the supposition that such structures result from pressures acting from behind them (Taylor, 1955). The force of gravity produces the pressure gradient in the earth (Fig. 13.1). Recrystallization of rocks to denser varieties under the influence of this pressure can create nodes of stress as the surrounding rocks fill in the space gained.

A similar shrinkage would occur if the earth were losing its original heat. Such a process, if it occurred, could be a major cause of tectonic forces. The energy in this case comes both from the earth's heat and from gravitation. Table 16.3 shows typical values of the coefficient of linear expansion for some common rocks. A 1,000-km-long column of granite which cooled 50°C would be shortened by 400 m. It would also shrink horizontally the same amount, which would be equally or more important in terms of the stresses involved. The coefficient of volume expansion is approximately three times that of linear expansion, since, for a cube of length L on a side, the change in volume for a temperature increase ΔT is

$$\Delta V = (L + \Gamma_1 L\,\Delta T)^3 - L^3 = (3\Gamma_1\,\Delta T + 3\Gamma_1^2\,\Delta T^2 + \Gamma_1^3\,\Delta T^3)L^3 \approx 3\Gamma_1\,\Delta T\,V \qquad (16.25)$$

where Γ_1 is the linear coefficient of expansion. The volume coefficient is

$$\Gamma_v = \frac{\Delta V}{V\,\Delta T} \approx 3\Gamma_1 \qquad (16.26)$$

An increase in temperature of a rock would create powerful stresses tending to force the surrounding rocks outward.

Heat could act in other ways to create stresses. In a rigid solid material heat flows largely by conduction, but in a fluid or plastic material convection cells could be of far greater importance. Horizontal temperature gradients could cause convection. The difference in mass ΔM of two columns of equal volume but different density is the same as the mass of a volume of rock equal in size to the difference in volume ΔV of the same two columns if their densities ρ were the same:

$$\Delta M = \rho \, \Delta V \tag{16.27}$$

The pressure difference at the bottom of two such columns, neglecting any difference in the acceleration of gravity g between them and any variations with depth, would be

$$\Delta P = g \frac{\Delta M}{A} = g\rho \frac{\Delta V}{A} \tag{16.28}$$

where A is the cross section of the column. If A is the same for both columns and using (16.26), since $V = AL$,

$$\Delta P = g\rho\Gamma_v V \frac{\Delta T}{A} = 3g\rho\Gamma_1 L \, \Delta T \tag{16.29}$$

Two 1,000-km-long columns of gabbro would have a stress difference of about 2.3×10^8 dynes/cm² at their bases for a 50° temperature difference,

TABLE 16.3 TYPICAL VALUES OF THE LINEAR COEFFICIENT OF THERMAL EXPANSION Γ_1*
(Volume coefficient is approximately three times as great.)

Material	Temperature, °C	Linear expansion coefficient: $(1/L)(\Delta L/\Delta T)$
Granite and rhyolite	20–100	8×10^{-6}
Andesite and diorite	20–100	7×10^{-6}
Basalt, gabbro, and diabase	20–100	5.4×10^{-6}
Sandstone	20–100	10×10^{-6}
Quartzite	20–100	11×10^{-6}
Limestone	20–100	8×10^{-6}
Marble	20–100	7×10^{-6}
Slate	20–100	9×10^{-6}
Meteoric iron	20–100	14×10^{-6}
α-Quartz	20–100	10×10^{-6} (parallel to c axis)
		17.5×10^{-6} (perpendicular to c axis)
β-Quartz	600–1000	-3.5×10^{-6} (parallel to c axis)
		-1.7×10^{-6} (perpendicular to c axis)
Olivine	20–100	5×10^{-6} (a axis)
		10×10^{-6} (b axis)
		8.8×10^{-6} (c axis)
	600–1000	8×10^{-6} (a axis)
		15×10^{-6} (b axis)
		13×10^{-6} (c axis)

* After Dane, 1942.

assuming a density of about 2.94 and using the coefficient of linear expansion given in Table 16.3. This is probably more than the rocks of the mantle could stand and would result in a convection current which would exert large forces on the overlying crust. The heat generated by radioactive disintegration might keep such a process going in the earth for billions of years if properly distributed (see Chap. 21). The energy of radioactive disintegration is thus one of the major possible sources of energy to explain tectonic deformation. The heat escaping through the earth's surface is about 6×10^{12} cal per sec (2.5×10^{20} ergs per sec; see Sec. 5.5).

16.7 Observed Earth Movements. In order to understand better which of these processes have been of importance in molding the earth into its present form, we must look to conditions as they exist today. Geologic history shows that relative changes in sea level of up to hundreds of meters, either by rising and falling of the land or by changes in ocean volume, have been frequent throughout recorded time. Every continent has been submerged to a large extent at one time or another. Terraces and submerged valleys mark nearly all shore lines. Few coast lines have been fixed in position even since Pleistocene time. Paleontologists have proposed land bridges connecting the continents. In such places as the rift valleys of Africa and the Basin and Range province of western North America large blocks of the earth have been shifted vertically relative to adjoining areas. Vertical movement is a universal characteristic of the earth's surface.

The evidence for horizontal movements is not so clear, since there is no readily available plane of reference to play the role of sea level. But a study of the attitudes of faults shows no predominance in high over low dips or of dip-slip over strike-slip movements. On the contrary, horizontal displacements on surface faults are observed as commonly as vertical in earthquakes, and horizontal faulting has been deduced as being more common than vertical from studies of seismograms (Byerly, 1957; Hodgson, 1957; Ritsema, 1957).

In the older geological literature there may sometimes be found an implicit assumption that it is easier to move rocks vertically than horizontally. This is because the surface of the earth is very nearly a free surface and there appears to be a place for the raised block to go when it moves upward. This represents a misunderstanding of the nature of faulting. Breaks occur because strains already exist. Whatever movements occur are a relief of stress. Nothing has to be pushed out of the way to make room for the shifting fault block. The movements which created the stresses took place long before the earthquake occurred (see Sec. 8.5). Chapters 18 to 21 will deal in greater detail with the actual observations of tectonic processes and theories as to their cause.

CHAPTER 17

ORIGIN OF THE CONTINENTS

The contrast between land and ocean has stimulated mankind for many centuries. Much of the history of civilization has been controlled by man's growing ability to travel on and over the seas. But it is only in the last two centuries that knowledge of the far-flung reaches of the oceans has become complete enough to make clear their pattern with respect to the land.

If one were to stand upon the moon and draw a map of the earth, one would observe first of all that most of its surface is covered with water. Approximately 71 per cent of the surface of the earth is occupied by 11 great oceanic basins (Table 17.1) and a multitude of smaller embayments, straits, channels, shelves, and other water-covered areas, not counting the numerous lakes, rivers, tidal flats, and smaller bodies of water. We who dwell upon the land tend to play down this predominance of water. On most of our maps the land occupies the most prominent positions. Topographic features beneath the upper few meters of ocean are but vaguely known to us. Its geologic structure is only just beginning to be understood. Compared with the land, the oceans represent a vacuum of knowledge to the exploration of which men's minds must inevitably turn with increasing intensity in the years ahead. Before we can understand the place of the continents on the earth, we must know their relation to the larger area of the oceans.

17.1 Distinctive Features. The continents are distinguishable from the ocean basins by four principal characteristics: (1) their topographic elevations; (2) their chemical and mineralogic composition; (3) their peculiar arrangement tapering, with the exception of Antarctica, southward away from the Arctic basin; and (4) their geologic structure, especially along their boundaries.

Although by definition the continents are large land areas, structurally they extend at least to the edge of the continental shelves at around 200 m below sea level. Between here and the ocean floors is a transitional zone, the continental slopes, dropping off at an angle of about 2 to 3.5°. The ocean floors lie principally in the depth range 3,000 to 6,000 m, averaging a little over 5,000 m. The mean depth of the whole ocean-covered area is about 3,800 m (Sverdrup, et al., 1942). The average elevation of the subaerial crust is 840 m above sea level. This is not the average elevation of the continents as a whole because of the area involved in the water-covered continental shelves, which constitute about 5.4 per cent of the area of the whole earth. Also, half of the area of the continental slopes, or another 4.9 per cent of the total area of the earth, might be included as a part of the continents, giving a total of 39.5 per cent of the area of the earth. Two predominant levels of the earth's surface, the ocean floor and

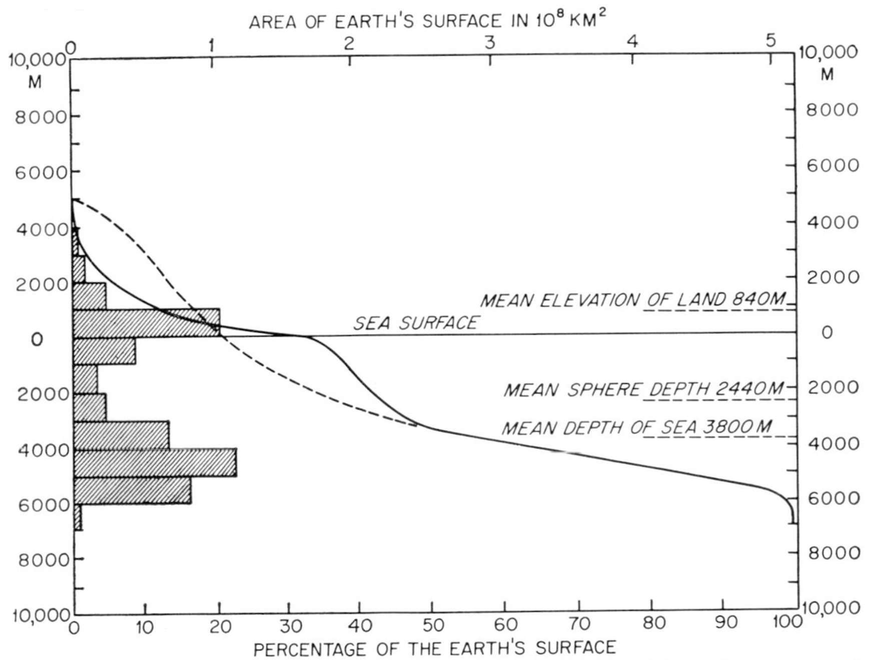

FIG. 17.1 Hypsographic curve of land surface elevation. *(After Sverdrup et al., 1942, and Kossinna, 1921.)*

the seacoast, can be clearly recognized by plotting the percentage of the earth's surface above a given elevation against elevation (Fig. 17.1). The approximate volume and mass of matter above −3,800 m depth is given in Table 17.1. The average elevation of the slopes above −3,800 m is estimated roughly to be 1,600 instead of 1,800 m to allow for the curvature of the hypsographic profile. The figure −3,800 m was also estimated roughly to be the average depth of the foot of the continental slopes. It is clear from the hypsographic profile only that the average depth of the foot of the slope probably lies between −3,000 and −4,000 m.

The reason for the height of the continental masses is quite evident when one considers the densities of the rocks which constitute them.

TABLE 17.1

	Area of continental material in		Average height above −3,800 m, m	Volume, km³	Mass if density is 2.75 gm/cm³, kg
	% of earth	Km²			
Subaerial...	29.2	148,900,000	4,640	6.9×10^8	19×10^{20}
Shelves.....	5.4	27,500,000	3,700	1.0	2.8
Slopes......	9.8	50,000,000	1,600	0.8	2.2
Total....	44.4	226,400,000		8.7×10^8	24.0×10^{20}

Washington (1922) estimates the average density of exposed continental rocks to be somewhere in the range 2.72 to 2.81 gm per cm³. The oceans are underlain at a shallow depth by heavier rocks in which the continents float. Assuming Airy's theory of isostatic compensation the depth of the root can be calculated by equating the masses of the continental and oceanic columns:

$$(D_n + h_n)\rho_a = h_w\rho_w + (D_n - h_w)\rho_b \tag{17.1}$$

where D_n is the depth of the root, h_n is the average elevation of the continents, h_w is the average depth of the oceans, and ρ_a, ρ_w, and ρ_b are the average densities of the continents, oceans, and the suboceanic material on which the continents are assumed to be floating. This can be solved for D_n, giving

$$\begin{aligned} D_n &= \frac{h_w(\rho_b - \rho_w) + h_n\rho_a}{\rho_b - \rho_a} \\ &= \frac{(h_w + h_n)\rho_a + h_w(\rho_b - \rho_a - \rho_w)}{\rho_b - \rho_a} \end{aligned} \tag{17.2}$$

If we assume that the area of the continents includes the shelves and half of the continental slopes, then their average elevations will be somewhere a little below 840 m above sea level, and the average depth of the oceans will be similarly slightly greater than the mean sea depth of 3,800 m.[1] Since both average elevations are changed in the same direction (h_w increases, h_n decreases) by a shift in the depth picked as the boundary between the continents and oceans, and since the first term in the numerator of Eq. (17.2) is much greater than the second, the exact depth selected will not be critical. In a similar manner, D_n depends more on the difference between the values of ρ_b and ρ_a than on their absolute values.

[1] The average depth of the oceanic basins exclusive of the shelves and slopes is naturally greater than this, probably about 5,300 m.

Assuming that h_n is 0.84 km, h_w is 3.8 km, $\rho_a = 2.75$ gm per cm^3, $\rho_w = 1.025$ gm per cm^3, and $\rho_b = 3.05$ gm per cm^3, D_n is found to be 33.3 km. The root of the continent extends 29.5 km below the ocean floor. The continental column is 7.36 times as long as the part rising above the sea bottom.

Use of Airy's hypothesis as is done here is an oversimplification (see Chap. 15). The actual crust is more complicated, having a complex variation in density both horizontally and vertically. Airy's method will give an accurate root depth only to the degree that the chosen density difference $\rho_b - \rho_a$ approximates the average density difference in the earth. The depth obtained here agrees roughly with figures obtained by more accurate studies (e.g., Hess, 1955; Ewing and Press, 1955), so it can be assumed to be a reasonable first approximation.

Chemically this density difference is believed to result from a greater abundance of silica and the sodium and potassium aluminum silicates in the continental rocks as compared with the iron-calcium-magnesium-rich rocks believed to underlie them. This difference can be seen by comparing columns (1) and (2) of Table 17.2. Exact figures on the composition of the two layers cannot be given, as only surface rocks are available for analysis. Exposed continental rocks are probably more sialic (silicon and aluminum rich) than the average for the continents as a whole. This may also be true of the surface rocks under the oceans. The lavas of oceanic and continental volcanoes are not strikingly different, basalts being common in both places. However, quartz-bearing, salic igneous rocks are found only on the continents (Umbgrove, 1947). A line can be drawn encircling most of the Pacific basin, called the andesite line, oceanward from which there is no acidic volcanism (Fig. 11.15). This line is believed to mark a truer border of the continents than can be distinguished on the more obvious evidence of topography. Beneath the oceans a sedimentary overburden is generally present hiding the basement, which adds further to the uncertainty of the composition differences.

One of the most striking features of the continents is their irregular distribution. Looking at a globe most of the land is seen to be concentrated in northern latitudes. It spreads southward from the edges of the arctic depression in great tapering wedges. The pattern is not symmetrical, for the land is spread southward most extensively in a broad zone lying equally on either side of 0° longitude, but with more of the land east than west of this. Figure 17.2 is a plot of percentage of land against latitude. The maximum occurs at 66°N. The concentration of continental material just south of the Arctic Circle is even more striking if the continental shelves are included in the land area (Fig. 17.3 and Table 17.3). At 66°, over 89 per cent of the earth's surface stands above

TABLE 17.2

Compound	(1) Gm/100 gm plateau basalt*	(2) Average crust, gm/100 gm†	(3) Composition of material which combined with 100 gm of (2) would give 200 gm of (1)	(4) Add to 50 gm of (1) to get 100 gm of (2)	(5) Composition of 100 gm of stony meteorites‡
SiO_2 . . .	48.80	59.12	38.48	34.72	38.41
Al_2O_3 . .	13.98	15.34	12.62	8.35	2.86
Fe_2O_3 . .	3.59	3.08			
(Fe_2O_3 + FeO)	13.37	6.88	19.86	0.20	14.52
FeO . . .	9.78	3.80			
MgO . . .	6.70	3.49	9.92	0.14	23.66
CaO . . .	9.38	5.08	13.68	0.39	1.88
Na_2O . .	2.59	3.84	1.34	2.54	0.82
K_2O . . .	0.69	3.13	−1.74	2.78	0.16
H_2O . . .	1.80	1.15	2.45	0.25	0.47
TiO_2 . . .	2.19	1.05	3.34	−0.05	0.16
P_2O_5 . . .	0.33	0.30	0.36	0.13	1.89
MnO . .	0.17	0.12	0.22	0.03	0.23
Other . .	0.00	0.50	−0.50	0.50	14.94 (12.35 gm metallic Fe)

* After Daly, 1933.

† After Clarke and Washington, 1924.

‡ After Daly et al., 1942.

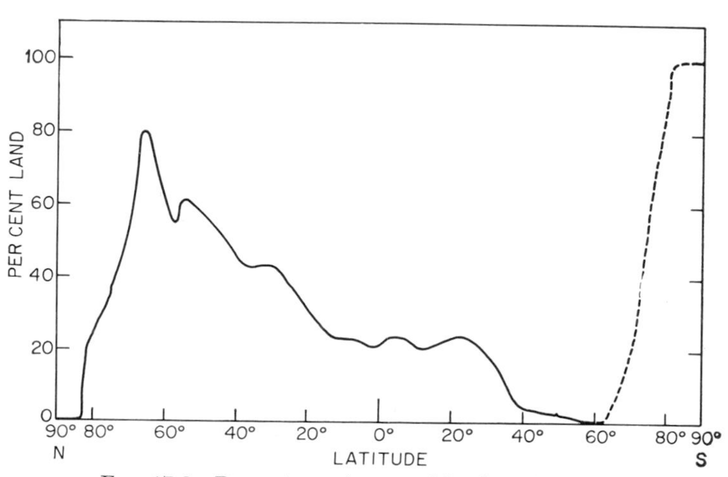

FIG. 17.2 Percentage of exposed land vs. latitude.

−200 m. The minimum shown in Fig. 17.2 at 57.5°N would probably disappear if the shelves were included in the land, as along this latitude lie Hudson Bay, the North and Baltic Seas, the northern part of the Bering Sea, and the Sea of Okhotsk, all largely shallow areas.

The concentration of land in northern latitudes is in part a result of the tapering of all the larger continents southward. North America tapers to Central America and Florida; South America to Tierra del Fuego; Eurasia to Africa, India, and the Malay Peninsula. Australia can be looked upon as the southern tip of east Asia, since the area separating it

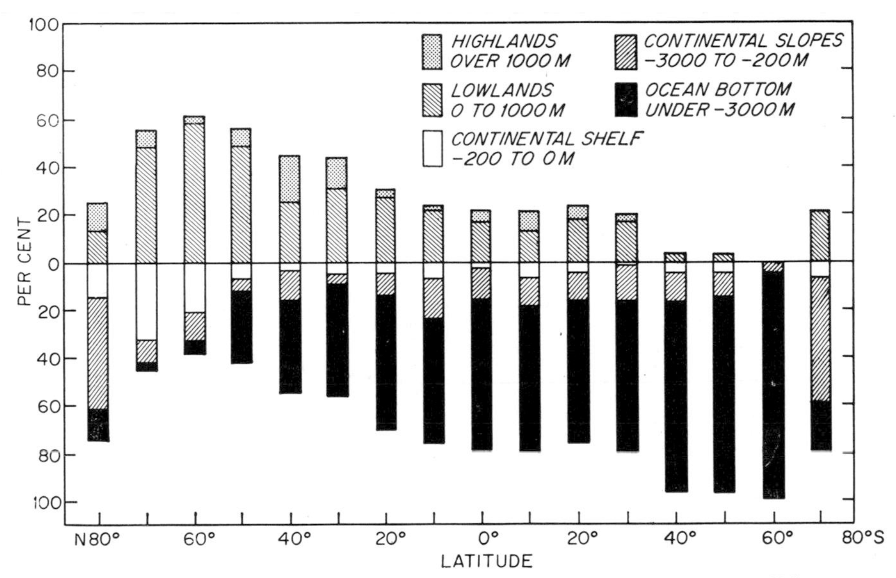

Fig. 17.3 Variation of elevation with latitude along selected parallels.

from the main continent, though depressed, is in its main structural features not unlike other parts of Asia. Australia and Antarctica alone, the two smallest and southernmost of the continents, lack the tapering shape of the other major land bodies. Antarctica is the only large land mass south of 30°S latitude, and its dimensions are still not established in detail. Because of the ice blanket covering it, the height of the land surface has been measured at relatively few places, though the general outline of the continent has been established.

Another notable feature of the earth is the antipodal arrangement of the land and oceans (Fig. 17.4). This is not so much an independent feature as it is a result of the concentration of the land around the arctic basin. If the earth is divided into two hemispheres, one centered at 0°E-W, 38°N, 40 miles off the coast of southeastern Spain, and the other at the antipodes of this point, over 80 per cent of the land is in the former

TABLE 17.3 PERCENTAGE OF PROFILE IN PRINCIPAL ELEVATION RANGES

Latitude	Highlands over 1,000 m	Lowlands 0 to 1,000 m	Continental shelf −200 to 0 m	Continental slope −3,000 to −200 m	Ocean bottom below −3,000 m
90°N					100 (?)
80°N	10.5	13.9	15.0	46.7	13.9
70°N	6.8	48.0	32.4	10.8	2.4
60°N	2.2	59.3	21.0	11.8	5.7
50°N	8.5	48.7	6.8	5.1	30.9
40°N	20.1	25.3	4.0	11.5	39.1
30°N	12.8	30.8	4.3	4.8	47.3
20°N	2.5	27.4	5.6	8.5	56.0
10°N	2.5	21.4	6.7	16.8	52.6
0°	4.1	17.3	3.7	10.9	64.0
10°S	6.7	13.7	7.0	12.4	60.2
20°S	5.8	17.8	4.9	12.1	59.4
30°S	2.3	17.5	1.4	15.1	63.7
40°S	0.3	3.0	4.5	10.1	82.1
50°S	0.4	2.2	4.3	14.9	78.2
60°S	0.0	0.0	0.0	4.3	95.7
70°S	0.0	20.8	6.7	53.2	19.3
80°S	83.3 (?)	3.4 (?)	13.3 (?)		
90°S	100 (?)				

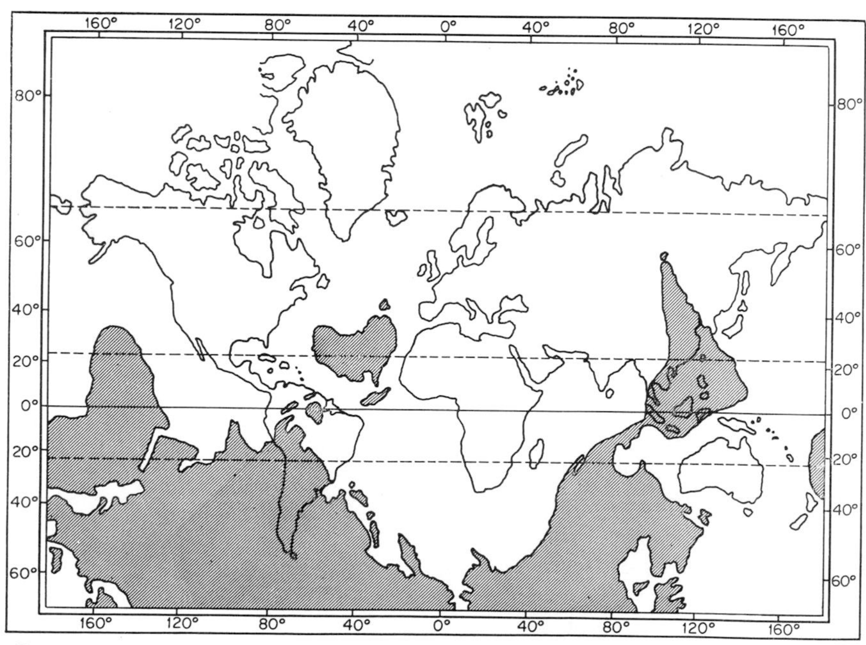

FIG. 17.4 Illustrating the antipodal position of land and water. *(Gregory, 1899.)*

hemisphere. The land hemisphere contains 47 per cent land, 53 per cent water, while the water hemisphere contains 11 per cent land and 89 per cent water (Fig. 17.5). Of the land in the water hemisphere 37 per cent is opposite land and 63 per cent opposite water. This is not a very striking contrast, as a shift of only 2,700,000 km^2 of land, less than 2 per cent of the land area of the world, from a position opposite water to one opposite land would change the 37 to 63 per cent ratio to the 47 to 53 per cent ratio of land to water in the land hemisphere. A change of this size in the ratio might be found if the continental shelves were included in the land area in making the calculations. Thus the antipodal arrangement is little more than would be expected from the degree of concentration of the land in one hemisphere.

Another condition to which reference is commonly made is the tetragonal arrangement of the continents (Gregory, 1899). The land is pictured as lying roughly at the apices and along the edges of an equilateral tetrahedron, whose points are one near the South Pole, one in Europe, one in Asia, and one in North America. South America, Africa, and the East Indian-Australian archipelago lie along the edges. This concept, in this form, fits the land distribution poorly. The maximum land exposure lies at 66° north latitude where there is 80.1 per cent land above sea level compared with 43.6 per cent at 30°, where the maximum would be required according to the tetragonal concept. The south-pointing fingers fall most nearly at 20°E, 135°E, and 70°W longitude, or at intervals of 115, 155, and 90° rather than every 120°. A trigonal pyramid can be fitted to this distribution, but the land masses stretching south from the base are aligned askew to the edges of the figure, and it is so long and pointed that it is hard to see any significance to it in relation to the ellipsoidal shape of the earth.

Structurally the continents can be described roughly as basins fringed by mountains. At places these fringing mountains are on land, as in the case of the western borders of North and South America; at places they lie as fringing island strings, as from Kamchatka to New Guinea and New Zealand. Elsewhere islands and continental segments alternate. In the case of the Atlantic sides of Africa and South America, the fringing ranges are more topographically than structurally striking, but they still exist to a notable degree.

Large parts of the central basins are underlain by crystalline rocks, sometimes exposed and at other times covered by sediments, which often lie nearly flat. Such large areas of exposed crystalline rocks are called continental shields or bucklers. Only in the case of parts of the Alpine-Caucasus-Himalayan system, the Urals, and the ranges of central Asia are the bucklers cut by high mountains which do not closely follow the continental fringes.

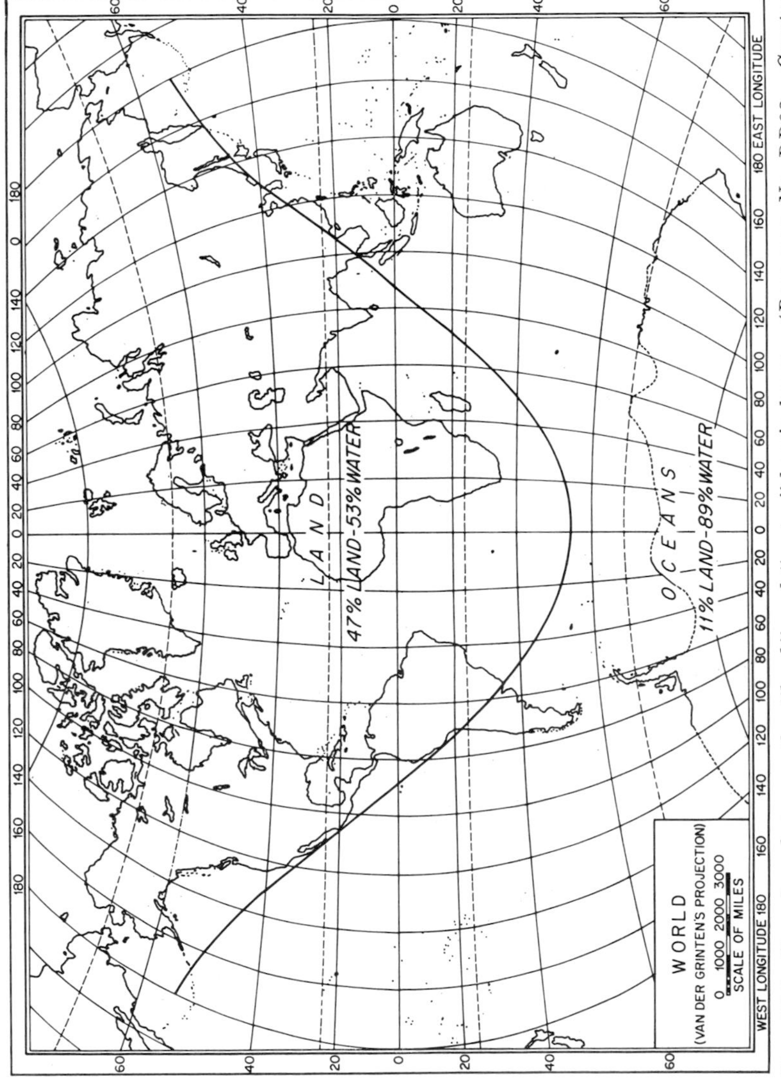

Fig. 17.5 Boundary between the "land" and "water" hemispheres. (*Base map No. DD98. Courtesy of A. J. Nystrom and Co., Chicago.*)

On the oceanward side of these mountain chains there is commonly a belt of sediments, or where mountain building is currently active, there is an oceanic trough with an associated gravity anomaly and earthquake pattern (see Chaps. 19 and 20). The belt of sediments may be either narrow or wide. In the case of the Pacific Ocean border, it is generally narrow. In the case of the North Atlantic it often reaches several hundred miles in width, partly exposed and partly submerged. Studies

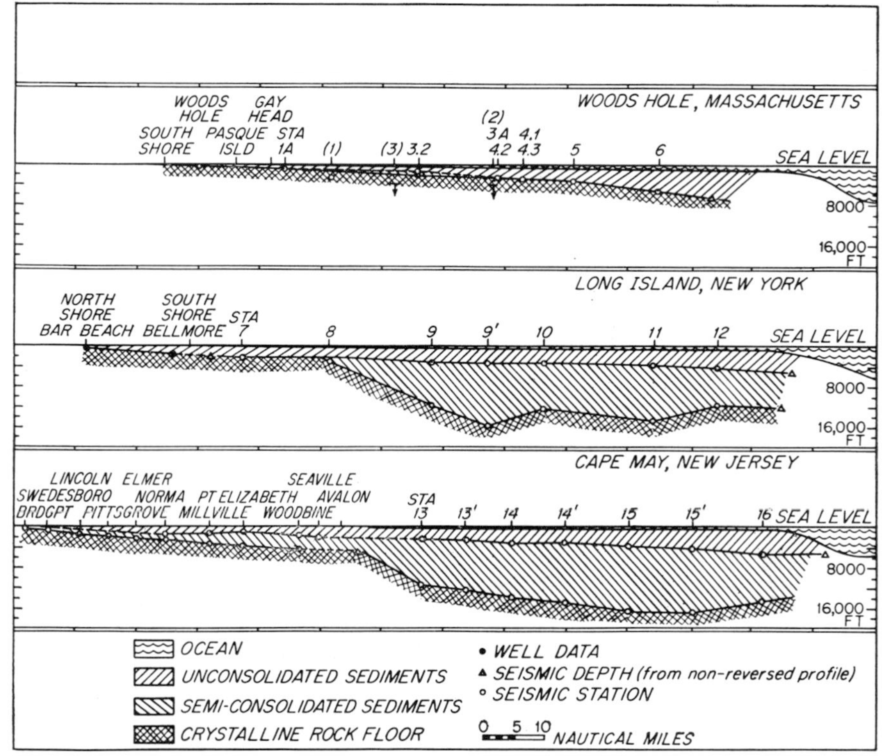

FIG. 17.6 Cross section of Atlantic coastal plain based on seismic evidence. (*Ewing et al., 1950.*)

of the structure of this shelf in the western North Atlantic show it to be a thick wedge of sediments tapering in places both shoreward and oceanward (Fig. 17.6). That part of the material being eroded from the continents which is not trapped in interior basins is continually being deposited in this fringe zone and is not carried toward the center of the ocean basins to any great extent. The greatest thickness of these sediments is generally under the continental shelf or the inner part of the continental slope, which therefore must be the locus of maximum sedimentation (Bentley and Worzel, 1956; Officer and Ewing, 1954). The sediments of the continental slopes appear to be the overflow of the shelves, piling up at the angle of repose. Thus, we must picture the continents as continually spreading by enlarging this sedimentary border.

The presence of mountain ranges of folded sediments parallel to the continental edges is the result of a counterprocess opposing this expansion. The amount of folding and thrusting in these ranges is the compression by which the spreading of the continents has been limited and complete submergence of the land beneath the sea prevented. This is a pattern in

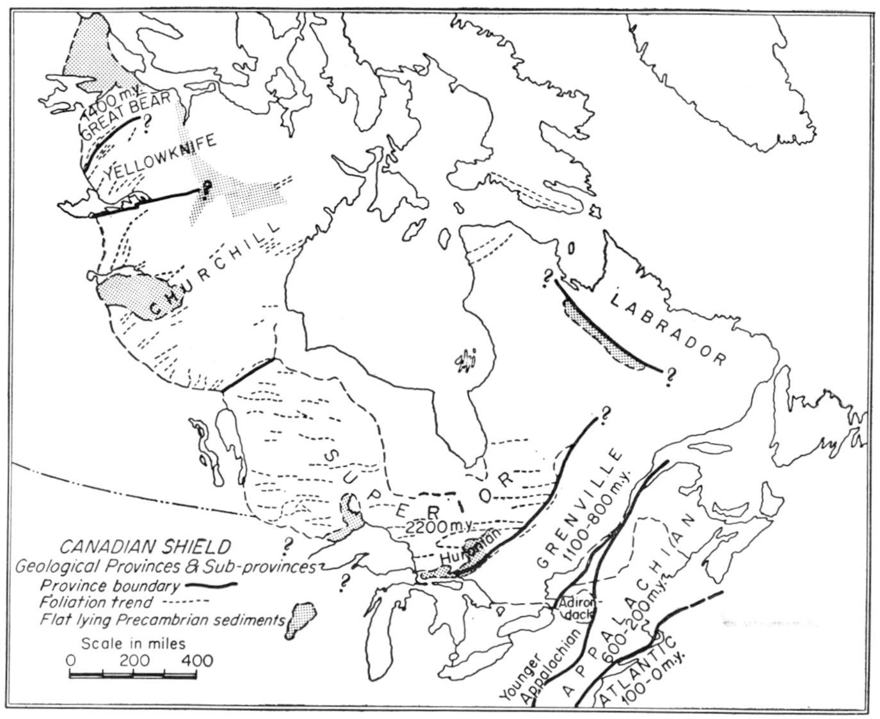

FIG. 17.7 Geologic provinces which correspond to former orogenic belts in the Canadian Shield. (*Wilson, 1950.*)

time as well as space. There is a tendency for the younger mountains to lie on the seaward side of older ones. Thus, in eastern Asia and Australia Mesozoic and Paleozoic mountains lie on the land and the fringing island chains are Cenozoic in age. The pre-Cambrian mountain structures of the bucklers lie largely inside the Paleozoic and younger fringing mountains.

In North America, where the structural pattern of the Canadian Shield is beginning to be understood, it is apparent that this concentric pattern exists even in this central core of the continent (Fig. 17.7). The Grenville province of Ontario and Quebec is older than the Appalachian province to the southeast and the Labrador province to the northeast but is younger than the Superior province to the northwest (Wilson, 1948, 1949, 1950). Some of the oldest rocks discovered anywhere on the earth come from near the center of the continent in southeastern Manitoba (Ahrens, 1955). To the northwest, the Yellowknife and Great Bear areas appear to be younger. Along the northern fringes of the continent in eastern Greenland and in Ellesmere Land are orogenic systems of Paleozoic and Mesozoic age (King, 1951).

However, there are exceptions to this pattern. In North America, the Jurassic Sierra Nevada compression lies between the Cenozoic Coast Ranges and the Cretaceous (Laramide) Rocky Mountains. Beneath the late pre-Cambrian sediments of the southwestern United States are highly deformed older pre-Cambrian rocks. The concentric pattern is suggestive but not so clearly defined as the other features discussed above.

These, then, are the principal facts which stand out above all others as characteristic of the continents. Any theory of the origin of the continents must explain most of these features, and it must not be inconsistent with any of them. To be acceptable, no theory may require that there be other major characteristics which are not present.

17.2 Origin by Local Differentiation. Almost all theories of the origin of the continents suppose that the material of which the land is composed was derived from the underlying mantle. The first possibility is that separation took place only locally over parts of the earth, leaving the remaining areas with little or no sialic encrustations. It is thought that a homogeneous magma intruded into a solid crust will generally result in a variety of bodies of differing compositions. The process responsible for this is magmatic differentiation. The detailed nature of magmatic differentiation is a subject of considerable debate, although it is commonly supposed by the majority of petrologists that fractional crystallization is the dominant process. The following factors, taken together, appear to be capable of explaining most of the broad compositional variations in the igneous rocks:

1. Gravitational differentiation (fractional crystallization) by the sinking of crystals in the liquid. As a magma cools, the early-formed crystals are often considerably richer in lime, magnesia, and iron than the liquid and are ordinarily denser than the liquid. Consequently it is expected that these early-formed crystals will settle, leaving the liquid enriched in alkalies, alumina, and silica. Silicon-aluminum-rich (sialic) material is therefore being displaced upward by the sinking calcium-magnesium-rich (simatic) crystals, resulting in a generally decreasing basicity going upward.

2. Gravitational differentiation by the rising of crystalline phases having a density less than the liquid. There is very little evidence in the rocks to support this concept, but in some environments such a process

might be possible. As the light phases would probably be alkali-rich silicates, the tendency to produce decreasing basicity upward would be present in this process also.

3. Differentiation by filter-pressing. When crystallization proceeds to the stage where the liquid makes up the lesser part of the total volume, it is possible by squeezing the crystal-liquid mesh to separate the liquid from the crystals. The residual liquid is expected to be less basic than the rock as a whole. Upward escape would occur more easily than downward, resulting in compositional layering with more basic material below.

4. Differentiation by gas streaming. As crystallization proceeds in magma, the dissolved gases will become concentrated, since the early-formed crystals do not contain volatile components. This concentration will cause the volatiles to exert an increasing vapor pressure on the magma chamber during crystallization. In some cases the volatiles may exert a pressure in excess of the strength of the chamber, and the gas will escape upward. Bubbles will rise throughout the magma. It is believed that this escaping gas may sweep some of the residual liquid out of the crystal mesh during the later stages of crystallization.

Other processes of differentiation, such as diffusion in the liquid magma, may be important in certain instances, but in general fractional crystallization is believed to be the most important process responsible for producing the great variety of igneous rocks exposed at the earth's surface. If the continental rocks have solidified, melted, recrystallized, and remelted many times, as seems likely from the geologic record, then there will have been a tendency to develop a scum of light constituents at the surface, the continental masses, which because of their low density stand above the undifferentiated ocean floors.

It has been suggested (for instance, Daly, 1926) that the outer mantle and the crust immediately beneath the oceans and deep beneath the continents is composed of a material in composition close to basalt. Column (3) in Table 17.2 shows what materials combined with 100 gm of average exposed crust would produce 200 gm of plateau basalt. This material in general differs from basalt in the direction of the composition of stony meteorites [column (5)]. It is thought by some that stony meteorites may be similar in composition to the average of the earth's mantle. The suggested layering in the crust thus is a regular sequence of rocks of increasing acidity outward, consistent with what would be expected to result from the types of magmatic differentiation discussed above.

The principal weaknesses of the differentiation-in-place theory are the difficulties in explaining the limited extent of the continents, their sharp boundaries, and their peculiar distribution on the earth's surface, all of which are important features of the continents. Any differentiation process would be expected to take place with considerable uniformity everywhere on the earth. Although it is perhaps too much to expect that continental-composition material would be formed everywhere on the earth at the same rate, the thickness of the crust, where it changes, would be expected to taper gradually from one place to another, and over any large segment of the earth an approximately equal amount of sial should have separated from the underlying column. The present distribution of

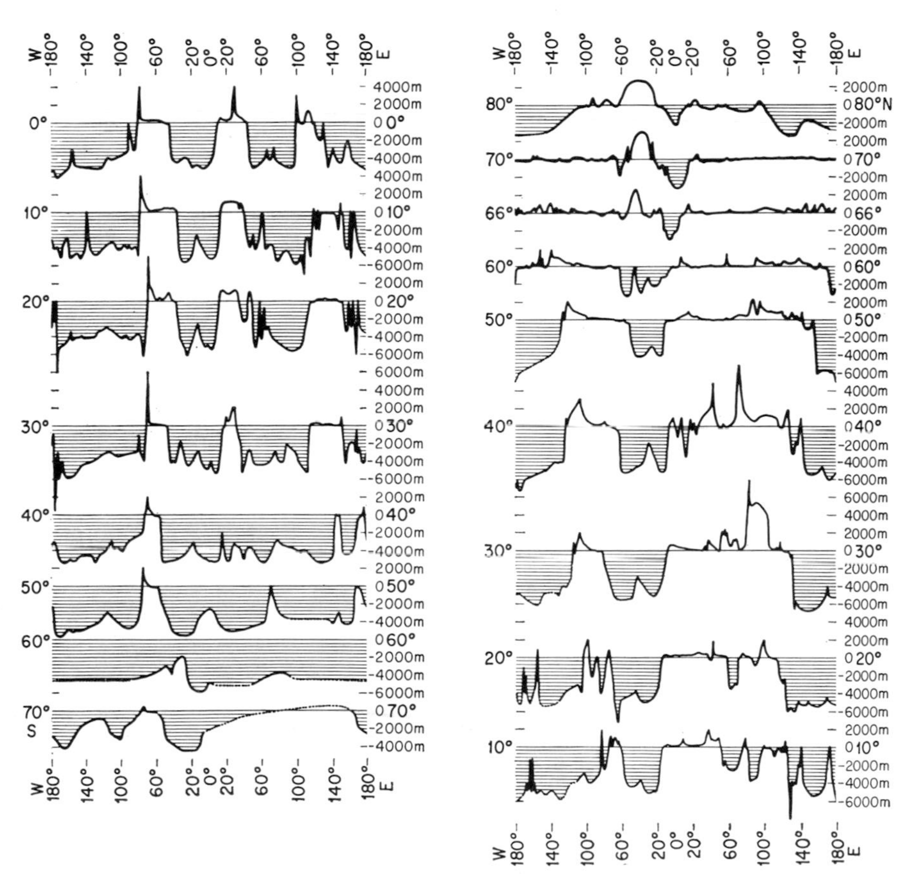

FIG. 17.8 Land-elevation profiles along selected parallels of latitude.

the continents is in striking contrast to this. The continents are largely concentrated in one hemisphere (Fig. 17.5), and their boundaries are sharp (Fig. 17.8).

Furthermore, it is questionable if an undifferentiated column of rock would occupy less space than a differentiated one. Jeffreys (1952) has pointed out that differentiation would produce denser as well as lighter products, and as a result, a differentiated column of rock may be no longer than an undifferentiated one. It is more likely that the elevation of the land results from the presence of material beneath the continents which is absent at any depth beneath the oceans.

Nor does there seen to be any good reason why continents formed by magmatic differentiation would have a concentric arrangement of their orogenic belts. However, this pattern may have developed after the continents were first formed, and it may be only a reflection of the tendency of mountains to develop where thick lenses of sediments accumulate at the edges of any continent once it has come into existence. If this is the case, it tends only to emphasize the variability of crustal thickness, as the present continental profile must then have been derived from a distribution such as that shown by the dotted line in Fig. 17.1, wherein the continents were once much higher than now and the continental shelves resulted from the shift of material from the crest of the land to the depositional zone on the slopes. Such a peaked character to the original hypsographic profile is reasonable only if there is some tendency for differentiation, once started, to accelerate relative to less differentiated zones.

17.3 Sedimentary Segregation. The concentric pattern of orogenies is better explained if it is assumed that the separation of sialic material was controlled by erosion and sedimentation (see, for instance, Wilson, 1949*b*, 1954). According to this hypothesis the continents grew around belts of volcanoes. The volcanic material must still be assumed to have been a sialic fraction of the underlying more simatic rock. Detrital material from the volcanoes filled adjoining geosynclines and was folded into mountain ranges. Further volcanism, a normal part of the orogenic cycle, added more material to the continental core. According to this theory, the existence of a plate of sialic material is assumed to stimulate acidic volcanism in comparison with the activity in the ocean basins. Compression and metamorphism of the sediments derived from the volcanoes built each continental block. The larger the block became, the more area there was to erode and the more sedimentation and the more orogenic disturbance there were, including volcanism. Thus the bigger the continent, the more it grew. The total present volume of continental material (Table 17.1), including the roots, is $7.36 \times 8.7 \times 10^8$ km^3, or about 6.4×10^9 km^3. If all this material originated by volcanic action over a period of 4 billion years, the average rate of sial production would be 1.6 km^3 per year. This is of the same order of magnitude as Kuenen's (1950) estimated current rate of efflux of material from volcanoes of 0.75 km^3 per year and only 3.3 times his estimate of 0.5 km^3 per year for the average rate throughout the earth's history. Allowing for the presence also of intrusive materials, the figures are in reasonably close agreement.

Although this theory explains the concentric pattern of the continents and the sharpness of their borders better than the one involving only igneous processes, it has the other weaknesses of the latter. It does not explain the concentration of the continents in one hemisphere or their fingering to the south. Furthermore, it requires that volcanic rocks be more acidic than the average for all crustal rocks, which is doubtful. This is not true of the volcanoes at present in the ocean basins, which produce only basic lavas.

Removal of the more basic components by sedimentary processes could overcome the last of these objections if it were quantitatively sufficient. Iron, magnesium, and calcium are more soluble than are silicon and aluminum and therefore are carried to sea in solution in greater quantity and contribute more heavily to abyssal sediments. This leaves the clastic sediments more sialic in composition than the materials from which they are derived. However, there are not nearly enough abyssal sediments to account for the mafic constituents which volcanic rocks would have to lose, even if the average composition of abyssal sediments is of the correct composition, which is doubtful. The only other possibility is that a part of the material removed from the continents and deposited in the oceans has somehow been remelted beneath the sea floor to become a part of the basic basement known from seismic evidence to underlie the oceans.

17.4 Suboceanic Assimilation Theory. It is conceivable that the continents could have formed by assimilation of the sial beneath the ocean basins (Pettersson, 1954, p. 21). The idea would be that beneath what are now the oceans a once-universal continental layer has been destroyed by absorption of the sialic material into the underlying sima, resulting in a shorter column of rock. This theory suffers all the disadvantages of the igneous differentiation theory plus the fact that there is no petrologic evidence suggesting that such recombination is likely. The main argument in favor of it is that it would explain the sinking of the ocean basins, for which there is much evidence. At many places in the oceans there are found flat-topped mountains, called guyots, with their summits sometimes thousands of feet beneath the sea surface (Fig. 17.9). These oceanic buttes are most easily explained by supposing that marine erosion truncated their summits at a time when they rose above sea level. Similarly, there are large canyons in the continental slopes which some geologists think must have been formed above sea level (Fig. 17.10). Also, paleontological evidence suggests former land bridges beneath areas now deeply submerged. Lastly, the coral atolls of the Pacific are believed to cap submerged volcanoes and to have grown as the peaks became submerged. Unless the volume of sea water has fluctuated very greatly in recent geologic history, parts at least of the ocean basins must have sunk.

17.5 Concentration by Gravity. Various processes have been proposed to explain how a sialic crust originally formed everywhere on the earth's surface could be subsequently concentrated into the present distribution. Poldervaart (1955, p. 140) suggested that early in the earth's life when the oceans were first coming into being, the higher parts of an original pumiceous crust were carried by subaerial erosion into such shallow depressions as then existed. These sediments later were forged by folding and metamorphism into the cores of the present continents, which then grew by volcanic activity as described in Sec. 17.3 above.

Daly (1926) suggested that gravity accomplished the concentration

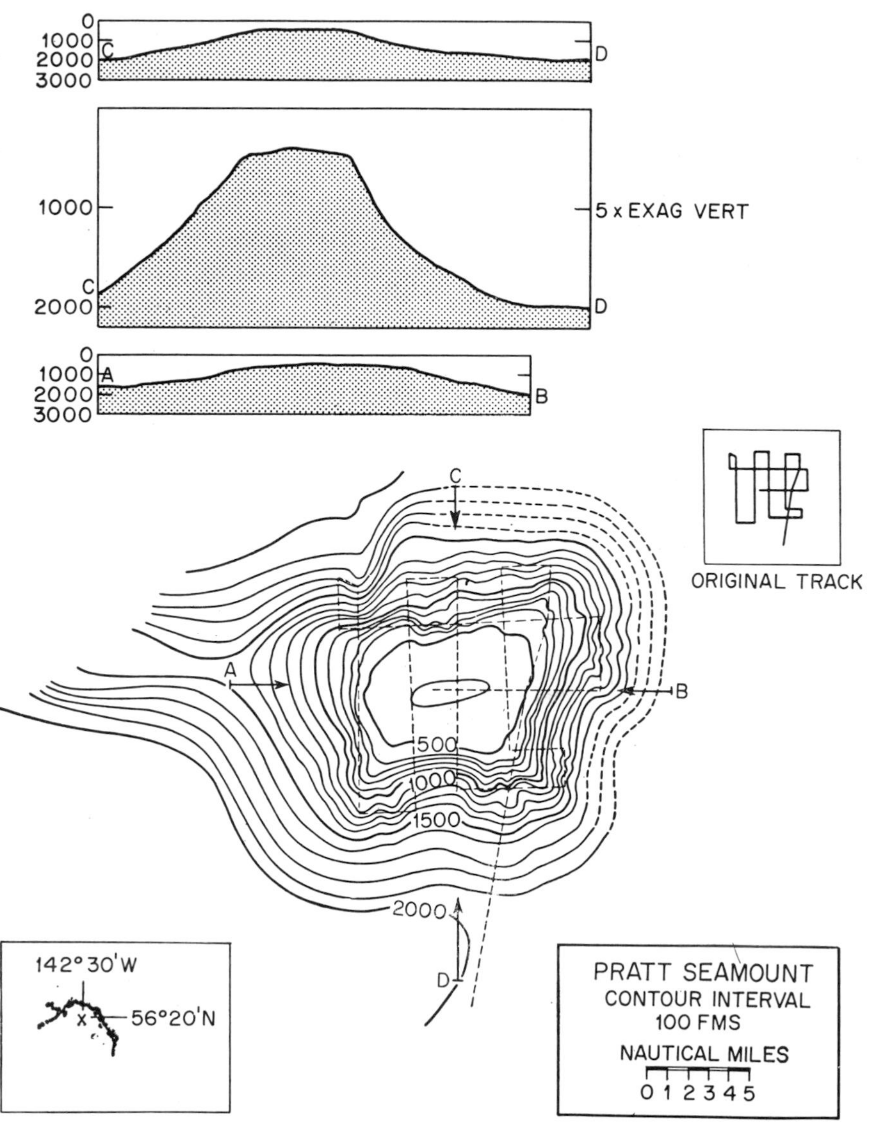

FIG. 17.9 Pratt Seamount, a guyot in the Gulf of Alaska. (*Menard, 1955.*)

more directly (see also Sec. 21.4). He postulated that the interior of the earth has cooled and shrunk unevenly. After the solidification of a once universal sialic crust, certain areas corresponding to the present continents sank to lower elevations than the rest of the surface owing to decrease in the volume of the underlying material. The rest of the crust slipped into the depressions thus formed, sliding on the still liquid or plastic substratum which lay under what was to become the oceans. After this concentration of the crust, the newly exposed areas cooled and shrank to form the present ocean basins, leaving the continents standing

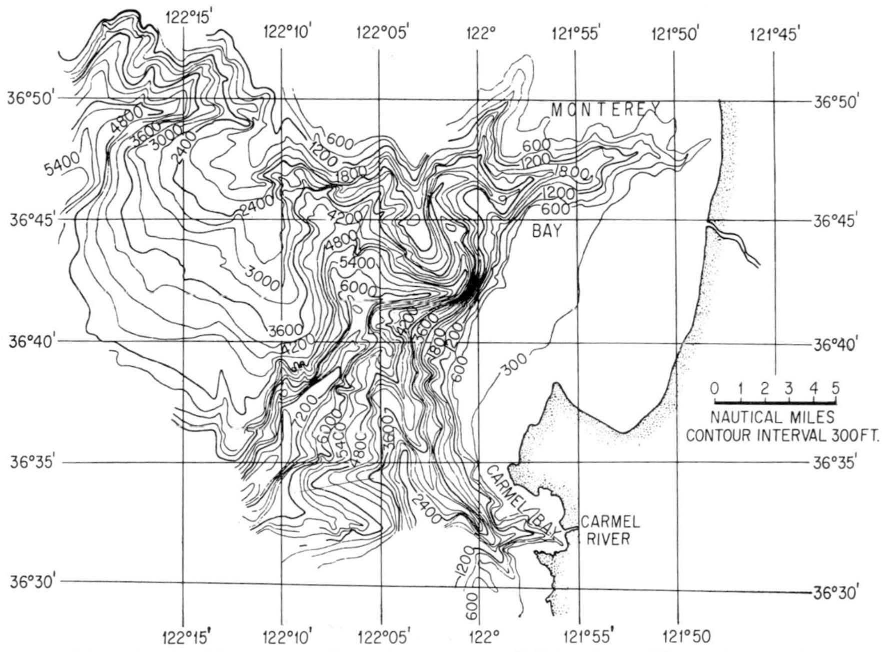

FIG. 17.10 Monterey submarine canyon, California. (*Shepard, 1938.*)

high above them. As cooling progressed, the solid shell of the earth thickened and the mobility of the crustal masses was decreased. Further differentiation and tectonic action is presumed to have altered only details of this general pattern. The depressions filled with water as the oceans were formed, and the world took on its present aspect.

These concepts explain adequately continental composition and resulting elevation. However, the processes by which it is proposed that the continental material would be concentrated are unlikely ones. It is hard to see why there should be an alternation of first high and then low elevations (and vice versa) for parts of the earth's surface. Isostasy would have been as active then as today, perhaps more so if the earth was more nearly fluid. Irregular shrinking would not have been expected to be so systematic as to have reversed the positions of the land and ocean areas. Even the cooling itself is open to question because of the heat generated by radioactivity.

17.6 Concentration by Subcrustal Convection Currents. Such a gathering together of the land is more reasonable if it is supposed that in the interior convection currents were stirring the mantle. Umbgrove (1947) and Vening Meinesz (1945) have suggested that a pattern of four convection cells would account for the tetragonal distribution of the

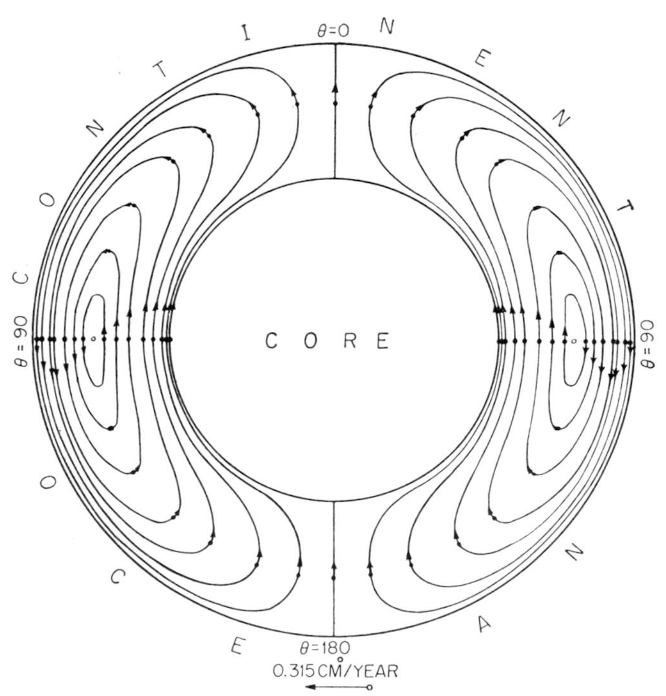

FIG. 17.11 Flow patterns in a spherical convective cell. (*Pekeris, 1935.*)

land areas. Beneath the four oceans, Atlantic, Pacific, Indian, and Arctic, were the centers of four rising currents of magma, driven by heat escaping from the hot interior and generated by radioactive disintegration in the core and mantle. These rising currents swept the sialic scum off their tops, piling it up in what are now the continental areas. As crustal thickness increased with cooling, the pattern was frozen. The subcrustal currents continued to flow, but more slowly, as perhaps they still do today, forming mountain ranges, earthquake zones, volcanic belts, and gravity anomalies (see Chaps. 19 and 20).

Theoretical support of this concept of subcrustal currents came from the work of Pekeris (1935), who showed that certain patterns of convection were probable in a cooling sphere of liquid. The simplest system would be a rising current at one pole and a descending one opposite it (Fig. 17.11). A double cell could have rising currents at both poles and an equatorial descending stream (Fig. 17.12). The next stable case is the tetragonal, with rising and descending currents corresponding to the poles and faces.

Perfect symmetry would not be expected in such a system. Some cells might be stronger than others. Certainly this would be necessary to

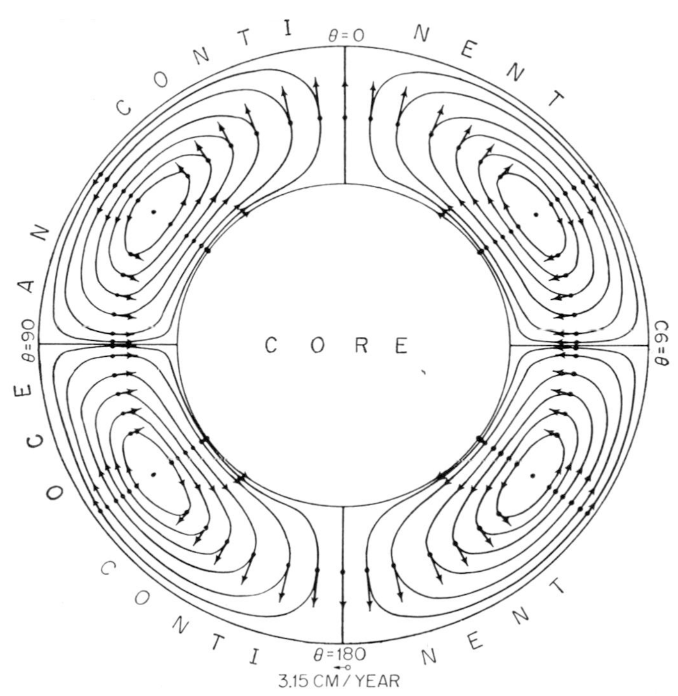

FIG. 17.12 Flow patterns in a spherical convective double cell. (*Pekeris, 1935.*)

explain the observed pattern of the continents. Perhaps an original tetragonal pattern was later replaced by a single current rising under the Pacific Ocean and descending under the land hemisphere. Such a current under a nearly rigid but still deformable shell would have the effect of squeezing the previous pattern out of shape, decreasing its symmetry. Such a current, still persisting, could be used to explain the circum-Pacific ring of tectonic activity (Fig. 19.4).

This is an appealing theory. It accounts moderately well for the major features of the continents, their concentration in one hemisphere, much of their fingering to the south, and their sharp boundaries. Even their mountainous borders are to be expected as a result of the subcrustal currents which, flowing horizontally from the region of upwelling to the downward column, exert their greatest tangential force on the crust in these regions.

One strong objection can be made to it. It requires that the descending currents be under the continents. It is commonly believed that the radioactive material of the earth is concentrated in the sialic rocks as compared with the underlying sima (see Sec. 5.5). Thus, they should represent heat blankets, preventing conductive loss from below. This would force the rising part of the convective cells to be under the insulating continents, the descending parts under the cooling oceans. This objection loses force when one observes that such measurements as have been made indicate that the heat loss is as great beneath the oceans as on land (Birch, 1954). One is led to suppose that an insulating crust, preventing conductive heat loss from below, tends to slow down convection and force the flow into new patterns. The convective system would then shift with time, the present arrangement of cells differing from the ones which swept the continents into their present positions earlier in the earth's history.

17.7 The Tidal Resonance Theory. A historically important hypothesis is that part of an originally world-wide crust was removed to become the moon (see Chap. 3). The density of the moon, 3.34 gm per cm^3, is much less than that of the earth, 5.51 gm per cm^3, being what would be expected for a body composed of a mixture of terrestrial crust and mantle without any constituent corresponding to the rocks of the earth's core or, perhaps, even the deeper part of the mantle. Following the separation of the moon from the Pacific basin, the remaining continental material is presumed to have broken apart and the pieces to have floated toward the newly formed depression on the still fluid subcrust, leaving the Atlantic, Arctic, and Indian Oceans between them. Before the pieces had time to reach a more symmetrical distribution, the sima froze, holding them fixed where they are today.

The arguments against this have been presented in Chap. 3. Although the theory explains reasonably well all the features of the continents except the concentric arrangement of mountain belts, the objections to it are so powerful that it is no longer considered important.

17.8 Origin by Addition of Mass to the Earth. One other possibility remains. From purely geometrical considerations, if the continents can be explained by postulating removal of a part of the crust to leave isolated blocks of material contrasting in composition to the rest of the surface, then it is equally reasonable to suppose that they can have originated by the addition from outside the earth of material of composition different from that of the rest of the earth. The time of such an event would most likely be early in the earth's life, before any of the detailed characteristics of its surface had been formed but after it had solidified sufficiently to immobilize a crustal layer on which the added material would sit. The continental material might even have been added as the last stage of the coagulation of the particles from which the earth was formed.

The continents together with their roots consist of 6.4×10^9 km^3 of material of density about 2.75+ gm per cm^3 (Table 17.1). The mass is therefore about 1.76×10^{22} kg. Separated from the earth, the continental masses would form a body 1,150 km in radius, or three-tenths of the volume of the moon, whose radius is 1,740 km. However, only about half this much material (915 km radius) would be required if the composition was right. In column (4) of Table 17.2 is shown what would have to be added to 50 gm of plateau basalt to get 100 gm of average crustal material. If a large block of such sodium-potassium-aluminum silicate were placed on a basaltic crust, it would sink to maintain isostatic equilibrium; spread by flow, erosion, and sedimentation; be intruded by various igneous bodies; and become mixed with the underlying strata by the folding and faulting of mountain formation. Today, 3 billion or 4 billion or more years after the addition of the lighter material, no pure block of the original additive might remain. An even smaller body might be sufficient if the presence of a thin acidic crustal block were to form a heat blanket, stimulating differentiation beneath it at a faster rate than elsewhere and hence tending to multiply its thickness.

Possible sources for such a body include the planetoids, although all known bodies of this type are much smaller than the theory requires. However, some of the planetoids pass periodically very close to the earth. In 1937 Hermes missed the earth by only 600,000 miles, about 2.5 times the mean distance of the moon (Krogdahl, 1952). It is believed also that many of the meteorites which impinge on the earth may be minute planetoids. Early in the life of the solar system there may have been many more of them, including larger ones. A second possibility is that the earth formerly had a second moon. If this satellite were in an unstable orbit, it might have fallen to the earth.

It is not necessary to suppose that there was only one such giant meteor, though it is simpler to suppose that there was one, or a single shower consisting of several principal pieces. The southward-pointing fingers of the continents suggest that this giant meteoric mass fell somewhere near the North Pole, splattering southward. Only Antarctica lies so far south that it is hard (but not impossible) to explain by this mechanism, and its size is still not completely certain because of the large ice-covered areas. The simplest hypothesis is to suppose that each continent began as a single fragment falling in the meteoric shower or broke from a single mass by the impact of its contact with the earth. The distribution of material is such that the meteor must have struck the earth at an oblique angle, coming in somewhere near 180° longitude, since the land hemisphere lies symmetrically about 0° (Fig. 17.5).

This theory explains adequately the limited distribution of the continental material, its elevation and composition, and the southward fingering of the continents. The concentric arrangement of the mountain ranges is explained by the tendency of the initial cores to grow by spreading and orogeny from the original centers where the pieces of the meteorite fell. There are two main objections to it. First, it calls for a much more acidic meteorite than any which are known to be striking the earth today. However, it is possible that this is only because sialic meteorites have not been recognized as such. It has been suggested that tektites, small glassy bodies found in many places, are supersiliceous meteorites (Rankama and Sahama, 1950). The second objection is that so large a meteorite striking the earth would have completely melted and possibly vaporized itself, with the result that its fragments would have been widely scattered instead of remaining in the proposed limited distribution. The energy acquired by a body of mass m falling to the earth through its gravitative field is

$$E = \int_{\infty}^{R_e} gm\, dr = \int_{\infty}^{R_e} \gamma M_e m r^{-2}\, dr = 6.3 \times 10^{11} \text{ ergs per gm} \quad (17.3)$$

Common minerals such as albite and orthoclase require energy only of the order of magnitude of 2×10^{10} ergs for fusion, even starting at low temperatures. Evaporation energies are largely unknown but are not likely to exceed 6.3×10^{11} ergs per gm.

Therefore, it must be concluded that all the theories proposed for the origin of the continents have important weaknesses. The true origin is still a matter of conjecture.

CHAPTER 18

CONTINENTAL DRIFT

Vertical movements of the earth's surface are easily demonstrated. Any alternation of emergence and submergence beneath sea level leaves clear evidence (e.g., unconformities) in the rocks. The distribution of sedimentary rocks is such that it is certain that almost all parts of what is now land have lain repeatedly beneath sea level. For these movements to have occurred while isostatic equilibrium was at the same time approximated there must have been large mass currents beneath the crust. Such transfer of material must be occurring today to balance the shift of surface material by erosion and deposition.

If there were no disturbing forces, the earth would be getting more and more even. The continents would be gradually worn away until their surfaces became everywhere covered by the oceans. The present is a period of emergence, in contrast to much of the time since the Cambrian. Large stresses must have acted in the earth's crust to produce this emergence. These stresses must be greater than the fundamental strength of the rocks of the crust inasmuch as they have deformed them.

There is no reason to suppose that these forces are not just as capable of causing horizontal as vertical movements. Indeed, horizontal movements may require less stress than vertical, since no part of the force is used in raising a part of the crust above the level of isostatic equilibrium against the earth's gravitational attraction.

18.1 Proof of Drift. The existence of folded mountain ranges proves that there have been large horizontal movements in the past. According to Van der Gracht (1928) the rocks of the Alpine belt were shortened from an original length of 600 to 1,200 km to a folded width of 120 to 150 km. The mountains of central Asia, from the Himalayas on the south to the Altai-Sayan group separating Mongolia from Siberia, show a compression of about 3,000 km. Elkins (1942) estimates that the original width of the Appalachian Mountains was 1.5 to 2.5 times the present figures of 300 to 600 km, which means that this belt has been shortened by at least 150 km. Although some authorities question the magnitude of these compressions, substantial crustal shortening is clearly indicated. Since in each of these cases there has been horizontal movement of very large blocks of continental crust relative to other large blocks, these constitute continental drifts.

In California we can measure a drift of the land to the southeast relative to the adjoining ocean. In the 1857 Tejon earthquake the estimated displacement was 20 ft. In the case of the 1906 San Francisco earthquake, the maximum shift was 21 ft. In 1940 in the Imperial Valley earthquake, a horizontal displacement of over 12 ft occurred (Secs. 8.2 to 8.4). Over the exposed length of the fault the average horizontal movement in the last hundred years is of the order of magnitude of 10 ft. This estimate of the amount of movement is more likely low than high, inasmuch as it is logical to suppose that movement is greater near the focus than at the surface. Whitten (1948) has shown that the geodetic evidence suggests a drift rate of about 15 ft (4.6 m) per century in California, but Hill and Diblee (1953) estimate only 2 ft per century from geologic evidence. The presence of folded mountain ranges suggests that the rocks yield to a considerable extent by plastic flow in addition to the observed fracture.

The deformation of the California Coast Ranges has been going on at least since Miocene time. The dissimilarity of the fault blocks on either side of the San Andreas fault suggests that this shear zone may have been active during the whole of this interval, possibly even since the Jurassic. A drift of 0.1 ft per year since the early Miocene, a little over 2×10^7 years, would result in a shift of about 400 miles. We can conclude that drift such as is seen to be occurring today is entirely sufficient to cause large shifts in the relative positions of parts of the earth's surface. This raises the question of what drifts have actually occurred. No large drifts of one continent with respect to another have ever been proved in spite of the extensive postulates presented, several samples of which follow.

18.2 Taylor's Theory. One of the oldest of the drift theories is that of F. B. Taylor (1910, 1928). He was impressed by the sudden inception of mountain building at the start of Tertiary time in contrast to quieter conditions of the mid-Cretaceous, and he concluded that some new source of stress must have become active then. He felt that, in order to have started acting so suddenly, the source of this energy must have been external to the earth, and he suggested that it resulted from the capture of the moon by the earth in late Cretaceous time. This would have caused a sudden increase in the tides. Taylor thought that tidal action would have increased the rate of rotation of the earth and hence increased its ellipticity. Polfluchtkraft would have caused a drift of the continents equatorward. As evidence supporting this view he pointed to the Alpine-Caucasus-Himalayan mountain belts (Fig. 18.1). With the exception of South America, most of the Tertiary mountains lie along the equatorward sides of continental blocks. Furthermore, all continents except Antarctica and those already lying on the equator have Tertiary mountains in the proper location. The largest continent, Eurasia, has the most strongly developed mountains.

As further evidence of the drift, Taylor pointed to tensional features which he believed existed in the arctic region from which the continents would have come. He cites Baffin Bay, Davis Strait, and the Labrador Sea as examples of rift valleys indicating stretching of the crust as it moved southward. The arctic basin is nearly 2,000 km across from

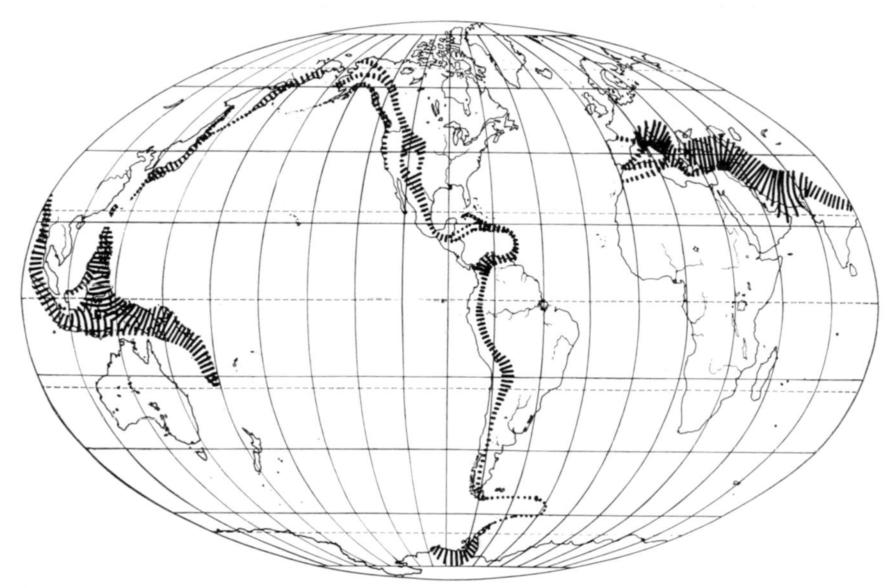

FIG. 18.1 The Tertiary tectonic belts. (*Largely after Davies, 1956; Hess, 1938; Wilson, 1954; Umbgrove, 1947.*)

Greenland to Siberia and according to this theory is the largest of the tension-produced basins.

Taylor suggested that South America separated from Africa before the Tertiary, probably in Permian time. The shape of the east coast of the former is remarkably similar to the west coast of the latter, the two fitting like parts of a jigsaw puzzle. The south coast of Australia has a like relationship to the edge of Antarctica facing it, the Great Australian Bight fitting over Wilkes Land, and Victoria and Tasmania occupying the Ross Sea.

The objections to this theory are many. One of its main weaknesses is the assumption that tidal forces would increase the earth's rotation. This is the reverse of what happens. The speed of rotation is decreasing (Sec. 2.3). Thus this part of Taylor's stress system is nonexistent.

Another difficulty is the weakness of the polfluchtkraft compared with the force necessary to produce mountains (Sec. 16.6). Also, it is difficult to see why South America would have moved westward at 90° to the direction of the force supposedly causing the drift.

18.3 Continental Drift as an Explanation of the Origin of Mountains. One of the main reasons why theories of continental drift appeal to the imagination is that they seem to offer an explanation of the origin of mountain ranges. It is suggested that the front edge of the moving block was crumpled by the resistance of the material against which it was thrust. To understand how this would occur, it is necessary to keep in mind the relative strengths and breaking strengths of the rocks involved. It is common in discussing continental drift to picture the continents as sialic material floating in a layer of basalt which outcrops under the oceans. The basalt is pictured as a plastic material, incapable of offering resistance to long-continued forces. This is incorrect. Beneath the continents at the temperatures and pressures which exist at a few tens of kilometers depth, the evidence of isostasy proves that the strength of the rock must be relatively small. However, at the surface the strength of basic rocks such as diabase and gabbro, which are the plutonic equivalents of basalt, is of the same order of magnitude as that of granite. The average crushing strength of 41 samples of gabbro and diabase was 1,800 kg per cm^2 compared with 1,480 kg per cm^2 for 154 samples of granite (Griggs, 1942; see also Table 16.1). There is no reason to expect that such rocks where they constitute the sea floor are significantly weaker than similar rocks of the continents. If anything, they would be expected to be stronger. Nor is there any reason to assume that the strength decreases more rapidly with depth under the oceans than on the land. Therefore, the continents cannot be pictured as surrounded by a sea of plastic material beside as well as beneath them.

To move, the continents must break rigid basalt or be broken by it. Any drifting which they do is against the resistance of the ocean basins. Any crushing which occurs will take place where the stress is greatest or where the crust is weakest. The point of maximum stress will depend on its source. In the case of the polfluchtkraft, this will tend to be at 45° latitude (see Sec. 16.6). There is no sign of the compression being greater here than elsewhere. Thus, the location of compressive mountain ranges must be due to some other set of forces or to weaknesses of the crust.

In considering the problem of whether a particular theory of continental drift is a good one or not, two classes of arguments are commonly involved. The first involves the ability of the theory to explain otherwise difficult-to-explain geological facts. It was in the attempt to explain the distribution of mountains on the earth that Taylor and other proponents of continental drift developed their ideas. There is no value to any theory that does not offer an explanation of observed facts. The second group of arguments relates to the source of the forces causing the drift. These arguments should be kept separate from those regarding the existence of drift. Even if the proposed cause can be proved to be incorrect, this does not disprove that the drift occurred. Taylor's explanation of the cause of continental drift, which involved the acquisition of the moon in the Cretaceous, has caused his theories to be generally discarded, whereas those of other writers who started from the same facts are still given consideration.

18.4 The Wegenerian Hypothesis. F. B. Taylor first published his theory in 1910. Two years later a somewhat similar proposal was

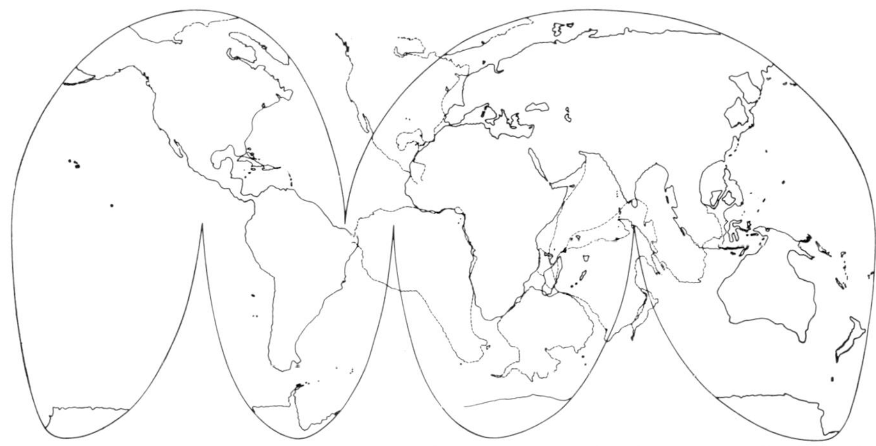

FIG. 18.2 The grouping of the continents previous to drifting as conceived by A. Wegener. Map is drawn at the edge of the continental shelf. Note that North America must be greatly distorted and India drawn out to join Africa. Wegener also stretched North and South America so that they were joined from the start.

made by Alfred Wegener, apparently independently (Wegener, 1924). Wegener postulated that previous to the Silurian, the sial was all one large continent which he called Pangaea. This block floated in the world-wide basaltic layer. In the late Paleozoic it broke to pieces under the influence of tidal forces, polfluchtkraft, and forces generated by movements of the earth's axis of rotation.

The separation proceeded at first slowly and then more rapidly as the continents became completely separated. In the Jurassic, the southern and western edges of this great land mass started to split from the rest as shown in Figs. 18.2 and 18.4. The free, eastern end swung out like a loose flap. Australia was first left behind and swung to the east; Antarctica only recently became separated from South America.

While this southward drift was occurring, South America traveled westward, opening the South Atlantic Ocean between it and Africa.

North and South America, which Wegener somehow pictured as having been attached previous to drifting, rotated about a point in North America and were drawn apart, leaving in between only the narrow stringer of Central America and the scattered fragments which now constitute the West Indies. Not until the Quaternary did Labrador and Newfoundland part from Europe. As they swung southwest, Greenland was left behind as a separate block.

While this was going on, India moved north against the main mass of the Asiatic continent, separating it from Africa, leaving Madagascar behind as a fragment, and throwing up the Himalayan mountain chain where it pressed against the resisting land.

In favor of this theory, Wegener and his followers have pointed to the similarities of the coast lines of the blocks once thought to be adjacent, especially South America and Africa. The comparison must be made at the edge of the continental shelf, not at the present shore line. They point to the chains of mountains all along the western edge of the Americas, which they believe were thrown up by the resistance of the sima to the thrust of the continents over it.

Central Africa is underlain in large part by pre-Cambrian rocks, covered in places by basins containing little-deformed sediments of lesser age. Madagascar and southern India consist largely of similar rocks. This is true also of Brazil and to some extent of western Australia. It is claimed that if these parts are fitted together on a globe in their predrift positions, the tectonic trends of the joined blocks are continuous across what are now their boundaries. The Mesozoic folding exposed at the southern tip of Africa (Cape Mountains) would be continuous with mountains of similar age in eastern Argentina (Sierra de la Ventana). The Tertiary features, on the other hand, are completely dissimilar, showing that the separation occurred before that time.

Similar relations exist between North America and Europe. The Appalachian Mountains strike northeastward across Newfoundland at exactly the place where this island is supposed formerly to have fitted against Ireland. Both the early (Taconic) and late Paleozoic (Appalachian) folding have similar trends and structures on both continents.

Faunal and floral similarities also exist among areas presumed by Wegener's theory formerly to have been continuous. One of the most remarkable of these is the distribution of the fossil plant *Glossopteris*. This has been found in Argentina, South Africa, India, Western Australia, and Antarctica, all areas presumed originally to have been close together.

Similarly, peculiarities of the climatic variations in the past can be explained if one supposes that the whole crust moved with respect to the earth's axis of rotation. Between the Carboniferous and the present, the total cumulative shift is claimed to have been 60° (Fig. 18.3), and the total movement much more than that as a result of the pole's having followed a sinuous path. In southern Africa there is much evidence of Carboniferous and Permian glaciation. The distribution of coal beds (common in tropical and temperate climates), salt and gypsum deposits,

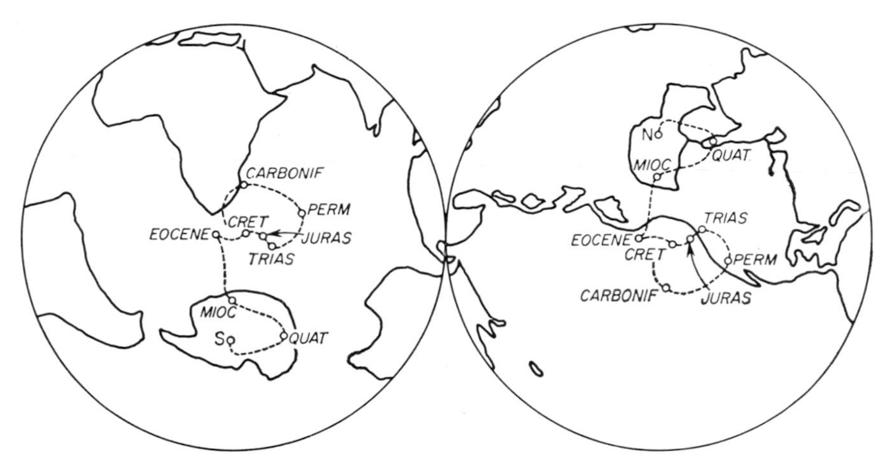

FIG. 18.3 Postulated wanderings of the poles. (*After Köppen and Wegener, 1924. Courtesy of Verlagsbuchhandlung Gebrüder Borntraeger, Berlin.*)

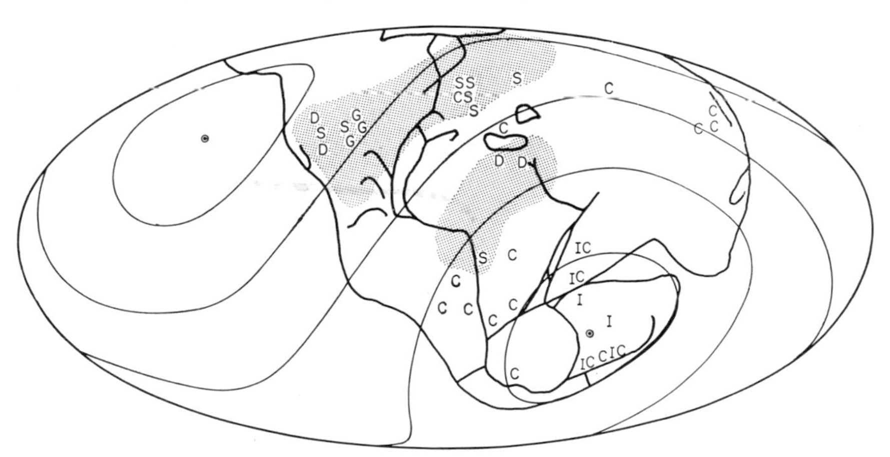

FIG. 18.4 Evidence for Wegener's postulated pattern of Permian climatic zones. *I*, ice; *C*, coal, *S*, salt; *G*, gypsum; *D*, desert sandstone; dotted areas, arid regions. (*After Köppen and Wegener, 1924. Courtesy of Verlagsbuchhandlung Gebrüder Borntraeger, Berlin.*)

and desert sandstones (typical of subtropical arid conditions) is consistent with the continents having been grouped in Pangaea and the South Pole having been in western Australia or the adjoining part of Antarctica (Fig. 18.4). Throughout the Mesozoic the climatic belts were shifted with respect to their present distribution but were still consistent with a

Pangaea which had split apart very little. By Miocene time, it is necessary to suppose a further shift of the pole and the separation of Australia from the other continents. By Pliocene time the distribution of the land was more nearly what it is today but the pole was still some 20° from its present location. If the continents had had their present

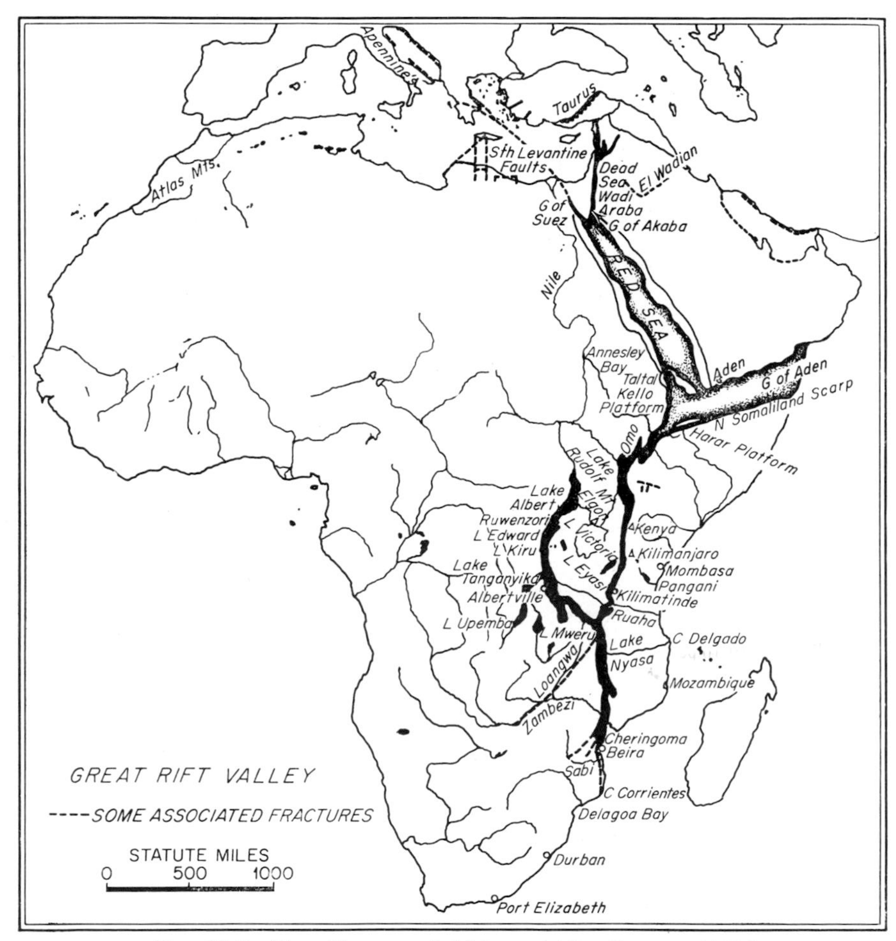

FIG. 18.5 The rift zones of Africa. (*After Gregory, 1920.*)

positions, it would be impossible to explain many of the climatic conditions of the past.

Separation of the continents and drift such as that proposed by Wegener necessitate tension in the crust behind the moving blocks. Most of the evidence for this would be beneath the sea, where it cannot be easily observed. However, there are some structures on land which are generally thought to be the result of tension. The most remarkable of these is the system of rift valleys in Africa and adjoining parts of Asia (Fig. 18.5). This system extends from Lake Nyasa in the south to the Dead Sea in Israel on the north. Throughout this belt there appear to be one and at places two lines of downdropped graben wedges, as though the crust were just starting to break apart. The Rhine Valley in Germany may be a similar structure, the zone of tension extending out under the North Sea.

18.5 Objections to Wegener's Ideas. The surest proof of Wegener's hypothesis would be a set of measurements of longitude of two of the blocks showing that they were moving with respect to one another. Wegener estimated that Greenland became separated from Europe by about 1,000 km in the last 50,000 to 100,000 years. This is an average velocity of 10 to 20 m per year. If this motion is still going on, it should be detectable by measurements of longitude. Measurements made in 1823, 1870, 1907, and 1922 on Greenland suggested a drift of this order of magnitude, but more recent measurements using more accurate methods have failed to detect any evidence of drift (Markowitz, 1945).

Many of the objections to Taylor's theory apply also to Wegener's. Wegener's drift has a predominantly westward direction. He suggested that tides in the body of the earth provided the forces which accomplished the drift. But even if the tides had been many times larger than they are, it is doubtful if they could have generated sufficient stress to overcome the resistance of the basaltic layer underlying the oceans or have folded and broken the crust into mountains. There is no reason to suppose that the fundamental strength of the rocks of the crust is anywhere small enough to permit yielding to forces as small as those which would be caused by tidal friction no matter how long they acted. For drift of this sort to have occurred, the whole continent would have to slide over to the ocean bottom. This would require a force strong enough to raise the advancing continental edge some tens of kilometers against the pull of gravity or to depress the ocean floor correspondingly, for the granitic layer extends to 30 km depth at places.

An insurmountable objection to Wegener's concepts would be the presence beneath a part of the Atlantic Ocean of a granitic layer (Sec. 11.7). Rothé (1951) has summarized the available evidence on the structure of the Atlantic sea bottom. He concluded that the granitic slab which forms the European and African continents extends west as far as the mid-Atlantic ridge, which rises above sea level at Iceland, the Azores, São Pedro and São Paulo, Ascension, Saint Helena, Tristan da Cunha, Gough, and Bouvet Islands. If any large part of the eastern Atlantic basins is floored by continental rocks, then the similarities of the coast lines are without significance. Search for a submerged continental area has so far been unsuccessful.

However, large areas in the Atlantic are underlain by up to 12,000 ft of red clay (Pettersson, 1954). The rate of accumulation of such materials is about 3×10^{-4} in. per year. Thus it would take about 500 million years to accumulate the observed sediments under the Atlantic in a basin claimed by Wegener to have formed less than 160 million years ago in Jurassic or later time. These deposits are as thick as or are thicker than similar deposits in the Pacific, suggesting that the Atlantic basin has been in existence equally long.

Other scientists have questioned the facts which Wegener uses to support his theory. R. T. Chamberlin (1928) has pointed out that petrographic analysis of the rocks on either side of the Atlantic shows that their resemblance is only superficial. The very formations claimed by Wegener to prove previous nearness on closer examination do not turn out to be much alike. Schuchert (1928) claims that the geologic histories of Ireland and Newfoundland are more different than would be expected if they had been linked until the Tertiary. Similar arguments apply elsewhere.

The similarity of the Paleozoic fauna and flora has been declared to be much less than Wegener claims. Schuchert states that the similarities across the Atlantic are about what one would expect if these continents had always had their present separation. Gregory (1928) points out that just as great biological resemblances exist between tropical America today and the lands on the opposite side of the Pacific as Wegener uses to prove that the continents must once have been closely grouped.

The climatological evidence is also in doubt. Glacial deposits of late Paleozoic age are found in New England and elsewhere in the middle of what Wegener postulates would be a tropical rain forest. Individually, no one of the arguments concerning climatic or biological similarities is sufficient to invalidate the drift theory, but taken all together the disagreements on the basic facts of evidence make it seem unlikely that the extreme movements proposed by Wegener have occurred.

Even Wegener's arguments as to the direction of motion required to fit the continental blocks back together has been questioned. Wegener claimed that as the Americas drifted westward, they moved farther apart. Schuchert (1928) believes that, on the contrary, they must come about 1,200 miles nearer one another to reach their present positions from where Wegener maintains they started. This is in conflict with paleontological evidence, which indicates that North and South America have been connected since long before the late Tertiary or early Quaternary, the time at which Wegener postulates the drift of North America to have occurred. In a like manner, the separation of Alaska and Siberia by 600 miles previous to this time, which is required by Wegener's theory, also conflicts with paleontological evidence, which suggests that the continents have been connected at this point since the Cambrian.

Lastly, Bailey Willis (1928) has pointed out that forces great enough to have built the Andes Mountains would almost certainly have deformed South America so greatly that any similarity of its eastern coast line to that of Africa facing it would have been destroyed. Whether or not drift in general is an important geologic phenomenon, Wegener's version in particular seems to be very unlikely.

CHAPTER 19

TECTONIC PATTERNS[1]

Geophysics has much to contribute to the rest of geology which can be of great help in understanding the changes which have taken place in the earth's interior in the past and which are taking place today. In particular, if we study how the earth is currently changing, we may come to an understanding of how it has changed previously. Tectonics, sometimes called tectonophysics, is the branch of geophysics which deals with the deformation of rocks by naturally generated stresses. In this chapter certain of the manifestations of currently or recently active deformation will be described.

19.1 Classification of Areas. The earth's surface can be classified into six principal types of area, three on land and three oceanic. These are (1) the continental shields, (2) the covered shield areas, (3) the continental mountain ranges, (4) the continental borderlands, (5) the ocean basins, and (6) the oceanic ridges. Although the boundaries between each are rarely sharp, each type of area can usually be recognized easily.

In the central parts of all the continents (except Antarctica) large areas of crystalline igneous and metamorphic rocks, mostly of pre-Cambrian age, are exposed. They appear to have rested in their present positions for many geologic periods with no greater disturbance than gentle upwarpings and resultant erosion. Such areas are called shields or bucklers (Fig. 19.4). At some places they are covered by flat or gently dipping sediments, the covered shield areas. Where this occurs, the old crystalline rocks are called the basement. Basement rocks of this kind may underlie mountainous areas also, but here it is not easy to distinguish them from relatively recent igneous and metamorphic formations.

Where exposed, the basement rocks are typically highly complex in structure and are truncated by a sharp nonconformity, indicating great deformation followed by a long period of erosion. The overlying sediments are typically little disturbed, showing that since the unconformity

[1] It is recommended that the reader have a good world map such as that published by the National Geographic Society (1951) available for easy reference while reading this chapter and the one which follows it.

the areas have undergone little deformation. The thickness of the sediments varies from zero to many thousands of meters but is rarely over 5,000 m. The geologic section is notable for many hiatuses representing periods of erosion.

The continental borderlands in many ways resemble the covered shields. They include the coastal plains where these are structurally a landward continuation of the shelves, as is commonly the case. The typical continental borderland, composed of the shelf and slope, is underlain by a thick wedge of little-deformed sediments. From the limited evidence available, this material seems to overlie a basement which on land is similar to the exposed shields but which, at the seaward end, may consist only of the more basic simatic phase of the crust (Fig. 17.6). Near the borders of the continents, sedimentary thickness increases, at places to over 10,000 m. Ewing and associates (1955) report such thicknesses in the Gulf of Mexico. In contrast, along the Atlantic seacoast of the United States, thicknesses of over 5,000 m are rare (see, for instance, Ewing et al., 1950). The continental borderlands are the natural location of the greatest volume of erosion products. Nearly all the clastic debris torn from the land is dropped on the continental shelves and slopes. Very little is carried out to sea.

The deep oceans are underlain by an entirely different type of sediment, largely chemical and fossil sediments with some wind-blown dust. This material has accumulated to depths as great as 3,500 m (Pettersson, 1954). Little is known of the structure of these sediments, but they, too, are believed to be generally flat-lying and to have been undisturbed for a long time.

In contrast, the mountain ranges, both continental and oceanic, are typified by igneous rocks and, on the continents, by deformed sediments. Volcanism is prevalent; in the case of the oceanic ridges it is the dominant feature. Continental mountains are often made up in large part of folded and faulted sediments. Deep troughs are often associated with the high ridges. On land these troughs are usually sediment-filled.

In addition to their purely topographic and stratigraphic features, the six types of area are notable for tectonic differences in the form of earthquake activity, volcanism, and gravity anomalies. Although these features are less easy to use in classifying the areas, since they are transient in nature and not easily recognized in the geologic record of the rocks, they are of the greatest importance in understanding geologic history.

19.2 Seismicity of the Earth. Figures 19.1 and 19.2 show the epicenters of all large earthquakes which occurred between 1904 and 1952.[1]

[1] More detailed epicenter maps and a more thorough discussion of earthquake occurrences will be found in Gutenberg and Richter's (1954) book "Seismicity of the Earth."

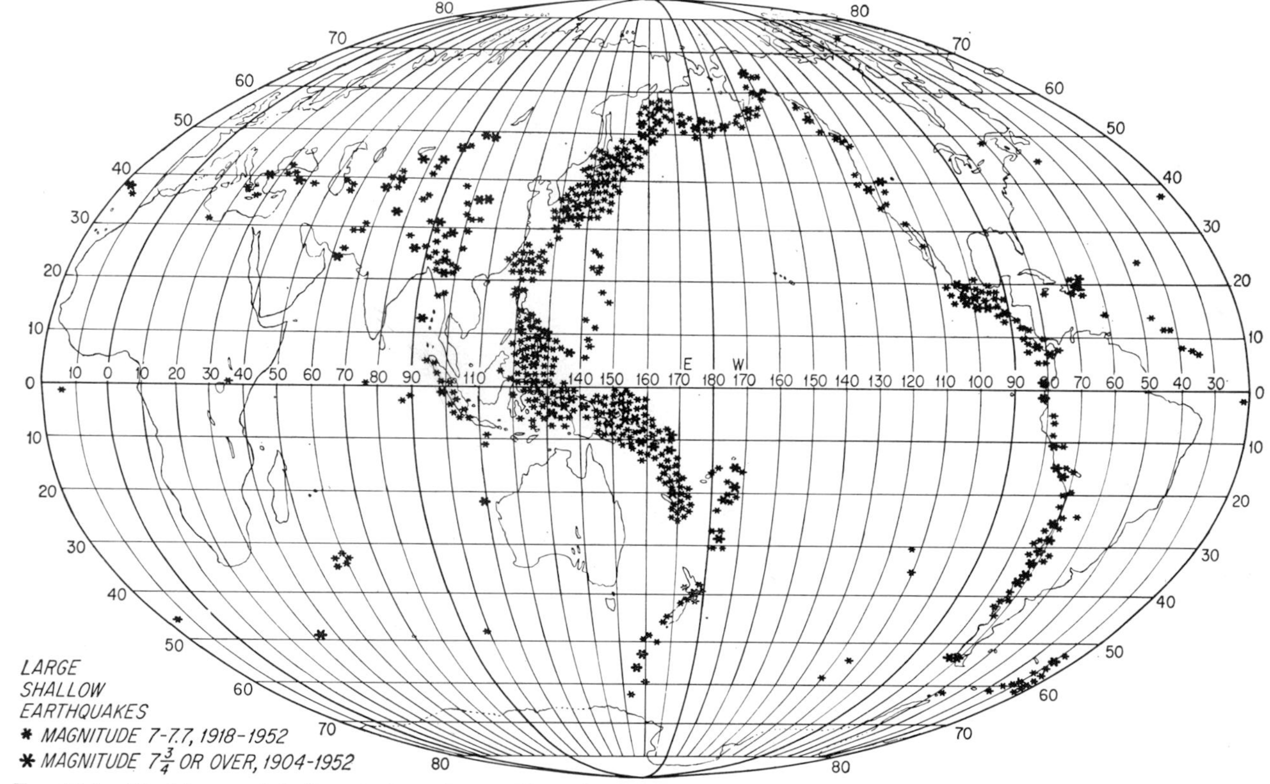

FIG. 19.1 World map of shallow earthquakes. (*From Gutenberg and Richter, 1954, "Seismicity of the Earth," p. 15. Courtesy of Princeton University Press.*)

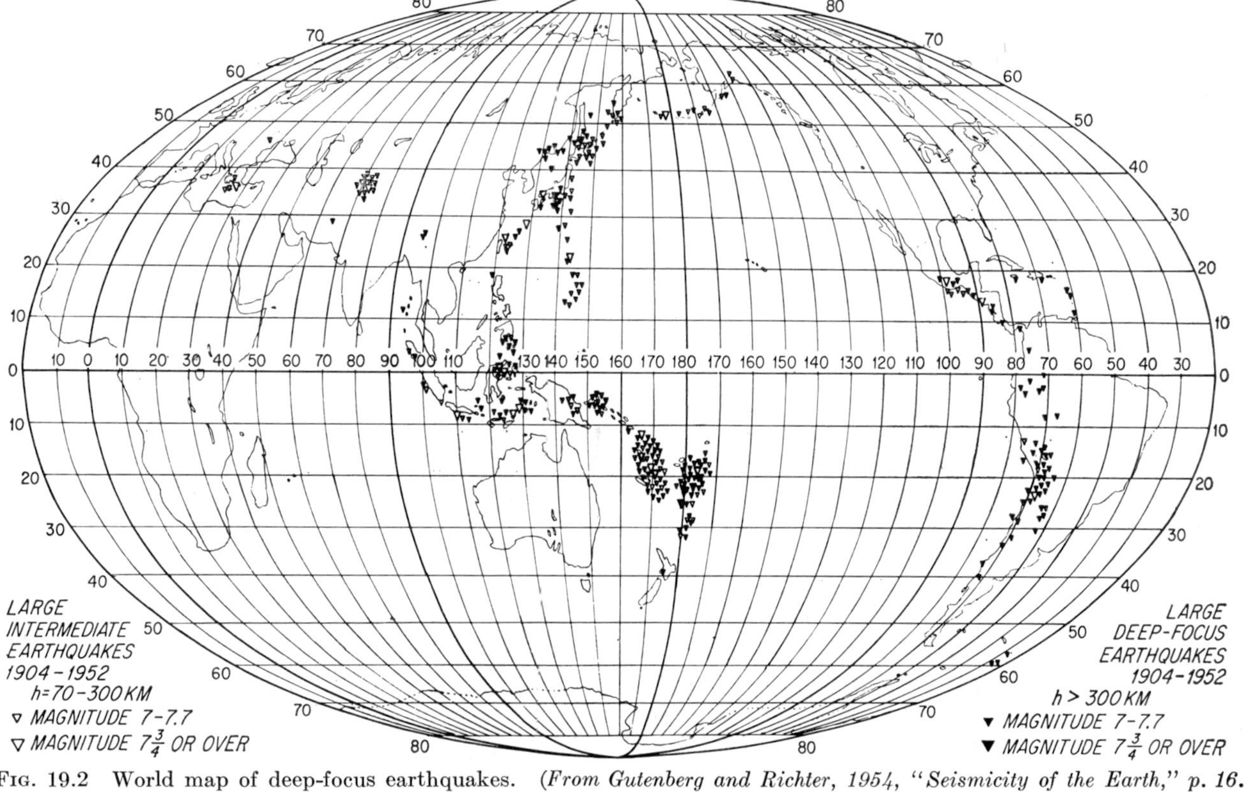

FIG. 19.2 World map of deep-focus earthquakes. (*From Gutenberg and Richter, 1954, "Seismicity of the Earth," p. 16. Courtesy of Princeton University Press.*)

One map is for shallow shocks; the other for intermediate and deep ones. Shocks of magnitude 7¾ or greater are indicated by a large symbol; 7 to 7.7 by a smaller one. To keep the map from becoming overcrowded, the smaller shallow shocks for the period 1904–1917 are omitted. Inclusion of these shocks would not change the main features of the pattern of earthquake distribution.

The most notable feature of the distribution of earthquakes is their concentration in a ring surrounding the Pacific Ocean. This shows clearly on both maps. The frequency of earthquakes is less along some parts of the loop than along others. For instance, in western North America earthquakes are scarcer than in the adjoining regions. Although California is often thought to have frequent earthquakes, actually they are surprisingly uncommon considering the state's location in the circum-Pacific earthquake belt. If smaller shocks had also been plotted, they would have filled this gap, making the continuity of the belt clearer.

Closure of the southern end of the ring is uncertain. From Tierra del Fuego at the southern tip of Chile the belt swings about 4,500 km to the east along the Falkland Island ridge, returning westward to reach Antarctica at the Palmer Peninsula (Graham Land). South of this, the Antarctic region seems to be largely free of earthquakes. In part, this may be due to the scarcity of seismic observatories south of 45° south latitude. Smaller shocks may often be undetected. But shocks of magnitude 7 or more are usually recorded all over the world, and none are known to have originated south of the Antarctic Circle.

In the eastern hemisphere the belt begins again southwest of New Zealand. From the vicinity of Macquarie Island it extends through New Zealand to the Kermadec and Tonga Islands and finally to Samoa. West of the belt of shallow earthquakes lie the epicenters of the intermediate and deep shocks. Beyond these, starting in the vicinity of the New Hebrides, the belt continues again to the northwest past the Solomons, along the north side of New Guinea to the Molucca Islands. Here the trend splits into three branches. One swings south and east to follow the Indies and constitutes the start of an independent trend. Another swings out into the Pacific to the Palau Islands, Guam, Saipan, and the Mariana and Bonin Islands and eventually joins the third, main branch in Japan.

The main branch extends northward by way of the Philippines, Formosa, and the Ryukyu Islands, of which Okinawa is one, to the Japanese archipelago. From here the line of epicenters follows the Kuril Islands to Kamchatka, then the Aleutians to Alaska. From there south, fortunately for the United States and Canada, the most active region lies off the coast coming back on the land only a little north of San Francisco. The axis of maximum activity closely follows the San Andreas fault and strikes into the Gulf of Southern California.

In Mexico the belt closely follows the western coast line. Near the southern border of the country it splits. The main trend continues along the west coast of Central America to Colombia. A minor arm runs east to Jamaica, Hispaniola, around the West Indian arc and returns through Venezuela to rejoin the main trend in Colombia. From here it continues south to the tip of the continent, with shallow shocks near the coast and deeper ones inland.

The East Indian trend is the second most important. It is known as the Alpide-Himalayan belt. From where it joins the circum-Pacific ring it follows the south side of the Indonesian archipelago, passes west of the Nicobar and Andaman Islands, and reaches the mainland in Burma. At the east end of the Himalaya Mountains this trend ceases to be a narrow belt and broadens as it turns east to include the whole of central Asia as far north as Lake Baikal. The belt narrows again to the west. Large deep shocks are rare, and intermediate ones are limited to a few areas such as the Pamir Mountains, where large earthquakes occur frequently at a depth of about 220 km. The belt is broad through Iran and Afghanistan. West of here it swings northward to include Turkey, the islands of the Aegean Sea, Greece, and Italy. Shocks of intermediate depth are common in Rumania, and small shocks occur throughout the Alpine region. The southern edge of the belt includes the regions around Tripoli and the Atlas Mountains in Africa. The center of the belt reaches the Atlantic near Gibraltar. The great Lisbon earthquake of 1755 is believed to belong to this group. The belt extends westward as far as the Azores.

Dividing the Atlantic into two series of basins is the mid-Atlantic ridge. Closely following it is another less completely developed line of epicenters. South of Saint Helena few shocks are observed, but from there north to Iceland the belt is well defined. Beyond Iceland the belt passes northwest of Spitsbergen to within 10° of the pole, ending near the mouth of the Lena River in northern Siberia.

Another minor belt lies largely in the Indian Ocean. Its northernmost epicenters lie in the Gulf of Aden and adjoining parts of the Arabian Sea. It passes between the Seychelles and Maldive Islands. It swings south of Africa, passing near the Prince Edward Islands (approximately 38°W, 46°S) and Bouvet Island, and joins the circum-Pacific trend at the Falkland Islands. Earthquakes are common west of this line in a belt which starts around the south end of the Red Sea and follows the rift zones of Africa, with scattered epicenters as far south as 30°.

Probably no region in the world is completely free of earthquakes, though in some areas like Antarctica none have been observed. The eastern and central United States, although nearly free of damaging shocks since 1886, have a history which includes heavy shaking (Fig.

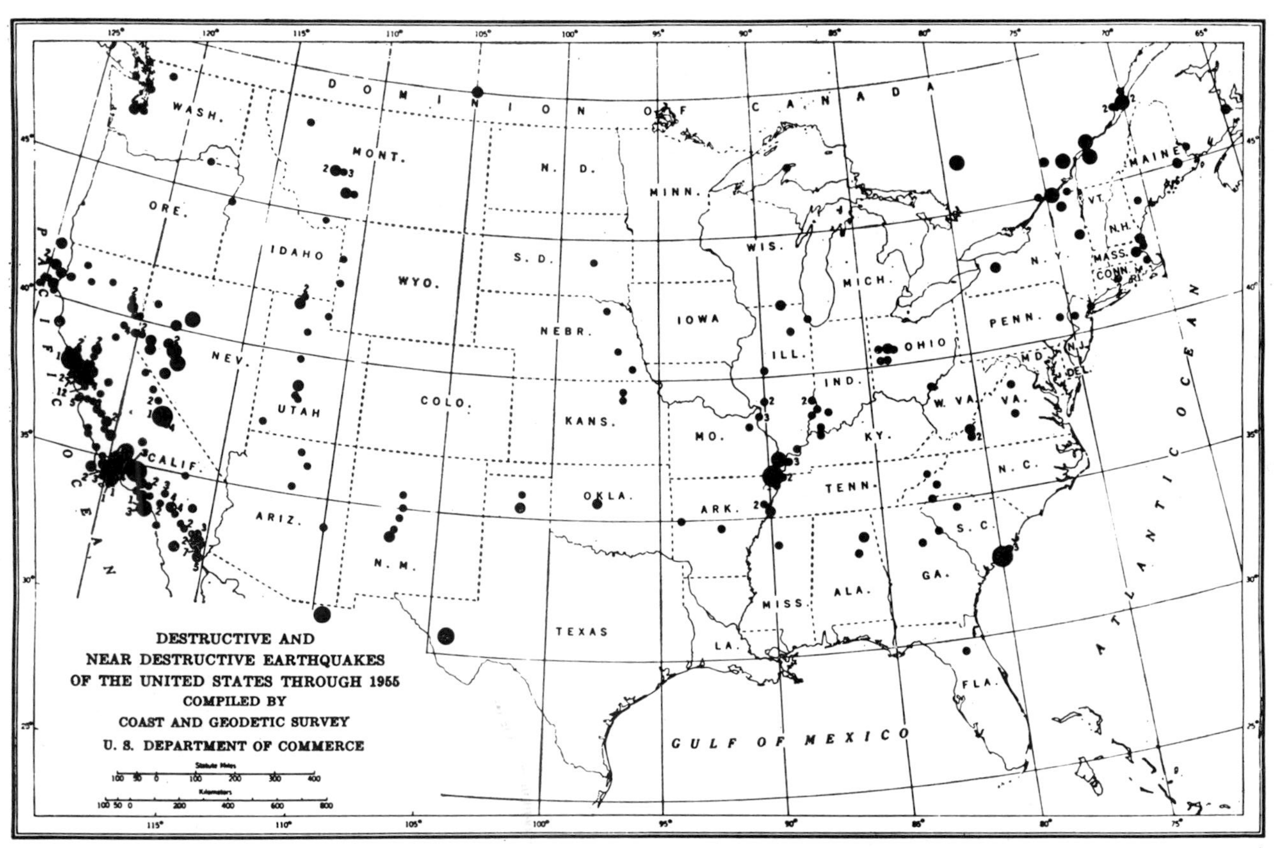

FIG. 19.3 Epicenters of the larger United States earthquakes through 1955. *(Courtesy of U.S. Coast and Geodetic Survey.)*

19.3). Some of the most violent earthquakes known to have occurred in the United States shook the central part of the Mississippi Valley in 1811 and 1812 (Davison, 1936). The exact locations of the epicenters are unknown, but they are thought to lie in the extreme southeastern corner of Missouri on the east side of Saint Francis Lake. Small earthquakes are not uncommon in the Saint Lawrence River Valley. The Charleston earthquake of 1886 is the largest to shake the southeastern United States in historic time (see Sec. 9.7).

19.3 Stable Areas. The shield areas, both covered and exposed, are notable for infrequency of earthquakes. The northern part of the Great Plains of the United States is an example (Fig. 19.3). A similar situation exists throughout central Canada. This stability is the principal characteristic of the shields. They appear to have been land areas throughout much of the interval since the pre-Cambrian. From time to time they have been partially submerged, acquiring a thin veneer of sedimentary cover. Repeatedly they have been gently bowed, allowing erosion to cut into the crust and to expose rocks once deeply buried. They appear to be near a state of equilibrium. Sometimes they are nearly peneplained. Nowhere in the shield areas is there evidence of strong current diastrophism. They seem to have withstood the paroxysms of Paleozoic, Mesozoic, and Cenozoic deformation largely untouched, yet they are fringed in general by mountain ranges of intensely folded and faulted formations. They give the impression of being rigid masses against whose resisting borders the surrounding deformable rocks were forced until they bent or broke.

In many cases the shields occupy the centers of the continents (Fig. 19.4). This is true of the North American (Canadian) shield, the African shield, the Scandinavian shield, and the Siberian shield. It is true also of the three Chinese and the Siamese shield areas if we suppose that the true border of the Asian continent lies along the island chains reaching from the East Indies to Japan. It is not true of the South American or Australian shields, which lie near edges of their continents, and it is not true of the Indian shield, which is separated from the bulk of Asia by the Himalaya Mountains.

There may be additional shield areas beneath the oceans. Gutenberg and Richter (1949) postulate that such an area may lie west of Chile and separated from it by the deep depression which fronts the South American continent on this side. Studies of seismic pulses reflected under the area suggest that it is continental in character (see Sec. 11.9). If this is the case, the true boundary of the ocean may follow the series of suboceanic ridges which extend southward from Central America to the Galápagos Islands, along the Easter Island rise, and thence southwestward, eventu-

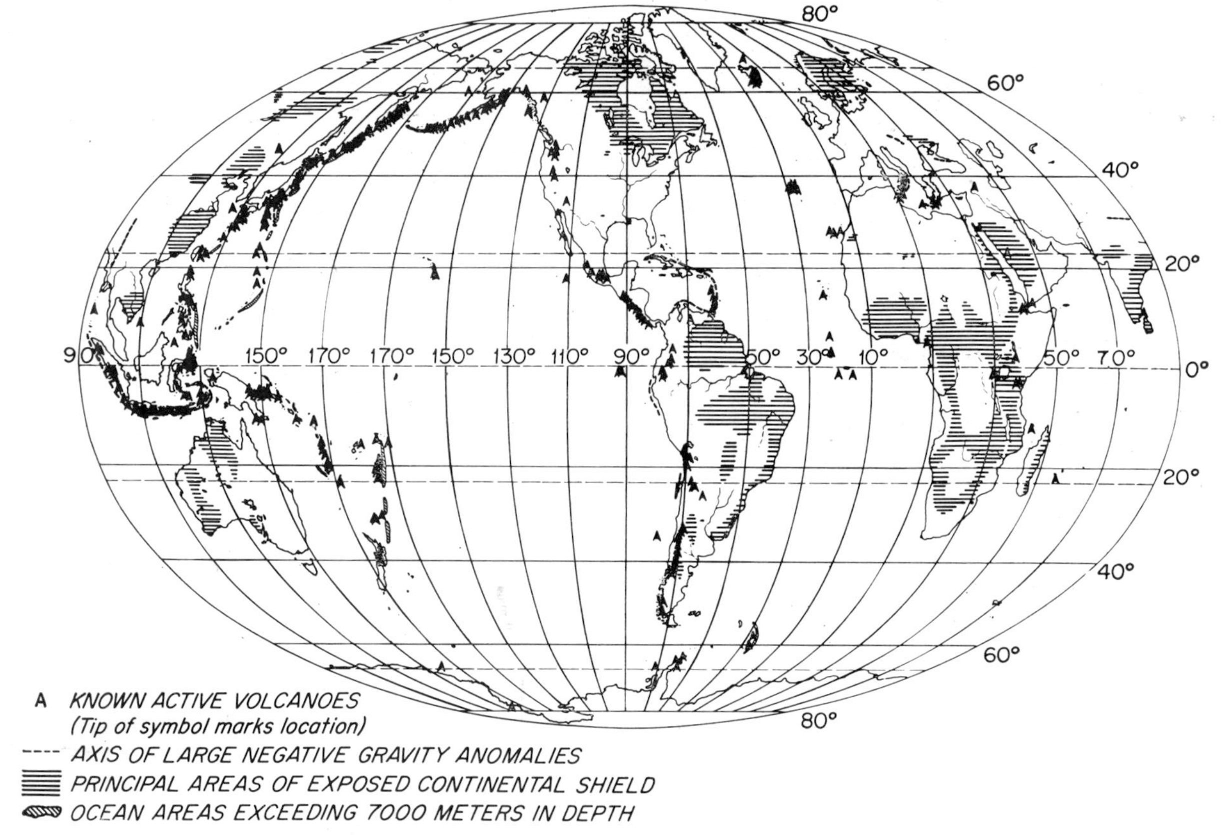

FIG. 19.4 World map of principal tectonic features.

ally joining the ridge which runs south from New Zealand toward Antarctica. Scattered earthquakes occur along this line.

It has already been noted that the Antarctic lacks significant seismic activity. It, too, may be a shield area. Too little is as yet known of it to generalize as to its geologic features. A few earthquakes south of Australia and near Amsterdam and Saint Paul Islands may be part of a group similar to the South Pacific belt. They occur along a submarine ridge which separates the central basin of the Indian Ocean from the Indian-Antarctic basin.

The ocean basins themselves are stable areas. Almost no earthquakes have been reported anywhere in the Pacific basin except around the Hawaiian Islands, where occasional shocks are felt, some of them possibly related to volcanic activity. The Atlantic Ocean is considered to consist of 15 basins in four main groups, a northeast group, a northwest one, a southeast one, and a southwest one, besides the Arctic and Atlantic-Antarctic basins (Sverdrup et al., 1942). All are stable areas. So are the Indian Ocean basins and the Pacific-Antarctic basin in so far as can be told from the limited information available on these remote regions.

The continental borderlands are also relatively stable. The eastern seaboard of the United States, the Gulf of Mexico, the west coast of Europe, and the China Sea are all quiet areas seismicly.

In a sense all four stable areas are of one nature. They differ from one another only in the thicknesses of the underlying crust and the superficial veneer of sediments. Because the continents tend to be fringed with mountains, there is no well-mapped, good example of a continuous transition from buckler through covered shield to continental borderland to ocean basin. It may occur along the north Brazilian coast, but here the details of the structural profile are unmapped. It is approximated by a section from Canada to the Caribbean Sea except that the covered shield is separated from the continental borderland by the buried Ouachita Mountain system.

19.4 Mountain Belts. In contrast to the four relatively even-surfaced regions described above, long, narrow belts of mountains and deep sea troughs surround the basins and shields and often follow the border of the continents. On land the mountains may be formed of intensely buckled sediments, upraised and eroded igneous and metamorphic masses, or piles of volcanic effluvia. Beneath the sea their nature is less well known. Some submarine ridges appear occasionally as volcanic island chains, but many are recognizable only by sketchily mapped submarine contours.

The most outstanding of these ridges are distributed in a pattern markedly similar to that of earthquake distribution. From the southern tip of South America to northern Colombia the Pacific border of the land is edged by a double and sometimes triple chain of mountains, largely of late Mesozoic and Cenozoic age. From Colombia, one chain of mountains swings east to become the islands of the Antilles, rejoining the mainland as three submarine ridges at Yucatán, British Honduras, and Nicaragua. Topographically, Central America is the continuation of the western ranges.

In the United States and Canada three parallel elements are apparent. The Rockies constitute the eastern arm, extending into central and northern Alaska. The Sierra Nevada, Cascade Mountains, and Coast Mountains of British Columbia are the central part; the southern extension of this ridge is the peninsula of Baja California. The Aleutian Islands are its expression to the north. The westernmost division begins with the islands off the southern California and Baja California coasts. It is best developed as the Coast Ranges of California, Oregon, and Washington and continues to the north in the form of the islands which shelter the inside passage to Alaska. From Mount Saint Elias, the line swings westward, leaves the land at the Kenai Peninsula, forms Kodiac Island, but cannot be traced beyond the Shumagin Islands.

In detail, particularly in geologic structure, the situation is much more complicated than this simple picture would indicate. The geologic age of mountain upheaval varies from place to place. There are major structural trends which cut across the lines of mountains, as in the case of the Transverse Ranges north of Los Angeles. The San Andreas fault crosses both the westernmost and the central ridges of the cordillera between San Francisco and Indio, California. The individual ridges cannot be traced continuously but join together and split apart repeatedly along their length.

The Bering Sea is a basin between two ridges of this system. These ridges join on the Kamchatka peninsula. The Sea of Okhotsk lies between two mountain ridges which join on Hokkaido. The Sea of Japan is similarly outlined. Other ranges stretch in a complex array from Bering Strait along the Anadyr, Kolyma, Stanovoi, Yablonoi, Sayan, Altai, and Tien Shan Ranges, which border Siberia, to the mountain swirl of the Pamir-Hindu Kush area. From Honshu one belt of islands swings southwest to Formosa, the Philippines, and East Indies; another forms the Bonin and Mariana Islands, Saipan, Guam, and the Palaus and rejoins the main trend at Halmahera.

The morphology of the East Indies is complex. Here the circum-Pacific belt joins a second major trend which extends westward, forming the Himalaya, Caucasus, Alps, Pyrenees, and Atlas Mountains. It joins the mid-Atlantic ridge at the Azores. In the other direction the mountain complex swings east along New Guinea, the Solomons, New Hebrides, New Caledonia, and the Tonga Islands. New Zealand may be the continuation of this trend, although its mountains are older than those of most parts of the system. The ridge continues south to Antarctica by way of the Auckland Islands, Macquarie Island, and the Balleny Islands. Victoria Land, Marie Byrd Land, and the Ellsworth Highland seem to provide a continuous system of ranges across Antarctica to the Palmer Peninsula. From here the ridge follows the South Orkneys, South Sandwich group, South Georgia and Falkland Islands to close the circum-Pacific loop at Tierra del Fuego.

The mid-Atlantic ridge separates the Atlantic into four groups of basins. Ridges divide the Indian ocean into a northwestern, an Antarctic, and a main (eastern) basin. Suboceanic rises outline basins surrounding Antarctica on its Pacific and Atlantic sides as well.

Elsewhere the shield areas are separated by older mountains. The Fennoscandian and Siberian shields have the Urals between them. The Appalachians and the Caledonian Mountains of Great Britain and Norway face the Atlantic basins. At the tip of Africa lie the Cape Mountains. The Chinese shield areas are separated by Mesozoic mountain ranges (Umbgrove, 1947). Comparison of the earthquake and mountain belts shows a remarkable restriction of the shocks to these regions of elevated rocks. Furthermore, the vast majority of epicenters lie in the belts of Tertiary or Quaternary disturbance, showing a relation between earthquakes and the processes of mountain formation.

19.5 Volcanoes. The small islands of Micronesia and Polynesia are of an entirely different nature from the peaks discussed above. Most or all of them are believed to be the tops of volcanoes, although the exposed parts of the islands are often composed entirely of coral reefs. With a few exceptions, as on Hawaii, the volcanoes are inactive. They have no clear relation to tectonic activity elsewhere on the globe. It has been suggested that they may be primarily the result of tensional cracking of the crust, though this is by no means certain. A similar explanation may apply to the volcanoes of the rift zones of Africa and Arabia. Because of the lack of exposures through most of the Pacific area the composition of the volcanic material is known for only a few islands. All of it is believed to belong to the alkali olivine-basaltic suite.

Extinct marine volcanoes are not restricted to the southwest Pacific region. Even off the coast of North America truncated cones called guyots are common (Menard, 1955). They are believed to have been planed by erosion at a time when sea level was much lower than at present.

On the other hand, the distribution of the majority of active volcanoes is closely related to the seismic belts (Fig. 19.4). In general they lie on lines parallel to the seismic belts but not coinciding with them. Generally the volcanoes are on the continental side of the earthquake activity, and such large shocks as occur near them are often at intermediate depth.

Gutenberg and Richter (1954) list 459 volcanoes which are known to have been active in historic times.

The region of the East Indies has the greatest concentration of these. Some of them are submarine, and their locations are known only from ships' reports. From the Banda Sea they follow the arc of the islands across Flores, Java, and Sumatra. There is one active volcano in the Andamans, and one reputedly active in Burma.

The distribution of active volcanism within this belt is more erratic than that of the other tectonic features discussed above. Only one additional part of the Alpide-Himalayan tectonic belt has experienced recent volcanism. This district is the Mediterranean. In Italy, Sicily, and the Aegean sea are a group of active cones. Four islands of the Canary group also have volcanoes. The Azores can be included either in the above group or the mid-Atlantic one. The latter belt starts with two submarine vents almost on the equator, one north of Ascension Island and the other west of there. The volcanic belt does not follow the mid-Atlantic ridge but lies in large part east of it, including the Cape Verde and Canary Islands. At the north end, Iceland exhibits activity, and there is one volcano on Jan Mayen Island.

Almost all parts of the circum-Pacific belt are active. Mount Erebus in Antarctica is active, as is one island in the Balleny group. There are five active vents on the North Island of New Zealand, several west of the Kermadecs, and a group in the Tonga and Samoan Islands. Like the seismic belt, west of here the trend is offset to a point southeast of the New Hebrides and extending through the Solomon, New Britain, and New Guinea Islands. It includes Halmahera and Celebes in the East Indies, the Philippines, Formosa, and the Ryukyu Islands. A second line of volcanoes stretching south to the Bonin and Mariana Islands joins this group at Fujiyama in Japan. The arc of the Kuril Islands and Kamchatka exhibits strong volcanism. There are several vents on the mainland in Manchuria. The circum-Pacific line follows the Aleutians to Alaska.

In the United States, Mount Baker, Mount Rainier, Mount Saint Helens, Mount Hood, Mount Shasta, Cinder Cone (in California), Lassen Peak, and Sunset Crater (in Arizona) have all shown some activity within historic times. The most recent eruption was a small outpouring of lava from Lassen Peak in 1917.

There are two vents in Baja California. A vigorously active belt crosses central Mexico and includes the new volcano Paricutin. Another group lies along the Pacific Coast of Central America. The Lesser Antilles are marked by a chain of volcanoes. There is one in Venezuela, a group in Colombia and Ecuador, more in the southern Andes. Along the Falkland Island ridge, there is activity in the South

Sandwich Islands, the South Shetlands, on Lindenberg Island off the Palmer Peninsula, and at one place in the Bellingshausen Sea to the west. The close connection between the volcanic belts and the seismic belts makes it certain that there is some fundamental connection between the two types of activity.

19.6 Troughs. Along the borders of the continents great elongate troughs, called deeps, are commonly found (Fig. 19.4). There may be more of them than have as yet been mapped. In some cases they present greater topographic relief than the highest mountains above sea level. The Cape Johnson Deep east of the Philippines is 34,440 ft deep compared with Everest's 29,000 ft height. The largest deeps are those lying off island arcs. Depths of over 30,000 ft have been measured in the Tonga-Kermadec Trench, south of the Marianas, south of Japan, east of New Britain, and east of the Philippines.

The most characteristic feature of these troughs is not their depth, but their position with respect to the seismic, volcanic, and mountain belts. Elongate troughs lie south of the East Indies and all along the Japanese, Kuril, and Aleutian arcs. A great depression hugs the west coast of South America, reaching a maximum depth of 25,050 ft west of northern Chile. East of the southern Antilles, east of Tonga, west of the New Hebrides, west of the Solomons, and south of New Britian there are elongate trenches. At 61°S latitude just west of the 180th meridian a depth of 28,152 ft has been measured, suggesting that a trough lies here, adjoining the ridge connecting New Zealand and Antarctica. Where these trenches lie in front of arcuate segments of continental borderland, they are often called foredeeps.

Near land such troughs would be quickly filled with debris as a result of erosion and sedimentation. Such a basin is known to lie along the south edge of the Himalayas. The Persian Gulf may be such a structure. In western North America, a remarkable chain of valleys begins south of Mount Saint Elias in Alaska, forms the inside passage behind Vancouver Island, and extends along Puget Sound and the Willamette Valley. It is interrupted by the Klamath Mountains in Oregon but continues as the Sacramento and San Joaquin Valleys in California. The Tehachapi Mountains and the Transverse Ranges separate this area from the Ventura and Los Angeles basins to the south. The basement is believed to be 45,000 ft deep in the latter region (Gutenberg and Buwalda, 1936). A continuous valley connects with the Salton Sink and continues to the southeast as the Gulf of California. Umbgrove (1947) believes that similar depositional troughs lay along the edges of the Alps and older mountains of Europe and elsewhere during their formation.

19.7 Gravity Anomalies. One might expect to find abnormal values of gravity over such striking topographic features as the recently formed mountain ranges of the Alpide-Himalayan belt and the deep depressions of the oceanic troughs. In most places, especially in the mountainous areas, isostatic adjustment has wiped out whatever anomaly there ever was. In some cases where the deformation was very recent, considerable departure from normal still remains. To some extent the anomalies may exist as a result of stresses still being exerted on the area. In other cases, they may be already shrinking as adjustment takes place.

The patterns which remain are as distinctive as those of the seismic epicenters and volcanoes. Figure 19.4 shows some of the strongest anomalies. This map is far from complete, especially at sea, as detailed gravity surveys have been carried out only in a few parts of the earth. Many of the surveys which have been made have not been integrated with other surveys. In most cases, mapped local anomalies have not been corrected for isostatic adjustment and hence cannot be fitted into a world-wide picture.

The great anomaly south and east of the East Indies is the largest and best known and is typical in general form of the others (Fig. 19.5). The lowest value of attraction is represented by an anomaly of −204 milligals between Halmahera and Celebes. The trough of the gravity low lies along the inside edge of the oceanic deep. It coincides with a topographic ridge lying off the coast of Sumatra and rising above the sea in places as islands. At the west end these include Simeuloeë, Nias, and Siberut. Where the ridge rises highest, the gravity anomaly decreases. At Soemba the gravitational attraction rises to above average values in contrast to the negative anomalies to the east and west. From Timor to Tanimbar it is large and below average. The zone curves around past Ceram, again becomes positive for a section under the Banda Sea, follows the eastern arms of Celebes, and swerves north along the coast of Mindanao. On either side of the negative strips are wider areas of positive anomalies. The deviations from normal pull are less under the broad positive areas than in the adjoining narrow negative belt.

Similar areas of negative gravity with associated positive anomalies lie along the foot of the Himalaya Mountains and their extension to the south through Burma, along the Japanese deep, along the Brownson trough north of the Greater Antilles, and looping around the east side of the Lesser Antilles in the West Indies. Negative areas are also known at several places off the west coast of South America. In Europe, belts of positive and negative anomalies occur in the Mediterranean and Black Seas and along the north edge of the Carpathian Mountains.

The similarities in the trends of all these features can only mean that they have some connection with one another. The seismic activity shows that deformation of the crust is currently taking place. The volcanism proves either that the crust here is warmer than usual or that hotter rocks from beneath are being forced up into the surface formations. The gravity anomalies indicate that large current or recent forces have bent or broken the crust out of its equilibrium position. Clearly these are belts of active mountain building. Whatever the cause of the deformation, the pattern is clear. Today, especially around the Pacific, we can see the mountains forming. If this is typical of mountain building in general, it is here we can expect to learn how it takes place.

CHAPTER 20

TYPICAL TECTONIC PROFILES

In Chap. 19 the areal distribution of tectonic activity was described. It showed primarily the surface outcrop of processes extending deep into the earth. Lacking the opportunity for direct observation, the deeper events must be deduced from such geophysical evidence as is available. To do this let us examine the belts of tectonic activity in cross section.

20.1 Japan. The pattern of tectonic activity in the Japanese region is similar to that found all around the Pacific basin. In Fig. 20.1, the earthquake foci lying in a northwest-southeast belt across the island of Hokkaido have been projected onto a vertical plane through the line *A-B*. The distribution which results suggests that a narrow zone of shear dips under the continent at an angle of about 30°. It strikes the surface near the bottom of the foredeep, whose maximum known depth is 10,550 m. A negative gravity anomaly of approximately 100 milligals has its axis between here and the shore line. Belts of positive anomalies lie on either side. That on the landward side is the larger, having a maximum of nearly 100 milligals at the shore line.

In the center of the island are Cenozoic mountains. There are five active volcanoes on Hokkaido. To the northwest is a shallow basin, the north end of the Sea of Japan. On the continent proper the land is fronted by Mesozoic mountains, the Sikhote Alin Range.

The gravity minimum cannot be caused by the absence of rock in the trough, as it lies at the side, not over the center of the depression. The explanation must lie in a thickening of the layer of low-density rocks along the margin of the islands. This could be caused by a greater abundance of light sediments under the inner edge of the trough than on its oceanic side, by folding of the crustal layers, or by overthrusting of the continental mass onto the sea bottom. In the case of the similar anomaly over the Puerto Rico trench, Ewing and Worzel (1954) have concluded that it can best be explained as a result of sedimentation. On the other hand, the distribution of earthquakes suggests that the continent is rising on a fault. The vulcanism might result from magma rising along subsidiary breaks.

If the earthquake foci were plotted in three dimensions instead of two, their distribution would be seen to be zonal rather than planar, showing that structure is more complicated than a single large fault. Probably many of the shallow shocks are not closely related to the main zone of shear. This may be true for some of the intermediate and deep shocks also. Furthermore, studies of the direction of displacement show that

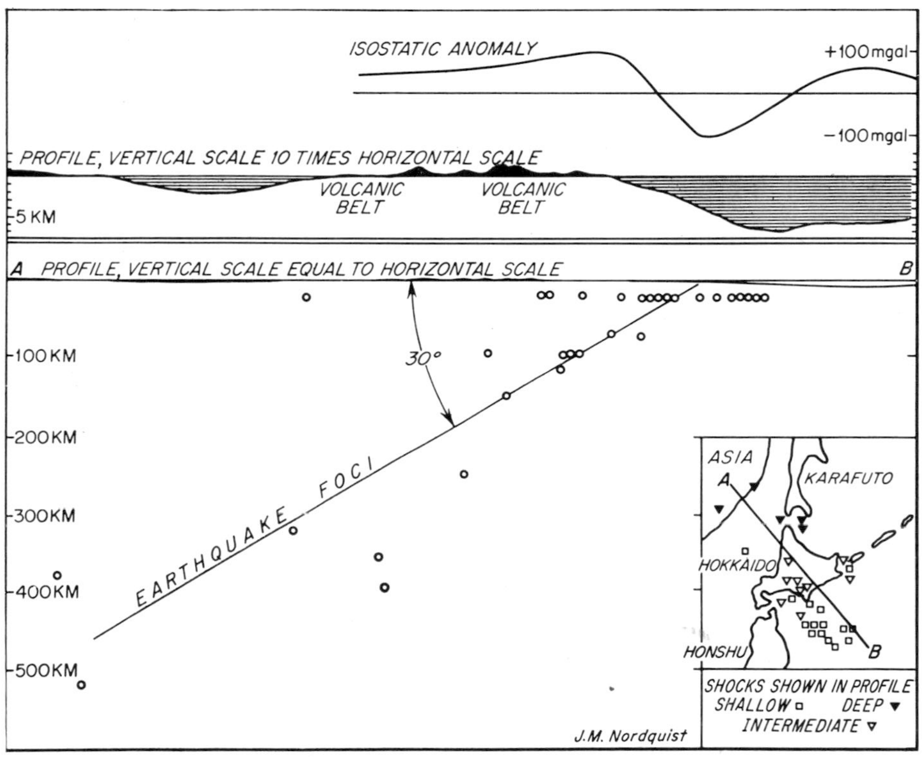

FIG. 20.1 Tectonic profile, northern Japanese region, showing earthquake foci, relief, and isostatic gravity anomalies. (*After Gutenberg and Richter, 1941.*)

there is more of a tendency to lateral than vertical motion (see Sec. 9.5), which is inconsistent with the concept of an overthrust.

A more complicated picture is obtained if we visualize Hokkaido as a part of the Kamchatka-Kuril Island arc (Fig. 20.2; Benioff, 1955). The profiles again exhibit the foredeep, ridge with volcanic activity, and the shallow basin behind, in this case the Sea of Okhotsk. Information is lacking on the northward extend of the gravity anomaly in this region. The seismic profile seems to break into two parts, the zone of shallow and intermediate earthquakes dipping less steeply than the zone of deep shocks.

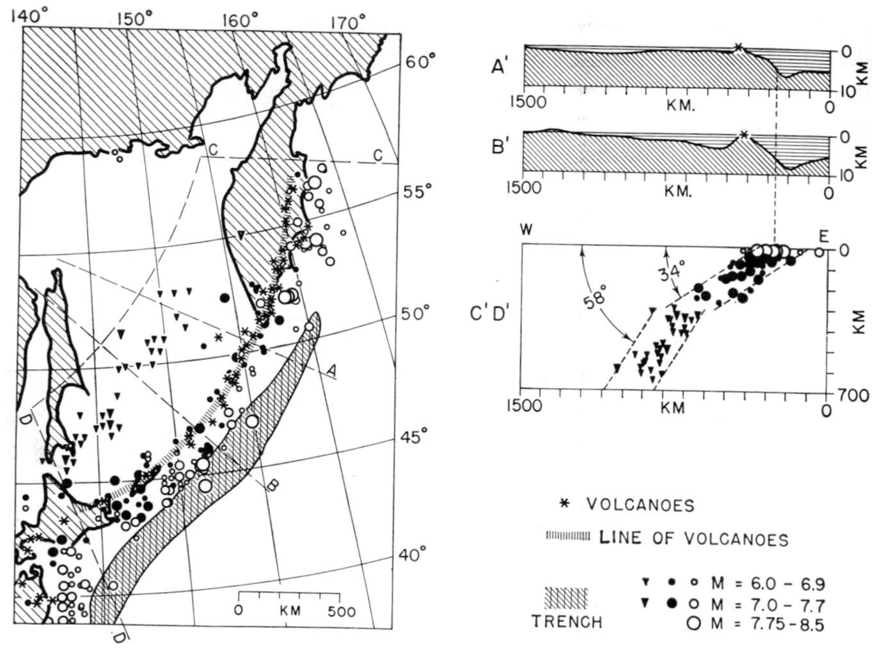

FIG. 20.2 Tectonic profile, Kamchatka-Kuril Island region. (*Courtesy of H. Benioff, 1955.*)

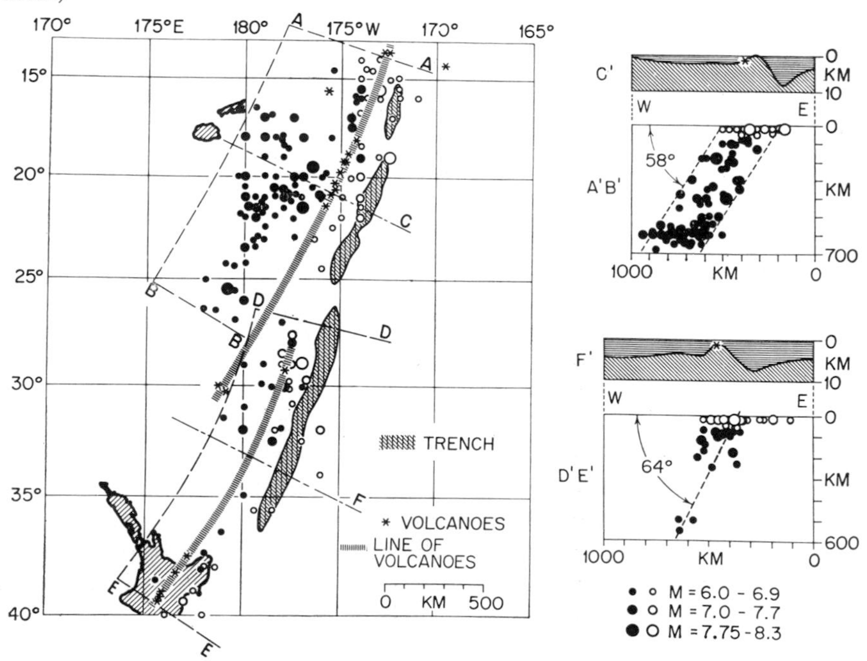

FIG. 20.3 Tectonic profile, Tonga-Kermadec region. (*Courtesy of H. Benioff, 1955.*)

20.2 Tonga-Kermadec Region. Benioff (1949, 1955) has studied the Tonga-Kermadec region in a like manner (Fig. 20.3). The pattern is similar in plan and section. This time the postulated fault dips more steeply, about 60°. There appear to be two parts to the region, a northern and a southern arc. Data on the variation of gravity are lacking, but there is the same arrangement of a foredeep fronting the islands, volcanoes, in this case mostly submarine and lying west of the crest of the ridge, and beyond them a basin which rises to another ridge outcropping between New Zealand and New Caledonia at Norfolk Island.

As a result of studies of the rate of release of energy by the shallow and deeper-than-normal sequences of earthquakes, Benioff concluded that they represent two independent sequences (Figs. 9.3 and 9.4). Thus, the activity beneath the crust may be caused differently from the shallow shocks. The evidence is not good enough to prove that the subcrustal and crustal deformation are on a single structure, even though one can draw in one fault zone which seems to contain the earthquakes at all depths.

20.3 South America. The seismic belt along the Pacific Coast of South America has a general resemblance to that on the west side of the Pacific Ocean (Fig. 20.4). However, there is a notable lack of shocks throughout the belt at depths between 300 and 550 km and, in the northern part of the area, between 200 and 550 km. When the belt is plotted in section, a single plane is not always apparent. The ocean deep is not so large as in the two cases described above but is definitely present. Some measurements have been made indicating the presence of an axis of low gravity. The volcanic belt, while not continuous, lies in its typical position above the zone of intermediate-depth earthquakes.

The topographic high is much larger and more complicated than in the case of the island arcs. A large part of the cordillera is older, having been folded in the Mesozoic, though Cenozoic deformation is also prevalent. To find a low-lying basin behind the mountains we must go to Argentina and Brazil. Because of erosion from the mountains, this basin has been filled with Cenozoic sediments (Levorsen, 1945; Oppenheim, 1948).

The shallow and intermediate shocks seem to define a different plane from that on which the deep shocks lie. However, a sudden change of rate of energy release affecting both the intermediate and deep sequences occurred in 1922. This seems to indicate that there is a connection between them. Benioff (1949) suggests that such changes in energy rate result from the freezing or breaking of points of a single fault surface (see Sec. 9.4). If he is correct, then the foci must define the surface of a truly great fault. It certainly is not a plane, as its outcrop follows the coast line of the continent. The energy released by these earthquakes, which lie in a belt 4,500 km long, can be plotted on a single set of graphs giving a picture of a steady, regular process of strain relief (Figs. 9.6, 9.7, and 9.8). This seems to indicate that all of South America is moving as a unit. Otherwise, the pattern would be unlikely to be nearly so regular.

Geophysical observations have given us a picture of what is going on in the earth. In the next chapter different theories of what causes mountain formation will be discussed. Keep in mind the facts of geophysical observation. To be tenable, a theory of tectonic deformation intended to explain the type of mountains we see forming today must lead to a pattern in plan and profile such as has been outlined above. The areas

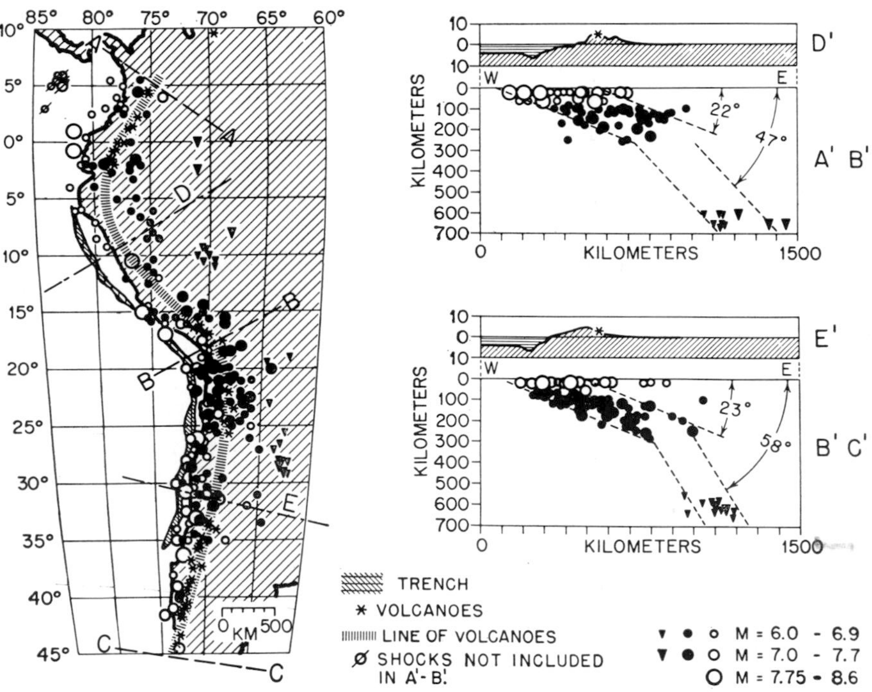

FIG. 20.4 Tectonic profile, west coast of South America. (*Courtesy of H. Benioff, 1954.*)

described in profile here are all active today. Thus, we do not see completely formed structures, but only partly made ones. The exposed mountains are being eroded. The troughs filled in. The volume of sediment accumulated to date is relatively small compared with what is found in old geosynclines. Folded sediments are a prominent feature of most old mountain ranges. If the current tectonic belts are eventually to become typical folded mountains, the sediments accumulating currently are the ones which must be involved. We should ask ourselves, will continuation of what we see occurring today lead to mountains like the Alps, the Rockies, and the Appalachians?

CHAPTER 21

CAUSE OF MOUNTAIN BUILDING

21.1 Geological Features of Mountain Ranges. The principal geophysical features of present tectonic activity were outlined in the last two chapters. When we regard the mountain ranges of the world, there are in addition, as Daly (1938) has pointed out, eight principal groups of geologic facts to be explained. These characteristics have been discovered almost entirely through study of the mountain ranges of the continents. For obvious reasons, the detailed structures of the submerged oceanic ranges are less well known. It must be remembered, therefore, that Daly's characteristics are necessarily typical only of the continental mountains, and future studies could prove that oceanic mountains have different distinctive features.

The first characteristic feature is that mountains occur in long, narrow belts. The width of the belts may vary. Several belts may merge or split along their length. Chains of different ages may be parallel, overlapping, or intersecting, but each group occupies only a small part of the total surface area of the earth (Fig. 18.1). This pattern means that the forces which built the mountains acted over only a small part of the earth's surface at any one time. No such marked restriction of the mountains to one area in one period and to another locality at another time could have resulted from a uniformly distributed system of stresses.

Second, the presence of a geosyncline is a typical feature of a mountain chain. The axis of the geosyncline and the axis of the mountain range are generally nearly parallel. The sedimentary rocks exposed in the chain are largely those which were deposited in the geosyncline. During most of the time of deposition the geosyncline was submerged beneath the sea.

This does not mean that the forces which build mountains are restricted to geosynclinal areas. It means that a typical range results only where a thick lens of sediments has been deposited. When we understand the process better, we may find that old lineaments in the centers of the oceanic basins and even the continental stable areas are the result of forces which, acting in the presence of sufficient deposits of soft clastics, would have built great cordilleras. Thus, along the Marianas Islands today, there is too little sediment being deposited ever to give a typical folded range. The end result will be very different from what can someday be expected along what is now the Ganges River basin in India. Here already the deposits are being deformed (Fig. 21.1). The Siwalik Hills may be the beginning of a new mountain range.

Third, the rocks originally deposited nearly horizontally in the geosyncline have been compressed as a part of the mountain-building cycle. If the individual formations were flattened out so that each anticline and syncline was unfolded, the edges of the beds which make up the geosynclinal prism would be moved apart by tens and sometimes hundreds of kilometers. Thus, mountains represent a shortening of the crust. The basement rocks everywhere show evidence of some sort of tectonic

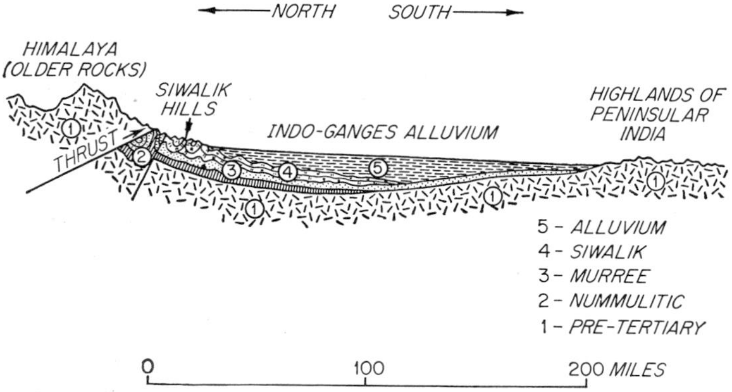

FIG. 21.1 The geosynclinal prism of northern India, a potential mountain range. (*Courtesy of R. A. Daly, 1938.*)

activity either certainly or probably connected with mountain building. The area of the continents must, therefore, have been reduced by mountain formation.

Fourth, the direction of the shortening was at right angles to the axis of the geosyncline. Since mountains are long, narrow structures, the force must have acted largely perpendicular to the axis also. Since the length of individual mountain systems is very great, we are dealing with a system of forces, not a single force.

Fifth, compression of the geosynclinal prisms must have increased the amount of low-density rocks present along the axis of the folding. Folding and overthrusting of the sediments would provide this thickening even if the more rigid granitic layer of the crust was not compressed at the same time. Seismic evidence confirms this. The Alps in Europe and the Sierra Nevada in California have roots of light rocks which extend downward much deeper than the height of the mountains (Gutenberg, 1943).

Sixth, for millions of years after the mountains were formed, the whole folded belt continued to rise. The crest was eroded off, exposing the mountains in cross section.

Seventh, a batholith is generally found in the center of the folded belt. The composition of this is often not greatly different from the average composition of the sediments. Theories of the origin of batholiths include melting of the rocks in place, alteration of the deeply buried sediments by invading mineralized solutions (metasomatism), and volume-for-volume replacement by invading magmas. In any case, the core of the range was hot at a late stage in the orogenic process, and it subsequently cooled, allowing the melt to solidify to form a batholith.

The detailed characteristics of batholiths are so remarkable and so significant to a proper understanding of the origin of mountains that a summary of them is included here. Daly lists 10 features which are common to all batholiths.

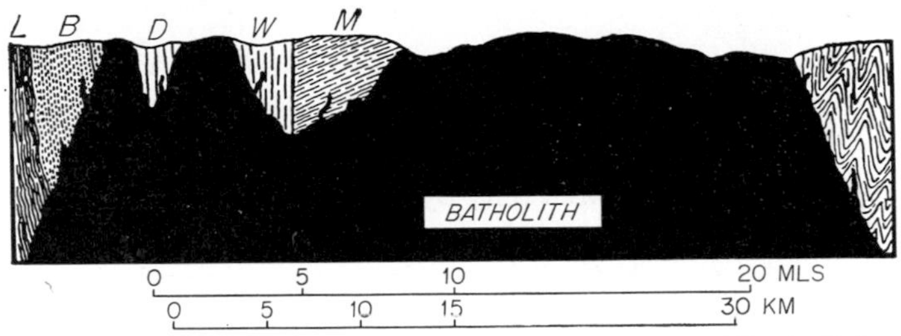

FIG. 21.2 Cross section of a typical batholith. (*Courtesy of R. A. Daly, 1938.*)

1. They are of great horizontal cross section. This feature is not always illustrated clearly by exposed rocks, but it is presumed that if erosion cut deeply enough, it would be. By definition, batholiths are distinguished from local intrusive bodies on the basis of size. The area of a batholith may be 50 per cent or more of that of the whole mountain range.

2. They are elongated parallel to the ranges they have invaded. They are not a local feature of a part of the chain but are an integral part of its whole extent. At great depth the area of the batholith may even exceed that of the folded sediments exposed at the surface.

3. They are dome-shaped, increasing in size with depth (Fig. 21.2). Where streams have cut into them, their horizontal dimensions are greater than where they are exposed at higher elevations. Their upper surfaces are irregular, not smooth. Spurs of the igneous mass extend outward into the surrounding formations. Elsewhere, great blocks of the roof which once covered the melt extend down into it.

4. No one has ever seen the bottom of a batholith. It extends to great depths into the crust. What happens as one goes down into a batholith

is unknown. It may expand and merge into one of the crustal layers or ultimately be floored by rocks of a different nature.

5. Batholiths were generally emplaced after the main paroxysm of tectonic activity. The sedimentary formations which the batholith invaded were already folded when intrusion occurred (Fig. 21.3). In most cases, the batholith itself shows relatively little evidence of great compression. The intrusion appears to occur at a late stage of the

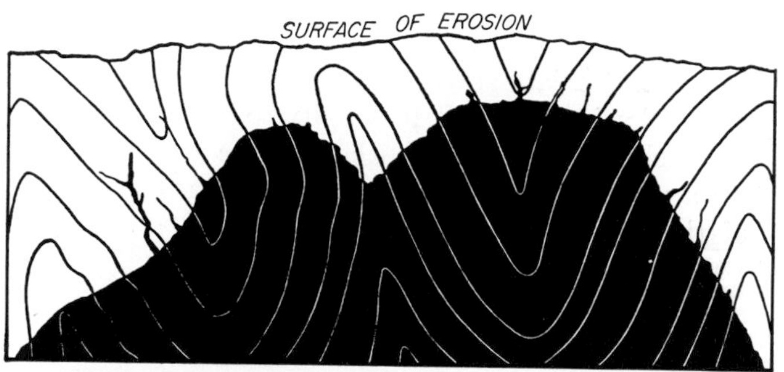

Fig. 21.3 A batholith replaces folded rocks in the root of a mountain range. *(Courtesy of R. A. Daly, 1938.)*

tectonic cycle, usually followed only by the gradual uparching and erosion of the deformed belt.

6. The boundaries of batholiths are in crosscutting relationship to the invaded formations. The igneous melts did not reach their present positions primarily by squeezing their way in between older rocks or by opening up gaps across continuous formations. Their contacts have a random direction with respect to the boundaries of the invaded rocks.

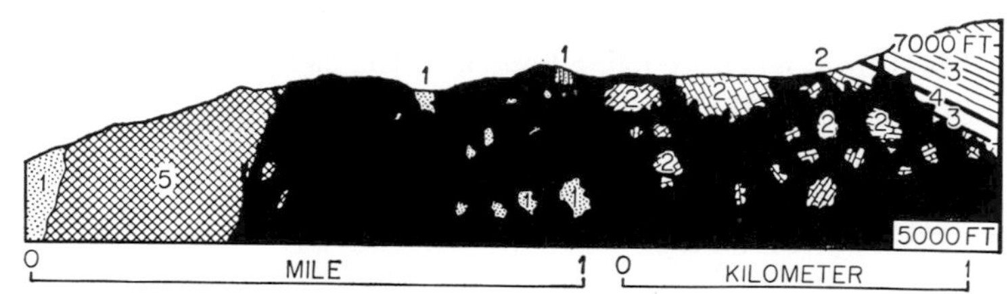

Fig. 21.4 Xenoliths in a batholith, Tintic district, Utah. *(Courtesy of R. A. Daly, 1938.)*

The energy of the magma was so great that it could in large measure ignore local trends of the intruded formations.

7. To a large degree, batholiths took the place of the invaded formations in volume, with relatively little distortion of the enclosing walls. Batholiths occupy space where other rocks were previously. There is only one place for the latter to have gone. They must have sunk into the batholith. Such foundered blocks are commonly observed, especially

near the tops of batholiths (Fig. 21.4). They are called xenoliths. It is generally believed that they melt eventually and, hence, that the average composition of a batholith must tend in time to become more similar to that of the invaded rocks. Field evidence of the assimilation of xenoliths is scarce. Grout (1932) states that xenoliths which have been greatly metamorphosed by the magma in which they are included are common but that they almost always retain their identity. It seems likely that complete assimilation, if it occurs, takes place largely in the deeper part of the batholith. The sinking of blocks of solid rock will help to keep the batholith stirred.

8. Chemical and thermal reactions commonly occur between the magma of the batholith and the surrounding rocks. This results in recrystallization and alteration of their composition. In some cases, addition or subtraction of one or more elements may result in considerable change in the chemical composition of the wall rock. In other cases, only the mineralogical composition is involved, and there has been no change of atoms. One of the basic rules of geology is the environmental law. This states that there is a tendency for any assemblage of chemical elements to group themselves into a mineral assemblage which is stable under the conditions of temperature, pressure, and contact with other elements in which it occurs. Thus, the heat of the intruded magma may be sufficient to form a new mineral grouping without any direct reaction between the two rock bodies. That the batholith is the cause of the alteration is clear from the distribution of the changes in a shell-shaped aureole around the intrusion, the degree of metamorphism decreasing with distance from the igneous body.

9. The compositions of batholiths cover a wide range. A granite[1] batholith is rare. Most batholiths are probably intermediate in composition between the ideal granite and diorite. The range includes some which are definitely of the latter composition, at least in large part.

10. Furthermore, there is usually some variation in composition from place to place in the intrusive. In some cases, this can be related to melting and assimilation of the adjoining rocks (Jahns, 1948). In other cases it is more likely due to differentiation of the main magmatic mass. There is a general order of intrusion for the chemically different rocks which are involved in mountain building. In some cases basalt or more coarsely crystalline rock of similar composition appears to have penetrated the surface formations at an early stage of the tectonic cycle. Later intrusions are commonly of less basic composition. The last intrusives to be emplaced are often acidic pegmatites.

[1] By definition, granite is a plutonic rock consisting largely of alkalic feldspar and quartz, commonly with some sodic plagioclase and a small amount of mica and hornblende or pyroxene (after J. V. Howell, 1957).

The last general observation on mountains concerns the places where they occur. Except for the oceanic ridges, which are largely or entirely volcanic as far as is known, all mountain ranges occur on the continents or along their borders (see Sec. 19.4). This applies both to current mountain belts and to older ranges. The predominant ranges of Cenozoic folding are the circum-Pacific belt and the Indo-Himalayan-Alpine belt. Mesozoic folding is found at many places on the continentward side of this, as in Siberia, China, Malaya, and Borneo, between Cenozoic folding or west of it on the Pacific shore of the Americas, and with no close relation to Cenozoic folding in South Africa (Umbgrove, 1947). The principal Paleozoic mountain belts are the Appalachians, the Urals, the complex of ranges along the Atlantic Coast of Europe from Spain to Norway, the mountains of eastern Australia, and those surrounding the Siberian shield. The shield areas are laced with a complex but generally concentric pattern of even older ranges (Wilson, 1954).

This apparent restriction of folded ranges to the continents may be more apparent than real. The suboceanic ranges are largely unknown except for the few places where they rise above sea level. The islands in the central part of the Pacific Ocean are all volcanic. This is in general true of the islands which rise above sea level along the mid-Atlantic ridge and in the Indian Ocean. However, these few highest peaks may not be typical of the suboceanic ranges as a whole, and there are some exceptions to the rule of universal volcanic rocks. For instance, Umbgrove (1947) reports that there are granitic xenoliths on Ascension Island. However, the exceptions are so rare that they lead one to suspect that the structural patterns of the suboceanic ranges are unlike those of the folded ranges of the continents.

One explanation may be that the oceanic ridges rise to less height than the continental welts because the crust is thinner here. Folded mountains are found in New Zealand, far from any large land mass, and separated from the nearest continent, Australia, by the oceanic Tasman basin. Officer (1955) found from studies of seismic-wave transmission that the crust under New Zealand and the Tonga-Kermadec rise to the north is between 20 and 30 km thick. This is less than in larger continental areas, but several times the crustal thickness in the adjoining oceanic areas. The crust is slightly thinner but still probably continental along the oceanic ridges to the northwest of New Zealand. This would seem to indicate that oceanic ridges can have structures similar to those on the continents but that lack of sediments in these areas may inhibit their development into typical folded ranges.

The above eight discussions summarize the geologic facts of observation. Like the geophysical data of Chaps. 19 and 20, these facts must be explained by any theory of mountain formation for it to be tenable.

21.2 Laboratory Experiments. One of the most prominent features of mountain ranges is their compression. To gain a better understanding of how this may have occurred, numerous investigators have attempted to duplicate in laboratory models structural forms observed in the field (e.g., Griggs, 1939; Kuenen, 1937; MacCarthy, 1928; Willis, 1923).

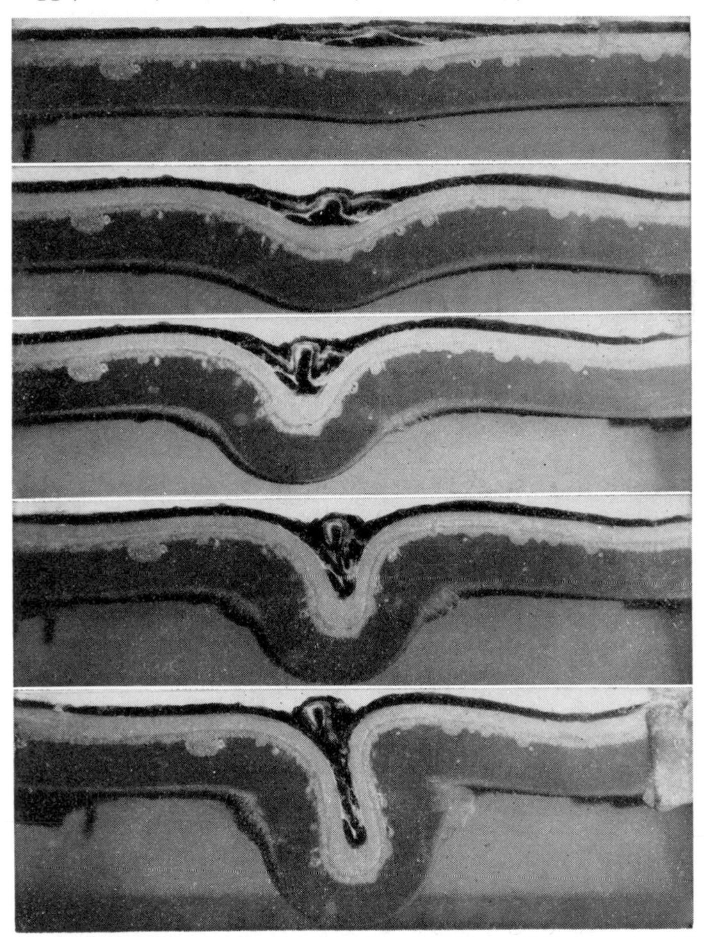

FIG. 21.5 Model experiment illustrating downbuckling of the crust. (*Courtesy of P. H. Kuenen, 1937.*)

Their experiments resulted in a variety of deformations resembling earth structures in a general way. The biggest problem to be overcome in setting up such an experiment is the selection of proper scaling factors. The mechanical properties of the model must have values of such size that the small model will behave exactly as its large natural counterpart (Hubbert, 1937). This requires the use of weak, plastic materials in the model.

The results of carefully scaled experiments by David Griggs (1939) are particularly helpful in visualizing how mountains may have formed. Griggs applied linear compression to a thin sequence of layers, corresponding to the earth's crust, overlying a plastic substratum. Using a stiff substratum, Willis (1923) had obtained upfolding and faulting of such a layered section. Using a liquid substratum, Kuenen (1936) had obtained simple downbuckling (Fig. 21.5). Using a substratum carefully proportioned to the stiffness of the surface rocks, Griggs found that the surface layers would not slide over the underlying material. Stress applied at one end of the model was not transmitted along the crustal layer but resulted only in a thickening of the crust immediately adjoining the place

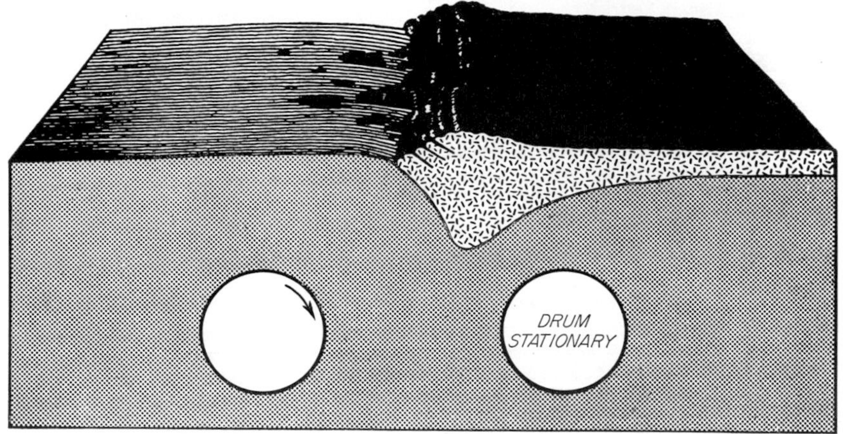

Fig. 21.6 Crustal downbuckle resulting from a single subcrustal current. (*Griggs, 1939.*)

where the pressure was applied. The structures which resulted did not look like those found in mountain ranges.

An entirely different behavior resulted when stress was applied tangentially to the bottom of the crust by stirring the plastic substratum. In this case, the crust was shoved along by the motion of the material beneath it, buckling downward and thickening in front of the area pushed by the subcrustal current (Fig. 21.6). If the current was caused to continue long enough, the whole of the crust above it was swept into a broad, asymetrical heap, with a root which was much larger than the hump above the surface. The root dropped down steeply on the side facing the current which caused it. On the opposite side the compression died off more slowly, yet most of the compression occurred within a horizontal distance from the front edge of the thickened wedge equal to the thickness of the crust.

Griggs produced his subcrustal currents by rotating a drum in the plastic material beneath the firmer crust. The plastic substratum was drawn around the turning axis by viscous friction. By using two rotating drums, he created a down current between two converging horizontal currents. For slow currents, all that happened was a slight thickening of the crust and a depression of its surface over the down current. More rapid currents caused a narrow downfold of the crust and greater thickening. The layer became folded irregularly with compression structures in the central part of the buckle, and it continued to be depressed over the down current. When the currents were stopped, the crust rose, the folded material in the center of the welt forming a ridge which stood higher than the surrounding less deformed areas. In cross section, fold and fault structures comparable to those found in mountain ranges were displayed.

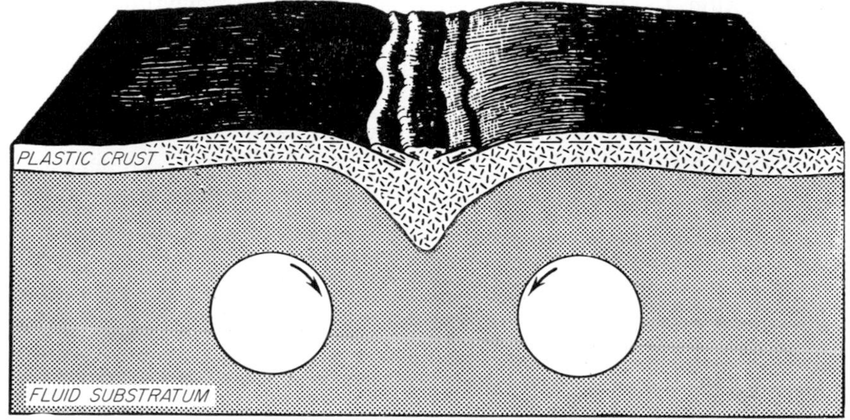

Fig. 21.7 Crustal downbuckle resulting from two opposing subcrustal currents. (*Griggs, 1939.*)

If these experiments represent truly the way the crust will deform under natural forces, they can be used to judge the reasonableness of the various theories of mountain deformation which have been proposed. However, they can be used for this purpose only to the extent that the materials used in the experiments were properly scaled to represent the materials of the earth. It must be remembered that the physical properties of the rocks that constitute the crust and mantle are not known accurately and the degree of their variability from place to place can be only guessed. Conditions in nature can be expected to be more complex than in the best conceived laboratory experiment.

21.3 Contraction Theory. In Chap. 18 mountain ranges were considered an evidence of the probability of continental drift. One of the principal inadequacies of all drift theories is that the forces available to produce the observed deformations are almost certainly inadequate for the task. For the same reason, tidal forces and the various stresses such as polflucht force which are dependent on the earth's rotation or changes in its shape do not seem to offer much promise as causes of mountain building. One energy source alone remains when all the others have been eliminated which has the potential to be a major orogenic factor, namely, the earth's heat. All the explanations which currently seem reasonable depend on heat to some extent for the energy needed to produce the observed structures.

The first geologists, observing the heat of volcanoes, rightly concluded that the interior of the earth was hot. Since temperature increases with depth within the earth, it is also obvious that heat is being conducted to the surface. Before the discovery of radioactivity, this was interpreted to mean that the interior of the earth was becoming colder. According to this deduction, the earth must have been hotter in former times than it is today.

The encounter theory of the earth's origin postulated that our globe is composed of matter drawn from a star. Hence, initially it would probably have consisted of a hot gas. This would have cooled rapidly. The rate of heat loss, assisted by convection, would at first have been large. Jeffreys (1952) has estimated that 5,000 years after its formation, the earth would have cooled to the point where the rocks would have liquefied. As the liquid cooled, it would have become more viscous, and the rate of cooling would decrease as convection slowed. Thus, an appreciable temperature gradient between the surface and center of the earth would have developed.

As more heat was lost, any immiscible materials present would tend to separate into layers according to their densities. Liquid iron and nickel would sink to the center; silicates would float on top of this core. There might be an intermediate layer containing mixed iron and silicates. The possibilities are summarized by Mason (1952, pp. 32–37) and Umbgrove (1947, pp. 8–11). At the surface, crystals would begin to settle out. They would sink until they reached a depth where the temperature was great enough to remelt them or until they reached a place where their density equaled that of the surrounding melt.

As the liquid became still more viscous, the rate of sinking of this shower of crystals would decrease. Eventually they would form so fast at the cold surface that they would not have time to sink before a network of solid particles was formed. This initial crust would at first tend to break up and be flooded with hotter liquid. It would sink as large blocks. Later, as its strength increased, it would become rigid and strong enough to form a continuous layer around the earth. Thereafter, only locally could the underlying melt break through to the surface. This crust would consist largely of the lighter minerals which had least tendency to sink.

As the earth continued to cool, the shell would become thicker and thicker. The average temperature of the enclosed material, whether solid or liquid, would be dropping. As it cooled, it would shrink. The temperature at the surface is controlled by the heat from the sun. Once the atmosphere formed, it would have stayed at approximately the value it has today. Hence, the crust would not shrink as the interior did. Its rigidity would tend to maintain its shape. Great stresses would be developed as the shrinking underlying material ceased to support the crust, and it would yield by folding and thrusting along belts of weakness, which would become mountain ranges.

As cooling continued, the interior would go on shrinking. Mountains would be thrown up first in one place, then in another as the crust constantly adjusted itself to an ever-smaller interior. Thus, at some time in geologic history, nearly every part of the surface would be deformed into a mountain range.

The discovery of radioactivity upset this picture. The amount of radioactive material in the exposed rocks is so great that if this concentration continued to any great depth, it would require that the interior be warming to an unbelievable extent (see Sec. 5.5). Even if one assumes that radioactive material occurs only in the crust, there may still be enough there to account for the whole observed heat loss under the continents. Thus, it is doubtful if the earth has ever contracted to a significant extent as a result of cooling.

An alternative explanation starts with a version of the condensation hypotheses. It is assumed that the earth was formed by the gathering together of cold, solid particles and since its formation has been getting hotter (Urey, 1952). According to this theory, as the minerals become hotter, transformations occur whereby new compounds are formed, better adapted to the conditions of great pressure under which they occur. These transformations result in a shrinking of the interior which allows the crust to buckle (Gutenberg, 1951*e*). The process of readjustment could be accelerating as the interior becomes warmer. As temperature increases, recrystallization might take place at a faster pace, and sorting of the material into layers might aid in the formation of denser mineral forms. This is consistent with the theory that mountain formation has been more intense and more frequent in the latest geologic eras.

Possibly the greatest weakness of the contraction hypothesis is the necessity of accounting for large amounts of compression in individual groups of ranges. It has been postulated that the mountain belts of the Himalayas and central Asia may represent a shortening of the crust of as much as 3,000 km, though the true figure is probably much less than this. If all of the radial shortening in a great circle perpendicular to this belt had been concentrated at this one place, then the decrease in the earth's radius R to give this change in circumference C could be found from the equation

$$C = 2\pi R \tag{21.1}$$

The radius would have to decrease by nearly 480 out of 6,370 km, or 7.5 per cent. This is a very large amount to have occurred since the early Paleozoic, which is probably not more than one-eighth of the earth's history. Furthermore, this is only one of many belts of mountains formed during this time. The Alps represent a shortening of the circumference in the Tertiary alone of perhaps 120 km. This requires a radial shrinking of about 20 km in less than 70 million years. Other great mountain ranges were simultaneously being formed all around the Pacific Ocean.

On the other hand, Bucher (1955) believes that many of the published estimates of the amount of shortening of the crust in mountain chains are off by nearly an order of magnitude. He has shown that formations undergoing extreme compression may be stretched by a factor of 6 to 8, so that the measured length of a folded bed may greatly exceed its undeformed length. If the total compression is substantially less than the figures quoted suggest, then the amount of contraction required is correspondingly reduced.

Regardless of the amount of contraction, it is difficult to explain why the buckling was concentrated in so few belts in any one period, yet shifted so greatly from time to time. Griggs (1939) has shown that the crust is too thin and weak to transmit the thrust which would be generated by contraction over large distances. Hence, the mountain ranges should be more evenly distributed. And if the crust does have the strength to concentrate the yielding in one place, then it should have always buckled there throughout geologic time, for contraction would be a continuous process.

The contraction hypothesis can be further tested as it relates to the known nature of the circum-Pacific deformation. Wilson (1954) has pointed out that the two major belts of Tertiary tectonism may be visualized as series of circular arcs whose centers lie on or near two great circles intersecting nearly at right angles (Fig. 21.8). Each of the individual arcs defines a plane dipping under the compressed mountain range like a great fault. The mountains can be pictured as rising along these faults, with compression of the front edge of the overriding block and depression of the underriding one. According to this concept each arc encloses a chip of the earth's rigid crust which had broken under the stress produced by the shrinking of the earth's plastic interior. The outcrop of the fault occurs along the trough where the more rigid block has pushed down the underriding edge of the crust. Sediments forming in

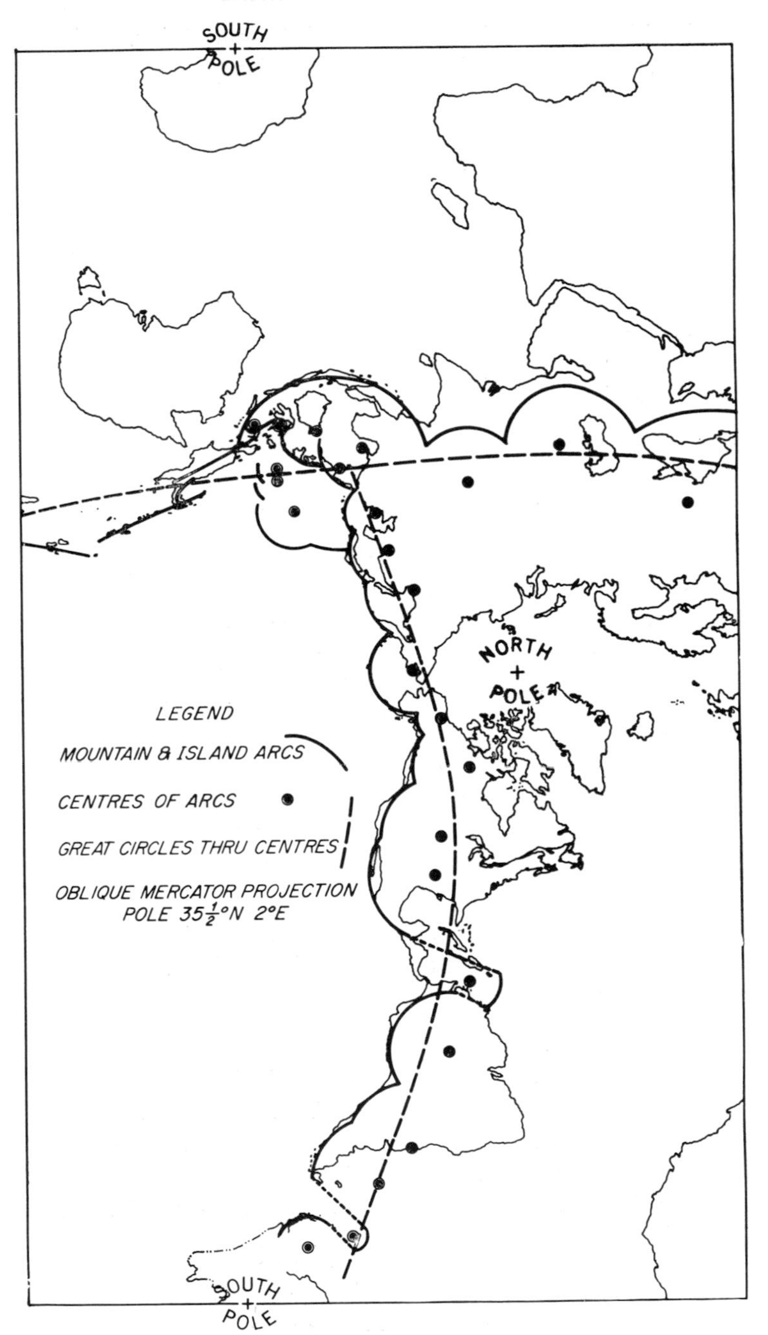

FIG. 21.8 The two belts of Tertiary tectonism and the arcs which constitute them. (*Wilson, 1954.*)

this trough will eventually become folded into mountains. The crust will be thickened. The observed gravity anomalies result from the excess of low-density crustal material where the blocks are overriding one another.

It is supposed that cracking of the thin exposed end of the overriding wedge has allowed basaltic magma to flow to the surface, producing the belts of volcanism. The heat of friction on the great fault and the radioactivity in the thickened crustal wedge will eventually cause melting and the formation of a batholith. Since the two strings of arcs intersect at right angles, they are capable of taking up all the compression for a time. Eventually, the site of the yielding will shift to relieve the stresses currently accumulating elsewhere in the crust. Compression along two belts relieves only a part of the stresses in a shrinking spherical shell. Considered qualitatively for the present moment in the long span of geologic time, the general features of the observed facts are consistent with what might be expected for a contracting shell.

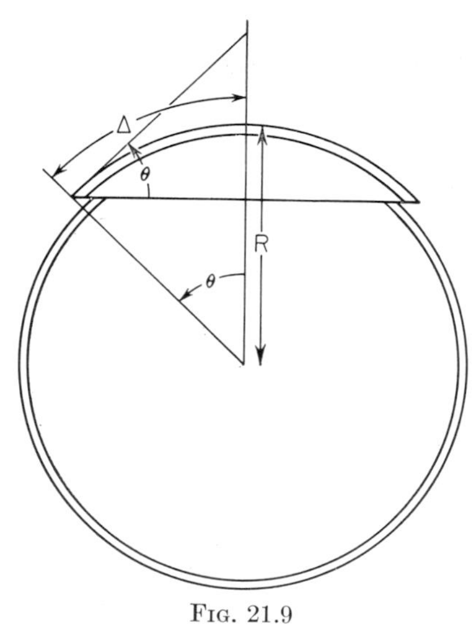

Fig. 21.9

Considered quantitatively, however, the dip of individual faults is not what this theory would predict. It was previously noted (Chap. 20) that the shear planes had dips of 30 to 60°. The angle θ between the outcropping arc and its center equals the angle of dip of the fault plane, as shown in Fig. 21.9. For the Japanese arc, this angle is only 8°, far less than the seismicly determined dip of the fault plane.

Scheidegger and Wilson (1950) have suggested that the deep and intermediate shocks are on separate structures from the shallow ones and are the result of tension in the zone of cooling. If this is the case, then compression is confined to a layer only a few tens of kilometers thick. This implies a very small amount of shrinking of the interior, whereas great shrinking would be required to explain quantitatively the amount of compression in mountain ranges. Furthermore, an upper mantle rigid enough to break under very slowly developing tension is hard to reconcile with a layer plastic enough to yield to isostatic forces.

21.4 Gravitative Sliding. Daly (1926, 1938) has proposed a less extreme contraction theory. He supposes that the primordial earth was irregular in shape and that appreciable elevation differences existed. Any material which was free to slide would tend to be pulled down these slopes by gravity. Sediments deposited along the foot of such a slope would be squeezed into mountain ranges as blocks of crust slid against them. To obtain the variations in elevation necessary to cause the sliding, Daly supposed that the earth cools unevenly. Where there are continents, the sialic rocks prevent the escape of heat. The rocks expand; the column rises. Beneath the oceans, where there is no blanket of rocks of relatively great radioactive mineral content, the rocks cool, contract, and sink. Thus, the continental blocks will slide into the oceans, forming mountains along their fringes, as is the case around the Pacific Ocean today.

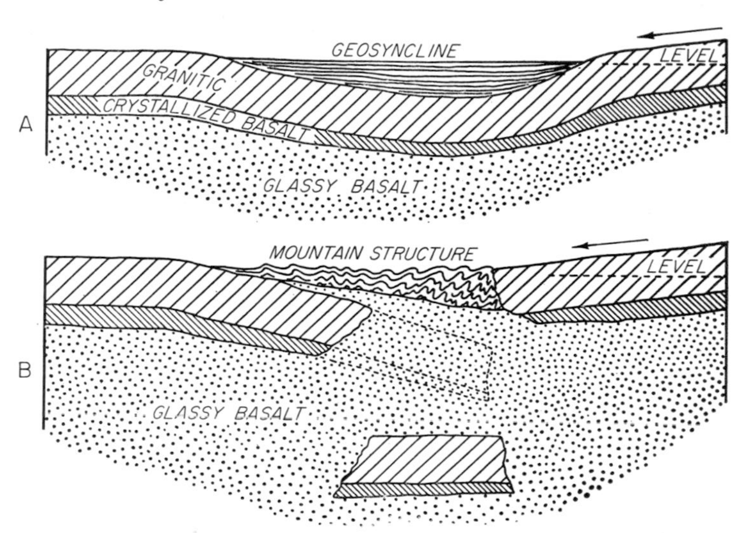

Fig. 21.10 Compression of a mountain range by a slab of the crust sliding against it. (*Daly, 1926.*)

The sliding will be made easier by weakening of the crust due to heating beneath the wedge of geosynclinal material at the toe of the moving block. As the crust is depressed here, it heats and cracks. Pieces of it may break off and sink into the underlying plastic sima (Fig. 21.10). Warmer rock flows in to take its place, invading the folded belt in the form of a batholith and rising to the surface through cracks to form volcanoes.

A quantitative check on the expectable slope which can be produced by differential heating of two columns can be obtained if we examine the thermal coefficient of expansion of rocks. Typical figures are given in Table 16.4. Since the rocks are free to expand only vertically, the expectable enlargement will be approximately three times what is given in the table. In general, at higher pressures the rate of expansion is less. Taking as a coefficient of expansion for basalt 16×10^{-6} per degree centigrade, the temperature change in a 1,000-km column of rock to raise the top 10 km (32,808 ft) can be found from the formula

$$\frac{\Delta L}{L} = 16 \times 10^{-6}\,\Delta T \tag{21.2}$$

$$\Delta T = \frac{10}{1{,}000 \times 16 \times 10^{-6}}\,{}^\circ\mathrm{C} = 625^\circ\mathrm{C} \tag{21.3}$$

Since the maximum temperature at the earth's center is probably of the order of 2000°C (Sec. 5.6, Fig. 5.6) and the temperature gradient is probably small below 100 km, it is unlikely that temperature changes can ever have raised the crust more than a small fraction of the height of the highest mountains on the earth today.

However, it is not necessary to suppose, as Daly did, that whole continents slid. A thick wedge of sediments would have a tendency to slide and fold in this manner under its own weight if it were deposited on a slope or on a block which subsequently tilted. This may account for many individual folds and especially for some thrust faults in mountain ranges; but there is no reason to believe that gradients ever existed of sufficient steepness to cause whole continents or even individual ranges to shift in this way.

One could argue, as Hess (1955) has done, that phase changes from one mineral species to another could increase substantially the possible changes in column length. However, this concept cannot be quantitatively evaluated because knowledge is lacking of what transitions of this sort actually occur.

The sliding hypothesis gets into difficulty also with observed tectonic patterns. There is no obvious relation to the pattern of deep earthquakes. Positive rather than negative gravity anomalies would be expected in the regions into which more mass is sliding. Volcanism would be concentrated far from the arc of mountain building in the region of tension, not where it is observed.

21.5 Subcrustal Convection Currents. The universal presence of a batholithic core at the center of all old mountain ranges suggests that beneath such belts the subcrustal material was at one time molten. If the lower part of the crust was fluid when orogeny was occurring, then it is at least equally likely that the underlying mantle was in a similar state. If this material has a low enough viscosity, the heat generated by radioactive disintegration within it or deeper in the earth would tend to produce convection currents. This would be true whether the material was actually liquid or only plastic. Pekeris (1935) has shown that, assuming reasonable conditions within the earth's mantle, convection cells would be expectable. Such cells will tend to have a regular pattern. In so far as possible, in adjoining cells uprising currents would be adjacent to one another and, similarly, downflowing currents would merge (Figs. 17.11 and 17.12).

Such currents will exert frictional forces on the bottom of the crust. The stresses will be greatest where the currents flow horizontally. Tensional structures are to be expected over areas where the horizontal stress is increasing, because the front edge of the affected block will be pulled along harder than the rear edge. Compression should occur over areas of negative stress gradient, because the rear edge of the block will be shoved against the front edge (Fig. 21.11).

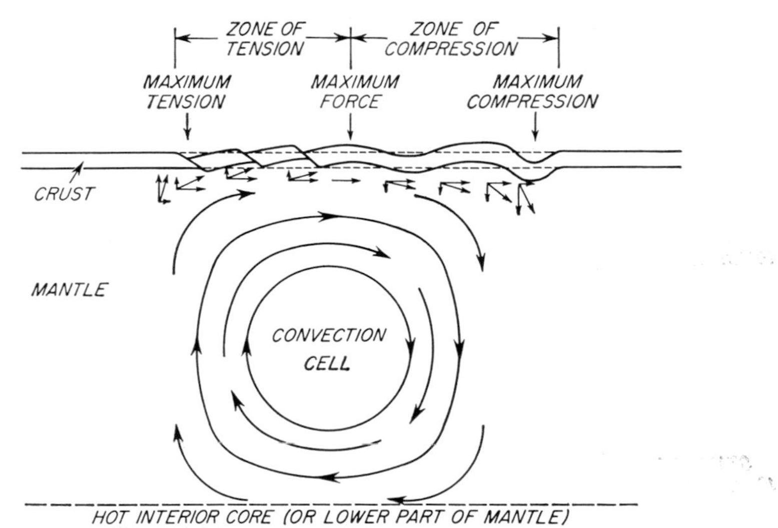

FIG. 21.11 Forces on the crust due to a convective cell in the earth's mantle.

At first, as stress is applied to it, the crust will yield elastically. In the compression zone, gentle swells and broad basins will be formed, with greatest amplitude over the zone of greatest stress. Sediments will be eroded off the crests and deposited in the basins, tending to depress them further. In one of these hollows, probably where the surface slope is greatest or where the most exposed land is available to supply sediments, deposits will accumulate more rapidly than elsewhere. This area will become a geosyncline, sinking under the weight of the sediments and being pressed downward by the continued compression of a wide belt of crust.

As the crust is thickened by the filling of the geosyncline, the down-bent root will begin to warm. This will weaken it still further. Finally it will be folded into a downbuckle as shown in Fig. 21.12. Such a structure is called a tectogene. It may break on one side, one block of the crust overriding the other. The sediments in the geosyncline will be faulted and folded into mountains.

In the upbent portions on one or both sides, the crust will crack along the crests owing to tension at the upper surface. Hot magma brought near the surface by the convection cell will fill these cracks and will enter similar breaks in the floor of the geosyncline, even extending into the sediments themselves. This material will be largely of basic composition. It will form small intrusive bodies of various sorts beneath the surface, and it will form volcanoes and lava flows above it.

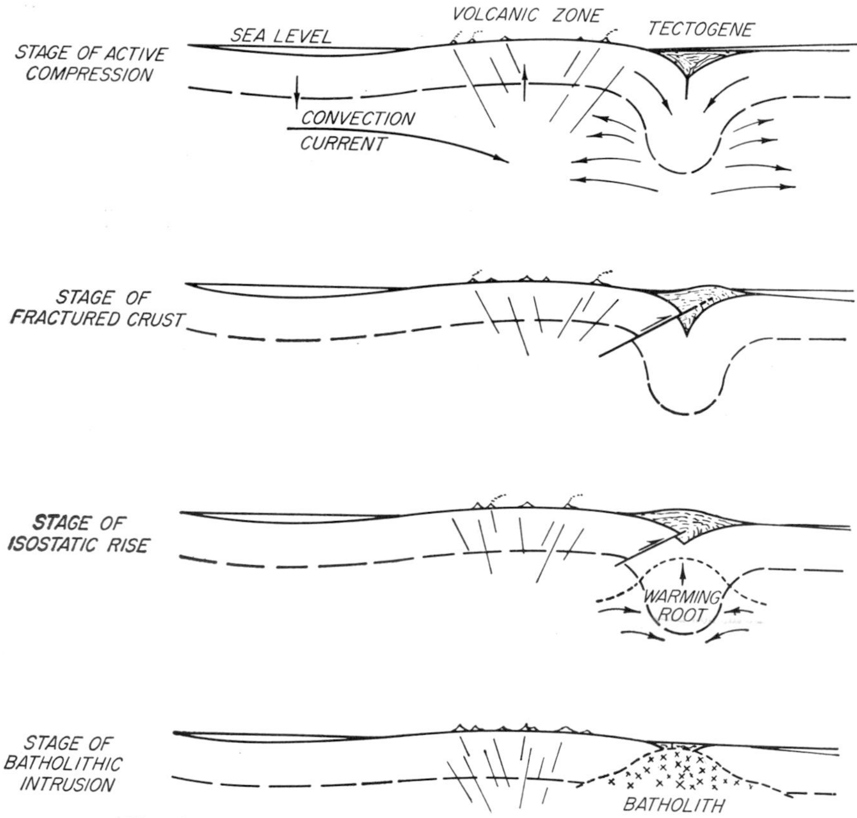

FIG. 21.12 Tectogene formed by compression of the crust.

Once it is forced down, either by folding or thrusting, the root of crustal rocks beneath the folded belt will start to warm. Given enough time, it will melt itself by its own radioactive heat generation. In this way a batholith will be formed and will melt its way into the folded sediments until it gets near enough the surface for the heat to escape by conduction.

If the convection cell slows down, lessening the force depressing the downbuckle, or if the whole crust should fracture, allowing relief of stress by a large over- or underthrust, then the tectogene will rise owing to isostasy. Erosion will attack its surface. As the cover becomes thinner, the batholith will cool. As erosion progresses, the whole area will continue to rise isostatically, so that eventually the top of the batholith will be exposed. While this is going on, the lower portion of the batholith will be spreading outward as it is pressed up by the greater density of the more basic rocks it has displaced. Eventually the root will be largely dispersed.

This picture fits the facts moderately well. The batholith, the folded sediments, the volcanism, and the broad, shallow trough of the adjoining flexure all correspond to what is observed around the Pacific Ocean today. The gravity anomalies are explained by the presence of the low-density downfold. The oceanic deep represents the trough where one crustal block is overriding another along the broken tectogene, or it may even be the visible expression of the downbuckle itself.

The seismic picture at intermediate and great depths is harder to explain. It may be that it represents a zone of maximum shear in the flowing convection current (Vening Meinesz, 1947*a*). This could explain why it departs so greatly from a perfect plane. Or it may be that the convection cell reaches upward only to about 700 km from the surface and all the material above this depth is being compressed.

A major problem is to decide which way the convection current flows. One theory holds that the sialic rocks of the crust, being richer in radioactive elements than the rocks underlying the ocean basins, must cause higher temperatures to be present beneath the continents than beneath the sea. The continents, then, would be the site of the upwelling, whereas sinking cells would underlie the oceans. Along the oceanic borders, where the flow is horizontal, the zones of maximum stress would be found.

There are two difficulties with this concept. First, the theory predicts that the centers of the continents should be under tension. There is no evidence that this is the case. Second, the theory predicts that more heat should be escaping from beneath the continents than below the oceans. This is not only because of the greater radioactivity in the continental rocks but also because the rising convection current will bring up hot material here from deep within the mantle. Such evidence as is available indicates that the rate of heat loss beneath the oceans is about the same as beneath the continents, 1.2×10^{-6} cal per cm^2 per sec $\pm$ 50 per cent (Birch, 1954*b*).

What, then, are the possibilities of the currents flowing in the opposite direction, from the oceans toward the continents? It has already been pointed out in Sec. 17.6 that such currents have been proposed to explain the origin of the continents. The pattern of tectogene, volcanism, gravity anomalies, deep-sea troughs, and shallow basins can result as well from force in one direction as in the other. The locations of these structures are fixed only by the locus of the maximum stress gradient, and their detailed characteristics may be more the result of crustal composition than of the direction of the convection current. It is easier to explain the intermediate and deep earthquakes by a landward-directed flow, as they would in this case lie near the outer edge of the flowing cell. The fact that the steepness of the earthquake belt sometimes increases with depth (Figs. 20.2 and 20.4) could be a result of the turning downward of the convective flow. The earthquakes may be theorized to be occurring at the edge of the convective cell where flowing plastic rock adjoins a more rigid block which can yield only by breaking.

For a continentward-directed convection current, the area of tension would underlie the oceans. This is more reasonable than the previous alternative. The volcanic islands of the Pacific basin have been cited as evidence of extensive tension cracking in this area in the past. Many of these volcanic chains occur in long lines, as though they marked individual cracks in the crust through which molten magma flowed to the surface (Umbgrove, 1947). The Hawaiian Islands, the Cook and Tubuai Islands, the Society Islands, and the Taumoto Islands are examples of such lineaments.

Another possibility is that rising cells underlie both the land and the sea and that the tectogenes occur over the descending currents, where the crust is squeezed together most strongly (Vening Meinesz et al., 1934).

It must be remembered that there is no direct evidence to prove that convective cells exist at all. They are postulated to provide the forces which cause horizontal compression of the crust. In spite of the lack of proof of their existence, it is generally agreed that they are very probable. No other theory accounts so satisfactorily for the large forces which must have existed to form mountains. No other theory can explain so easily the localization of the folding in one area in one period and in another area in a later period as would occur if the locus of the cells shifted from place to place in the earth with time.

Support for the existence of currents comes from a study of the earth's magnetic field (Sec. 23.5). The most satisfactory explanation of the cause of the earth's magnetism is that it is the result at least in part of electrical currents in the earth's interior. These can most easily be explained if they are associated with mass currents (movements of solid or liquid rock). It is to be hoped that future research in this field may contribute to our knowledge of subcrustal convection.

21.6 Thermal Cycles. Theories of the origin of mountain ranges depend largely upon the earth's heat for the source of the energy needed for orogeny, excepting certain versions of continental drift which assume tidal or polflucht forces. In the case of the contraction theories, the loss of heat creates a state of inequilibrium, which is relieved by compression of the crust. In the case of convection currents, the generation of radioactive heat causes the mass movements, and the stressing of the crust is simply a superficial manifestation of their existence. These thermal processes are continuous and must have supplied a steady or only slowly changing amount of energy throughout geologic time. Yet one of the peculiar features of mountain formation is that it does not appear to be uniform in time. In certain periods of the earth's history tectonic activity seems to have been much greater than in others. In the late Paleozoic and late Tertiary, mountain building seems to have been particularly intense. Other moderate maxima occurred in Silurian, Devonian, Jurassic, and early Tertiary times. Ordovician, Triassic, and the middle of the Cretaceous were relatively quiet (Umbgrove, 1947).

This alternation of quiet and activity may be only apparent. We know the geology of only a very limited part of the earth. Over 70 per cent of its surface is buried beneath the oceans. Other areas are covered by recent sediments. Still others, like Antarctica, are so inaccessible or ice-sheathed that we know little of their nature. The geologic time scale was originally divided into periods with the idea in mind that each period was a time of quiet preceded and followed by an interval of unrest. Geologists have long abandoned so simple a view. As the whole world picture has become better understood, the distribution of tectonic activity is seen to be more and more even. Different areas were disturbed at different times. The formation of mountains at one place coincided with quiet deposition elsewhere. Perhaps eventually it will be discovered that there was no periodicity for the world as a whole, only a shift of the site of activity from place to place (Gilluly, 1949).

On the other hand, our present limited knowledge suggests that there is a periodicity to orogeny. Joly (1925, 1928) has attempted to show how this could be caused. Consider the heat generated in the earth's mantle beneath the crust. If the mantle had a concentration of radioactive matter equal to that in basalt at the surface, heat would be formed much faster than it could be removed by conduction. The conduction loss would be least from the bottom of the layer. This would warm up more rapidly than the shallower material. The layer would melt from the bottom upward. Melting would be a gradual process. During a long period, both solid and liquid phases would be present. The later-melting crystals would form a spongy network filled with liquid. Finally, the whole would be disrupted by tidal forces. Cooler material from just beneath the crust would settle to the bottom of the mantle, and warm material would rise close to the surface.

The relative positions of the hot and cold materials would then be reversed. Since the melting point increases with pressure, the rising fluid would become more liquid as it rose. The colder falling blocks would stiffen. Thus, once the inversion had occurred, the subcrustal currents would cease. The hot melt, now near the surface, would cool by conduction. The sunken solids would be heated by their own radioactivity. After a period of time the cycle would be repeated.

The periodicity would be aided by the contrast in rate of heat loss under the continents and under the oceans. Much heat is lost by conduction beneath the sea. The radioactivity of the continental rocks must hold back the heat beneath the land. Thus, the material beneath the continents must warm in contrast to the cooling oceanic segments.

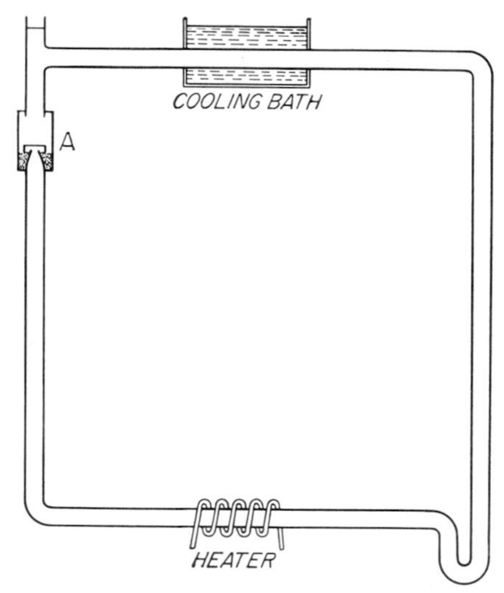

FIG. 21.13 Experimental cell to demonstrate periodic convection in a system subject to constant heating and cooling. (*Griggs, 1939.*)

When the melting cycle reaches its climax, the continents can drift more easily than at other times. Tidal or other forces might more easily shift them westward to new positions. Thus, even their locations might be involved in the tectonic cycle.

Joly's ideas have done much to encourage the acceptance of the idea of subcrustal currents. The concept of periodicity is not so well established as that of convection. If the subcrustal material contains enough radioactive material to melt in the first place, then it is hard to understand how it can ever cool enough by conduction to solidify. This is particularly true if its composition is that of surface basalt, which contains significant amounts of the radioactive elements. Actually, it is likely that it is more ultrabasic than this and is poorer in radioactive material. Heat may also be supplied continually from the earth's core. This would tend to keep the bottom of the mantle melted. The periodicity of convection would be impeded, and continuous circulation would be more likely.

An interesting experiment by Griggs (1939) supports Joly's explanation of how periodicity might be brought about. Griggs built a system consisting of a tube of fluid as shown in Fig. 21.13. The lower arm of the tube was heated and the upper arm was cooled, causing a vertical temperature gradient to develop. A pressure valve kept the fluid from flowing until the temperature gradient reached the point where the force was sufficient to open the valve. The valve then remained open until convective flow had inverted the column. Flow then slowed, the pressure gradient across the valve was reduced, and it closed. It remained closed until the gradient had again built up sufficiently to reopen it. Griggs theorized that a plastic solid with finite strength would behave in the same way. No flow would occur until the strength of the system was exceeded. Convective overturn would then occur, but flow would stop as soon as the hot material had risen to the top of the cell. Convection would cease when the temperature gradient had been reduced by the flow of the material to the point where the strength of the rocks was no longer exceeded. A period of quiescence would follow while the risen hot material cooled and the sunken colder material heated. Then the process would be repeated. Such inversions might take place first in one part of the world, then in another. Wherever they occurred, an alternation of orogeny and quiescence would result.

It is clear from the geologic evidence that the formation of a mountain range follows a definite sequence of steps, at the end of which deformation slows down or ceases. This could be the result of the thickening of the crust slowing down the rate of heat loss by conduction beneath it and driving the cell pattern to some new distribution, or the flow could stop solely because the turnover of cold and hot rock was completed. In the former case, the subcrustal currents would keep flowing continuously, but they would periodically shift in location from one place to another. In the latter case the currents would be periodic in any one area, while in other areas the periodicity could be the same or completely different. Even if the length of a cycle were the same everywhere, the phase might vary from place to place.

More study of individual mountain ranges throughout the world is needed to show to what degree each of the theories presented above can explain the distribution of the rocks as they actually occur.

CHAPTER 22

GEOMAGNETISM

The date of the discovery of magnetism is unknown, being lost in mythology. There are some claims that the Chinese knew of it as early as 2600 B.C. The Greeks were acquainted with the ability of the lodestone[1] to attract iron at least as early as the sixth century B.C. but did not realize that the earth itself acts as a magnet. Primitive compasses are believed to have been first used for navigation by the Arabs and Persians in the latter part of the eleventh century. The Chinese had knowledge of the directive properties of the magnet at about the same time, as reported by the encyclopedist Shon-Kua, who lived from A.D. 1030 to 1093. Early compasses sometimes consisted of a piece of magnetite or a needle suspended by a thread or attached to a piece of wood or straw and floated on water. First reference to their use for navigation in Europe was toward the end of the twelfth century. By the fourteenth century the compass was widely used. A sailing needle and dial are listed as a part of the equipment of a British naval vessel in 1338. Without the compass the long sea voyages of discovery begun in the fourteenth century by the Portuguese would have been impossible.

At first it was thought that the compass pointed straight north, but by the latter part of the fifteenth century it was realized by a few that this was not always true. The common seaman had a superstitious respect for the compass, looking upon it as almost sacred. One of the reasons why Christopher Columbus's men threatened to mutiny is that they were disturbed by the fact that, as they proceeded westward, the compass needle swung from a little east of north to a little west of it.

The man who did the most to found the science of geomagnetism was an Englishman, William Gilbert (1540–1603). His discoveries are described in his book "De Magnete," published in 1600. He investigated the properties of iron magnets and lodestones, showed that the earth acts like a giant magnet, and discussed the variations in the direction of the earth's field in the then explored parts of the world. Systematic quantitative observations of the direction of the earth's field were begun in

[1] A lodestone is a piece of magnetite or other iron oxide exhibiting polarity.

London during Gilbert's lifetime (Fig. 22.1). It is from long-continued accurate observations such as these that man has learned much of what he knows of the variations of the earth's field. Thus, in 1635 Henry Gillibrand, studying these data, was the first to realize that they proved the magnetic field to be changing with time.

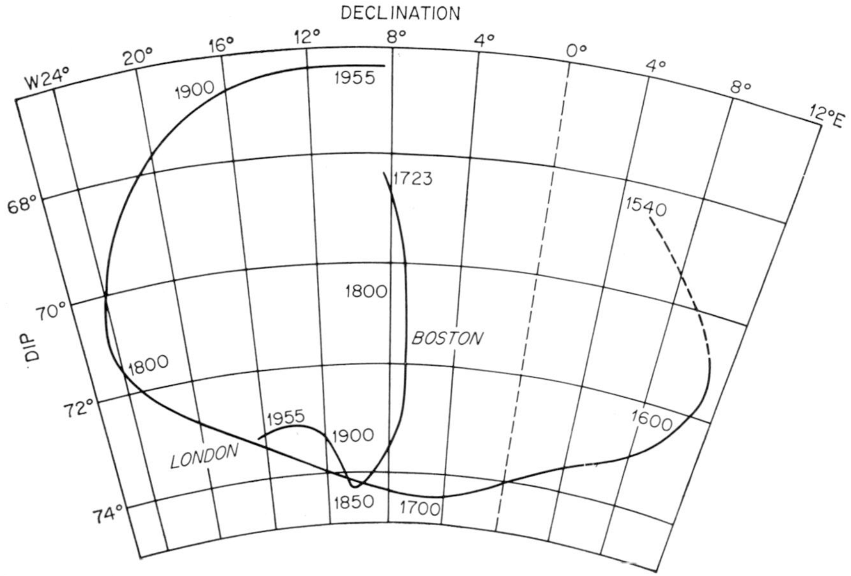

FIG. 22.1 Secular change in magnetic declination and inclination. *(After Bauer, 1902; Howe and Knapp, 1938; Deel and Howe, 1948; and U.S. Navy Hydrographic Office charts.)*

22.1 Description of the Magnetic Field. The earth's field may be pictured to a first approximation as the field of a single large magnetic dipole situated in the core of the earth, but not exactly at the center (Fig. 22.2). The magnetic axis misses the center of the earth by 1,200 km. In 1947 the north magnetic pole[1] was at 73°N, 100°W (Madill, 1948), while (in 1945) the south magnetic pole was at about 68°S, 146°E, but they are not fixed in position. Between 1922 and 1945 the north magnetic pole moved several hundred miles northwestward. At any point on the earth's surface the magnetic field can be described by stating its strength and direction. Direction is described in terms of declination,

[1] The magnetic pole is defined as the point at the surface of the earth where a freely suspended magnetic needle would point straight down, hence the place where the field is vertical. The north magnetic pole of the earth is a south-seeking pole, while the north-pointing end of a compass needle is a north-seeking pole. The custom of calling a north-seeking pole a north pole sometimes leads to confusion, as such a pole has the opposite polarity of that of the earth's north magnetic pole. In this book the expression "north pole" of a magnet will always mean north-seeking pole, and in referring to the north magnetic pole of the earth the adjective "magnetic" will always be used.

the deflection of the field from north-south, and dip[1], the deflection of the field from horizontal. Maps of variations of field strength, declination, and dip are published by national and international agencies. In the United States, the Coast and Geodetic Survey and the Navy Hydrographic Office are the Federal agencies responsible for supplying up-to-date information. Every 10 years the former issues a report on geomagnetism in this country, the latest being a description of conditions in 1945 (Deel and Howe, 1948). The vertical and horizontal components of the field are given more often than the total field. Figure 22.3 shows the

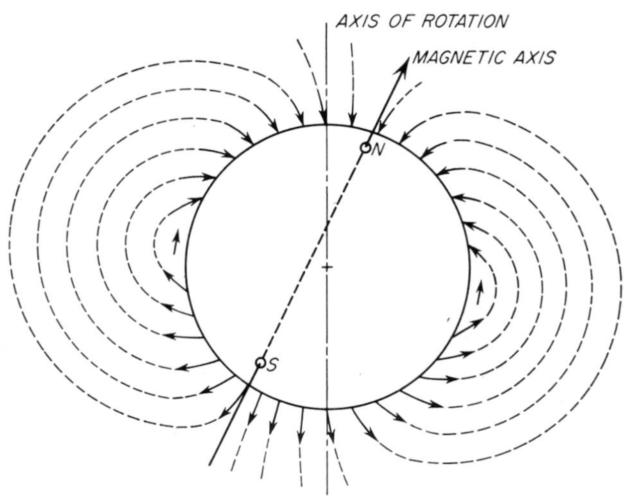

FIG. 22.2 The earth behaves like a giant magnet.

world-wide variation of declination. Lines connecting points of equal declination are called isogonic lines. Similarly Fig. 22.4 is an isoclinic map showing dip, and Fig. 22.5 is an isodynamic map showing magnetic intensity.

The field is strongest in the neighborhood of the poles, though the maxima are displaced somewhat from them, and it decreases toward the magnetic equator. The south magnetic pole is stronger than the north one, indicating that the effective center of the dipole is nearer that end of the earth. The field is measured in oersteds,[2] being slightly over 0.7

[1] Dip is also called inclination in the geophysical literature. This is confusing, since navigators use the latter term for declination.

[2] One oersted is the strength of a field which exerts a force of one dyne on a unit magnetic pole. A unit pole is one which repels a like pole one centimeter away with a force of one dyne. Magnetic fields are commonly visualized in terms of lines of force per square centimeter, and their strength measured in relation to the density of such lines. In these terms, the oersted is the strength of a field of one line per square centimeter. Because the oersted is such a large unit, fields are often measured in gammas, 10^5 gammas equaling 1 oersted.

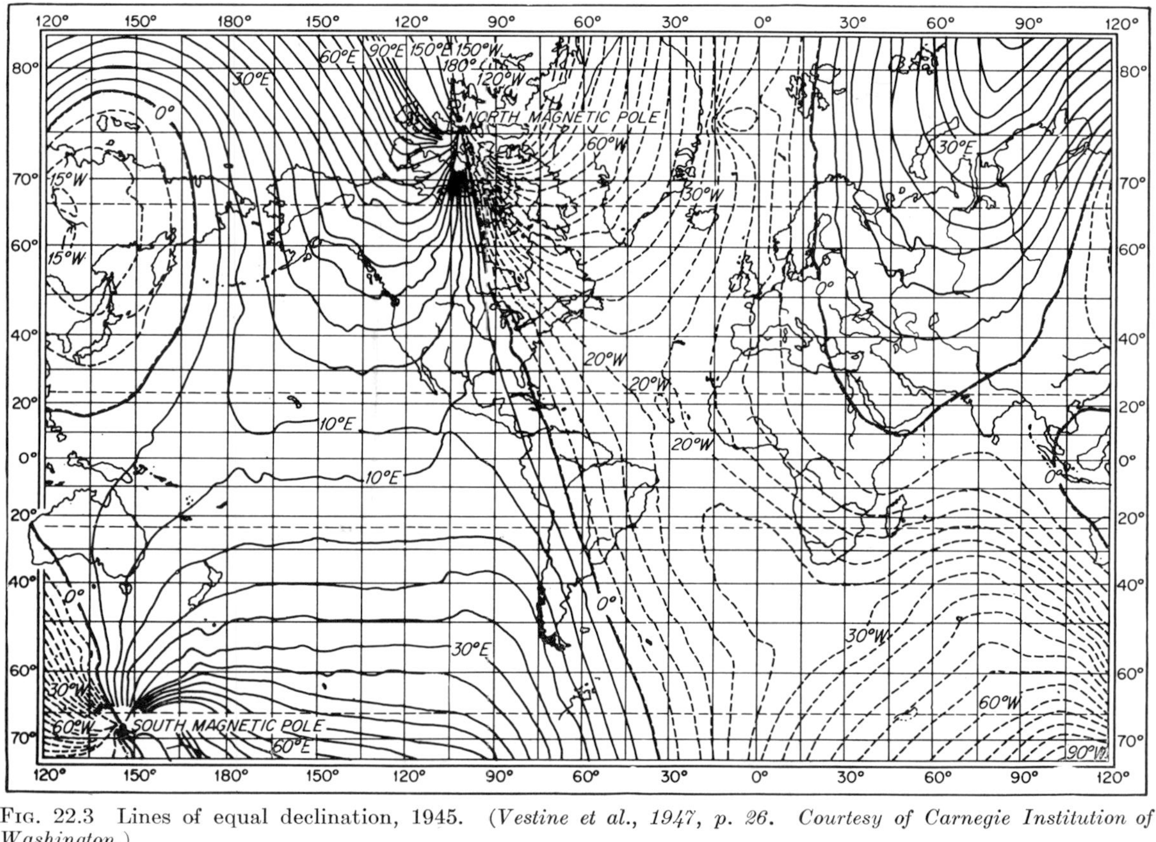

FIG. 22.3 Lines of equal declination, 1945. (*Vestine et al., 1947, p. 26. Courtesy of Carnegie Institution of Washington.*)

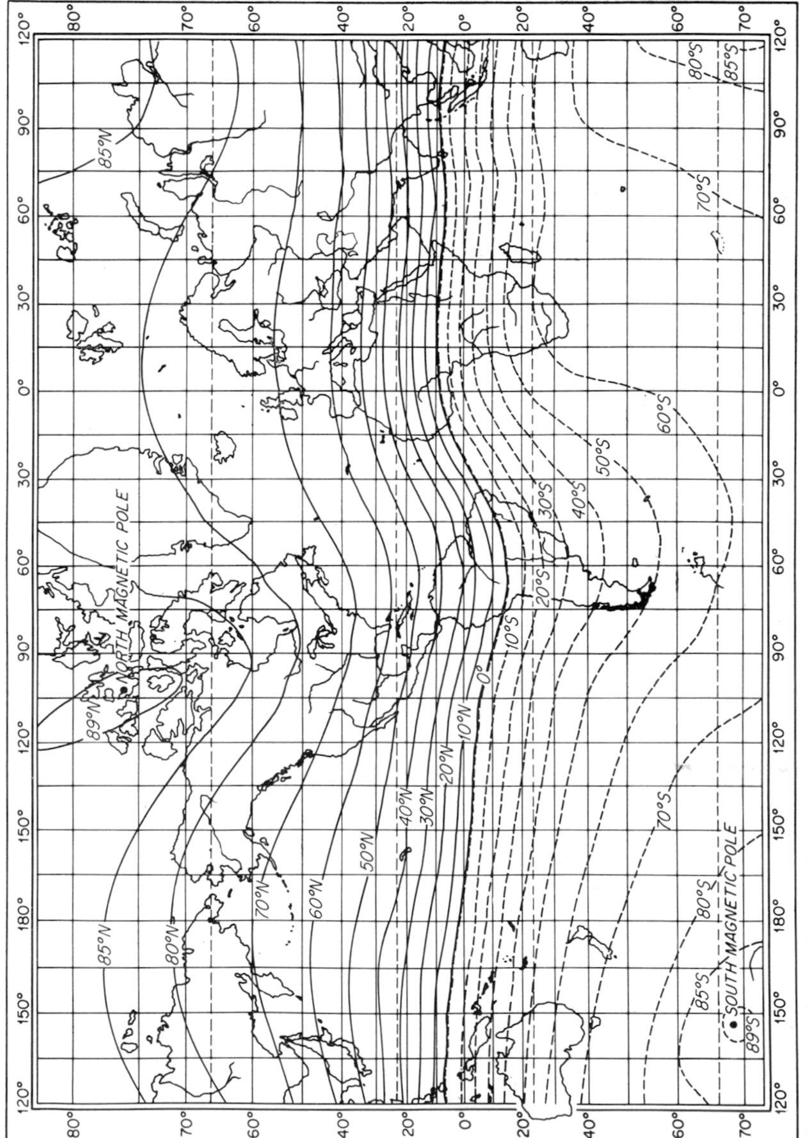

FIG. 22.4 Lines of equal inclination, 1945. (*Vestine et al.*, 1947, p. 27. Courtesy of Carnegie Institution of Washington.)

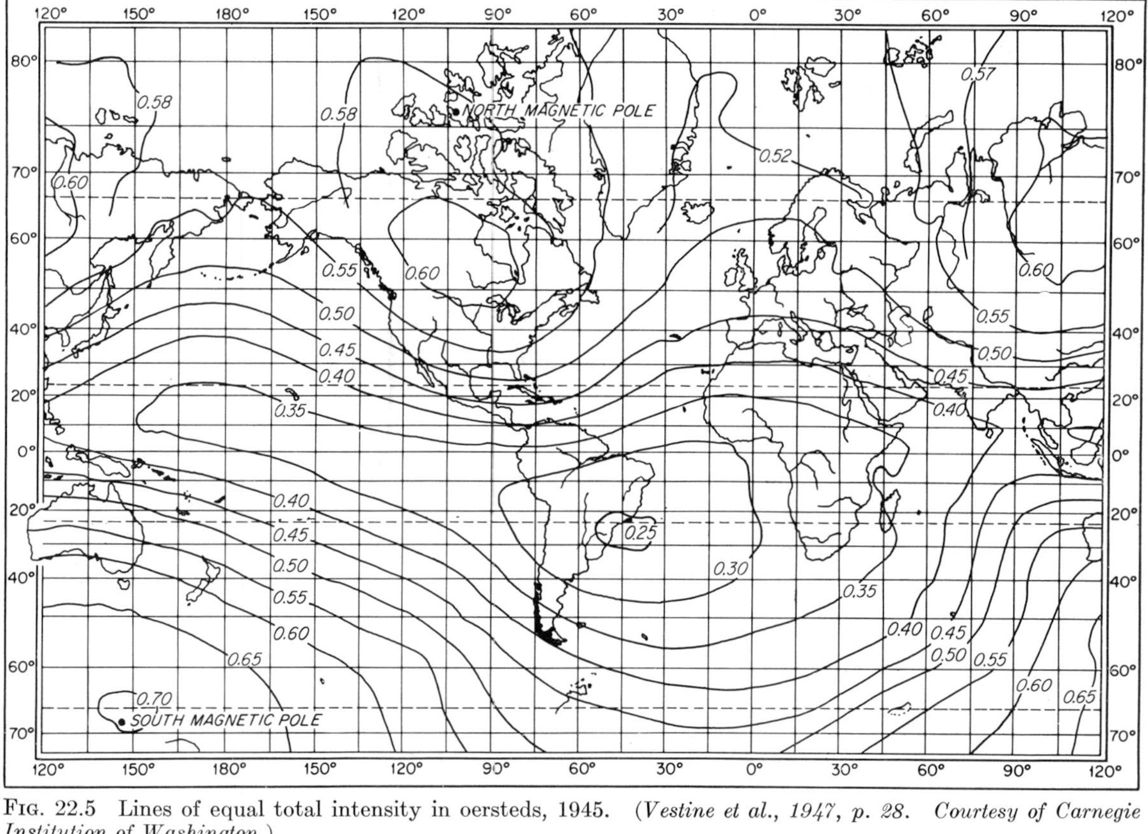

FIG. 22.5 Lines of equal total intensity in oersteds, 1945. (*Vestine et al., 1947, p. 28. Courtesy of Carnegie Institution of Washington.*)

oersted at the south magnetic pole. It can be shown that 94 per cent of this comes from within the earth and 6 per cent comes from above the surface or is generated by currents flowing through the surface. The two parts are called internal and external components of the field.

22.2 Magnetic Properties of Rocks. The irregularity of the contours in Figs. 22.3 to 22.5 shows that the concept of a single dipole is too simple to describe the earth's field. Better approximations are obtained by assuming larger numbers of dipoles variously distributed, but as the actual field is studied in greater and greater detail, the number of such dipoles required becomes very large. One reason for the complexity is that the field strength at any point depends on the nature of the immediately underlying rocks and on those in neighboring areas. Within any magnetized body such as the earth, each part is polarized. At any place

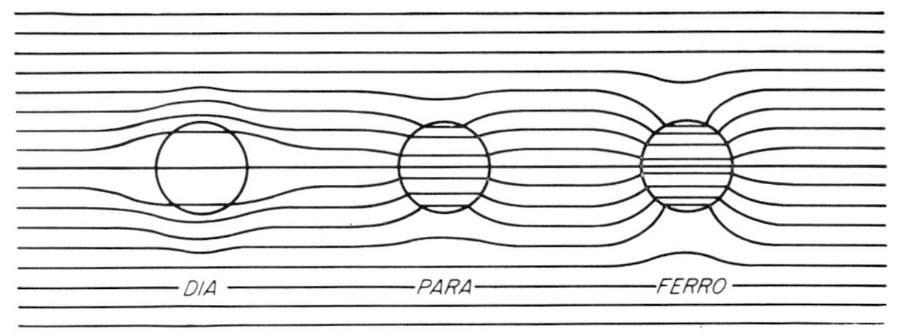

FIG. 22.6 Effect of dia-, para-, and ferromagnetic materials on a magnetic field.

the field can be described in terms of the amount of magnetic flux which it produces. Field H and flux B are related by the equation

$$B = \mu H \tag{22.1}$$

where μ is called the permeability. If field strength is expressed in oersteds, flux will be in gauss. The permeability of a vacuum is unity. Matter in a magnetic field will generally tend either to concentrate or to repel flux as compared with a vacuum. Bodies which repel it are called diamagnetic (Fig. 22.6). Those which attract the field are called paramagnetic. A few substances such as iron, nickel, and certain alloys of cobalt, iron, and nickel attract magnetic fields very strongly. Where their permeability is a function of field strength, they are called ferromagnetic.

The magnetic flux in a body results in part from the externally applied field and in part from the fact that the body itself becomes polarized. For most materials, the intensity of magnetization I_m is related to the field strength H by the formula

$$I_m = kH \tag{22.2}$$

where k is called susceptibility. Susceptibility and permeability are often confused. The former refers to the ability of a body to become magnetized; the latter to the ease of passing a flux through it. The two are related by the formula

$$\mu = 1 + 4\pi k \tag{22.3}$$

The situation becomes more complex for ferromagnetic bodies, as in this case μ and k are not constant but depend on the strength of the magnetic field and the previous history of the material. Thus, if an unmagnetized piece of magnetite is placed in a magnetic field and then removed, it will retain some of the induced magnetism. This property is exhibited to a lesser degree by a few other minerals such as pyrrhotite. Materials exhibiting the ability to retain magnetism in this fashion are called magnetic. The relation between the flux and the magnetic field is most easily described by a diagram like Fig. 22.7. As the field H is increased from zero, the flux B increases along the line *oa* until a value, saturation, is approached above which it will not rise. If the field is then decreased, the flux falls off more slowly than it rose. When the field intensity reaches zero, some flux b remains. This is called remanent magnetization. To reduce the flux to zero, a field c of the opposite polarity must be applied to the sample. The degree of remanent magnetization exhibited by a magnetizable material will vary depending on how near to saturation it was driven in previous magnetization cycles.

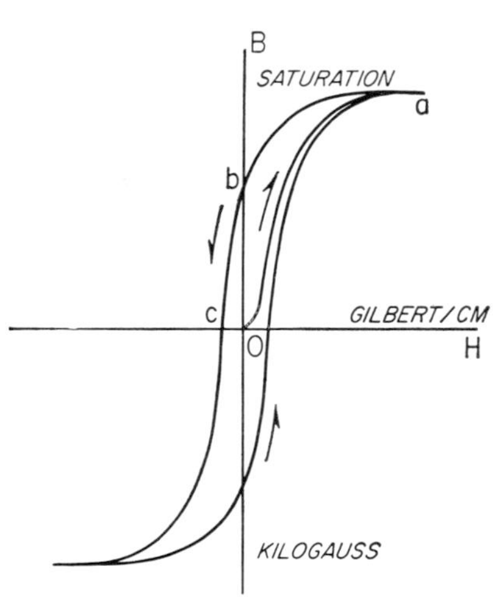

FIG. 22.7 Hysteresis loop.

The intensity of the magnetic field varies from place to place at the earth's surface owing to the permeability and magnetization of the rocks beneath the surface. Since magnetite is by far the most permeable of the common minerals (Table 22.1) and also the only common magnetic mineral, its distribution in the rocks has a strong effect on the earth's magnetic field. The largest magnetic anomaly known is over a magnetite body at Kursk in Russia. The vertical field is nearly 1.4 oersteds at its peak, and the horizontal field 0.7 oersted (Dobrin, 1952). Magnetite is commoner in igneous and metamorphic rocks than in sediments, being most abundant in basic intrusives. Consequently, local variations in magnetic intensity are controlled largely by the topography of the crystalline basement and by basic formations in the basement and intruded into the overlying sediments.

In some cases, local magnetization may oppose the earth's field. The Pilansburg volcanic dike system in Transvaal is magnetized to an intensity of over 0.16 oersted oppositely to the earth's field (Fleming, 1939).

TABLE 22.1 TYPICAL VALUES OF SUSCEPTIBILITY OF SOME COMMON ROCKS AND MINERALS*

Material	*Susceptibility (electromagnetic cgs units)*
Magnetite†	0.3
Pyrrhotite†	0.3
Hematite	0.003
Quartz	−0.000001
Rock salt	−0.000001
Calcite	−0.000001
Basalt	0.003
Diabase	0.003
Gabbro	0.001
Granite	0.002
Gneiss	0.0001
Sandstone	0.00002
Shale	0.00004
Dolomite	0.00001

* For additional data and references see Slichter (1942) and Heiland (1940).

† Since these minerals are ferromagnetic, their susceptibilities depend greatly on field strength. Since the susceptibilities of most rocks depend greatly on their magnetite content, this will also be true of most rock susceptibilities. The situation is further complicated by the fact that the susceptibility of a finely powdered mineral such as magnetite depends on the per cent void space in the sample tested (Slichter, 1929).

To what extent changes in the magnetite and metallic iron concentration inside the earth influence the larger regional differences in intensity is unknown, though they may account for much of this variation. Differences in permeability have the same effect on the magnetic field at the surface as do changes in magnetization. If iron concentration is an important cause of field-strength variations, deep-seated effects must be due to permeability variations, not to differences in remanent magnetization, since all materials lose their ability to retain magnetism at high temperatures. The temperature at which this occurs is called the magnetic inversion temperature, or Curie point. For magnetite this occurs at 580°C; for iron, at 780°C; for nickel, at 350°C (Chapman and Bartels, 1940). These temperatures are probably reached in the lower part of the crust or just below it. Pressure has very little, if any, effect on the Curie point, so that at least most of the mantle and all the core of the earth are believed to be without permanent magnetization.

The observed field at any time and place is thus the resultant of (1) the main magnetic field of the earth, as concentrated or repelled by nearby and distant rocks, plus (2) the effect of any remanent magnetization of the local formations plus (3) the fields generated by any electrical currents which may be flowing in the area. More will be said about electrical currents and the cause of the principal field in Chap. 23.

22.3 Variability of the Field. If nothing occurred to alter it, the earth's magnetic field would remain constant. In earlier chapters it has been shown that the earth is undergoing slow but continous changes. Mountains are formed and worn away; large bodies of rock melt, cool, and solidify; there may be convective cells of liquid or plastic rock within the earth. Small wonder, then, that the magnetic field undergoes alterations. The changes in the magnetic field are rapid in comparison with most geologic processes. If the alterations in the earth's magnetism currently taking place are caused by changes in the interior of the earth, then things are happening there much faster than large-scale changes are taking place on the surface.

The variations are of three types: (1) a secular variation, (2) short-term regular periodic variations, and (3) irregular transient fluctuations. The records of the older magnetic observatories show that there is a gradual shifting of the direction of the earth's field. Whether this is truly a permanent drift or actually a very long period cyclic change cannot be determined from the brief record of observations. The pattern of Fig. 22.1 suggests that there may be a cyclic change in direction taking place with a period of about 600 years. There are also secular changes in intensity, though these are less well known, because accurate observations of this were begun only in 1832. The nonaxial part of the earth's field appears to be drifting westward.

An entirely different line of evidence comes from the study of the permanent magnetization of rocks (Blackett, 1956). It has been observed that successive lava flows in Iceland are magnetized in different directions (Runcorn, 1954). It has been postulated that the direction and intensity of magnetization were controlled by the direction and strength of the earth's field at the time the solidifying lava cooled through the Curie point. The alternating polarity of successive lava flows would indicate that the earth's field may reverse itself cyclicly.

Other observers (Graham, 1954) have noted variations in the directions of magnetization of sediments. This can be explained by supposing that the magnetized sand grains tend to align themselves parallel to the varying direction of the earth's field as they are deposited. These theories are difficult to prove or disprove, as most rocks are only weakly magnetized and the magnetization of specimens is easily destroyed or altered in handling. It is possible that over a long period of time part or all of the original magnetization of a formation may be lost, possibly owing in part to the demagnetizing effect of the known fluctuations of the earth's field.

Reversed magnetization may also be a result of the tendency of a magnetic field to induce an opposing field in certain minerals. Balsley (1954) observed a systematic variation of the magnetization of certain Adirondack Mountain rocks related to the hematite and ilmenite content. He also found in the laboratory that a mixture of these minerals which had cooled through the Curie point in the earth's field had remanent magnetization opposite to the impressed field. Much more study of the magnetization of rocks is needed.

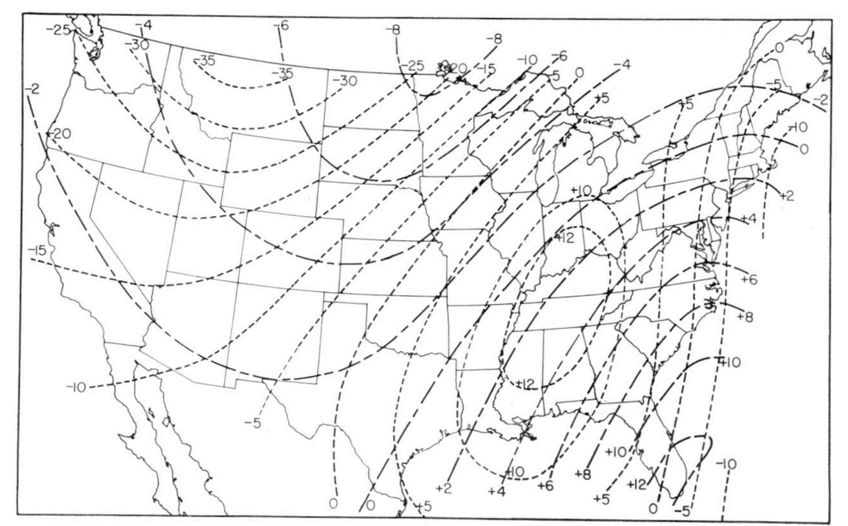

Fig. 22.8 Rate of change of magnetic declination (——) and inclination (- - - -) in minutes per year in the United States. (*After Deel and Howe, 1948.*)

The local rates of secular variation are well known. Figure 22.8 shows the rate of change of magnetic declination and dip in the United States, and Fig. 22.9 shows the world-wide variation in total intensity. Accurate knowledge of the direction of the magnetic field is essential for navigation and surveying, and hence this subject is under continuous study by government agencies.

In addition to the secular changes, there are periodic daily variations. These have a regular pattern whose amplitude depends primarily on latitude (Fig. 22.10). The changes do not depend greatly on longitude but follow the sun, being generally similar for a given local time for all stations at any one latitude. Their connection with solar radiation is further shown by the contrast in activity between the changing daytime values and the more steady nighttime conditions. There is also a considerable seasonal change in the amplitude of the variation, it being

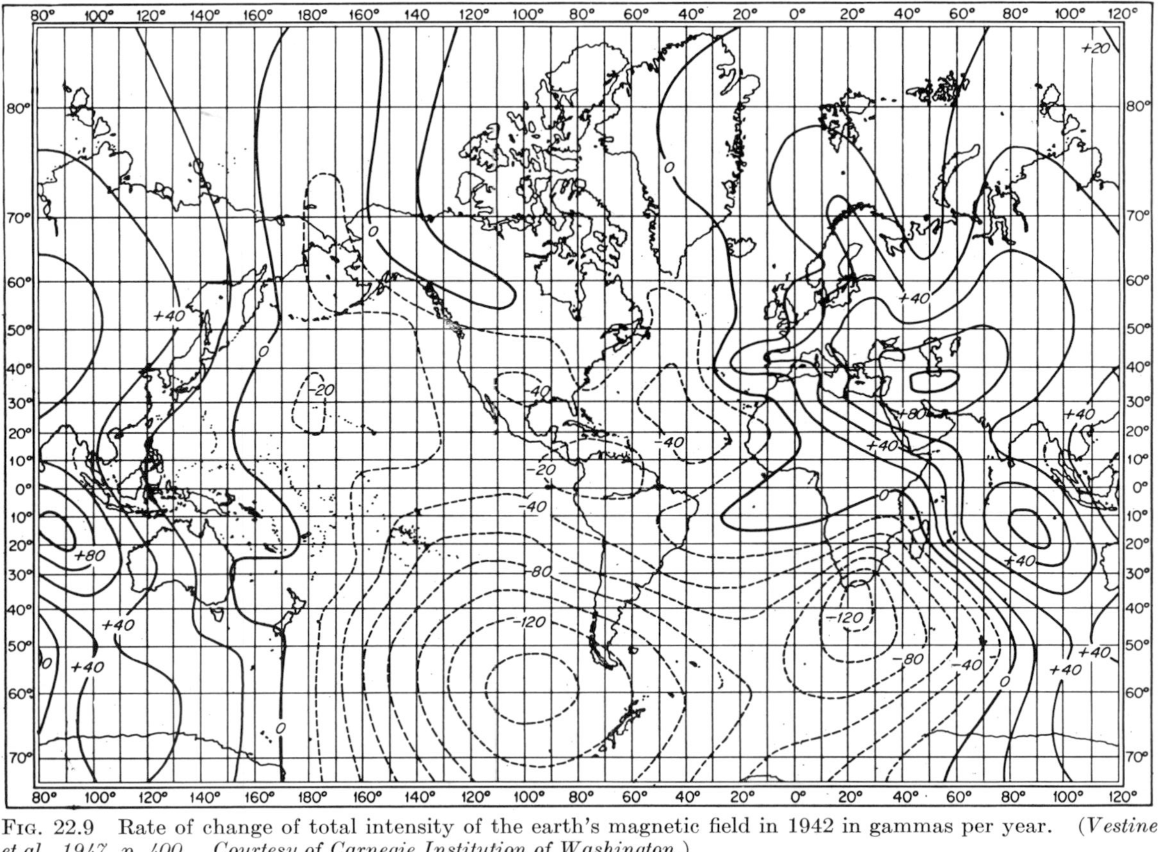

FIG. 22.9 Rate of change of total intensity of the earth's magnetic field in 1942 in gammas per year. (*Vestine et al., 1947, p. 400. Courtesy of Carnegie Institution of Washington.*)

greater in summer than in winter. The maximum amplitude of the variation in intensity is only a very small fraction of the total field, generally less than 0.05 per cent at temperate latitudes. The variations in dip and inclination amount to only a few minutes (generally less than five).

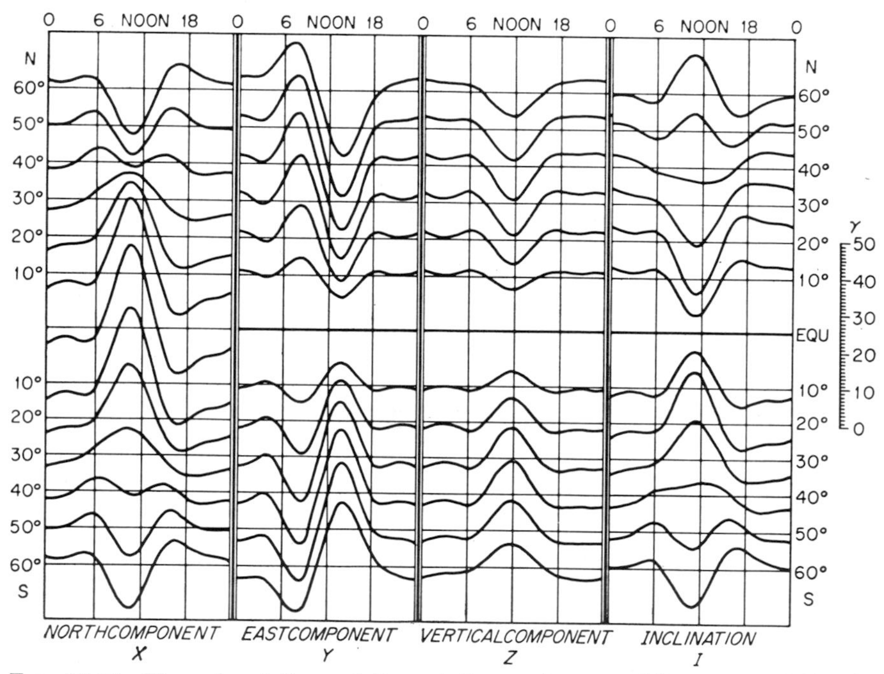

FIG. 22.10 The solar daily variation at the equinoxes. (*Chapman and Bartels, 1940. Courtesy of Oxford University Press.*)

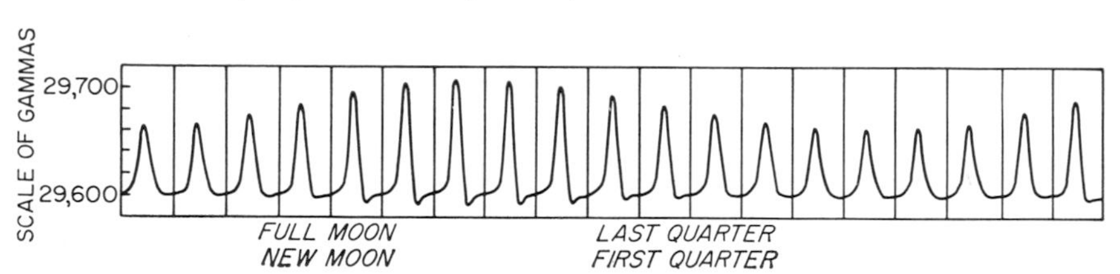

FIG. 22.11 Solar plus lunar variation patterns at Huancayo, Peru. (*Chapman and Bartels, 1940. Courtesy of Oxford University Press.*)

There are also monthly and annual cycles. Figure 22.11 illustrates the variation of the solar cycle with the phase of the moon. The lunar "day," the period between times when any point on the earth faces the moon, is 50 min longer than the solar day, so that the solar and lunar daily changes are shifting in phase. The lunar variations are on the average less than one-tenth the solar variations. Their mean cycle goes through two maxima and two minima daily. The annual periodic variation is even smaller than this.

More striking than these regular, predictable variations are the irregular transient fluctuations called magnetic storms (Fig. 22.12). These occur most commonly at times of unusual sunspot activity (Fig. 22.13). As will be seen from the next chapter, they appear to be a result of the

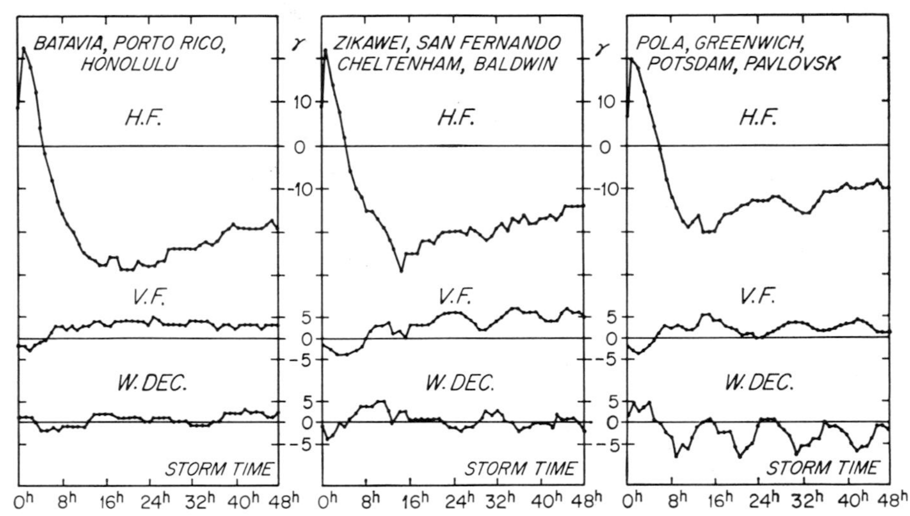

FIG. 22.12 Typical storm-time magnetic field changes. H.F. = horizontal intensity; V.F. = vertical intensity; W.Dec. = west declination. *(Chapman and Bartels, 1940. Courtesy of Oxford University Press.)*

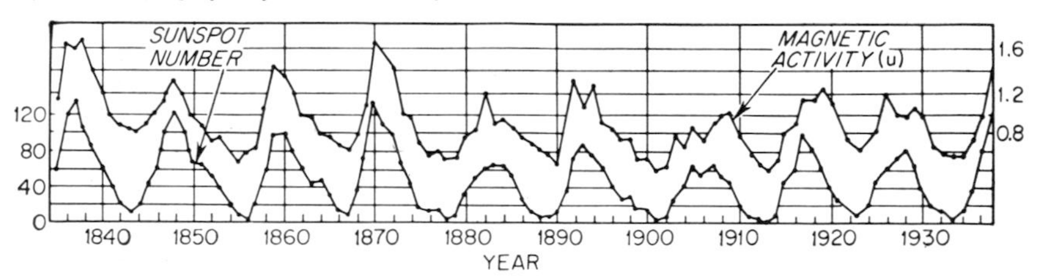

FIG. 22.13 Comparison of magnetic activity (upper curve) and sunspot number (lower curve). *(After Chapman and Bartels, 1940.)*

bombardment of the earth by high-energy particles from the sun. During a magnetic storm the horizontal field undergoes the largest variations, sometimes several times the normal daily fluctuation (Fig. 22.12). The vertical component and the direction also change, though not so strikingly. At first the horizontal field increases, reaching a maximum on the average in about 1 hr, then falling off more slowly. It remains above its initial value for 2 to 4 hr. This period is called the initial phase of the storm. The decrease continues for several hours until a minimum is reached about 15 hr after the start of the disturbance. The depth of the minimum is generally greater than the height of the maximum which preceded it. Thereafter, there is a gradual return to normal, the rate of recovery decelerating with time and lasting at least several days. The period from the initial phase to the time of minimum intensity is called the main phase of the storm, and the subsequent period is called the last phase or phase of recovery (Chapman, 1951).

Magnetic storms start within less than a minute at all points on the earth. The range of the fluctuation in intensity varies from a few to over 1,000 gammas. The disturbances are much greater in polar latitudes, above 60°, than in middle and low latitudes. The zone of auroral activity expands and moves toward the equator during periods of intense magnetic disturbance, showing a connection with the storms. Certain types of transient disturbances are accompanied by interference with radio and telegraph communications, often interrupting these services. The reason for this will become apparent when the relation between magnetism and electrical currents has been demonstrated, as will be done in the next chapter.

CHAPTER 23

TERRESTRIAL ELECTRICITY

The variation of the earth's magnetic field cannot be properly understood without some knowledge of the electrical currents which flow in its solid body and in the atmosphere and oceans which envelop it. These constitute a complex system of largely interrelated moving charges. Deep within the earth, much of the current flow may be electronic, but in the water-saturated sedimentary rocks, the oceans, and the atmosphere, it is largely ionic. The distinction is a question of whether the moving charges are free electrons, as is the case in electronic conduction, or charged particles of atomic or larger size, as is the case in ionic conduction. Electronic conduction is the most familiar type because of the common use of metals and radio tubes to carry current for many useful purposes. The most familiar example of ionic conduction is in a storage battery, where charge travels from one plate to another as an electrolytic current consisting of dissolved salt ions drifting to opposite poles of the battery.

23.1 Electrical Conduction in Rock. In the case of rocks, near the earth's surface conductivity is determined largely by the distribution of salt water in the pores of the rocks (Howell, 1953). Below the sedimentary layers and even in some of the more deeply buried sediments, the pressure is probably so great that all pores are closed and only the conductivity of the solid rock framework remains to carry current. The conductivities of dry rocks are much lower than those of water-saturated rocks. For this reason most igneous and metamorphic rocks are less conductive than the average sedimentary formation, as shown in Table 23.1.

23.2 Conduction in Air. The conductivity of air depends primarily on the degree of ionization, the number of charged particles per unit volume. Some of the charges are free electrons, but most of the time these attach themselves to larger particles, such as individual atoms, molecules, moisture droplets, dust grains, or other colloidal aggregates. Since the removal of an electron from an atom leaves that atom with a positive charge, both positively and negatively charged particles are present in the air. The solid earth appears to have an excess of negative charges,

TABLE 23.1 TYPICAL VALUES OF THE RESISTIVITY OF SOME COMMON MATERIALS*

Miscellaneous substances	Resistivity, ohm-cm	Temperature, °C	Reference
Air (at earth's surface)	2×10^6–5×10^7	...	1
Water:			
Distilled	2×10^7	...	2
Surface	3×10^3–10^5	...	2
Mine	40–6×10^4	...	2
Sea	21	20	2
Copper:			
Pure	1.7×10^{-6}	20	6
Native (ore)	0.1	...	3
Iron:			
Pure	10^{-5}	...	5
Meteoritic	3×10^{-6}	...	4
Minerals:			
Calcite	5.5×10^{15}	...	3
Galena	0.001–0.25	...	2
Magnetite	0.008–0.5	...	2
Pyrite	0.002–9	...	2
Quartz	4×10^{12}	...	3
Rock salt	10^6–10^7	...	2
Sulfur	10^{14}–10^{17}	...	3
Rocks:			
Granite	5×10^5–10^9	...	2, 3
Gabbro	10^6–10^9	...	2, 3
Gneiss	2×10^7–10^9	...	2, 3
Schist	10^3–3×10^9	...	2, 3
Limestone	6×10^3–3×10^5	...	2, 3
Sandstone	10^2–10^5	...	7
Shale	2×10^3–10^7	...	2, 3, 7
Clay and soil	10^2–10^6	...	2, 3

* For more extensive data and bibliography see references.

References: 1. Gish, 1939
2. Slichter and Telkes, 1942
3. Heiland, 1940
4. Jakosky et al., 1932
5. Knowlton, 1957
6. I. A. C. Standard, National Bureau of Standards, 1956
7. Well logs, Geophysical Laboratory files, Pennsylvania State University

causing a steady drift of positively charged ions from the air toward it. Although the size of this negative charge fluctuates greatly with time and varies from place to place, it is continuously maintained in some unknown fashion. The falling of positive charges to the surface constitutes an electrical current, which must be compensated by a corresponding undetected current in the reverse direction if the earth is not to be gaining positive charge. There is considerable uncertainty as to the actual size of this current. From measurements of air conductivity and potential gradient it is estimated to average about 10^{-12} amp per cm^2. The current i can be calculated by taking a line integral of the horizontal component of the earth's magnetic field H around a closed loop:

$$\oint_L H\,dl = 4\pi i \tag{23.1}$$

The currents measured in this way are outward over some areas, inward over others (Chapman, 1951). Many investigators believe that this nonpotential field does not exist and that the failure of magnetic loops to

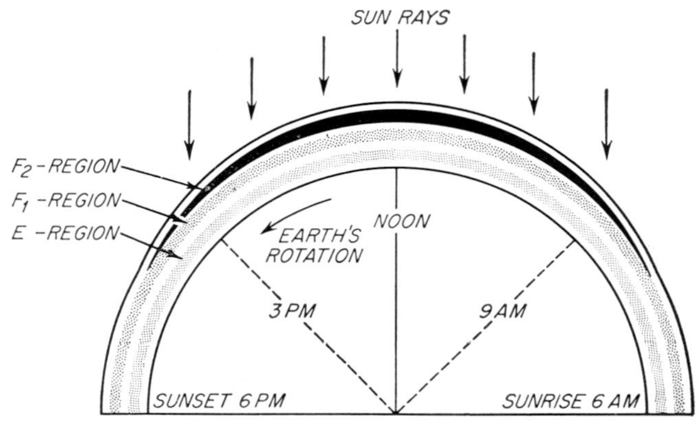

FIG. 23.1 Idealized view of ionized regions of the atmosphere, equatorial section as viewed from the North Pole.

indicate zero current is only a result of the inaccuracy of the data. It is also possible that the downward current observed at most places is balanced by upward currents elsewhere, perhaps in the polar regions (McNish, 1939).

The degree of ionization of the air varies greatly with elevation, time of day, and latitude (Fig. 23.1). Near the earth's surface the ionization is small, a few thousand ions per cubic centimeter. Around noon on a summer day near the equator, ionization begins to increase at a height of about 65 km, the rate of augmentation becoming greater with elevation. Around 100 km, ionization changes by a factor of 10 in a few kilometers. A little above this a maximum density of 180,000 electrons per cubic centimeter is reached. Above this there is a slight decrease, followed by another rapid increase in ionization at 190 km. The second peak is reached at 220 km. Continuing upward, there is little change until 300 km, where there is another sharp increase to 10^6 electrons per cubic centimeter. The three regions of rapidly increasing ionization are called the E, F_1, and F_2 layers, respectively.

The uppermost of these, F_2, exists only in the daytime. It forms a sort of electric blister where the direct rays of the sun strike the atmosphere. Moving toward the poles or the dark side of the earth its height falls till it merges with the F_1 layer as shown in Fig. 23.1.

The main agents causing the ionization of the air are believed to be cosmic rays below an elevation of 80 km and ultraviolet radiation above this. Minor causes are radioactive emanations, electrical discharges such as lightning and corona discharges on power lines, open flames, and industrial chemical and mechanical processes. A large percentage of the ions thus generated are much bigger than molecular in size and because of their great inertia contribute little to air conductivity. Fog and smoke, though often charged as much or more than normal air, usually have small conductivities because of the low relative mobility of the ions.

Above 80 km, electronic conduction is more important than ionic. The mean free path of an electron is inversely proportional to the distance between molecules, so that in the uppermost part of the ionosphere a large percentage of the charges present may be free electrons. As the mass of an electron is much smaller than even the lightest atom, free electrons are correspondingly more mobile and play a more active role in electrical conduction where they are plentiful.

23.3 Cause of the External Magnetic Field. A cloud of ions (or electrons) in the air will constitute an electrical current if it moves relative to the earth. Such movements do occur. The most prominent regular motions, aside from winds, are the atmospheric tides which result from the attraction of the sun and moon. As these bulges rise and fall above the earth's surface, the ions are carried along. The situation is complicated by the variation of ionization with time of day and by the generator action of the earth's magnetic field, which tends to make the charges move at right angles to both the tidal motion and the field. The solar atmospheric tide at high elevations is probably increased by expansion due to the heat of the sun's rays. Tidal resonance may also make a contribution to its size. As a result of this and the higher daytime ionization, the solar component of atmospheric current is larger than the lunar.

Such currents will produce a magnetic field. Indeed, it is these currents which are believed to cause the daily variation in the earth's field. The average current pattern necessary for this purpose is shown in Fig. 23.2. This current system follows the sun about the earth in a daily cycle. The daytime current loop in each hemisphere at the equinoxes has a flow of 62,000 amp. The nighttime current is only 32,000 amp. In June the summer hemisphere daytime current is increased to 89,000 amp, while the winter hemisphere current is only 36,000 amp. Similar variations occur in the nighttime current. The daytime current flows counter-clockwise in the Northern Hemisphere, clockwise in the Southern Hemisphere. The nighttime flow is the opposite.

Because the atmosphere contains no magnetizable constitutents, the nonperiodic externally caused part of the earth's magnetic field must also

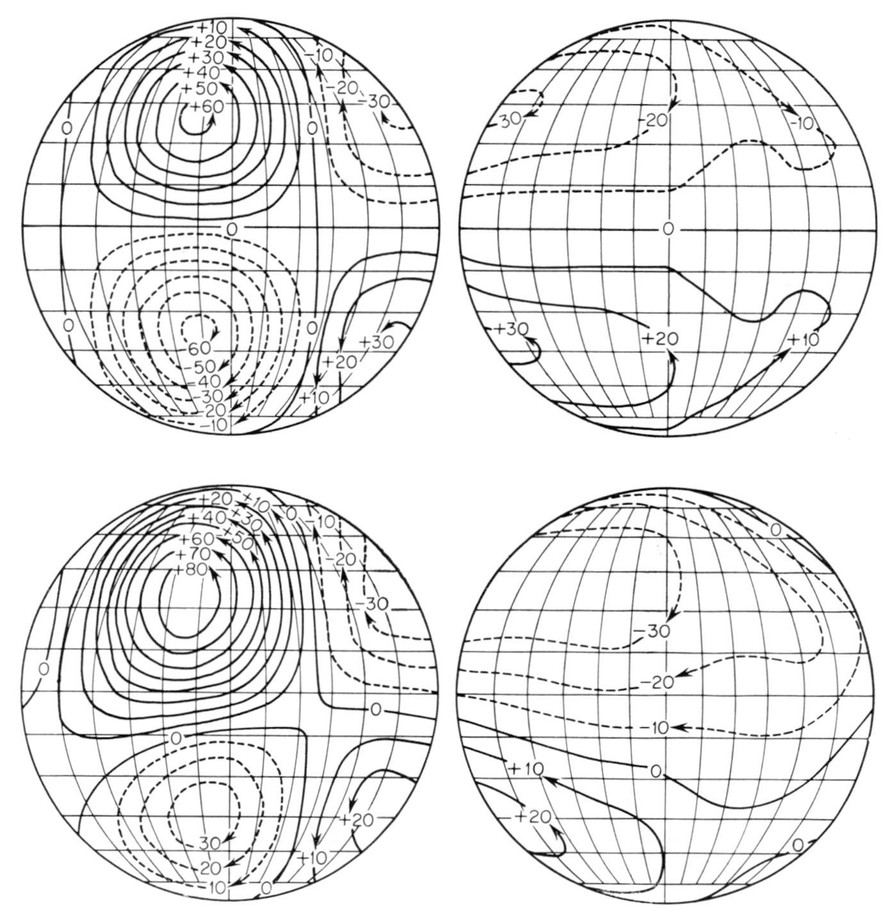

FIG. 23.2 Atmospheric electric-current systems responsible for magnetic field variations: at left, daylight hemisphere; at right, nighttime hemisphere; at top, at the equinox; at bottom, northern summer. *(Chapman and Bartels, 1940. Courtesy of Oxford University Press.)*

result from some sort of atmospheric flow of electricity. A current above the earth in the equatorial regions would explain its observed strength.

There are other possible but less likely explanations for the external magnetic field (McNish, 1939). One of these arises from the probability that in the hot, rarefied gas of the upper atmosphere the individual gas molecules have high velocities. Those which are electrically charged will tend to move in spiral paths between collisions with other particles because of their motion in the earth's magnetic field. Where the mean free path between such collisions is large, as it is in the upper part of the atmosphere, the cumulative effect of the spiral current elements which these particles represent may produce an appreciable magnetic field. The possible magnitude of this effect is enough to account for part or all of the solar daily variation but is not believed capable of explaining the lunar change.

23.4 Earth Currents. Roughly two-thirds of the diurnally varying magnetic field is of external origin. The remaining third results from

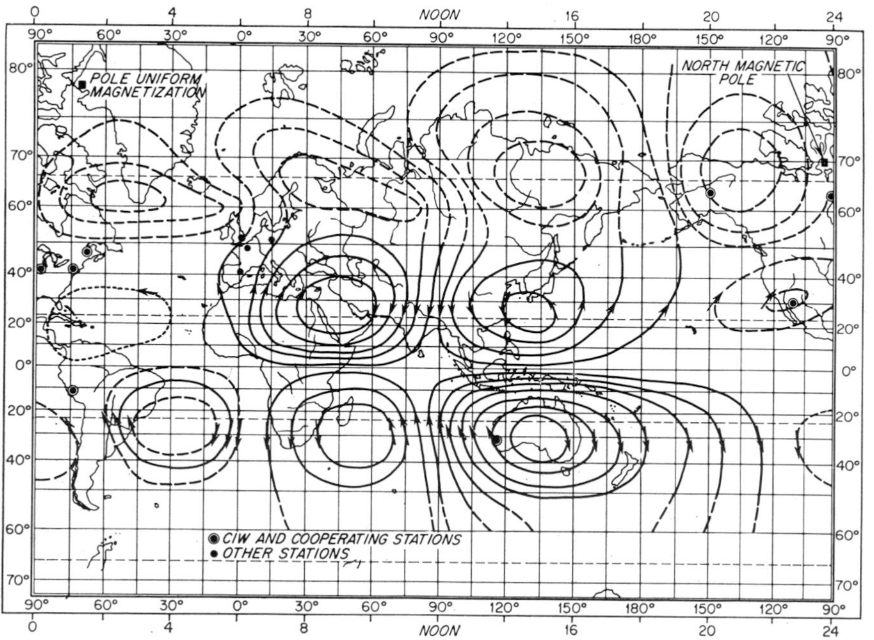

Fig. 23.3 Earth-current system at 6h G.M.T. (*Chapman and Bartels, 1940. Courtesy of Oxford University Press.*)

currents flowing in the ground. If one attempts to calculate the current distribution within the earth which would give the observed internal component to the magnetic field variation, some difficulty is experienced in finding an earth model to satisfy all the observations. The magnetic field can be most simply explained by a nonconducting surface layer 250 km thick overlying an interior with a resistivity of 2.7×10^3 ohm-cm (McNish, 1939). This is certainly too simple a model of the earth. The resistivity probably decreases more nearly continuously with depth. Some pattern of rapid decrease beneath the crustal rocks is required to satisfy observed data.

The recorded pattern of earth currents at the surface is shown in Fig. 23.3. It rotates about the earth following the sun. This is believed to be a part of a current system distributed through at least several hundred kilometers depth and induced by the atmospheric diurnal current system. No vertical currents have been successfully demonstrated to exist in the earth at the surface aside from local deflections of horizontal currents caused by variations in conductivity of the rocks (Rooney, 1939). Because Fig. 23.3 is based on observations at only a few stations, it is only a diagrammatic representation subject to further modification of its details as more data become available.

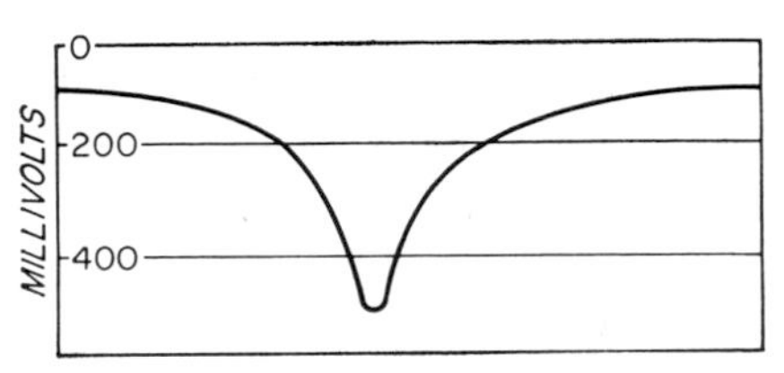

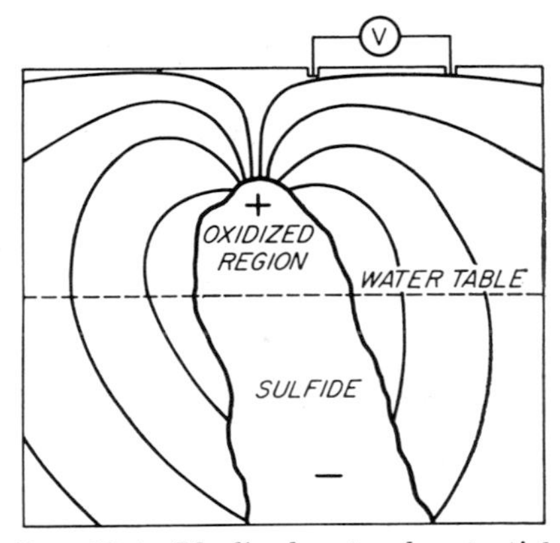

FIG. 23.4 Idealized natural potential profile over a sulfide body oxidizing at the top.

No nonperiodic part of the world-wide current pattern has as yet been detected at the surface. This does not mean that such a current is absent. It would be very difficult to observe if it was present because of local earth potentials and contact potentials at the electrodes of the measuring instruments. Earth currents are not measured directly but are determined from the potential gradient and resistivity using Ohm's law:

$$i = \rho_e \frac{dE}{dl} \tag{23.2}$$

where i is current density, ρ_e is resistivity, and dE/dl is the potential gradient.

Local voltages arise from several causes. Chemical reactions cause distinctive patterns around certain ore bodies (Fig. 23.4). In the case of sulfide ores, especially those rich in pyrite, oxidation commonly occurs above the water table. Sulfuric acid, iron sulfate, and hydrous iron oxide (limonite) are formed. Reducing reactions occur at the lower end of the deposit where the ground water is low in oxygen.

Heiland (1940) gives the following equations as representing the reactions which occur in the zone of oxidation:

$$FeS_2 + 7O + H_2O \rightarrow FeSO_4 + H_2SO_4 \tag{23.3}$$

$$2FeSO_4 + H_2SO_4 + O \rightarrow Fe_2(SO_4)_3 + H_2O \tag{23.4}$$

$$Fe_2(SO_4)_3 + 6H_2O \rightarrow Fe_2O_3{\cdot}3H_2O + 3H_2SO_4 \tag{23.5}$$

Polarization occurs in the ground because of differences in chemical activity where ore bodies are in contact with solutions and because the flow of current causes changes in the ion concentration in the neighborhoods of the ore bodies. This type of reaction can occur also at electrodes. The contact potential between two metallic bodies in contact with solutions of different concentration C_1 and C_2 is

$$\Delta E = \frac{GT}{nF} \ln \frac{C_1 S_{p2}}{C_2 S_{p1}} \tag{23.6}$$

where S_{p1} and S_{p2} are the solution pressures of the two metals involved (Heiland, 1940). In the study of natural earth currents, changes in concentration with time are particularly serious, as they cause gradual changes in the associated potential differences which cannot be distinguished from changes in natural earth potentials.

Potential differences will also occur without the presence of metallic bodies solely owing to differences in salt concentration in ground water. Where there are two solutions in contact having different ion activities and mobilities, an electrochemical diffusion potential is generated, as given in the following equation (Wyllie, 1949):

$$E = \frac{(v - u)GT}{(v + u)nF} \ln \frac{a'}{a''} \tag{23.7}$$

where v = cation mobility; u = anion mobility; G = gas constant, 8.314 joules per °C; T = absolute temperature; n = ionic valency; F = Faraday, 96,000 coulombs; a', a'' = mean activities of the solutions; ln = natural logarithm.

Where the solutions are not in simple contact but are separated by earth materials, the relationship is more complex. An additional voltage is observed between solutions separated by ion-active earth materials. This is called a Mounce potential. For the simple case of two different concentrations of one monovalent salt, the Mounce potential is given by the formula (Wyllie, 1949)

$$E = \frac{GT}{F} \ln \frac{a'}{a''} \tag{23.8}$$

The potentials represented by (23.7) and (23.8) must be added to get the total potential.

Potentials are also generated by the flow of solutions through permeable rocks. Such potentials are called electrofiltration or streaming potentials and are given by the formula (Heiland, 1940)

$$E = \frac{UP\kappa}{4\pi \nu_f \sigma_e} \tag{23.9}$$

where U is the adsorption potential (potential of a double layer of charge, whose size depends on ion concentration, on the wall of the capillaries), P is the difference in pressure between the points where E is measured, κ is the dielectric constant, ν_f is the viscosity, and σ_e is the conductivity of the solution. Voltages as high as several hundred millivolts are often generated by the above causes.

23.5 Cause of the Main Magnetic Field. It has been shown above that the short-term periodic changes in the earth's magnetic field can be explained by electrical currents in the mantle and the atmosphere. It is logical to postulate that the secular and permanent fields also owe their presence to earth currents. Progress in understanding the possible distribution of such currents has resulted from a study of the secular variation. It was found that to a considerable degree this has a regional rather than a planetary character (Runcorn, 1954). The field in individual areas grows and decays independently of that elsewhere, as though it resulted from a distribution of horizontal current loops at the surface of the earth's core. The magnetic field variations for each individual area can be approximately represented by the field of a system of magnetic dipoles 1,000 km within the core beneath the current loops. Runcorn suggests that these are lobes or eddies of a larger electrical current pattern resulting from thermal convection currents in the molten, conducting metal of which the core is believed to be composed.

This concept of convective flow is supported by two other types of observation. The nonaxial field of the earth is known to be drifting slowly westward at the rate of 20 km per year at the equator (Vestine, 1954). This is what would result if there were a rotation of the core of the earth with respect to the surface and if the nonaxial field was generated in the core. There is reason to believe that this drift is not completely regular in rate. It has been demonstrated that changes in the length of the day of as much as 0.003 sec have occurred in comparatively short periods. Such changes are known to occur every few decades (Runcorn, 1954). They are thought to result from readjustments of the distribution of angular momentum between the core and overlying material. Such changes might be the result of shifts in the convection-cell pattern in the core. The flow of matter at the upper boundary of such a cell system might exert frictional forces on the bottom of the mantle which could bring this about, though such forces are thought to be small. Electromagnetic forces could also be brought into play, owing to the mutual induction between currents in the lower mantle and in the core. The westward drift of the magnetic field appears to be of the right order of magnitude to be explainable by this theory.

The details of the electric currents which are required to produce the observed magnetic field at the surface are not easy to describe or establish.

It is not a case of a few simple loops of current. The earth's core must be likened to the armature of an electric generator. The convection cells in the core move conducting material in whatever magnetic field is present. Electrical currents in this conducting material will result. These will contribute to the total magnetic field, which at the earth's surface will be the resultant of all the current loops in the core, mantle, crust, and atmosphere, plus any small contribution made by the permanent magnetization of materials near the earth's surface where temperatures are below the Curie point.

It is possible that not all the currents are due to self-induction in this fashion. Temperature differences of a few hundred degrees may result in electrical potentials of the order of a volt, which for large bodies of low conductivity could cause large currents. Thus the earth's thermal gradient could contribute to the current pattern directly as well as by causing convection.

The energy source for all this is believed to be the heat produced by the disintegration of radioactive elements. This radiogenic heat could maintain both the temperature gradients necessary for the thermoelectric potentials and the convective cells required for the generator action. Because of the large volume of matter involved, the self-induction of the current loops would be large and rapid changes in this pattern would be inhibited.

It has also been proposed that the current system which causes the magnetic field is not being continuously regenerated but is the slowly decaying remnant of a once much larger circulation created in an unknown fashion. The earth is so huge that, provided the core is conductive enough, currents therein once started could continue to exist for millions of years, even though the energy stored in the magnetic field would be decreased gradually by resistive losses. This theory must be considered to be purely speculative unless some reasonable means can be proposed for generating a magnetic field that was formerly much larger than that which exists today. The only evidence that can be brought to support it is a slight tendency of the magnetic field to decrease with time. This can be just as easily explained by the generator theory.

Another concept is that a magnetic field is a fundamental property of all rotating matter, there being in all cases a field proportional to the angular momentum. If this theory is correct, then it can be shown that magnetic intensity should decrease downward in the earth. But the field increases downward more commonly than it decreases (Runcorn et al., 1951), so this theory appears to be an unlikely explanation of the earth's magnetism. At best, this theory could explain only the axial and not the transverse component of the field. The latter is about 20 per cent of the total in the case of the earth.

23.6 Magnetic Storms. Magnetic storms are less easy to explain than the other characteristic forms of geomagnetism. Their coincidence with sunspot activity led to a search for some sort of radiation of a corpuscular or electromagnetic nature whose influence on the earth's atmosphere would result in electrical currents which would explain the magnetic effects. In Fig. 23.5 is shown the type of current pattern which would be required. The region of reversal of current flow coincides with the region of maximum auroral activity. The connection between the cause of magnetic storms and the aurora borealis is further emphasized by the tendency of the latter to be more widespread and intense at times of magnetic disturbances.

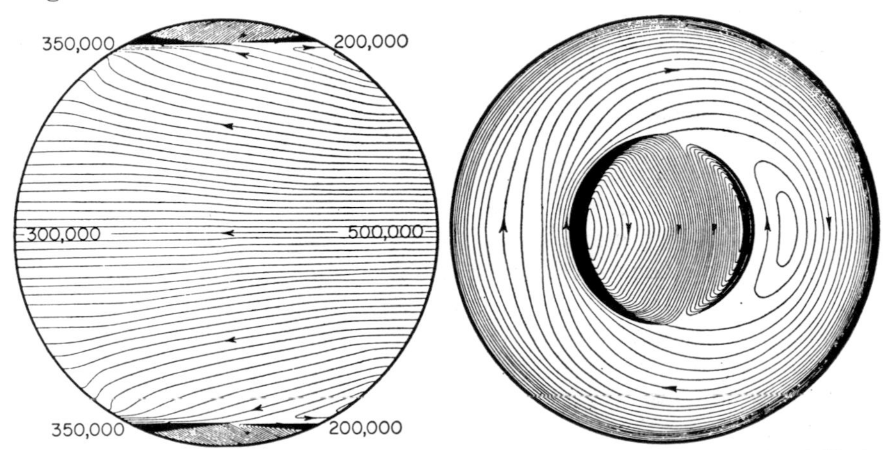

FIG. 23.5 Idealized electric-current system which could produce the regular field of a geomagnetic storm; at left, viewed from the sun; at right, looking down on the North Pole. (*Chapman and Bartels, 1940. Courtesy of Oxford Uuiversity Press.*)

Magnetic storms are also accompanied by disturbances of the ionization of the atmosphere, especially the F_2 layer. During a typical storm the ion density at the top of the F_2 region is reduced while the height of the F_2 region increases. The latter effect could be due to heating of the outer part of the atmosphere. There also appears frequently to be an increase in ionization of the lower part of the E region, causing it to absorb electromagnetic waves. This may result in poor radio communications at frequencies in excess of 500 kc per sec. Communication at lower frequencies is improved owing to the lowering of the reflecting surface. The improved nighttime reception of radio signals at standard broadcast frequencies is similarly due to a decrease in ionization of the air just below the E region where these signals are reflected.

The agency which causes these disturbances has not yet been determined. It has been suggested that the changes result from a temporary increase in ultraviolet radiation, but it is difficult to see how this can cause the auroras and the magnetic pattern in the polar regions, where the intensity of the sun's rays is small. Another theory is that the sun emits bursts of particles which on their approach to the earth are deflected by the magnetic field in such a fashion that they are focused in the auroral belt. To be so deflected they must be charged. If they are of only one polarity, then the cloud would dissipate itself too quickly ever to reach the earth. Therefore, it is suggested that both negatively and positively charged particles are present. According to this theory, these are deflected in opposite directions by the earth's magnetic field as they approach the earth, effectively constituting a circulating current which causes the magnetic effect. It is conceivable, also, that an originally uncharged cloud of particles somehow acquires a charge as it approaches the earth. Since the storms start nearly simultaneously at all points on the earth, some mechanism such as deflection of the particles by the earth's field is needed to bring the active agent into the shadowed side of the earth.

Particles traveling approximately along the earth's lines of magnetic force enter the polar regions and are thought to produce the auroral effects observed. There is some spectral evidence from auroras of hydrogen particles entering the earth's atmosphere at velocities of at least 3,000 km per sec (Chapman, 1951). These might be some of the corpuscles required by the theory described above.

23.7 Solar Flares. There is one type of terrestrial electrical disturbance which can be definitely correlated with solar energy. Occasionally it becomes impossible to get reflections of radio waves from the ionized layers of the earth's atmosphere. This is believed to be caused by absorption at a height between 60 and 100 km, due to an increase in ion density in this region. The fade-out of radio waves is usually complete in less than a minute and may last from 10 min to several hours, though usually less than 15 min. Unlike magnetic storms, such disturbances occur only on the sunlit hemisphere of the earth. The fade-outs are always accompanied by bright chromospheric eruptions on the surface of the sun, though the inverse is not always the case (Berkner, 1939). The fade-outs tend to occur in groups rather than singly. They cause an increase in the diurnal magnetic variation. The cause is thought to be ionization by the selective absorption of ultraviolet light from the solar eruption. Prolonged periods of low-layer absorption also occur, with gradual beginnings and endings and lasting several hours (Terman, 1943). They usually occur at times when the sudden fade-outs are common, suggesting a similar cause.

CHAPTER 24

GEOMAGNETIC AND GEOELECTRIC INSTRUMENTS

The variety of instruments used in studying geomagnetism and terrestrial electricity is too great for all of them to be described in an introductory text of this sort. Therefore, only a few typical examples will be discussed. These have been selected to illustrate some of the more important methods of measurement. More complete discussions of instrumentation will be found in such books as Chapman and Bartels' (1940) "Geomagnetism," Fleming's (1939) "Terrestrial Magnetism and Electricity," Jakosky's (1940) "Exploration Geophysics," and Heiland's (1940) "Geophysical Exploration."

24.1 Magnetic Compasses. The magnetic compass is so common an instrument that it is familiar to nearly everyone. Basically it consists of a magnetized needle and a circular scale of some kind. The needle may be either pivoted on a fine bearing or floated in a liquid, in which latter case it is usually attached to a bouyant disk on which the scale is drawn. Pivoted needles usually must have an adjustable weight attached to one end to counterbalance the moment resulting from the dip of the earth's field.

Compasses are used for aligning many types of surveying instruments with respect to north. Since the needle does not point north, but toward the magnetic pole, the alignment must be corrected for the declination. In some instruments this is done automatically by having an adjustable scale which is set to compensate for the declination of the needle. The accuracy with which direction can be read with a compass depends primarily on how accurately the scale can be read. Errors may also be introduced if the earth's field is distorted by the presence of polarizable bodies near the compass. Brass and many other metals as well as iron are often slightly magnetic, and great care must be taken in making sensitive magnetic instruments to use only nonmagnetizable alloys in their construction.

In the case of ships' compasses, because of the steel construction of the vessel, it is impossible to avoid completely stray fields from nearby iron. The usual solution is to counteract these fields by placing compensating

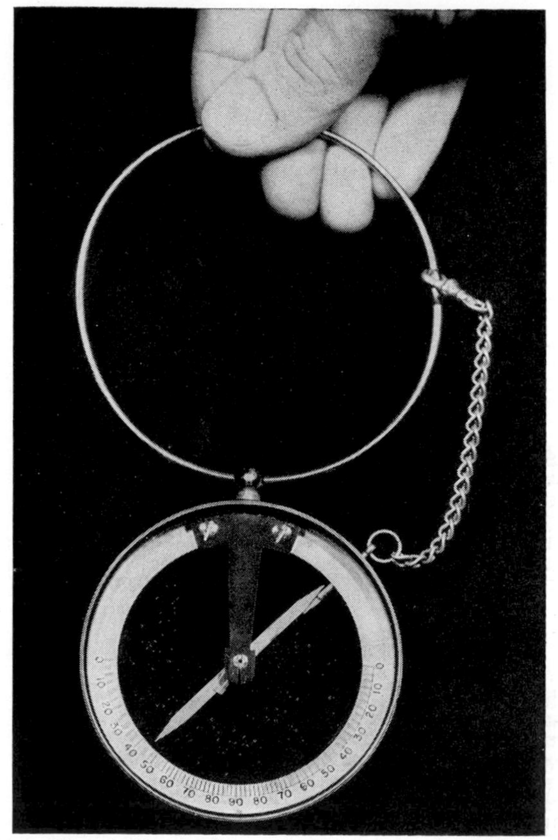

FIG. 24.1 Simple dip needle. (*Courtesy of United Geophysical Co.*)

magnets and iron bodies near the compass in such a manner that they cause the resultant total field to parallel closely that of the earth.

24.2 Dip Needles. Magnetic dip is measured by an instrument very similar to a compass. A balanced, magnetized needle is pivoted on a horizontal axis and allowed to rotate freely (Fig. 24.1). The axis must be aligned at right angles to the earth's field if the dip is to be correctly indicated.

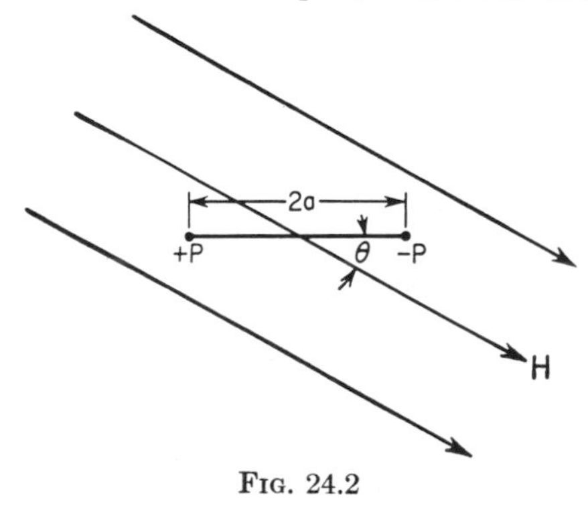

FIG. 24.2

Dip needles can be used also to measure the intensity of the earth's field, though more sensitive instruments are generally used. If a dip needle of known pole strength P and moment of inertia I is set in oscillation in a plane parallel to a field

FIG. 24.3 Wilson magnetometer.

H, the equation of motion of the needle is (Fig. 24.2)

$$I\ddot{\theta} = -2aPH \sin \theta \tag{24.1}$$

where $2a$ is the effective length of the magnet ($2aP$ is its magnetic moment). For small angles of oscillation, where $\sin \theta$ approximately equals θ, this has a solution of the form

$$\theta = \theta_0 \cos \left(\frac{2aPH}{I}\right)^{1/2} t \tag{24.2}$$

where θ_0 is the maximum deflection of the needle. If the swings of the needle are timed, the field can be measured, since the period of oscillation is

$$T = 2\pi \left(\frac{I}{2aPH}\right)^{1/2} \tag{24.3}$$

The horizontal component can be found similarly by swinging a horizontal needle, and the vertical component by swinging the needle in a vertical plane at right angles to the horizontal component. The accuracy of this method is limited by how accurately the magnetic moment and moment of inertia of the needle can be determined.

24.3 Deflection Magnetometers. The intensity of the magnetic field can also be measured by comparing the earth's field with that of another magnet of known intensity. The Wilson and Thalen-Tiberg magnetometers (Figs. 24.3 and 24.4) are simple instruments of this type. A small magnet of moment $M = 2aP$ is placed at an adjustable distance R from the compass needle and on a line from it at right angles to the field H being measured. The forces which must be in balance to give the

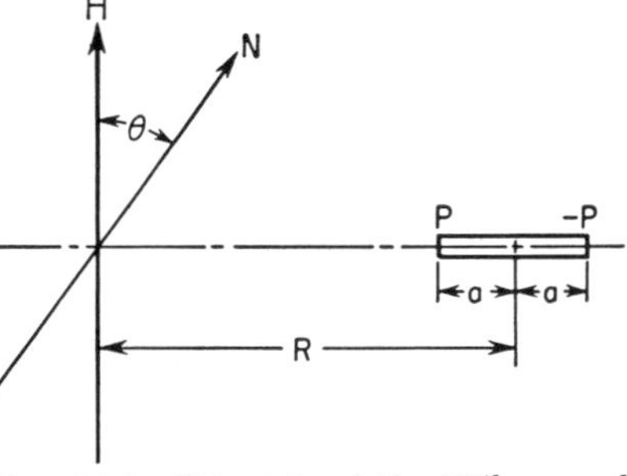

FIG. 24.4 Principle of the Wilson and Thalen-Tiberg magnetometers.

observed deflection are

$$H \sin \theta = \left[\frac{P}{(R - a)^2} - \frac{P}{(R + a)^2} \right] \cos \theta \tag{24.4}$$

which simplifies to

$$H = \frac{4aRP}{(R^2 - a^2)^2} \cot \theta \tag{24.5}$$

By adjusting R till θ is some simple angle such as 30 or 45°, the value of H is easily calculated. θ should not be close to 0 or 90°, or the sensitivity of the method of comparison is seriously reduced. The accuracy depends on how closely R and a can be measured and the moment $2aP$ determined. If R becomes too small, the field of the small magnet diverges appreciably as it passes the compass and formula (24.5) is no longer correct.

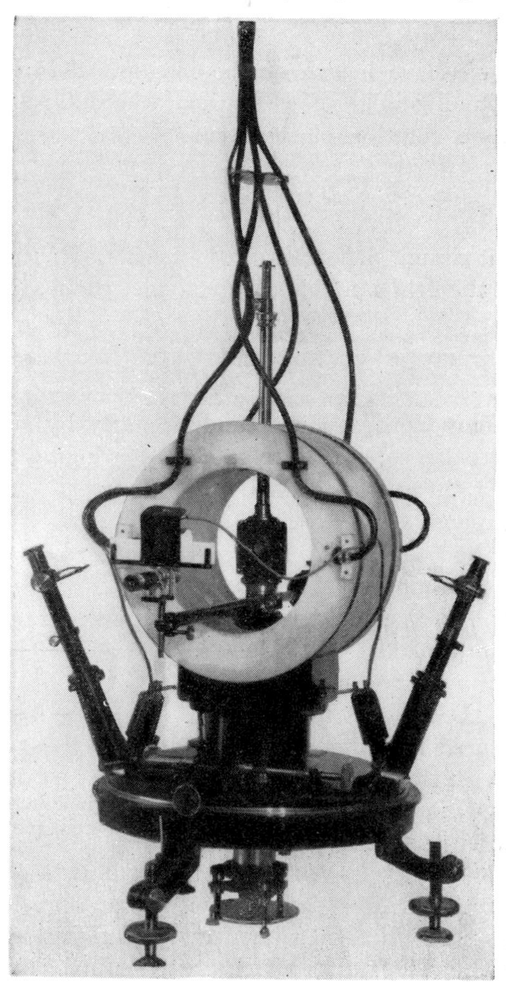

FIG. 24.5 Sine galvanometer. (*Courtesy of Carnegie Institution of Washington.*)

The auxiliary magnet may be replaced by a Helmholz coil. The sine galvanometer is such a device (Fig. 24.5). The Carnegie Institution of Washington uses this instrument in its magnetic observatories to measure the horizontal component of the earth's field. A Helmholz coil is actually two coils of the same size in parallel planes separated a distance R equal to their radii. With the same current i flowing in each, the field near the center of the system is

$$H = \frac{64\pi Ni}{(5)^{1/2}R} \tag{24.6}$$

where H is in gammas, i is in milliamperes, R is in centimeters, and N is the number of turns in each of the coils.[1] With the use of such a coil the field can be determined as accurately as R and i can be measured.

FIG. 24.6 Schmidt vertical component magnetometer in use.

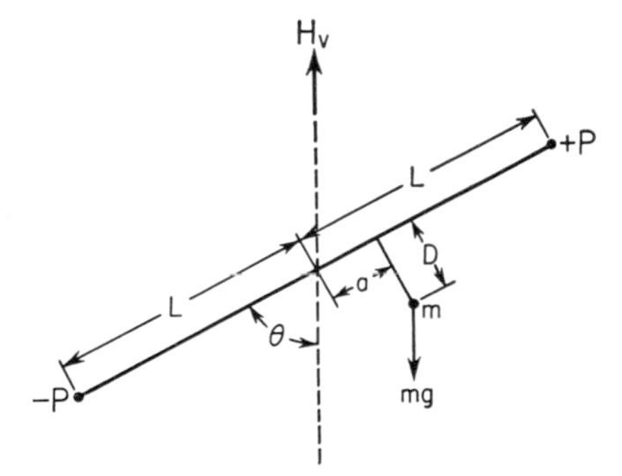

FIG. 24.7 Principle of Schmidt magnetometer.

Sensitive instruments can also be made by comparing the magnetic field with the gravitational attraction. The commonest instrument of this type is the Schmidt balance. Figures 24.6 and 24.7 illustrate one of these instruments designed to measure the vertical component of the magnetic field. The magnetic element is allowed to rotate in the vertical plane at right angles to the horizontal component of the earth's field. A small mass m is offset from the center of the magnet, so that as the magnet

[1] The field for each coil is (Harnwell, 1938, p. 288)

$$H_i = \frac{NiR^2}{2\left(R^2 + \frac{R^2}{4}\right)^{3/2}} \qquad i \text{ in amperes, } R \text{ in meters, } H_i \text{ in ampere turns/meter}$$

$$= \frac{16\pi Ni \times 10^{-3}}{(5)^{3/2}R} \qquad i \text{ in amperes, } R \text{ in meters, } H_i \text{ in oersteds}$$

$$= \frac{32\pi Ni}{(5)^{1/2}R} \qquad i \text{ in milliamperes, } R \text{ in centimeters, } H_i \text{ in gammas}$$

is drawn toward the vertical position, the gravitational torque on this mass opposes the rotation of the system. Balance is achieved when

$$2LPH_v \sin \theta = mg(a \sin \theta + D \cos \theta) \tag{24.7}$$

Solving for the field one gets

$$H_v = \frac{mg}{2LP}(a + D \cot \theta) \tag{24.8}$$

θ is measured by noting the shift of a scale reflected by a mirror mounted on the magnet. The instrument is generally used to compare the magnetic field at two different places, not to make an absolute measurement of H_v. For this purpose, the sensitivity can be expressed as

$$\frac{dH_v}{d\theta} = -\frac{mgD}{2LP \sin^2 \theta} \tag{24.9}$$

If a is of such length that θ is close to 90°, so that $\sin \theta \approx 1$, then dH_v is proportional to $d\theta$. In use, an auxiliary magnet is mounted below the balance in such fashion that enough of the earth's field is balanced out to make the beam sit nearly horizontally. The sensitivity can also be adjusted by changing the length D. The smaller D is, the greater $d\theta$ is for a given change in H_v. The sensitivity is determined by calibrating the instrument in known fields. Magnetic measurements can be made with such an instrument to a precision of about ±2 gammas.

24.4 Earth Inductors. Another means of measuring magnetic fields is to determine their effect on a rotating coil of wire. If a coil of wire is rotated through 180° about an axis in the plane of the coil, a transient voltage will be generated across the coil. If a galvanometer is connected to the coil, a pulse of current i will flow through it, causing it to deflect. The equation for the generated voltage in this case is

$$L_e \frac{di}{dt} + R_e i = -\frac{d\phi}{dt} \tag{24.10}$$

where L_e is the inductance of the system, R_e is its resistance, and ϕ is the flux being cut by the coil. By integrating Eq. (24.10) over the time required to turn the coil through 180°, the following relation is obtained:

$$R_e q = -\phi = -NAB \tag{24.11}$$

where q is the total charge in coulombs which has flowed, N is the number of turns of the coil, A is its area, and B is the magnetic induction in webers per square meter. The first term of Eq. (24.10) makes no contribution, since no current flows before or after the rotation. The charge q can be measured with a ballistic galvanometer or a fluxmeter.

If instead of turning the coil through only 180° it is rotated at a constant rate and the output rectified by properly spaced brushes, the average value of voltage generated can be measured to determine the flux using the equations

$$E = -\frac{d\phi}{dt} = -\frac{d}{dt}(N\phi_m \cos\theta)$$

$$= N\phi_m \sin\theta \frac{d\theta}{dt} = 2\pi f N\phi_m \sin\theta \qquad (24.12)$$

$$E_{av} = \frac{1}{\pi}\int_{-\pi}^{0} 2\pi f N\phi_m \sin\theta \, dt$$

$$= -4fN\phi_m = -4fNAB \qquad (24.13)$$

where f is the frequency of rotation, E is the instantaneous voltage, and E_{av} is the average rectified voltage. ϕ_m is the maximum flux (in webers) through the coil, encountered when the coil is in the position most nearly at right angles to the field. θ is the angle a perpendicular to the plane of the coil makes with the field at any instant.

A more accurate method is to use the rotating coil as a null indicator. Current through a Helmholz coil surrounding the rotating coil is adjusted to the size exactly necessary to balance out the field being measured. Field strengths can be determined to an accuracy of ¼ to ½ gamma using this system.

A rotating coil can also be used to determine the direction of the earth's field. The voltage generated by such a device is proportional to the sine of the angle between the field being measured and the axis of rotation of the instrument. Hence, when the coil is turned to a position where no voltage is generated, its axis is parallel to the field.

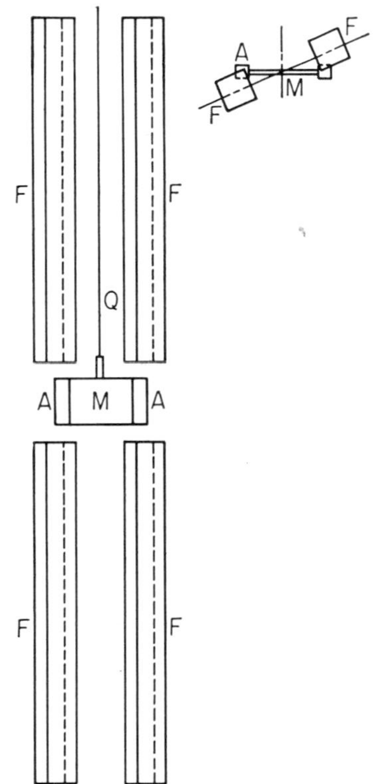

FIG. 24.8 Schematic view of induction variometer. A = armature pieces, F = field pieces, M = mirror, Q = quartz-fiber suspension. (*After Chapman and Bartels, 1940.*)

24.5 Induction Variometer. Another very sensitive instrument is the induction variometer (Fig. 24.8). In this instrument four field pieces of perminvar, an iron-nickel-cobalt alloy of constant permeability and negligible hysteresis loss, are mounted parallel to the field component to be measured. In the gap between the upper and lower pairs of field pieces is an armature with two small perminvar bars suspended by a torsion element so that they are rotated slightly out of alignment with the field pieces. The earth's field magnetizes all six elements. The magnetic torque drawing the armature into the line of the field pieces is balanced against the torque of the suspension, providing a very sensitive measure of the earth's field and one which is easily recorded.

24.6 Flux-gate Magnetometer. Most detailed studies of the magnetic field in local areas are now made with airborne magnetometers. A well-known example is the Gulf airborne magnetometer (Wyckoff, 1948). The essential element of this instrument is a flux gate (Fig. 24.9). This

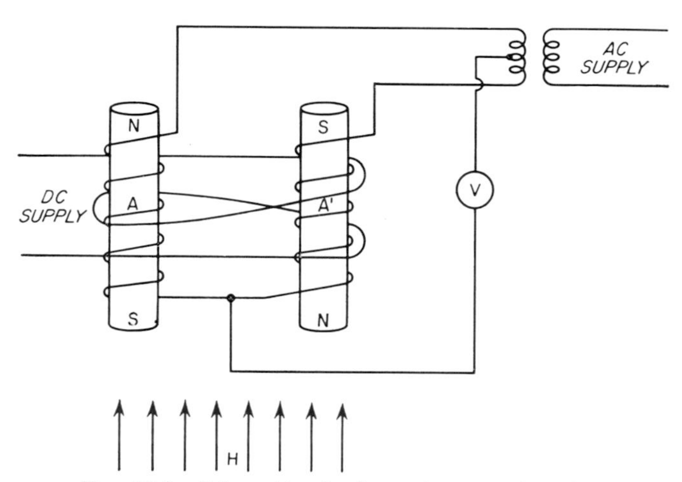

Fig. 24.9 Schematic of a flux-gate magnetometer.

consists of two identical saturable cores of high permeability, oppositely wound with identical coils. An alternating current in these coils magnetizes them first with one polarity, then in the opposite sense. If an additional field is present, such as the earth's field, it will add to the flux in one coil while decreasing that in the other. As a result, the voltage drop across the two coils will differ. The amount of this difference is proportional to the unvarying field, which can thus be measured by noting the average voltage difference between the two halves of the flux gate. This can be done to an accuracy of about ± 1 gamma. In use, a part of the earth's field is balanced out by an additional winding surrounding both cores and carrying direct current.

In airborne use, the recording flux gate is kept aligned with the magnetic field by the use of two additional flux gates. When these are at right angles to the earth's field, they generate no voltage, but if they depart from this position, they can be made to generate voltages which operate motors returning them to proper alignment. In this fashion the recording element is held always parallel to the total field.

24.7 Nuclear Resonance Magnetometer. Another method of measuring the strength of the earth's field depends on the magnetic moment of the atom (Waters and Phillips, 1956). Hydrogen atoms are generally used. The atoms can be in a compound such as water. Each hydrogen atom can be looked upon as a tiny electromagnet whose strength and direction are determined by the revolution of the electron of the atom about its nucleus. In a magnetic field, atoms of hydrogen have a tendency to align themselves in opposition to the field. If the direction of the field is suddenly changed, there will be a moment pulling the atoms toward the new direction. But each atom is a midget gyroscope, and instead of shifting directly to the new field direction, it will precess about this direction. The frequency of this precession will be a function only of the strength of the magnetic field.

To measure the strength of the earth's magnetic field, a bottle of water is subjected to a strong magnetic field at right angles to the earth's field. The voltage induced in a coil of wire wrapped around the bottle is observed when the auxiliary field is suddenly removed. This voltage will have a frequency of alternation of the order of 2,000 cycles per sec, its exact value depending on the strength of the earth's field. The time of 2,000 cycles of this voltage can be measured using a 100-kc oscillator and a high-speed counter, giving an accuracy of measurement of 1 part in 10^5, or of the order of $\pm \frac{1}{2}$ gamma.

24.8 Measurement of Variations of the Magnetic Field. Many of the instruments described above can be used to graph changes in the earth's magnetic field by combining them with suitable recording devices. Dip and declination variations are plotted by mounting mirrors on dip needles or compasses and recording the reflection of a light spot on a rotating drum. Instruments such as the sine galvanometer are easily converted into continuously recording devices in the same way.

Separating the effect of a change in direction from a change in field intensity is a problem in recording variations using any of the more effective deflection-type instruments involving a magnetized needle. This can be done by measuring all three components of intensity. Three earth inductors at right angles or three induction variometers can be used for this purpose.

24.9 Susceptibility and Permanent Magnetization. The effect of permanent magnetization cannot be distinguished from the effect of a susceptibility variation for rocks in place in the ground. In the laboratory the two are commonly determined simultaneously by one of several varieties of deflection magnetometer. The sample to be tested is placed in a magnetic field, where it behaves like a small magnet. If paramagnetic or ferromagnetic, it increases the magnetic field in its neighborhood. If diamagnetic, it opposes it.

To determine the susceptibility of an unmagnetized body, it is introduced into a previously measured magnetic field and the change in field strength is measured. The intensity of magnetization I_m is equal to kH [Eq. (22.2)], where k is susceptibility and H the magnetic field. Its equivalent magnetic moment will be I_mV, where V is the volume of the sample, and it will produce a field at a distance R along its axis of[1]

$$\Delta H = \frac{2I_mV}{R^3} = \frac{2kHV}{R^3} \tag{24.14}$$

The effect of permanent magnetization can be distinguished from that of susceptibility by turning the sample through 180°. If ΔH changes, then the change is twice the remanent magnetization, and the true susceptibility effect is the average of the two observations.

24.10 Earth Potentials. Potential differences in the earth are measured by setting two electrodes on the surface of the ground or burying one or both of them in the earth and measuring the potential difference between them with a potentiometer or a galvanometer. A potentiometer is generally used, as the current drawn by a galvanometer tends to increase the polarization which occurs at the electrodes even under the best of circumstances. For observatory work and in measuring the natural potentials in wells[2] recording potentiometers are commonly used. These have the advantage that they make a continuous record of voltage. The potentiometer is kept balanced by amplifying any unbalanced voltage and using it to drive a motor which moves the potentiometer toward the balanced setting.

The type of electrode used is important and varies with the purpose of the measurement. Surface surveys of natural potential generally use copper contacts set in a porous cup containing copper sulfate. This results in low contact resistance and minimum polarization at the electrode surface, which is desirable for accurate measurements. Contact potentials cannot be distinguished from earth potentials and hence must be kept to a minimum. Contact resistance interferes with measurements by providing a series resistance in the case of galvanometric recording, and by making it difficult to find and to maintain an accurate balance in the case of potentiometer recording.

In observatory work and in well logging, lead electrodes are commonly

[1] This is derived in the same manner as Eq. (24.5). The coefficient of cot θ in (24.5) reduces to $4aP/R^3$ when R greatly exceeds a. The magnetic moment I_mV is equal to $2aP$.

[2] Natural earth potentials are usually called S.P., which is short for self-potential or spontaneous polarization.

used. In the latter use it is generally not hard to get low contact resistance because the electrodes are normally immersed in salt water in the well bore. A good type of permanent observatory electrode is provided by 75 to 100 ft of lead wire in the form of a grid buried in the ground. This should be in moist soil such as clay to ensure low contact resistance. Porous-pot electrodes are undesirable for this type of application because of the extra work of keeping them filled with copper sulfate and because some of the solution gradually diffuses into the ground and causes a drift in the observed earth potential.

The connection from recorder to electrode is usually made with copper wire. The only problem here is to provide good insulation. Great care must be taken with this in permanent installations where much of the cable may be underground and pairs of electrodes may be as much as 100 km or more apart. Underground lines are better than above-surface ones because they are less subject to inductive disturbances, which are common particularly during atmospheric storms. However, they are more work to install and to maintain in proper operating condition.

24.11 Resistivity Measurements. The electrical resistance of a rock can be measured by noting the voltage required to force a measured current through it. To avoid the interference of contact potentials, low-frequency alternating current is generally used. In measuring the resistance of specimens in the laboratory, special precautions must be taken to be sure that the distribution of moisture in the sample is uniform and typical of the rock in place, or the resistivities measured will have little or no significance (Holmes, 1954*a*, 1954*b*). Porous-pot or metal electrodes are employed. In the majority of cases, most of the conduction is through the moisture in the rock.

In the field, if only two electrodes are used, the rock in the immediate vicinity of the electrode, where the current is concentrated, provides a greater part of the resistance measured than does the surrounding rock. Therefore, local inhomogeneities have a large effect on the measured value of resistivity. Because of this, it is common practice to use four electrodes (Fig. 24.10). The outer two of these introduce the current into the ground. Voltage is measured between the inner two. If the electrodes are equally spaced, this is called a Wenner configuration. The potential drop measured is that between the two equipotential surfaces on which the inner electrodes lie. This is equivalent, in effect, to increasing the area of the current electrodes to that of the equipotential surfaces. In this way the effect of contact resistancc is largely eliminated. The volume whose resistance is measured is indicated by shading in Fig. 24.10.

If the ground is electrically homogeneous and isotropic, resistivity can easily be calculated from the electrode spacing and the observed current and voltage. The resistance between two closely spaced concentric hemispherical shells of radius r a distance Δr apart in material of resistivity ρ_e is

$$\Delta R_e = \frac{\rho_e \Delta r}{2\pi r^2} \tag{24.15}$$

The potential drop between two such spheres with a current i flowing radially between them is

$$\Delta E = i\,\Delta R_e = \frac{i\rho_e\,\Delta r}{2\pi r^2} \tag{24.16}$$

The potential of a point on such a hemispherical surface of radius r with respect to infinity is

$$E_i = \int_{r_1}^{\infty} \frac{i\rho_e\,dr}{2\pi r^2} = \frac{i\rho_e}{2\pi}\left(-\frac{1}{r}\right)_{r_1}^{\infty} = \frac{i\rho_e}{2\pi r_1} \tag{24.17}$$

If, instead of flowing radially to infinity, the current converges to a second electrode at a distance r_2 from the point under consideration, then

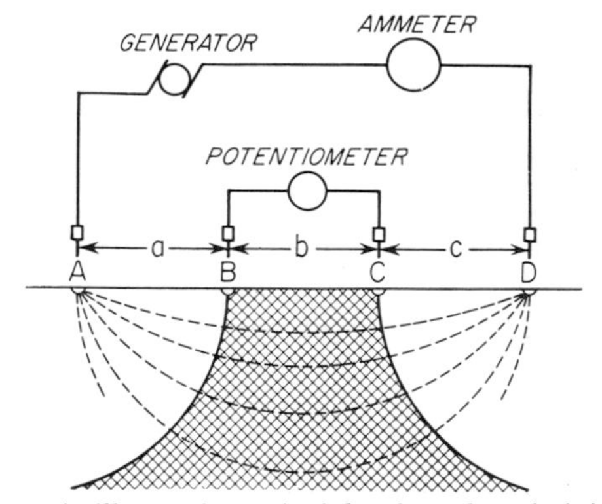

FIG. 24.10 Schematic illustrating principle of earth-resistivity measurement.

the potential at the point will be the sum of the two potentials which would exist, one for an isolated source $(+\,i)$ and the other for an isolated sink $(-\,i)$:

$$E_p = \frac{i\rho_e}{2\pi r_1} + \frac{(-i)\rho_e}{2\pi r_2} \tag{24.18}$$

If the geometry is as shown in Fig. 24.10, the voltages at B and C will be

$$E_B = \frac{i\rho_e}{2\pi}\left(\frac{1}{a} - \frac{1}{b+c}\right) \tag{24.19}$$

$$E_C = \frac{i\rho_e}{2\pi}\left(\frac{1}{a+b} - \frac{1}{c}\right) \tag{24.20}$$

The voltage measured is

$$E = E_B - E_C = \frac{i\rho_e}{2\pi}\left(\frac{1}{a} - \frac{1}{b+c} - \frac{1}{a+b} + \frac{1}{c}\right) \tag{24.21}$$

If a, b, and c are equal, the Wenner configuration, this becomes

$$E = \frac{i\rho_e}{2\pi a} \tag{24.22}$$

from which relationship ρ_e is easily calculated. Where the ground is not homogeneous, the resistivity calculated from Eq. (24.22) is a weighted average of the resistivities of the formations present.

24.12 Ionosphere Height Measurements. To measure the height of the ionized conducting layers in the earth's atmosphere, pulses of radio waves are directed vertically upward and the time is measured at which an echo returns. The waves travel over most of their path at the velocity of light, 3×10^{10} cm per sec, though they are slowed down slightly in passing through the conductive layers. Thus each microsecond delay in the time of the echo corresponds to a height of 0.15 km.

The height from which a reflection is returned depends on the frequency of the waves and the ion density in the air. Complete reflection occurs when the refractive index n is zero. From Snell's law,

$$n = \frac{V_1}{V_2} = \frac{\sin i_1}{\sin i_2} \tag{24.23}$$

where i_2 is the angle of refraction in the second medium, i_1 is the angle of incidence in the first medium, and V_1 and V_2 are the apparent phase velocities. (Note that these are not the group velocities, which never exceed the velocity of light in a vacuum.) If n is zero, this is equivalent to $\sin i_2$ being infinitely large regardless of what i_1 is, which requires complete reflection. Refractive index and ion density are related by the equation (Berkner, 1939, p. 444)

$$n = \left(1 - \frac{q^2 N}{\pi m f^2}\right)^{1/2} \tag{24.24}$$

where N is the number of charged particles of charge q in electrostatic units and mass m per unit volume and f is the frequency in cycles per second. The ion density necessary for reflection in equivalent numbers of electrons per cubic centimeter for $N = 0$ is $12{,}400 f^2_{\text{Mc}}$, where f_{Mc} is frequency in megacycles. If the charges are not electrons, as will be the case for some of them, then N will have to be larger to make the refractive index zero at a given frequency. The relationship is probably more nearly (Berkner, 1939, p. 445)

$$N = 1.86 \times 10^4 f^2_{\text{Mc}} \tag{24.25}$$

As a result of this relationship between N and f, successively higher frequencies are reflected by each of the different ionized layers of the atmosphere.

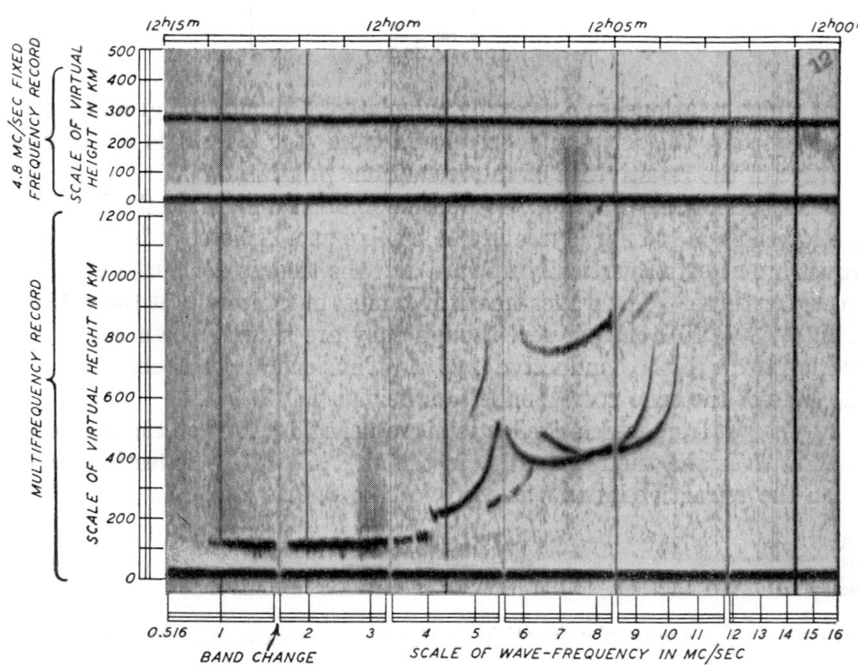

FIG. 24.11 Typical example of summertime record of ionosphere reflections near noon at middle latitudes: Watheroo, Australia, Nov. 26, 1939. (*Courtesy of Carnegie Institution of Washington.*)

The Carnegie Institution of Washington has developed apparatus for automatically recording radio reflections. One-hundred-microsecond pulses of successively greater frequency are transmitted several times per second, and the echoes recorded graphically as shown in Fig. 24.11. The frequency spectrum from 0.156 to 16 megacycles per sec is covered.

REFERENCES

Adams, J. A. S.
1954 Uranium and thorium contents of volcanic rocks: Nuclear Geology, pp. 89–98, Wiley

Ahrens, L. H.
1955 Oldest rocks exposed: Geol. Soc. Am. Spec. Paper 62, pp. 155–168
1956 Radioactive methods for determining geologic age: Chemistry and Physics of the Earth, vol. I, pp. 44–67, McGraw-Hill

Airy, G. B.
1855 On the computation of the effect of the attraction of mountain-masses, as disturbing the apparent astronomical latitude of stations in geodetic surveys: Phil. Trans. Roy. Soc. London 145:101–104

Aldrich, L. T.; G. W. Wetherill; G. R. Tilton; G. L. Davis
1956*a* Half-life of Rb87: Phys. Rev. 103:1045–1047

———; ———; ———; ———; P. M. Jeffrey
1956*b* Evaluation of mineral age measurements: Proc. 2d Conf. on Nuclear Processes in Geologic Settings: Natl. Acad. Sci.–Natl. Research Council Pub. 400:147–150

Anderson, J. A.; H. O. Wood
1925 Description and theory of the torsion seismometer: Bull. Seis. Soc. Am. 25:1–72

Arctowski, H.
1925 Geothermic researches made at Boryslaw: Geograph. Journal 66:422–427

Baldwin, R. B.
1949 The Face of the Moon: University of Chicago Press

Balsley, J. R.
1954 Discussion of paper by Runcorn (1954): The earth's core: Trans. Am. Geophys. Union 35:78

Barrell, J.
1925 The spheres of the earth and their effect on the lithosphere: Am. Jour. Sci. 210:499–529

Bauer, L. A.
1902 Magnetic declination tables and isogonic charts for 1902: U.S. Coast and and Geodetic Survey

Benioff, H.
1935 A linear strain seismograph: Bull. Seis. Soc. Am. 25:283–309
1949 Seismic evidence for the fault origin of oceanic deeps: Bull. Geol. Soc. Am. 60:1837–1856
1951 Global strain accumulation and release as revealed by great earthquakes: Bull. Geol. Soc. Am. 62:331–338
1954 Orogenesis and deep crustal structure—additional evidence from seismology: Bull. Geol. Soc. Am. 65:385–400
1955 Seismic evidence for crustal structure and tectonic activity: Geol. Soc. Am. Spec. Paper 62, pp. 61–74

1957 Tectonics of the Pacific continental margins: Unpublished paper presented before the annual meeting of the American Geophysical Union

———; B. Gutenberg

1951 Strain characteristics of the earth's interior: Chap. 15 of Internal Constitution of the Earth, 2d ed., Dover

———; ———; C.F. Richter

1953 Progress report, Seismological Laboratory, California Institute of Technology, 1952: Trans. Am. Geophys. Union 34:785–791

1954 Progress report, Seismological Laboratory, California Institute of Technology, 1953: Trans. Am. Geophys. Union 35:979–987

Bentley, C. R.; J. L. Worzel

1956 Geophysical investigations of the emerged and submerged Atlantic coastal plain, part X: Continental slope and continental rise south of the Grand Banks: Bull. Geol. Soc. Am. 67:1–18

Berckhemer, H.

1956 Rayleigh-wave dispersion and crustal structure in the East Atlantic Ocean: Bull. Seis. Soc. Am. 46:83–86

Berkner, L. V.

1939 Radio exploration of the earth's outer atmosphere: Chap. 9 of Terrestrial Magnetism and Electricity, McGraw-Hill

Birch, F.

1942 Thermal conductivity and diffusivity: Geol. Soc. Am. Spec. Paper 36, pp. 243–266

1952 Elasticity and constitution of the earth's interior: Jour. Geophys. Research 57:227–286

1954*a* Heat from radioactivity: Chap. 5 of Nuclear Geology, Wiley

1954*b* The present state of geothermal investigations: Geophysics 19:645–659

1955 Physics of the crust: Geol. Soc. Am. Spec. Paper 62, pp. 101–118

———; J. F. Shairer; H. C. Spicer

1942 Handbook of Physical Constants: Geol. Soc. Am. Spec. Paper 36

Blackett, P. M. S.

1956 Lectures on Rock Magnetism: Weizmann Science Press of Israel

Bowie, W.

1917 Investigations of gravity and isostasy: U.S. Coast and Geodetic Survey Pub. 40

1924 Isostatic investigations and data for gravity stations in the United States established since 1915: U.S. Coast and Geodetic Survey Pub. 99

1927 Isostasy: Dutton

Bucher, W. H.

1955 Deformation in orogenic belts: Geol. Soc. Am. Spec. Paper 62, pp. 343–368

Bullard, E.

1954 The interior of the earth: Part 3 of The Earth as a Planet, University of of Chicago Press

Bullen, K. E.

1947 An Introduction to the Theory of Seismology: Cambridge

1950 Theoretical travel-times of *S* waves in the earth's inner core: Monthly Notices Roy. Astron. Soc. Geophys. Suppl. 6, pp. 125–128

Byerly, P.

1955 Nature of faulting as deduced from seismograms: Geol. Soc. Am. Spec. Paper 62, pp. 75–86

Byrd, R. E.

1947 Our navy explores Antarctica: Natl. Geographic 92:429–522

Cancani, A.
1904 Sur l'emploi d'une double échelle sismique des intensités, empirique et absolue: Gerlands Beitr. Geophys. Verh. 2d Intern. Seis. Konf. II:281–283 (in French)

Cecchini, G.
1954 Relazione sull 'attivita' del servizio internationale delle latitudine dal 1952.0 al 1954.5: paper presented at International Union of Geodetics and Geophysics meetings in Rome (in Italian)

Chamberlin, R. T.
1928 Some of the objections to Wegener's theory: Am. Assoc. Petrol. Geologists Symposium on Theory of Continental Drift, pp. 83–87

Chapman, S.
1951 The Earth's Magnetism, 2d ed: Methuen

———; J. Bartels
1940 Geomagnetism: Oxford

Chubb, L. J.
1934 The structure of the Pacific basin: Geol. Mag. 71:289–302

Clark, D.
1951 Iceland tapestry: Natl. Geographic 100:599–630

Clark, J. S.
1940 An absolute determination of the acceleration of gravity: Phil. Trans. Roy. Soc. London A238:65–123

Clark, S. P., Jr.
1956 Radiative transfer and the temperature in the mantle (abstr.): Program of the 1956 annual meeting of the Geological Society of America, p. 35

Clarke, F. W.; H. S. Washington
1924 The composition of the earth's crust: U.S. Geol. Survey Profess. Paper 127

Cleland, R. H.
1933 Rock temperatures and some ventilation conditions in the mines of northern Ontario: Can. Mining Met. Bull. 36(256):379–407

Cooper, R. I. B.
1952 The distribution of radioactivity: Nature 169:350–352

Coster, H. P.
1947 Terrestrial heat flow in Persia: Monthly Notices Roy. Astron. Soc. Geophys. Suppl. 5, pp. 131–145

Crandell, F. J.
1949 Ground vibrations due to blasting and its effect upon structures: Jour. Boston Soc. Civil Engrs. 36:222–245

Daly, R. A.
1926 Our Mobile Earth: Scribner
1933 Igneous Rocks and the Depths of the Earth: McGraw-Hill
1938 Architecture of the Earth: Appleton-Century-Crofts
1940 Strength and Structure of the Earth: Prentice-Hall

Dane, E. B., Jr.
1942 Density at high temperature; thermal expansion: Geol. Soc. Am. Spec. Paper 36, pp. 27–37

Darling, F. W.; W. D. Lambert
1951 Density, gravity, pressure and ellipticity in the interior of the earth: Chap. 13 of Internal Constitution of the Earth, 2d ed., Dover

Davies, W. E.
1956 Antarctic stratigraphy and structure: Am. Geophys. Union Monograph 1, pp. 44–51

Davis, G. L.
1950 Radium content of ultramafic igneous rocks: Part III, Meteorites: Am. Jour. Sci. 248:107–111
———; L. T. Aldrich
1953 Determination of the age of lepidolites by the method of isotope dilution: Bull. Geol. Soc. Am. 64:379–380
Davison, C.
1927 Founders of Seismology: Cambridge
1936 Great Earthquakes: Thomas Murby
Deel, S. A.; H. H. Howe
1948 United States magnetic tables and magnetic charts for 1945: U.S. Coast and Geodetic Survey Bull. 667
De Golyer, E.
1918 The significance of certain Mexican oil field temperatures: Econ. Geol. 13:275–301
Dobrin, M.
1952 Introduction to Geophysical Prospecting: McGraw-Hill
Dole, R. B.; H. Stabler
1909 Denudation: U.S. Coast and Geodetic Survey Water Supply Paper 234, pp. 78–93
Duerksen, J. S.
1949 Pendulum gravity data in the United States: U.S. Coast and Geodetic Survey Spec. Pub. 244
Dutton, C. E.
1889 The Charleston earthquake: 9th Ann. Rept. Dir. U.S. Geol. Survey, pp. 203–528
Elkins, T. A.
1942 Test of a quantitative mountain building theory by Appalachian structural dimensions: Geophysics 7:45–60
Epstein, P. S.
1921 Uber die Polflucht der Kontinente: Naturwissenschaften 9:499–502 (in German)
Evans, R. D.; C. Goodman; N. B. Keevil
1942 Radioactivity: the earth's heat and geological age measurements: Geol. Soc. Am. Spec. Paper 36, pp. 267–277
Ewing, M.; W. S. Jardetzky; F. Press
1957 Elastic Waves in Layered Media: McGraw-Hill
———; F. Press
1950 Crustal structure and surface wave dispersion: Bull. Seis. Soc. Am. 40: 271–280
1955 Geophysical contrasts between continents and ocean basins: Geol. Soc. Am. Spec. Paper 62, pp. 1–6
———; G. H. Sutton; C. B. Officer
1954 Seismic refraction measurements in the Atlantic Ocean, part VI: Typical deep stations, North American basin: Bull. Seis. Soc. Am. 44:21–38
———; J. C. Worzel
1948 Long range sound transmission: Geol. Soc. Am. Mem. 27, part III
1954 Gravity anomalies and structure of the West Indies: Bull. Geol. Soc. Am. 65:165–174, 195–200
———; ———; D. B. Ericson; B. C. Heezen
1955 Geophysical and geological investigations in the Gulf of Mexico, part I: Geophysics 20:1–18

———; ———; J. B. Hersey; F. Press; G. R. Hamilton
1950 Seismic refraction measurements in the Atlantic Ocean basin: Bull. Seis. Soc. Am. 40:233–242

———; ———; N. C. Steenland; F. Press
1950 Geophysical investigations of the emerged and submerged Atlantic coastal plain, part V: Woods Hole, New York, and Cape May sections: Bull. Geol. Soc. Am. 61:877–892

Faul, H. (ed.)
1954 Nuclear Geology: Wiley

Finch, V. C.; G. T. Trewartha; A. H. Robinson; E. H. Hammond
1957 Elements of Geography, 4th ed.: McGraw-Hill

Fleming, J. A. (ed.)
1939 The earth's magnetism and magnetic surveys: Physics of the Earth, vol. VII, Terrestrial Magnetism and Electricity, pp. 1–58, McGraw-Hill

Foley, A. L.; W. H. Souder
1912 A new method of photographing sound waves: Phys. Rev. 35:373–386

Folinsbee, R. E.; J. Lipson; J. H. Reynolds
1956 Potassium-argon dating: Geochim. et Cosmochim. Acta 10:60–68

Freeman, J. R.
1932 Earthquake Damage and Earthquake Insurance: McGraw-Hill

Fu, C. Y.
1947 Propagation of elastic waves in the neighborhood of a free boundary: Geophysics 12:57–71

Gamow, G.
1951 Origin and evolution of the universe: Am. Scientist 39:393–406

Gilluly, J.
1949 Distribution of mountain building in geologic time: Bull. Geol. Soc. Am. 60:561–590

Gish, O. H.
1939 Atmospheric electricity: Chap. 4 of Terrestrial Magnetism and Electricity, McGraw-Hill

Graham, J. W.
1954 Discussion of paper by Runcorn (1954): Trans. Am. Geophys. Union 35:75–77

Gregory, J. W.
1899 The plan of the earth and its causes: Geograph. Journal 13:225–251
1920 The African rift valleys: Geograph. Journal 56:13–47
1928 Wegener's hypothesis: Am. Assoc. Petrol. Geologists Symposium on Theory of Continental Drift, pp. 93–96

Griggs, D.
1939*a* Creep of rocks: Jour. Geol. 47:225–251
1939*b* A theory of mountain building: Am. Jour. Sci. 237:611–650
1940 Experimental flow of rocks under conditions favoring recrystallization: Bull. Geol. Soc. Am. 51:1001–1022
1942 Strength and plasticity: Geol. Soc. Am. Spec. Paper 36, pp. 107–130

Grout, F. F.
1932 Petrography and Petrology: McGraw-Hill

Gutenberg, B.
1932 Beobachtungen von Erdbebenwellen: Handbuch der Geophysik, vol. 4, pp. 151–263, Borntraeger (in German)
1941*a* Mechanism of faulting in southern California: Bull. Seis. Soc. Am. 31: 263–302

1941*b* Seismology: Geol. Soc. Am. 50th Anniversary Vol., pp. 437–470
1943 Seismological evidence for roots of mountains: Bull. Geol. Soc. Am. 54: 473–498
1944 Energy ratio of reflected and refracted seismic waves: Bull. Seis. Soc. Am. 34:85–102
1951*a* The cooling of the earth and the temperature of its interior: Chap. 8 of Internal Constitution of the Earth, 2d ed., Dover
1951*b* Crustal layers of the continents and oceans: Bull. Geol. Soc. Am. 62:427–440
1951*c* Forces in the earth: Chap. 8 of Internal Constitution of the Earth, 2d ed., Dover
1951*d* Frequently used constants: Appendix of Internal Constitution of the Earth, 2d ed., Dover
1951*e* Hypotheses on the development of the earth: Chap. 9 of Internal Constitution of the Earth, 2d ed., Dover
1952 Waves from blasts recorded in southern California: Trans. Am. Geophys. Union 33:427–431
1954 Postglacial uplift in the Great Lakes region: Arch. Meteorol., Geophys. Bioklimatol. A7:243–251
1955 Wave velocities in the earth's crust: Geol. Soc. Am. Spec. Paper 62, pp. 19–34
1956*a* Great earthquakes 1896–1903: Trans. Am. Geophys. Union 37:608–614
1956*b* The energy of earthquakes: Quart. Jour. Geol. Soc. London 112:1–14

———; J. P. Buwalda
1936 Seismic reflection profile across Los Angeles Basin (abstr.): Proc. Geol. Soc. Am. 1935:327–328

———; C. F. Richter
1936*a* Materials for the study of deep focus earthquakes: Bull. Seis. Soc. Am. 26:341–390
1936*b* On seismic waves (3d paper): Gerlands Beitr. Geophys. 47:73–131
1941 Seismicity of the earth: Geol. Soc. Am. Spec. Paper 34 (see also 1949, 1954)
1942 Earthquake magnitude, intensity, energy and acceleration: Bull. Seis. Soc. Am. 32:163–191
1946 Seismic waves from atomic bomb tests: Trans. Am. Geophys. Union 27:776
1949 Seismicity of the Earth and Associated Phenomena: Princeton University Press (see also 1954)
1954 Seismicity of the Earth and Associated Phenomena, 2d ed.: Princeton University Press
1955 Magnitude and energy of earthquakes: Nature 176:795
1956*a* Earthquake magnitude, intensity, energy, and acceleration, (2d paper): Bull. Seis. Soc. Am. 46:105–145
1956*b* Magnitude and energy of earthquakes: Ann. Geofis. Rome 9:1–15

Hammer, S.
1938 Investigation of the vertical gradient of gravity: Trans. Am. Geophys. Union 19:72–82
1943 Note on the variation from equator to pole of the earth's gravity: Geophysics 8:57–60

Harnwell, G. P.
1949 Principles of Electricity and Electromagnetism, 2d ed.: McGraw-Hill

Hayford, J. F.; W. Bowie
1912 The effect of topography and isostatic compensation upon the intensity of gravity: U.S. Coast and Geodetic Survey Spec. Pub. 10

Heck, N. H.
1936 Earthquakes: Princeton University Press
Heiland, C. A.
1940 Geophysical Exploration: Prentice-Hall
Heiskanen, W. A.
1933 Die Erdkrustendicke und die Schweranomalien in dem vereinigten Staaten: Ann. Acad. Sci. Fennicae A36(3)
1938 Investigations on the gravity formula: Isostatic Inst. Intern. Assoc. Geodesy Pub. 1
———; F. A. Vening Meinesz
1958 The Earth and Its Gravity Field: McGraw-Hill
Henrich, F.
1904 Underground temperatures in the Paruschowitz No. 5 boring, Germany (abstr.): Trans. Inst. Mining Engrs. 27:592–593
Hess, H. H.
1938 Gravity anomalies and island arc structure with particular reference to the West Indies: Proc. Am. Phil. Soc. 79:71–96
1955 Serpentines, orogeny, and epeirogeny: Geol. Soc. Am. Spec. Paper 62, pp. 391–408
Heyl, P. R.; P. Chrzanowski
1942 A new determination of the constant of gravitation: Jour. Research Natl. Bur. Standards 29:1–31
Hill, M. L.; T. W. Diblee, Jr.
1953 San Andreas, Garlock, and Big Pine faults, California: Bull. Geol. Soc. Am. 64:443–458
Hobbs, W. H.
1910 The earthquake of 1872 in the Owens Valley, California: Gerlands Beitr. Geophys. 10:352–385
Hodgman, C. D., and associates
1953 Handbook of Chemistry and Physics: Chemical Rubber Publishing Co.
Hodgson, J. H.
1957 The nature of faulting in large earthquakes: Bull. Geol. Soc. Am. 68:611–644
Hollander, J. M.; I. Perlman; G. T. Seaborg
1953 Table of isotopes: Rev. Mod. Phys. 25:469–651
Holmes, A.
1947 The construction of a geologic time scale: Trans. Geol. Soc. Glasgow 21: 117–152
Holmes, C. R.
1954*a* Progress in electric logging research at the Penna. State University during 1952–1953: Producers Monthly 18(3):33–38
1954*b* Some factors relating to the measurement of the electrical properties of porous sandstones: Producers Monthly 19(1):21–27
Houston, W. V.
1948 Principles of Mathematical Physics, 2d ed.: McGraw-Hill
Howe, H. H.; D. G. Knapp
1938 United States magnetic tables and magnetic charts for 1935: U.S. Coast and Geodetic Survey Bull. 602
Howell, B. F., Jr.
1949 Ground vibrations near explosions: Bull. Seis. Soc. Am. 39:285–310

1953 Electrical conduction in fluid saturated rocks: World Oil 136:113–116, 142–146

———; D. Budenstein

1955 Energy distribution in explosion-generated seismic pulses: Geophysics 20:33–52

———; E. K. Kaukonen

1954 Attenuation of seismic waves near an explosion: Bull. Seis. Soc. Am. 44: 481–491

Howell, J. V.

1957 Glossary of geology and related sciences: Natl. Acad. Sci.–Natl. Research Council Pub. 501

Hoyle, F.

1950 The Nature of the Universe: Harper

Hubbert, M. K.

1937 Theory of scale models as applied to the study of geologic structures: Bull. Geol. Soc. Am. 48:1459–1520

Imamura, A.

1937 Theoretical and Applied Seismology: Mazuren, Tokyo

Jahns, R. H.

1948 Discussions of origin of granite by Read, Buddington, Grout, Goodspeed and Bowen: Geol. Soc. Am. Mem. 28, pp. 91–96

Jakosky, J. J.

1940 Exploration Geophysics: Trija

———; C. H. Wilson; J. W. Daly

1932 Geophysical examination of Meteor Crater, Arizona: Trans. Am. Inst. Mining Met. Engrs. Geophys. Prosp., pp. 63–98

Jeffery, P. M.

1956 The radioactive age of four Western Australian pegmatites by the potassium and rubidium methods: Geochim. et Cosmochim. Acta 10:191–195

Jeffreys, H.

1929 The Earth, 2d ed.: Cambridge (see also 1952)

1939 The origin of the solar system: Chap. 2 of Internal Constitution of the Earth, McGraw-Hill (see also 1951)

1951 The origin of the solar system: Chap. 2 of Internal Constitution of the Earth, 2d ed., Dover

1952 The Earth, 3d ed.: Cambridge

Johnson, H. F.; J. A. Fleming; H. E. McComb

1939 Magnetic instruments: Chap. 2 of Terrestrial Magnetism and Electricity, McGraw-Hill

Joly, J.

1925 The Surface History of the Earth: Oxford

1928 The theory of thermal cycles: Gerlands Beitr. Geophys. 19:415–441

Kelly, A. O.; F. Dachille

1953 Target Earth: published by the authors

Kessler, D. W.; H. Insley; W. H. Sligh

1940 Physical, mineralogical, and durability studies on the building and monumental granites of the United States: Jour. Research Natl. Bur. Standards 25:161–206

King, P. B.

1951 The Tectonics of Middle North America: Princeton University Press

Knopf, A.

1931 Physics of the Earth, vol. IV, Age of the earth: National Research Council

Knopoff, L.
1955 Small three-dimensional seismic models: Trans. Am. Geophys. Union 36:1029–1034

Knowlton, A. E.
1957 Standard Handbook for Electrical Engineers, 9th ed.: McGraw-Hill

Koch, T. W.
1933 Analysis and effects of current movement on an active fault in Buena Vista Hills oil field: Bull. Am. Assoc. Petrol. Geologists 17:694–712

Köppen, W.; A. Wegener
1924 Die Klimate der Geologischen Vorzeit: Borntraeger (in German)

Kossinna, E.
1921 Die Tiefen des Weltmeeres: Veröffentl. Inst. Meereskunde Univ. Berlin, Neue Folge A, Geogr.-naturwiss. 9:1–70 (in German)

Krige, L. J.
1948 Borehole temperatures in the Transvaal and Orange Free State II: Union S. Africa Dept. Mines Geol. Survey Ser. Bull. 18

Krogdahl, W. S.
1952 The Astronomical Universe: Macmillan

Kuenen, P. H.
1937 The negative isostatic anomalies of the East Indies (with experiments): Leidsche Geol. Mededeel. 8:169–214
1950 Marine Geology: Wiley

Kuiper, G. P.
1951 On the origin of the solar system: Chap. 8 of Astrophysics, McGraw-Hill

Kulp, J. L.
1955 Isotope dating and the geologic time scale: Geol. Soc. Am. Spec. Paper 62, pp. 609–630

Lamb, H.
1904 On the propagation of tremors over the surface of an elastic solid: Phil. Trans. Roy. Soc. London 20:1–42

Lambert, W. D.
1921 Some mechanical curiosities connected with the earth's field of force: Am. Jour. Sci., Ser. 5, 2:129–158
1922 An investigation of the latitude at Ukiah, Calif., and of the motion of the pole: U. S. Coast and Geodetic Survey Spec. Pub. 80

———; F. W. Darling
1951 Density, gravity, pressure and ellipticity in the interior of the earth: Chap. 13 of Internal Constitution of the Earth, 2d ed., Dover

———; F. Schlesinger; E. W. Brown
1931 The variation of latitude: Physics of the Earth, vol. II, pp. 245–277, Bull. Natl. Research Council 78

Larsen, E. S., Jr.; G. Phair
1954 The distribution of uranium and thorium in igneous rocks: Nuclear Geology, pp. 75–89, Wiley

Lawson, A. C., et al.
1908 The California Earthquake of April 18, 1906: Carnegie Institution

Leet, L. D.
1939 Ground vibrations near dynamite blasts: Bull. Seis. Soc. Am. 29:487–496
1946 Earth motion from the atom bomb test: Am. Scientist 34:198–211
1948 Causes of Catastrophe: McGraw-Hill
1950 Earth Waves: Harvard University Press

Levorsen, A. I.
1945 Geological map of South America: Geol. Soc. Am. Spec. Paper 59
Lipson, J. I.
1956 K-A dating of sediments: Geochim. et Cosmochim. Acta 10:149–151
Love, A. E. H.
1911 Some Problems of Geodynamics: Cambridge
MacCarthy, G. R.
1928 Experiments in underthrusting: Am. Jour. Sci. 16:51–67
Macelwane, J. B.
1951 Evidence on the interior of the earth derived from seismic sources: Chap. 10 of Internal Constitution of the Earth, 2d ed., Dover
Machado, F.
1954 Earthquake intensity anomalies and magma chambers of Azorean volcanoes: Trans. Am. Geophys. Union 35:833–837
Madill, R. G.
1948 The search for the north magnetic pole: Arctic 1:8–18
Markowitz, W.
1945 Redeterminations of latitude: Trans. Am. Geophys. Union 26:197–199
Marshall, P.
1912 Oceania: Handbuch der Regionalen Geologie VII (2): Carl Winters, Heidelberg
Mason, B.
1952 Principles of Geochemistry: Wiley
McComb, H. E.
1936 Selection installation and operation of seismographs: U.S. Coast and Geodetic Survey Spec. Pub. 206
McCrady, E.
1952 The use of lead isotope ratios in estimating the age of the earth: Trans. Am. Geophys. Union 33:156–170
McNish, A. G.
1939 On causes of the earth's magnetism and its changes: Chap. 7 of Terrestrial Magnetism and Electricity, McGraw-Hill
Menard, H. W.
1955 Deformation of the northeastern Pacific basin and the west coast of North America: Bull. Geol. Soc. Am. 66:1149–1198
Michell, John
1761 Conjectures concerning the cause and observations upon the phenomena of earthquakes: Phil. Trans. Roy. Soc. London 51:566–634. Reprinted 1818, Phil. Mag. 52:186–195, 254–270, 323–340
Nádai, A.
1950 Theory of Flow and Fracture of Solids: McGraw-Hill
National Bureau of Standards
1956 Copper Wire Standards, Circ. 31, 4th ed., GPO
National Geographic Society
1951 World Map, Van der Gritten's Projection, 1:40,000,000
Nettleton, L. L.
1940 Geophysical Prospecting for Oil: McGraw-Hill
Neumann, F.
1938 United States Earthquakes 1938: U.S. Coast and Geodetic Survey Rept. Serial 629
1954 Earthquake Intensity and Related Ground Motion: University of Washington Press

Niskanen, E.
1945 Gravity formulas derived by the aid of level land stations: Isostatic Inst. Intern. Assoc. Geodesy Pub. 14

Obert, L.; W. I. Duvall
1949 A gage and recording equipment for measuring dynamic strain in rock: U.S. Bur. Mines Rept. Invest. 4581

Officer, C. B.
1955 Southwest Pacific crustal structure: Trans. Am. Geophys. Union 36:449–459

———; M. Ewing
1954 Geophysical investigations of the emerged and submerged Atlantic Coastal Plain, part VII: Bull. Geol. Soc. Am. 65:653–670

Oldham, R. D.
1899 Report of the great earthquake of 12th June 1897: Mem. Geol. Survey India, vol. 29

Oliver, J.; F. Press; M. Ewing
1954 Two-dimensional model seismology: Geophysics 19:202–219

Oppenheim, V.
1948 Theory of Andean orogenesis: Am. Jour. Sci. 246:578–590

Patterson, C. C.
1956 Age of meteorites and the earth: Proc. 2d Conf. on Nuclear Processes in Geologic Settings, Natl. Acad. Sci.–Natl. Research Council Pub. 400:157–159

Pekeris, C. L.
1935 Thermal convection in the interior of the earth: Monthly Notices Roy. Astron. Soc. Geophys. Suppl. 3, pp. 343–367

Pettersson, H.
1954 The Ocean Floor: Yale University Press

Poldervaart, A.
1940 Chemistry of the earth's crust: Geol. Soc. Am. Spec. Paper 62, pp. 119–144

Preibsch, J. A.; G. Radinger; P. L. Dymek
1937 Untersuchungen über den Radium-Emanations gehalt der Freiluft in Innsbruck und auf dem Hafelekar: Beitr. Geophys. 50:55–77 (in German)

Press, F.; M. Ewing
1955 Earthquake surface waves and crustal structure: Geol. Soc. Am. Spec. Paper 62, pp. 51–60

Raitt, R. W.
1954 Some results of seismic studies on Capricorn expedition (abstr.): Bull. Geol. Soc. Am. 65:1348

Rankama, K.; T. G. Sahama
1950 Geochemistry: University of Chicago Press

Rayleigh, Lord (R. J. Strutt)
1885 On waves propagated along the plane surface of an elastic solid: Proc. London Math. Soc. 17:4–11; also Collected Works, vol. 2, pp. 441–447

Reid, H. F.
1910 The Mechanics of the Earthquake: vol. 2 of the California Earthquake of April 18, 1906, Carnegie Inst. Wash. Pub. 87

Richter, C. F.
1935 An instrumental earthquake magnitude scale: Bull. Seis. Soc. Am. 25:1–32

Ritsema, A. R.
1957 Pacific and Mediterranean earthquake mechanisms: Trans. Am. Geophys. Union 38:349–353

Rooney, W. J.
1939 Earth currents: Chap. 6 of Terrestrial Magnetism and Electricity, McGraw-Hill

Rothé, J. P.
1951 The structure of the bed of the Atlantic Ocean: Trans. Am. Geophys. Union 32:457–461

Rubey, W. W.
1951 Geologic history of sea water: Bull. Geol. Soc. Am. 62:1111–1147

Runcorn, S. K.
1954 The earth's core: Trans. Am. Geophys. Union 35:49–63

———; A. C. Benson; A. F. Moore; D. H. Griffiths
1951 Measurements of the variation with depth of the main geomagnetic field: Phil. Trans. Roy. Soc. London A244:113–151

Russell, H. N.
1935 The Solar System and Its Origin: Macmillan

Scheidegger, A. E.; J. T. Wilson
1950 An investigation into possible methods of failure of the earth: Proc. Geol. Assoc. Can. 3:167–190

Schuchert, C.
1928 The hypothesis of continental displacement: Am. Assoc. Petrol. Geologists Symposium on Theory of Continental Drift, pp. 104–144

Senftle, F. E.
1956 Half-life of Th 232 and branching ratio of Bi 212: Proc. 2d Conf. Nuclear Processes in Geologic Settings, Natl. Acad. Sci.–Natl. Research Council Pub. 400:187–194

Sezawa, K.; K. Kanai
1935 The M_2 seismic waves: Bull. Earthquake Research Inst. 13:471–475

Shepard, F. P.
1938 Submarine canyons off the California coast: Calif. Jour. Mines Geol. 34: 290–310

Slichter, L. B.
1929 Certain aspects of magnetic surveying: Trans. Am. Inst. Mining Met. Engrs. Geophys. Vol., pp. 238–260
1942 Magnetic properties of rock: Geol. Soc. Am. Spec. Paper 36, pp. 295–298

———; M. Telkes
1942 Electrical properties of rocks and minerals: Geol. Soc. Am. Spec. Paper 36, pp. 299–319

Sohon, F. W.
1932 Introduction to theoretical seismology, part II: Seismometry, Saint Louis University

Spicer, H. C.
1942 Observed temperatures in the earth's crust: Geol. Soc. Am. Spec. Paper 36, pp. 280–292

Stoneley, R.
1924 Elastic waves at the surface of separation of two solids: Proc. Roy. Soc. London A106:416–428
1926 The effect of the ocean on Rayleigh waves: Monthly Notices Roy. Astron. Soc. Geophys. Suppl. 1, pp. 349–356

Suyehiro, K.
1932 Engineering seismology: Proc. Am. Soc. Civil Engrs. 58(4), May, part 2

Sverdrup, H. V.; M. W. Johnson; R. H. Fleming
1942 The Oceans: Prentice-Hall

Swick, C. H.
1942 Pendulum gravity measurements and isostatic reductions: U.S. Coast and Geodetic Survey Spec. Pub. 232

Tarr, R. S.; L. Martin
1912 The earthquakes at Yakutat Bay, Alaska, in September, 1899: U.S. Geol. Survey Profess. Paper 69, pp. 1–135

Tatel, H. E.
1954 Note on the nature of a seismogram, part II: Jour. Geophys. Research 59:289–294

———; L. H. Adams; M. A. Tuve
1953 Studies of the earth's crust using waves from explosions: Proc. Am. Phil. Soc. 97:658–669

Taylor, F. B.
1910 Bearing of the Tertiary mountain belt on the origin of the earth's plan: Bull. Geol. Soc. Am. 21:179–226
1928 Sliding continents and tidal and rotational forces: Am. Assoc. Petrol. Geologists Symposium on Theory of Continental Drift, pp. 158–177

Taylor, H.
1955 Rock deformation by gravitational sliding: Paper presented before American Geophysical Union

Terman, F. E.
1943 Radio Engineers' Handbook, 4th ed.: McGraw-Hill

Thoenen, J. R.; S. L. Windes
1942 Seismic effects of quarry blasting: U.S. Bur. Mines Bull. 442

Tuttle, O. F.
1955 Degré geothermique et magmas granitiques: Coll. Int. Petrog. sur Les Échanges des Matières au Cours de la Genèse des Roches Grenves Acides et Basiques, C.N.R.S. Colloque 68, Paris (in French)

Ulrich, F. P.
1941 The Imperial Valley earthquake of 1940: Bull. Seis. Soc. Am. 31:13–31

Umbgrove, J. H. F.
1947 The Pulse of the Earth: Martinus Nijhoff, The Hague

Urey, H. C.
1952 The Planets: Yale University Press

Van der Gracht, W. A.; J. M. van Waterschoot
1928 The problem of continental drift: Am. Assoc. Petrol. Geologists Symposium on Theory of Continental Drift, pp. 1–75

Van Orstrand, C. E.
1934 Temperature gradients: Problems of Petroleum Geology, pp. 989–1021: American Association of Petroleum Geologists
1939 Observed temperatures in the earth's crust: Chap. 6 of Internal Constitution of the Earth, McGraw-Hill

Vening Meinesz, F. A.
1945 The division of continents and oceans over the surface of the earth (abstr.): Proc. Koninkl. Ned. Akad. Wetenschap. 46:115–116
1947*a* Major tectonic phenomena and the hypothesis of convection currents in the earth: Quart. Jour. Geol. Soc. London 103:191–207
1947*b* Shear patterns of the earth's crust: Trans. Am. Geophys. Union 28:1–61

———; J. H. F. Umbgrove; P. H. Kuenen
1934 Gravity Expeditions at Sea: Netherlands Geodetic Commission

Vestine, E. H.
1954 Discussion of paper by Runcorn (1954): Trans. Am. Geophys. Union 35:63–72

———; Isabelle Lange; Lucille Laporte; W. E. Scott
1947 The geomagnetic field, its description and analysis: Carnegie Inst. Wash. Pub. 580
———; Lucille Laporte; Caroline Cooper; Isabelle Lange; W. C. Hendrix
1947 Description of the earth's main magnetic field and its secular change, 1905–1945: Carnegie Inst. Wash. Pub. 578
Washington, H. S.
1922 Isostasy and rock density: Bull. Geol. Soc. Am. 33:375–410
1939 The crust of the earth and its relation to the interior: Chap. 5 of Internal Constitution of the Earth, McGraw-Hill
———; L. H. Adams
1951 The chemical and petrological nature of the earth's crust: Chap. 5 of Internal Constitution of the Earth, 2d ed., Dover
Waters, G. S.; G. Phillips
1956 A new method of measuring the earth's magnetic field: Geophys. Prosp. 4:1–9
Wegener, A.; trans. by J. G. A. Skerl
1924 The Origin of Continents and Oceans: Dutton
Whitten, C. A.
1948 Horizontal earth movement, vicinity of San Francisco, California: Trans. Am. Geophys. Union 29:318–323
Willis, B.
1923 Geologic Structures: McGraw-Hill
1928 Continental drift: Am. Assoc. Petrol. Geologists Symposium on Theory of Continental Drift, pp. 76–82
1944 Philippine earthquakes and structure: Bull. Seis. Soc. Am. 34:69–81
Wilson, J. T.
1949 The origin of continents and precambrian history: Trans. Roy. Soc. Can. 43(4):157–184
1950 Recent applications of geophysical methods to the study of the Canadian Shield: Trans. Am. Geophys. Union 31:101–114
1954 The development and structure of the crust: Part 4 of The Earth as a Planet, University of Chicago Press
Wood, H. O.
1933 Earthquake investigation in the field: Bull. Natl. Research Council 90: 41–66 (Chap. 6 of Physics of the Earth, vol. VI)
1955 The 1857 earthquake in California: Bull. Seis. Soc. Am. 45:47–66
———; F. Neumann
1931 Modified Mercalli intensity scale of 1931: Bull. Seis. Soc. Am. 21:278–283
Wyckoff, R. D.
1936 Study of earth tides by gravitational measurements: Trans. Am. Geophys. Union 17:46–52
1941 The Gulf gravimeter: Geophysics 6:13–33
1948 The Gulf airborne magnetometer: Geophysics 13:182–208
Wyllie, M. R. J.
1949 A quantitative analysis of the electrochemical component of the S.P. curve: Jour. Petrol. Technol. 1:17–26
Zeis, E. G.
1946 Temperature measurements at Paricutin Volcano: Trans. Am. Geophys. Union 27:178–180

INDEX